Fundamentals of Rotating Machinery Diagnostics

Fundamentals of Rotating Machinery Diagnostics

Donald E. Bently
Chairman of the Board and Chief Executive Officer
Bently Pressurized Bearing Company

With
Charles T. Hatch

Edited by
Bob Grissom

Bently Pressurized Bearing Press

The following are trademarks of Bently Nevada Corporation in the United
States and Other Countries: Bently Nevada®, Keyphasor®, Proximitor®, REBAM®,
Seismoprobe®, Velomitor®, Orbit Design.

The Bently Pressurized Bearing Co. logo is a trademark of
Bently Pressurized Bearing Company in the United States and Other
Countries.

MATLAB® is a registered trademark of The MathWorks, Inc.

Bently Pressurized Bearing Press is an imprint of
Bently Pressurized Bearing Company
1711 Orbit Way
Minden, NV, USA 89423

Phone: 775-783-4600
bpb.press@bpb-co.com
www.bpb-co.com

Library of Congress Control Number 2002094136

ISBN 0-9714081-0-6

Book design by Charles T. Hatch
Set in Adobe Kepler and Myriad Multiple Master typefaces

Printed in Canada
First Printing

Dedication
This book is 50 percent due to the brilliant work of Dr. Agnes Muszynska. Dr. Muszynska is a member of the Polish Academy of Sciences and worked with me for more than 18 years.

Dr. Muszynska is an excellent researcher in her own right and pioneered the first correct modeling of equations for modern rotor dynamics. Chapter 22 on instability illustrates much of the work we did in partnership on the development of modern rotor equations.

Donald E. Bently

Table of Contents

Data Plots

The Static and Dynamic Response of Rotor Systems

Malfunctions

Case Histories

Appendix

Acknowledgments

ANYONE WHO HAS WRITTEN A BOOK knows that it takes a great many people to make it a success. I envisioned this book more than fifteen years ago. Patience, faith, and support made this book possible.

During the writing of this book, I had the help of many others who provided information or reviewed the drafts. These people helped me add depth, breadth, and clarification to the book.

Agnes Muszynska formalized much of the mathematics of the rotor dynamic model that is presented in Chapter 10. Agnes developed some of the mathematics on her own; we worked together on other of the mathematical models contained in this book.

Several technical experts within the company provided me with a great deal of in-depth, specialized knowledge. Bill Laws' strong background in large steam turbines helped me improve the chapter on rotor bow. Throughout this project, Ron Bosmans and Richard Thomas have been patient teachers and excellent guides through the world of rotating machinery. Our many debates on obscure aspects of rotating machinery behavior have been both interesting and informative, and they provided many subtle technical details that appear in this book.

Each chapter of this book has been thoroughly reviewed by experts with many years of experience in machinery diagnostics. Ron Bosmans and Richard Thomas acted as primary reviewers and read every chapter. Other reviewers included Don Southwick, Rett Jesse, Paul Goldman, Wes Franklin, Bob Hayashida, John Winterton, Rob Bloomquist, Clair Forland, Dave Whitefield, Craig Sever, Mike Quinlan, and Pascal Steeves. We also obtained special help from two talented engineers, Ingrid Foster and Susan McDole; their detailed reviews of the appendix material kept me on my toes.

The case histories in this book originated in the field with Bently Nevada machinery specialists, and, when finished, were reviewed by them. In recreating these events, we read their reports and articles and, whenever possible, discussed the details with them. Peyton Swan was a valuable source of information for the compressor problem described in Chapter 25; Peyton is also an excellent writer, and we gratefully borrowed material from an article he wrote for *ORBIT* magazine. Peyton also worked with Kevin Farrell on the generator problem described in Chapter 27. We had several interesting discussions about the underlying rotor dynamic mechanism that was responsible for this unusual behavior. John Kingham supplied additional information for the draft fan problem he encountered, which is described in Chapter 26. Rob Bloomquist provided considerable detail concerning the pipeline compressor problem that is described in Chapter 29.

We want to thank Bob Grissom, who edited this book. Bob was an instructor in Bently Nevada courses for many years, and he possesses a broad knowledge of the subjects covered. During the writing and editing process, Bob reminded us of many technical details, which made his editing very thorough. Because of Bob's effort, this is a much better book than it would have been without him.

I am in debt to Walter Evans for his teachings on root locus. I worked with Walter at Rocketdyne in Downey, California. I also attended classes at University of California Los Angeles where Walter taught root locus and other principles of control theory. I have used root locus techniques extensively throughout my career; although over the years, I thought root locus had gone out of style. About five years ago, I was visiting at California Polytechnic University in San Luis Obispo, California. A professor there showed me the textbook, *Modern Control Engineering (Third Edition)* by Katsuhiko Ogata that was being used at the university. The principles presented in the book rely heavily on Walter Evans' method of root locus. I hope that today's students will find root locus as useful in their careers as I have found it.

Finally, it is important that Charlie Hatch's name appear with me on the cover of this book. Charlie is more than a hired gun or a professional editor; he is also a researcher. After earning his first degree in forestry, Charlie attended University of California Berkeley, where he earned B.S. and M.S. degrees in mechanical engineering. After graduation, he worked at Bently Nevada Corporation as a production engineer and later transferred to the research laboratory where he worked with Agnes Muszynska and me. His first job was to attempt to build rheologic bearings, which are oil bearings with unique magnetic particles suspended inside. When this approach proved not to be feasible, Charlie then helped write a paper on the behavior of damping on flexible rotor systems. This excellent work is taught at all Bently Nevada seminars. Charlie and I have since worked collaboratively to document several other research study results and projects. I taught Charlie root locus methods, and he promptly became an expert on it. It was only natural that he would be my choice to help develop this book. In addition to collating and editing, Charlie was an inspirational collaborator and contributing researcher on the many ideas that appear in this book.

Donald E. Bently
Minden, NV
March 11, 2002

Foreword

Rotating machinery vibration analysis requires the use of principles that are still quite unfamiliar to many mechanical engineers. These principles are probably the least understood of those in any other field, yet are critical to the design, operation, and diagnosis of high-speed, high-power machinery. Over the past 100 years, misconceptions, misstatements, and mistakes in the description of rotor dynamics have compounded the problems.

In this age of detailed mathematical study of shaft dynamics, the rapidly advancing technology is not being properly communicated to the practicing engineers and engineering students in straightforward, compelling terms. Certainly, these days, most engineers do not have the time to digest all the published material. One of the most powerful new ideas is Dynamic Stiffness.

The vibration we measure is a ratio, the ratio of the dynamic force to the Dynamic Stiffness of the machine. This book clearly shows how to use Dynamic Stiffness to understand and recognize malfunction behavior. It is also a single source for the description of the fundamental principles of rotor dynamics and how machinery behaves. It corrects the misconceptions that have plagued the discipline and opens new territory and routes to understanding the dynamics of rotating machinery.

For example, in existing literature, the cross stiffness terms, K_{xy} and K_{yx}, are treated as independent variables. We call these terms quadrature terms, which have a very simple relationship. The "cross stiffness" is actually a tangential stiffness term (quadrature term) that acts perpendicular to the direction of displacement. The tangential stiffness term, $D\lambda\Omega$, is defined in basic rotor dynamic parameters, which are much more useful when you're trying to diagnose machinery operation.

Exploring new territory is always a fantastic adventure, and never without problems. In exploring the basic nature of rotating machinery, I regularly hit unforeseen cliffs, swamps, or other impediments. Looking back, having solved the problem, these pitfalls are interesting.

Crossing into new territory, it sometimes was necessary to tread on old traditions where these traditions were wrong, or were nearly correct but had been slightly misinterpreted. Great resistance to progress was, therefore, encountered from people who had an incorrect view of the theory.

Since the invention of rotating machines, the pursuit of higher power output has driven machine speeds higher and higher. With the breaking of the first balance resonance "barrier" (achieved by De Laval with a steam turbine in 1895), rotating machines were shown to be able to operate above the first balance resonance. However, with this new capability came a new problem for machines using fluid-lubricated journal bearings: fluid-induced instability. Over the years, many different methods have been developed by researchers to identify and understand the important parameters that influence rotor stability and, so, increase the reliability of the machinery.

Reliability is often thought to be synonymous with long, trouble-free life, and improved reliability to mean a longer, trouble-free life. But these are not acceptable definitions. A machine or component becomes reliable when its operation and actions are predictable. The accuracy with which these actions may be predicted is a true measure of its reliability. It follows, then, that reliability can best be improved by learning as much as possible about equipment operation and using this knowledge to reduce or eliminate as many unpredictable items as possible. Accurate predictions require accurate, meaningful data from which analysis can be made. When you have the data necessary to make accurate predictions of machine operations, you also have the data to improve designs, extend the life of components, probably even reduce its cost and increase its safety.

Meaningful information is the key. This book is a major step in assuring that good data can become meaningful information through the increased knowledge of the machinery specialist. It is a well-constructed foundation of the bridge to the future.

Machinery technology is rapidly changing, and new developments are always making their way into machines. One very promising new technology is the externally pressurized bearing, which Bently Nevada is developing. This bearing is an externally pressurized (hydrostatic), fluid-film bearing that can be operated in a passive mode, a semi-active mode, or in a fully active mode. In the passive mode, the bearing operates with a fixed design pressure and, by extension, fixed-by-design spring stiffness and damping. In the semi-active mode, the external supply pressure can be adjusted under operator control to change the values of stiffness and damping while the machine is operating. In its active mode, it is capable of producing fully automatic, instantaneous changes in stiffness and damping to control the rotor position in real time.

In June 2001, we demonstrated suppression of oil whirl by increasing bearing pressure at the International Gas Turbine Show in Munich, Germany. In August 2001, we demonstrated the suppresion of oil whip. This was the first demonstration of a supplementary bearing in the central span of a rotating machine.

These two successful innovations, never performed before in history, do not solve all instability problems, but they certainly make it possible to control two obvious problems that have presented challenges for rotating engineers for many decades.

This new technology promises to change the way machines respond dynamically and will require changes in the way we interpret and apply machinery data.

For example, the balance resonance is usually thought of as occurring at a fixed operating speed, where running speed coincides with a fixed rotor system natural frequency. With a semi- or fully active bearing, the natural frequency and balance resonance speed now become variables under the machine operator's control. By changing the bearing spring stiffness in semi-active mode, the balance resonance can be quickly moved to another speed, enabling the operator or machine control system to jump the resonance rapidly through the machine during startup or shutdown. This behavior will greatly alter, even eliminate, the usual balance resonance signature in a polar or Bode plot.

Changes in the balance resonance speed will also affect balancing. Active shifting of resonances will make polar plots look different, changing the way we identify the heavy spot. If a resonance is shifted to a different speed, then heavy spot/high spot relationships may change. For example, what was above a resonance might now be below, or vice versa. Response that was out of phase might now be in phase. Influence vectors may depend on bearing settings, and repeatability will require similar bearing settings.

Changes in bearing stiffness can also change the rotor mode shape. A mode associated with low bearing stiffness, for example, a rigid body mode, could be modified by higher bearing stiffness to a bending mode. This change in mode shape could change the match to the unbalance distribution, producing a change in balance state. It is possible that the existing unbalance distribution would become a better or poorer match to the new mode shape, and that the rotor would have to be balanced specifically at particular bearing settings.

Some malfunctions manifest themselves as a self-excited vibration at a system natural frequency. Because of the new, variable nature of the balance resonance, this natural frequency will exist somewhere in a frequency *band*, which will depend on the range of bearing settings and their effect on rotor modal stiffness. Under some circumstances, the bearing will allow the operator to move the natural frequency to a place where the malfunction vibration cannot occur. The diagnostician will need to understand how this kind of variable-parameter bearing operation will affect his or her interpretation of the data, and how it can be used to suppress unwanted vibration.

New technology will give us awesome new opportunities and new challenges. No matter what new developments occur, *the fundamental principles of rotor dynamics presented in this book will remain the same.* The machinery diagnostician who has a solid foundation in the fundamentals will be able to apply the basic principles presented in this book and solve machinery problems.

Introduction

WHY READ THIS BOOK? If you are responsible for the maintenance or operation of industrial rotating machinery, you know that catastrophic failure of a critical machine, large or small, can cause serious injury or death, result in the total loss of the machine, shut down the plant for an extended period, and be a public relations nightmare. For these reasons, it is not acceptable to wait until a machine fails before fixing a problem; the machinery manager must take a proactive stance. This book will give you the knowledge you need to detect problems with your machine *before* they cause economic losses associated with decreased plant efficiency, unplanned downtime, damage, or a serious loss of production.

This book will help you to understand the basic principles of machinery behavior that are common to all machines, ranging from very large steam and gas turbine generator sets in the power industry, to steam and gas turbine-driven compressors in the petrochemical industry, to motor-driven induced draft fans, cooling tower fans, blowers, and large and small pumps.

It will also give you a solid foundation in *machinery diagnostics*, the body of knowledge and technique that is used to identify the root cause of a machine malfunction through the use of vibration, position, and process data. Machinery diagnostics is a *science* in the sense that, during the diagnostic process, a hypothesis is formed that must be supported (or rejected) by the data and verified by inspection or corrective action. It is also an *art* in the sense that it requires detection of a meaningful pattern in what is often a bewildering array of data. Whether viewed as science or art, it first of all requires knowledge: the diagnostician must have a solid understanding of basic rotor dynamic behavior and of the various malfunction signal characteristics.

This book presents the fundamentals of that knowledge largely from an *intuitive* and *practical*, rather than theoretical, point of view. It is written for anyone who is responsible for the operation, maintenance, management, or malfunction diagnosis of rotating machinery. It also provides an information resource for those who write technical standards, or design transducers, monitoring systems, or software packages for rotating machinery application. This book also provides a valuable resource for the machinery designer; awareness and application of the basic principles in this book are essential to a good, robust machine design.

This book covers much of the material presented in Bently Nevada diagnostics courses over the years. These courses have long been recognized as some of the best in the world, but they are, by their nature, limited. This book greatly extends the depth of the material and provides a readily available reference.

The first section of the book, Chapters 1 through 3, presents the basic concepts of vibration, phase, and vibration vectors. Phase can, at first glance, be difficult to understand; because of this, it is often a neglected facet of machinery data. This is unfortunate, because the timing information it provides is a powerful tool; without phase, diagnosis becomes much more difficult, and efficient balancing is not possible. I hope that the discussion in Chapter 2 will help clarify this topic.

In vibration analysis, "vector" data is an important tool. Vibration vectors are actually complex numbers, which simplify calculations involving amplitude and phase. It is vital for the machinery diagnostician to understand their meaning and use. Chapter 3 discusses vibration vectors in detail, and this chapter should be thoroughly mastered. Throughout this book, vibration vectors, which possess both amplitude and phase, appear as ***italic boldface***, and scalars, which possess only amplitude appear as *italic*.

Data must be presented in a meaningful manner, and, to enhance communication, it must conform to accepted standards. The second section, Chapters 4 through 9, discusses the many different kinds of data plots that can be created from machinery data and how to construct and interpret them: timebase and orbit plots; average shaft centerline plots; polar, Bode, and APHT plots; spectrum plots; and trend and XY plots. Each chapter contains many examples of data from actual machines.

The next section looks at rotor dynamic behavior, starting in Chapter 10 with the development of a basic rotor dynamic model. A result of the model is a powerful new insight, Dynamic Stiffness, which is discussed in terms of rotor behavior in Chapter 11. Other chapters in this section deal with modes of vibration, the behavior of rotor systems with anisotropic stiffness, rotor stability analysis using root locus techniques, and torsional and axial vibration. The section ends with an introduction to balancing of rotors.

The fourth section introduces the most common rotor system malfunctions and the signal characteristics that can be used for their detection. The malfunctions include unbalance, rotor bow, radial loads and misalignment, rub and looseness, fluid-induced instability, and shaft cracks. Each chapter also lists other malfunctions that may have similar symptoms and provides guidelines for discriminating between them.

In the last section, several case histories show how this knowledge was applied in the real world to solve machinery problems. The case histories are well illustrated with data, and they discuss the sequence of thought that led to the solution. Every effort was made to present the events and data as accurately as possible, while protecting the privacy of our customers. Thus, certain details are fictionalized, but the data you will see is real, the problems you will read about did happen, and the resolution of the problems were as described.

Finally, the Appendix contains additional technical information for those who wish to pursue some topics further, as well as lists of common unit conversions and a glossary of machinery diagnostic terms.

For the most part, the material in this book is presented with a minimum of mathematics, but it cannot be avoided completely. The general reader should have a working knowledge of algebra and basic trigonometric functions; the advanced reader will benefit from a knowledge of differential equations, which are used in the development of the rotor model in Chapter 10 and in some material in Chapter 14. For those without this background, the more difficult mathematics can be skipped without a loss of understanding; the key concepts are always stated with a minimum of mathematics. It is more important to come away with a good understanding of the basic principles than to be able to duplicate a complicated derivation from memory.

This book primarily uses metric (SI) units of measurement, followed by US customary units in parentheses. At least that was the original intent. Unfortunately (or fortunately, depending on where you live in the world), much of the data that is used to illustrate this book originated as US customary measurements. Rather than attempt to convert all the data to metric, data plots are presented in whatever units of measurement were used when the data was taken. Thus, the reader will find many places in the book where the discussion is conducted in US customary units, followed by metric. I apologize for the inconvenience and ask for the reader's patience.

As in so many things, this book represents only a starting point; as the title says, it presents the *fundamentals* of rotating machinery diagnostics. The world of rotating machinery is extremely complex, and the science of rotor dynamics is young; that is what makes it so interesting. No single book can possibly address this topic in its full extent. I hope that it will help those getting started in this field, while at the same time providing new insight and serving as a useful reference for experienced practitioners. We are all in a continuous process of learning.

Fundamentals of Vibration

Chapter 1

Vibration

Vɪʙʀᴀᴛɪᴏɴ ɪs ᴛʜᴇ ᴘᴇʀɪᴏᴅɪᴄ, ʙᴀᴄᴋ ᴀɴᴅ ꜰᴏʀᴛʜ ᴍᴏᴛɪᴏɴ (oscillation) of an object. We encounter vibration in many different ways in our daily lives. Nearly all musical instruments utilize the periodic vibration of mechanical elements to make sound; for example, pianos and guitars use the vibration of a string and connected soundboard, clarinets use the vibration of a small reed, and trumpets use the vibration of the player's lips.

Vibration also exists in nature. The motion of the tides is an example of a very low frequency vibration that is produced by the gravitational force of the moon and sun. This motion is an example of forced vibration (and resonance, in the case of the Bay of Fundy). A sudden gust of wind acting on a tall pine tree can also produce a periodic, low frequency vibration of the tree, an example of free vibration resulting from an initial impulse. The wind blowing on aspen leaves produces a continuous, periodic motion of the leaves, an example of self-excited vibration.

Machines, because of internal and external forces, also vibrate. Machinery vibration involves the periodic motion of rotors, casing, piping, and foundation systems, all at the same time. Usually this vibration is so small that sensitive equipment is needed to detect it. To illustrate the small size of machinery vibration, we can compare it to the diameter of a human hair. The average diameter is approximately 130 µm (about 5 mil). This is an unacceptable vibration level on some steam turbine generator sets that are the length of a house.

Vibration in machines causes periodic stresses in machine parts, which can lead to fatigue failure. If the motion due to vibration is severe enough, it can cause machine parts to come into unwanted contact, causing wear or damage.

Because of this, the control of vibration is an important part of machinery management, and the concepts underlying vibration must be thoroughly understood by the machinery professional. This chapter will discuss the basic concepts of linear vibration, the vibration of machines, rotation, and the most commonly used vibration measurement units. Then, we will move onto a discussion of the concepts of free vibration at a natural frequency, forced vibration, and that most interesting marriage of the two, resonance. Finally, we will discuss self-excited vibration, where a system can internally transfer energy to produce vibration at a natural frequency.

The Basic Vibration Signal

A *vibration transducer* is a device that converts mechanical motion into an electronic signal. A displacement transducer can be used to measure the displacement, or position, of an object relative to the transducer. For most transducers this is, ideally at least, a one-dimensional measurement. If the object is

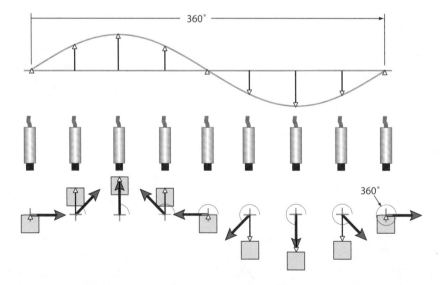

Figure 1-1. The relationship of a displacement vibration signal to the motion of an object. As the object moves relative to the measuring transducer, a time-varying voltage signal is created (top). A rotating position vector (red) rotates at the circular frequency, ω (Greek lower case omega). The projection of this vector on the transducer axis (yellow) represents the actual displacement of the object.

vibrating, the position of the object relative to the transducer will change in a repeating pattern over time.

Figure 1-1 shows an object that is vibrating toward and away from a transducer. The different images show the evolution of the system over time. The transducer converts the position of the box on the transducer's sensitive axis to an output voltage, which is displayed at the top of the figure. The transducer output voltage, or signal, is proportional to the distance from the transducer to the object, the *gap*. This changing voltage signal represents the relative position of the vibrating object versus time.

Note that the waveform reaches a maximum value on the plot when the object is closest to the transducer and a minimum value when the object is farthest from the transducer.

There are two primary characteristics that we can measure on this signal, frequency and amplitude. This signal has a simple, sinusoidal shape, and it contains only one frequency. More complex (and typical) signals contain several frequencies of vibration with different amplitudes.

Frequency

Frequency is the repetition rate of vibration per unit of time. The vibration signal in Figure 1-1 has only one frequency. The frequency of this signal is found by measuring the amount of time it takes to complete one cycle of vibration (Figure 1-3). This length of time is called the *period*, *T*, and is shown in the figure. It has units of seconds per cycle of vibration. The frequency, *f*, has units of cycles/second, or hertz (Hz) and is the reciprocal of the period in seconds:

$$f\,(\text{Hz}) = \frac{1}{T} \qquad\qquad (1\text{-}1)$$

In rotating machinery applications, we are often interested in expressing the frequency in *cycles per minute*, or *cpm*, so that the frequency can be directly compared to the rotative speed of the machine, measured in *revolutions per minute*, or *rpm*. The frequency in cpm can be calculated from the period using this expression:

$$f\,(\text{cpm}) = \left(f\,\frac{\text{cycles}}{\text{s}} \right)\left(60\,\frac{\text{s}}{\text{min}} \right) = \frac{60}{T} \qquad\qquad (1\text{-}2)$$

There are 2π radians or 360° in a circle; this concept can be extended to say that there are 2π radians or 360° in one cycle of vibration. Thus, the frequency can also be expressed in radians/second (rad/s):

$$\omega(\text{rad/s}) = \left(2\pi \frac{\text{rad}}{\text{cycle}}\right)\left(f \frac{\text{cycles}}{\text{s}}\right) = \frac{2\pi}{T} \qquad (1\text{-}3)$$

The frequency ω (Greek lower case omega) is sometimes called the *circular frequency*. The red vector in Figure 1-1 rotates at the circular frequency ω and completes one revolution for each cycle of vibration.

The rotating vector may seem like a complicated description for the simple system shown in the figure. But, in single-frequency vibration in rotating machinery, the rotor shaft moves in a two-dimensional circular or elliptical path, and the rotating vector is a logical model of its motion. In general, ω will be used to represent the vibration frequency of the rotor system. The one-dimensional position of a rotor can be expressed as the projection of the rotating vector onto the axis of sensitivity of the transducer (the yellow vector in Figure 1-1).

Several terms are commonly used to describe frequency ranges in machinery (Figure 1-2):

Synchronous, or 1X. The same as rotor speed. The "X" is equivalent to a mathematical multiplication symbol. Thus, 1X can be read as "1 times rotor speed."

Nonsynchronous. Any frequency *except* 1X.

Subsynchronous. Any frequency less than 1X. This can include simple integer ratios such as ⅔X, ¾X, etc., decimal ratios such as 0.48X, 0.37X, etc., or subharmonics (see below).

Supersynchronous. Any frequency greater than 1X. This can include simple integer ratios such as ³⁄₂X, ⁵⁄₂X, etc., decimal ratios such as 1.6X, 1.8X, etc., or superharmonics (see below).

Subharmonic. A frequency less than 1X that is an integer ratio with one in the numerator: for example, ½X, ⅓X, ¼X, etc.

Superharmonic. A frequency greater than 1X that is an integer multiple: for example, 2X, 3X, 4X, etc.

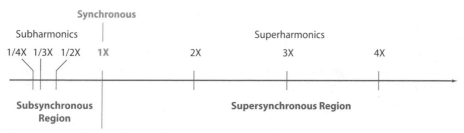

Figure 1-2. Machinery vibration frequency definitions. Synchronous, or 1X, is equivalent to the running speed of the machine.

Amplitude

Amplitude is the magnitude of vibration expressed in terms of signal level (for example, millivolts or milliamps) or in engineering units (for example, micrometers or mils, millimeters per second or inches per second, etc.).

The amplitude can be measured using several methods. One is to measure the total voltage change from the minimum of the signal to the maximum of the signal. This method is used for displacement signals and is referred to as *double amplitude*, or *peak-to-peak*, abbreviated pp. In Figure 1-3, the peak-to-peak voltage change represents a *total change* in position of 120 µm (4.7 mil).

Besides being used for the simple signal shown here, peak-to-peak amplitude is well-suited for the measurement and evaluation of complex vibration signals that contain many different frequencies. Often, the machinery diagnostician simply needs to know how much the machine rotor is vibrating relative to the available diametral clearance in the machine. Peak-to-peak measurement makes this comparison relatively easy.

The *single amplitude*, or *peak* method, abbreviated pk, measures the voltage change from the middle of the signal to the maximum value of the signal. This method yields an amplitude that is one half of the peak-to-peak value. This method of measurement is commonly used for velocity and acceleration vibra-

Figure 1-3. Three methods of amplitude measurement of a single-frequency (sine wave) signal. The period, *T*, represents the time to complete one cycle of vibration.

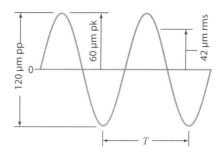

tion signals, but is not well-suited to the measurement of displacement signals for the reason given above.

When mathematically modeling rotor system behavior, the amplitude of vibration given by a model is equivalent to the peak method. This can sometimes lead to confusion when the amplitude of displacement vibration predicted by a model is compared the peak-to-peak vibration measured on a machine. Another potential confusion can occur when the Dynamic Stiffness of a machine (a peak kind of parameter based on a model) is calculated using peak-to-peak vibration data.

It is important to be aware of and keep track of the difference between the peak-to-peak and peak methods. It is easy to get confused about which system is being used and end up with an error of a factor of two. All vibration measurements should be written down with the complete units of measurement. Merely writing 250 μm or 10 mil *is not enough* and is an invitation to embarrassment. Is it peak, or peak-to-peak? Complete units should be written in all notes and calculations to avoid confusion: write 250 μm pp (10 mil pp), or 250 μm pk (10 mil pk).

The *root-mean-square* method, abbreviated rms, describes the amplitude of a continuously changing signal as a form of average. As the name suggests, it is calculated by taking the square root of the mean, or average, of the squares of the signal values.

If, *and only if*, the signal is a sine wave (single frequency), the rms amplitude will be equal to 0.707 times the *peak* amplitude, and it will be equal to 0.354 times the *peak-to-peak* amplitude. If the signal is *not* a sine wave, then the rms value using this simple calculation will *not* be correct. Most machine vibration signals are *not* sine waves. Instead, they contain a mixture of different frequencies (Figure 1-4).

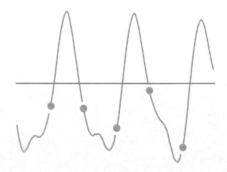

Figure 1-4. A vibration signal that contains several different frequencies. The Keyphasor marks (dots) occur once per revolution of the rotor shaft (See Chapter 2).

Displacement, Velocity, and Acceleration

Displacement describes the position of an object. *Velocity* describes how rapidly the object is changing position with time, and *acceleration* describes how fast the velocity changes with time. Figure 1-5 shows an oscillating pendulum observed by a displacement transducer and plots of displacement, velocity, and acceleration. The displacement of the pendulum is measured relative to the vertical, rest position.

Note that the peak velocity occurs when the pendulum passes through the vertical position and is moving toward the transducer. As the pendulum reaches the end of its motion and is closest to the transducer (the maximum positive value in the displacement plot), the velocity is zero, momentarily. The pendulum starts moving back in the opposite direction with negative velocity. When the pendulum passes through the vertical position again, the velocity reaches its maximum negative value. When the pendulum reaches the opposite displacement extreme, the displacement is at the minimum on the displacement plot, and the velocity is again zero.

Because the pendulum is driven by gravity, the acceleration is zero when the pendulum is in the vertical position. As the displacement approaches the positive peak near the transducer, the force due to gravity is acting in such a way as to reduce the velocity. Thus, the acceleration is negative, and it reaches its maximum negative value (the minimum on the plot) when the displacement is maximum. Then, as the pendulum starts back away from the transducer, the negative acceleration becomes smaller, heading up toward the zero crossing on the

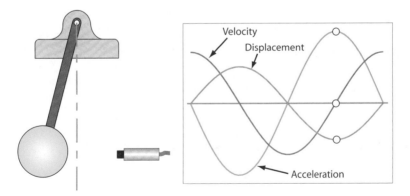

Figure 1-5. The motion of a pendulum. Curves of displacement (green), velocity (blue), and acceleration (orange) are shown versus time. The yellow dots represent the signal levels for the pendulum position shown.

plot. When the pendulum reaches the opposite extreme, gravity is trying to stop the pendulum and push it back toward the transducer. At this point, the acceleration reaches a maximum positive value on the plot.

For *single-frequency signals (sine waves) only*, such as shown in the illustration, there is a simple mathematical relationship between displacement, velocity, and acceleration:

$$d = A \sin(\omega t)$$
$$v = A\omega \sin(\omega t + 90°) = \dot{d} \qquad (1\text{-}4)$$
$$a = A\omega^2 \sin(\omega t + 180°) = -A\omega^2 \sin(\omega t) = \dot{v} = \ddot{d}$$

where d is the displacement, v is the velocity, a is the acceleration, A is the amplitude of the displacement (the maximum displacement possible, expressed as either pk, pp, or rms), and ω is the frequency of vibration in rad/s. The numbers 90° and 180° represent the *relative phase*, or *timing* between the signals. The dots (˙, ¨) represent the first and second derivatives with respect to time (d/dt and d^2/dt^2).

In Equations 1-4, velocity *leads* displacement by 90°; that is, it reaches its maximum one quarter of a cycle, or 90°, before (the reason for the plus sign) the displacement maximum. Figure 1-5 shows a set of plots of Equations 1-4; note that the velocity maximum occurs when the displacement is zero and rising.

Acceleration leads displacement by 180°, and acceleration leads velocity by $180° - 90° = 90°$. In the plot, the acceleration maximum occurs when the velocity is zero and rising, and the displacement and acceleration change in opposite directions.

Important note: the phase angles here are based on a mathematical definition of phase, not on phase measured by instrumentation. See Appendix 1 for a discussion of this important difference.

As shown in Equations 1-4, the amplitude of the velocity is related to the amplitude of displacement by a factor of ω. Similarly, the amplitude of acceleration is related to the amplitude of displacement by a factor of ω^2. This has important implications for transducer selection, because the amplitude of velocity and acceleration signals can become very small at low frequencies.

Why do we care about velocity and acceleration if we want to know the displacement vibration of the machine? Inside the machine, we can mount a displacement transducer on the machine casing or bearing structure and measure the displacement of the shaft relative to the casing. On the outside of the machine, displacement must be measured relative to something, and it is impossible to measure the displacement of a machine casing with a displacement transducer mounted on the casing. For this reason, velocity and acceleration transducers are used for casing vibration measurements on machines. These transducers provide their own internal inertial reference, and they can be mounted directly on the machine casing to provide casing vibration information.

Because these transducers are used for machine monitoring, it is important to understand the amplitude and phase relationships among displacement, velocity, and acceleration signals. Phase will be covered in detail in Chapter 2.

The Vibration of Machines

Machine rotors rotate and, because of forces in the machine, they also move laterally, or *radially*, in a plane perpendicular to the axis of the machine. This motion is periodic and usually occurs at the same frequency as rotor speed (primarily in response to unbalance), but can occur at frequencies below or above rotor speed. Often, several frequencies of vibration are present at the same time.

To visualize rotor vibration in its simplest form, imagine a short piece of metal rod (for example, a metal coat hanger) that is bent into a bowed shape. As the rod is rotated about its long axis, a point on the bowed part of the rod will move in a circle about this axis. This path of this point is called an *orbit*. In this example, the point will complete one orbit for each revolution of the rod, an example of 1X vibration.

All machine components (the rotor, machine casing, piping system, and support structures) can vibrate in several different directions. As already mentioned, radial vibration takes place in the plane (the *XY* plane) perpendicular to the rotor axis of the machine. Axial vibration takes place in a direction *parallel* to the rotor axis (the *Z* axis).

Angular vibration (the periodic change of the angular orientation of the machine component) is also often present. Some angular deflections are detected by radial vibration transducers, because the angular motion has a radial vibration component. Torsional vibration is a special case of angular vibration, where the relative angular deflection appears as a periodic twisting of the rotor shaft. This twisting of the shaft does not directly produce a radial vibration component and cannot be directly detected by radial vibration transducers.

Displacement transducers are mounted on the machine casing to observe the motion of the shaft. If the machine casing were absolutely still, then the rotor vibration would be measured relative to an absolutely motionless transducer, and the rotor vibration signal would be referred to as *shaft absolute vibration*. Shaft absolute vibration refers to the motion of the shaft measured relative to a fixed (inertial) reference frame.

Usually, however, there is some casing vibration present (Figure 1-6). This happens because forces are acting on the case, including the dynamic forces of the vibrating rotor that are transmitted through the bearings into the casing structure. These dynamic forces cause the casing to vibrate, too. The amount of casing vibration depends on the relative masses of the rotor and casing, the stiffness of the bearings, and the stiffness of the structure that supports the casing itself. Because casing vibration always exists in some amount, the displacement transducer is also in motion, and the measured rotor vibration is referred to as *shaft relative vibration*. In machines with heavy, well-supported casings, like high pressure compressors and most large steam turbines, casing vibration and, therefore, displacement transducer motion is often small compared to shaft vibration. In this case, the measured shaft relative vibration is a good approximation to shaft absolute. However, on machines with lightweight casings or soft supports, casing vibration can be so significant that shaft relative readings differ significantly from shaft absolute.

Casing vibration is also transmitted to and from any surrounding piping systems through the piping connections on the machine. Also, vibration can be transmitted into the foundation and through the building structure to other, remote locations. It is quite possible for casing transducers on one machine to detect vibration originating in another, nearby machine.

Radial vibration is the most commonly measured type of vibration, partly because it is the easiest to measure. However, radial vibration may not always be the most significant vibration of the system. For example, axial vibration can become extreme in surging compressors, and torsional vibration, the most

Figure 1-6. A comparison of types of machine vibration measurement. Casing absolute vibration (green) is measured relative to an inertial (fixed) reference frame contained in the casing transducer (not shown). Shaft relative vibration (red) is measured by the displacement transducer (shown), which is mounted on the machine casing. Shaft absolute vibration is the sum of the casing absolute and shaft relative vibration. It can be larger or smaller than shaft relative vibration, depending on the timing (phase) relationship of the vibration.

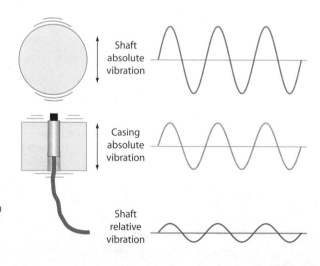

difficult of all to measure, can reach destructive levels with very little outside indication of its existence.

Rotation and Precession

Rotation is the angular motion of the rotor about its geometric center, or shaft centerline. Rotation can theoretically occur without any lateral motion of the rotor. In the absence of any external forces, a perfectly balanced rotor will spin in place around the geometric center of the shaft without any change in position (vibration) of that center (the left side of Figure 1-7).

Precession is the lateral motion, or vibration, of the rotor geometric center in the *XY* plane, which is perpendicular to the axis of the rotor. Precession is also known as orbiting or vibration; the *orbit* is a display of the lateral motion of the shaft centerline and is shown in light green in the figure. Precession can take place even if the rotor is stopped; it is completely independent of rotation (the right side of Figure 1-7). The orbit of the rotor can range from purely circular to a very complicated shape containing many frequencies of vibration.

It is possible for a rotor to rotate without vibrating, and it is possible for a rotor to vibrate without rotating. Usually, however, both rotation and precession occur at the same time.

The direction of rotation and precession can be expressed as *X to Y*, or *counterclockwise* (CCW), when the rotor moves in the positive mathematical angular sense (Figure 1-8). Motion in the opposite direction is expressed as *Y to X*, or *clockwise* (CW).

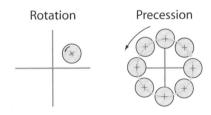

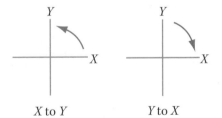

Figure 1-7. An end view of shaft rotation and precession. On the left, the shaft spins around its geometric center without vibrating, an example of pure rotation. On the right, the nonrotating shaft moves in an orbit, shown by the green path, an example of pure precession.

Figure 1-8. Rotation and precession naming conventions. On the left is *X* to *Y* (counterclockwise) angular motion. On the right is *Y* to *X* (clockwise) angular motion.

The terms X to Y and Y to X are preferred over CCW and CW because, once the coordinate system is fixed for a particular machine, the angular sense is invariant with viewpoint. For example, if you view a machine from the drive end, and the machine is turning X to Y (CCW), and then move to the opposite end of the machine, it will appear to be turning CW. However, the basic definition of X to Y still holds.

When the direction of precession is the same as rotation (for example, X to Y for both or Y to X for both), then the motion is defined as *forward precession*. When the direction of precession is opposite to the direction of rotation, then the motion is referred to as *reverse precession*. These concepts of forward and reverse precession have powerful application in full spectrum and in the diagnosis of certain types of malfunctions.

Free Vibration

When any underdamped mechanical system is displaced from its equilibrium position and then released, it will oscillate (vibrate) at a frequency that is called its *damped natural frequency*. In free vibration, once the system is released, it continues to vibrate until either the vibration dies out or is re-excited.

Vibration in most mechanical systems involves the periodic conversion of energy from potential energy to kinetic energy and back again. For example, if you displace a pendulum from its rest position, you have increased its potential energy. At the moment you release the pendulum, the potential energy is at a maximum, and the velocity is zero. Thus, the kinetic energy is zero. After release, the pendulum begins to move under the force due to gravity. As the pendulum reaches bottom, the gravitational potential energy is zero and the kinetic energy due to motion is maximum. As the pendulum reaches the opposite extreme of motion, the potential energy is again at a maximum, and the kinetic energy is zero as the pendulum comes momentarily to a stop. The pendulum continues to oscillate until frictional losses gradually remove the energy from the system.

Rotor system vibration involves the conversion of energy from the kinetic energy of motion to the potential energy of various spring-like components. Potential energy can be stored temporarily in rotor shaft deflection, bearing deflection, the deformation of the machine casing, the deflection of any attached piping system, and the deflection of the foundation system. Virtually every element of the rotor system can act as a spring that is available for temporary storage of the energy of vibration.

In free vibration, the energy is supplied by the force that caused the initial disturbance of the system away from its equilibrium position. This can be in the form of an impulse (like a hammer blow) or a step function, where a sudden magnitude change takes place in an applied force (Figure 1-9).

Stable, freely vibrating systems eventually stop vibrating because physical mechanisms remove energy from the system. Energy loss can be due to air resistance, viscous damping, plastic deformation, internal or external friction, or internal material losses (such as hysteretic damping).

Unstable systems possess a mechanism for converting energy from one form and transferring that energy *into* the system. Once disturbed, unstable systems tend to vibrate with increasing amplitude until either limiting nonlinearities come into play or the system is destroyed. Examples of unstable behavior are fluid-induced instability in rotor systems and aerodynamic flutter in aircraft. See Chapter 14.

Rotor systems are complex mechanical systems with distributed mass, stiffness, and damping, and they possess many different natural frequencies. It is possible for rotor systems to have several natural frequencies excited simultaneously. See Chapter 12.

Rotor systems also have torsional natural frequencies. Torsional vibration occurs as rotor masses (inertias) oscillate and twist the rotor shaft. The rotor shaft acts as the spring in the system, storing torsional potential energy during twisting, and the rotor masses undergo cyclic angular deflections around the

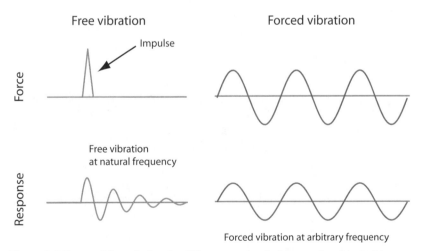

Figure 1-9. Free and forced vibration. When a mechanical system is subjected to a sudden impulse, it will vibrate (ring) at its natural frequency. Eventually, if the system is stable, the vibration will die out. Forced vibration can occur at any frequency, and the force amplitude and response amplitude are constant.

shaft axis. The angular velocities of the inertias store the kinetic energy of torsional vibration. The variation in torsional twisting occurs about the mean value of shaft twist caused by the static torque being transmitted through the shaft. Torsional vibration usually involves all of the coupled components of a machine train, including gearboxes.

Free torsional vibration can occur due to sudden changes in load in the system. For example, load switching in electrical generators can create an impulse that can excite a torsional natural frequency of the system.

Forced Vibration

A mechanical system can forcibly be moved at any frequency we wish. For example, a pendulum which is initially at rest can be moved by hand extremely slowly. The pendulum responds to the force provided by the hand. This force can be applied at any frequency we wish. If we increase the frequency of motion of the hand, the pendulum will respond at that frequency. This phenomenon is called forced vibration.

Forced vibration is caused by a periodic force acting through the *Dynamic Stiffness* of the rotor system. Dynamic Stiffness is the combination of various spring-like support stiffnesses and the dynamic effects of mass and damping. The vibration that we measure is the ratio of the force to the Dynamic Stiffness; thus, changes in either the force or the Dynamic Stiffness will produce a change in vibration. This basic principle of machinery behavior is key to successful machinery diagnostics and will be encountered throughout this book. Dynamic Stiffness will be derived in Chapter 10 and discussed in detail in Chapter 11.

Forced vibration differs from free vibration in two aspects. First, the frequency of vibration depends only on the frequency of the input force to the system. The forcing frequency may be completely independent of the natural frequency of the system. For linear systems, the frequency of the forced vibration response (the output) is the same as the frequency of the force (the input). Nonlinear systems can produce output that contains the fundamental forcing frequency and additional higher order harmonics. Rotor systems can exhibit both linear and nonlinear behavior.

The second difference between forced vibration and free vibration is the fact that, for a constant amplitude forcing input, the system vibration response remains at a constant amplitude and does not decay with time (Figure 1-9). This amplitude may be different for different forcing frequencies, but for any particular frequency it will be constant.

Unbalance is the most common force that produces vibration in rotating machinery. The asymmetric mass distribution of the rotor produces a centripetal force (sometimes called centrifugal force) that rotates with the rotor.

This rotating force causes a synchronous, or 1X, forced vibration response of the rotor.

Other examples of forced vibration include vane-pass excitation of pump impellers and housings (at a blade- or vane-pass frequency that is an integer multiple of running speed), turbine blade-pass excitation, or gear mesh frequencies. Because of the large shaking forces that can occur in machinery, forced vibration can extend to the surrounding piping and support structures and, on occasion, to nearby machinery.

Axial forced vibration can occur during surge in compressors, or because of balance piston problems or coupling problems in machine trains.

Torsional forced vibration can occur because of variations in gear geometry, periodic rotor-to-stator contact, electrical motor slip frequency or torque irregularities, misaligned couplings, reciprocating drivers or loads, or because of radial vibration. Radial vibration can couple into torsional vibration because the deflection of the shaft away from the spin axis of the machine increases the mass moment of inertia of the system, creating a torque disturbance to the system. It is also possible for torsional vibration to produce radial vibration through the same mechanism.

Resonance

When the forcing frequency is near the natural frequency of a mechanical system, the vibration response amplitude can become highly amplified. This phenomenon is called *resonance*.

Pushing a child on a swing is an example of resonance involving the periodic input of a relatively small force. The child and swing respond at the system natural frequency, like a pendulum. The system acts like an energy storage system, oscillating at the natural frequency. If successive pushes are timed correctly (the forcing frequency is equal to the natural frequency and in phase with the motion), each successive push on the swing puts more energy into the system, which increases the amplitude of vibration. The amount of amplification, expressed as the Synchronous Amplification Factor (SAF), will depend on the effective damping of the system.

In rotor systems, the force caused by a rotating unbalance produces a synchronous, 1X, forcing frequency that is equal to the rotor speed. When the rotor speed nears a rotor system natural frequency, the vibration amplitude will increase. At the natural frequency, the rotor will reach a *balance resonance* (also called a *critical speed*, or *critical*), and the vibration will reach a maximum amplitude. As the machine speed moves beyond the rotor system natural frequency, the amplitude will decrease (the amplitude plot in Figure 1-10).

Through this resonance region, important changes in the timing, or phase, of the vibration also occur. The amplitude and phase behavior through resonance is discussed in detail in Chapter 11.

While the majority of rotating machines operate below the first balance resonance, most large, critical-process machines operate above one or more balance resonances; thus, the amplification of rotor vibration in resonances during startup or shutdown is an important concern. High vibration at resonance opens up the danger of high rotor stresses, rotor-to-stator contact, and seal wear. For this reason, the American Petroleum Institute (API) sets recommended limits for maximum synchronous amplification factor values for acceptance testing of rotating machinery.

Torsional resonances can also occur whenever the frequency of a torsional disturbance is equal to a torsional natural frequency of the system. Torsional modes in rotor systems tend to be very poorly damped. Thus, torsional amplification factors tend to be very high. Operation for any length of time on a torsional resonance could produce very high torsional vibration amplitudes and likely machine damage; fortunately, because torsional resonances are very narrow, this rarely occurs in practice.

It is undesirable to operate machinery at any speed corresponding to either a resonance or half of a resonance frequency. Avoiding operation on a resonance seems fairly obvious (although it happens more than one would think), but because of nonlinearities present in most machinery, unbalance can produce some 2X vibration. Also, certain malfunctions can produce 2X vibration. If the machine operates at a speed close to one-half of a resonance frequency, then any 2X vibration will be amplified by the resonance that exists at twice running speed. This amplification can be large, resulting in a significant level of 2X vibration in the machine.

Figure 1-10. A Bode plot showing a resonance of an ideal rotor system. The upper plot shows the phase lag (see Chapter 2) versus rotor speed; the lower plot shows the amplitude of vibration versus rotor speed. When rotor speed nears the rotor system natural frequency, the amplitude of vibration increases. As the rotor speed passes beyond the natural frequency, the amplitude decreases. See also Chapter 11.

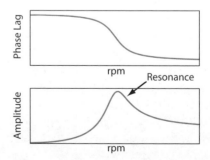

Self-Excited Vibration

Self-excited vibration can occur when a mechanism exists for converting non-vibration-related energy into energy of vibration. The oscillation of aspen leaves in a breeze is an example of this kind of vibration. The wind is the energy source that is converted, through the mechanism of vortex shedding, into the torsional and lateral vibration of the leaves.

On a larger scale, the destruction of the Tacoma Narrows bridge in 1940 was produced by a similar mechanism. The wind blowing across the bridge interacted with the bridge structure to produce an aerodynamic excitation of several different torsional modes of the bridge. Eventually, the amplitude of the torsional vibration became so large that the bridge was destroyed.

Self-excited vibration always involves the excitation of a system natural frequency by the energy conversion mechanism. So, in one sense, the phenomenon of self-excited vibration is similar to the phenomenon of resonance. The primary difference is in the way that energy is delivered to the vibrating system. Resonance involves periodic forcing at a natural frequency (for example, unbalance in rotors); self-excited vibration involves conversion from some other source of energy (for example, the energy in moving air).

One example of self-excited vibration in rotor systems is fluid-induced instability. The fluid circulation in a fluid-film bearing or seal acts as a mechanism to convert some of the energy of rotation to large amplitude, subsynchronous lateral vibration. The frequency of the subsynchronous vibration is a natural frequency of the system. See Chapter 22.

Another example is the subsynchronous vibration due to rub. Under certain conditions, periodic rotor-to-stator contact (similar to a periodic impulse) excites a rotor system natural frequency. At the rotor surface contact point, large tangential friction forces act as a mechanism to convert some of the kinetic energy of rotation to lateral vibration. At the next contact, the process repeats, supplying more energy that makes up for any energy losses that may have occurred. Thus, the rotor evolves into a steady state condition of self-excited vibration. Rotor vibration in this form of rub takes place at harmonic submultiples of running speed, ⅓X, ½X, ⅔X, ¾X, etc. See Chapter 21.

Summary

Vibration is the periodic, back and forth motion (oscillation) of an object. A transducer converts the vibration of an object into an electrical signal that we can measure.

Frequency and amplitude are two of the primary measurements of the vibration signal. (A third important measurement, phase, will be dealt with in the next chapter.) The frequency of a signal is found by taking the reciprocal of the period, the time to complete one cycle of vibration. Amplitude is normally measured as a peak-to-peak (minimum to maximum, abbreviated pp), peak (one-half of peak-to-peak, abbreviated pk), or root-mean-square (abbreviated rms) value.

Displacement is usually measured as a peak-to-peak value, while velocity and acceleration are usually measured as a peak value. For vibration at a single frequency, displacement, velocity, and acceleration can be simply calculated from each other. See Appendix 7 for conversion formulas.

Absolute vibration is the vibration of the rotor or casing relative to a fixed, inertial frame. Shaft relative vibration is measured relative to whatever the transducer is mounted on, using a transducer without an inertial reference.

Rotation and precession (vibration) are independent concepts. A machine can rotate or precess or both.

Free vibration is initiated by a disturbance to the system. Once started, the vibration occurs at the system natural frequency and dies away at a rate determined by damping or other frictional losses.

Forced vibration is produced by a continuous, periodic forcing of the system. If the amplitude of the force is constant, the amplitude of vibration will also be constant.

Resonance occurs when the forcing function is close to the natural frequency of the system. Vibration can be greatly amplified, when compared to the response at other frequencies.

Self-excited vibration occurs when a system has a method of converting a non-vibrating energy source to vibration energy. The self-excited vibration takes place at a natural frequency of the system.

Chapter 2

Phase

W<small>E HAVE SEEN THAT VIBRATION CAN BE MEASURED</small> with two parameters, frequency and amplitude. These are good and useful measurements. However, vibration never occurs in isolation; there is usually a root, or fundamental, cause of vibration in a machine. The machinery specialist needs to identify the root cause of any vibration problem, and it is often difficult to do this on the basis of frequency and amplitude alone. More information is needed.

One piece of information that can be very useful is the *timing* difference, or phase, between events. If we know the timing between a root cause and its effect, we can use our knowledge of rotor behavior to deduce the possible root causes of what we can measure. This gives us a powerful tool for the diagnosis of rotating machinery.

Phase is just such an essential piece of information. It really is basically a simple concept with some complex applications. It is, as we will see, one of the most powerful machinery diagnostic tools that we have.

In the following pages, we will define phase and try to identify some reasons why it is an important piece of information. We will discuss a special reference signal for measuring phase, the Keyphasor signal, and three types of phase measurements: absolute phase, relative phase, and differential phase.

What is Phase?

Phase is another name for the relative timing between two events in different signals. For example, in Figure 2-1, two similar vibration signals are shown. These two signals reach the positive peaks at different times. This timing difference is referred to as a *phase* difference.

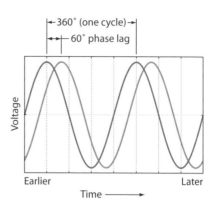

Figure 2-1. Relative phase difference between signals. The green signal peak occurs after the blue signal peak; the green signal has a phase lag of 60° with respect to the blue signal. (There are 360° in a complete vibration cycle.)

In machinery applications, the phase difference of equivalent events on different vibration signals is called *relative phase*. *Absolute phase* compares the timing of an event on the vibration waveform to a different type of reference signal, produced by a once-per-turn marker on a shaft. Both methods are commonly used, and both have their particular applications.

Even though phase compares the timing of events, it is expressed in units of *degrees* of the vibration cycle. In machinery instrumentation, the timing difference is usually expressed as a fraction of the complete 360° vibration cycle. This is a positive number with increasing time delay and is called *positive phase lag*. For example, in Figure 2-1, the green signal *lags* the blue signal by 60°.

Why Is Phase Important?

In an automobile engine, there may be spark and fuel, but if the timing is off, the engine may not run. In rotor behavior, the *timing* (phase) is just as important as vibration amplitude and frequency for effective diagnosis of machine behavior. It is also necessary for efficient balancing of machinery. Balancing requires us to know the angular location of the unbalance (the *heavy spot*). We deduce this location by using phase measurement of the vibration response of the machine combined with our knowledge of rotor behavior. Without phase information, we would have to perform many more runs to calculate an initial balance solution.

When rotors vibrate, they deflect away from the machine centerline. When the vibration is 1X, the point on the shaft which is on the outside of the deflected shaft is called the *high spot* (Figure 2-2). The timing of the rotor high spot passage under a transducer (the positive peak of displacement) provides important information about rotor behavior. It can be compared to the timing at different axial positions in the same machine. The amplitude and phase information can be combined to produce a picture of the deflection shape, or mode shape, of the

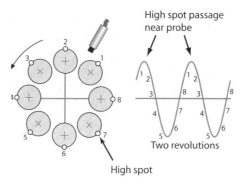

Figure 2-2. The high spot of vibration on a rotor shaft. The figure shows a sequence of images of the rotor as it moves in an orbit. For 1X circular orbits only, a spot (yellow) on the outside of the deflected rotor (the outer fiber or high spot) stays on the outside as the rotor orbits. When the high spot passes next to a probe, the vibration signal from that probe is at its maximum.

rotor at running speed. Phase can also be used to document mode shape of the casing or structure in a similar manner.

The vibration at the source of a machine problem always happens earliest in time. As vibration propagates away from the source location, it experiences a time delay (phase lag). Typically, the farther from the source, the longer the phase lag. Thus, by measuring the relative phase between different axial positions in a machine and looking for the earliest signal, we can sometimes determine the location closest to the source of the problem.

A healthy machine should operate and vibrate with a repeatable pattern day after day. Once the baseline vibration characteristics of a machine are known (including changes with load or other measurable factors), changes in vibration that break the pattern indicate that something may be wrong with the machine. Changes in phase are just as important as changes in vibration amplitude or frequency, and one may change independently of the others. Changes in phase, amplitude, or frequency can warn that something is happening to the machine.

For all of these reasons, phase is an important tool in machinery diagnostics.

The Keyphasor Event

The most common vibration in rotor systems is associated with rotor unbalance. The unbalance acts as a one-cycle-per-revolution rotating force on the rotor. This 1X forcing produces a 1X, or synchronous, vibration response in the machine. Because unbalance is so common, it is desirable to have a fixed, timing reference signal so that we can make phase measurements.

An eddy current displacement transducer looking at a keyway or key serves this purpose perfectly. Such a transducer is called a *Keyphasor transducer*. While a Keyphasor transducer is usually an eddy current transducer, it can be any type of transducer, as long as it provides a repeatable, once-per-turn reference signal.

Figure 2-3 shows a Keyphasor transducer observing a keyway and the resulting signal. As the leading edge of the notch passes by the transducer, the observed distance will increase suddenly, and the transducer signal voltage will abruptly become more negative. When the trailing edge of the notch passes by the probe, the transducer signal voltage will return to normal. Other shaft configurations for generating the Keyphasor signal are possible.

This pattern of voltage changes occurs once every revolution of the rotor and is referred to as the *Keyphasor event*. The Keyphasor event can be thought of as a timing signal. When the event occurs, a timing clock is set to zero and started. This event is used to measure the elapsed time between the Keyphasor event and an event on another signal. Each time the rotor completes a revolution, the Keyphasor event occurs again, resetting the imaginary timer.

This once-per-turn event is the timing reference used by instrumentation to measure the absolute phase of vibration signals at 1X and integer multiples (2X, 3X, ...). It is also used to measure rotor speed and other important characteristics of the dynamic response of the rotor.

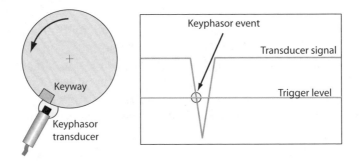

Figure 2-3. The Keyphasor event. When the *Keyphasor transducer* observes a once-per-turn mark (notch or keyway), it generates a Keyphasor (timing) event. The event is the sudden negative change in signal voltage when the leading edge of the keyway passes next to the probe.

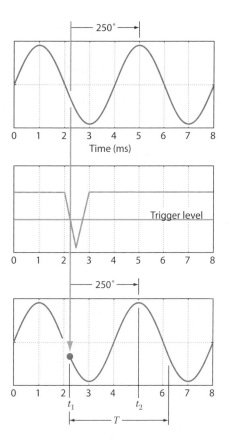

Figure 2-4. The Keyphasor event and absolute phase. The Keyphasor event is the fixed reference from which vibration phase lag is measured. When combined with the vibration signal (bottom), it produces a blank/dot display on the vibration plot (Bently Nevada convention) that simplifies phase measurement. In plots, measure phase lag from the dot to the next positive peak.

Phase Measurement

Phase is used to compare the timing of two events in different signals. If an event occurs later in time than a reference event, then it *lags* the reference event. Similarly, if an event occurs before the reference event, then it *leads* the reference event.

In order to make meaningful phase measurements, the signals being used must consist of a single primary frequency component or, in the case of the Keyphasor signal, one clearly identifiable reference event. For this reason, signals are usually filtered to the frequency of interest before making the measurement, although unfiltered signals can be used if they are dominated by one frequency.

The convention used in most vibration measurement instrumentation is to measure phase lag with a positive number, sometimes called *positive phase lag*. For example, take the vibration signal shown in Figure 2-4. The spike in the Keyphasor signal provides the timing reference. The event of interest is the first positive peak of the vibration signal that occurs after (to the right of) the Keyphasor event. Because the first positive peak occurs after the Keyphasor event, the time delay between the two events is referred to as the phase lag.

For convenience, the Keyphasor event can be combined with the vibration signal. This is shown in the bottom signal in the figure. The blank/dot sequence (a Bently Nevada convention) displays the Keyphasor event on the waveform. In data plots, the precise moment of the Keyphasor event is represented by the dot. (Oscilloscopes use a different convention, where a notch-driven Keyphasor event is indicated by the beginning of the blank.) Remember: *the period between two Keyphasor marks represents one revolution of the shaft.*

The numeric value of the phase lag is found by taking the measured time delay and comparing it to the time for one cycle of vibration:

$$\Phi = \left(\frac{t_2 - t_1}{T} \frac{\text{ms}}{\text{ms/cycle}} \right) \left(360 \frac{\text{deg}}{\text{cycle}} \right) \qquad (2\text{-}1)$$

where Φ (Greek upper case phi) is the phase lag in degrees, t_1 is the time in milliseconds at which the reference event takes place, t_2 is the time at which the event of interest takes place, and T is the time in milliseconds for one cycle of vibration.

Phase measurements are usually reduced to numbers between 0° and 360°. This is automatic in many instrumentation systems. For example, a calculated phase measurement of 395° would be reduced to 395° − 360° = 35°.

The measurement of phase using this instrumentation convention (positive phase lag) differs from the measurement of phase using a standard mathematical convention. In the mathematical system, phase lag would be a *negative* number, and phase lead would be *positive*. For a discussion of this important difference, see Appendix 1.

Absolute Phase

Absolute phase is the phase angle measured from the Keyphasor event to the *first* positive peak of the waveform. For 1X vibration in a circular orbit, this peak occurs when the rotor *high spot* is nearest the vibration transducer (the high spot and the orbit will be discussed in more detail in a later chapter). Thus, for 1X vibration, the absolute phase is sometimes said to represent the phase of the rotor high spot.

The absolute phase is found by measuring the time between the Keyphasor event and the time of the first positive peak ($t_2 - t_1$), measuring the time for one complete cycle of vibration, T, and using Equation 2-1.

In Figure 2-4, t_1 is measured as about 2.25 ms, and t_2 is about 5.0 ms. T is 6.25 ms − 2.25 ms = 4.00 ms. Applying Equation 2-1, the phase, Φ, is

$$\Phi = \left(\frac{5.0-2.25}{6.25-2.25} \; \frac{\text{ms}}{\text{ms/cycle}}\right)\left(360\frac{\text{deg}}{\text{cycle}}\right)$$

$$\Phi = 250° \text{ phase lag}$$

In Figure 2-5, an unfiltered vibration signal is shown along with its 1X- and 2X-filtered vibration components. Note that the 1X signal has one Keyphasor event per cycle of vibration; thus, the vibration frequency is one times (1X) rotor speed. The bottom signal has two cycles of vibration for each shaft revolution; the vibration frequency is twice (2X) running speed. Note that, in the 2X signal, the absolute phase is measured to the *first* positive peak; the second peak is ignored. Note also that the period, T, is measured for only one cycle of the 2X vibration.

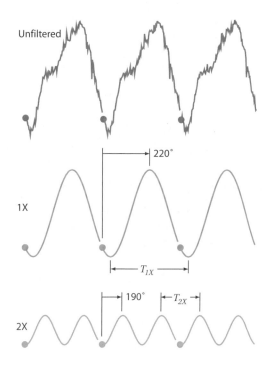

Figure 2-5. 1X, 2X, …,nX absolute phase. An unfiltered vibration signal is shown with its 1X- and 2X-filtered components. Absolute phase is found by comparing 1) the time from the Keyphasor event (dot) to the next positive peak of the vibration signal, to 2) the time for one cycle of the *vibration* signal, T. Note that, for all frequencies, the rules are the same; only the *first* positive peak is used for absolute phase measurement.

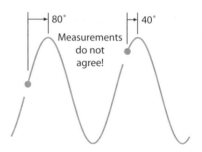

Figure 2-6. Absolute phase and nonharmonic signals. Absolute phase *cannot* be measured on vibration signals when their frequency is not a harmonic multiple of running speed (the signal is *not* 1X, 2X, 3X, etc.). The phase measurement from each successive Keyphasor dot produces a different result. Thus, absolute phase is meaningless for nonharmonic-related vibration.

Absolute phase can only be measured on vibration signals with a frequency that is a harmonic (integer) multiple of running speed, such as 1X, 2X, 3X, etc.

Attempting to measure absolute phase for frequencies that are not integer multiples, or that are subsynchronous, can lead to ambiguity. For example, in Figure 2-6, a vibration signal is shown that has a frequency slightly higher than 1X. Measuring absolute phase from successive Keyphasor marks results in different phase values. For signals with frequencies that are not integer multiples of running speed, absolute phase measurements are meaningless.

Note that, if the instrument cannot combine the Keyphasor signal with the vibration signal, it is still possible to measure absolute phase by displaying both waveforms. The top two plots in Figure 2-4 can be used to measure the absolute phase; the basic definition of absolute phase is unchanged.

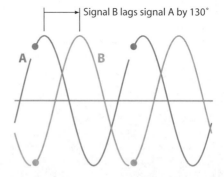

Figure 2-7. Relative phase between equivalent points on signals. In this example, signal A is the reference. Signal A reaches a maximum some time before (to the left of) signal B. That time, compared to the period of one vibration cycle, gives a relative phase of 130°. The relative phase is described as "Signal B lags signal A by 130°."

Relative Phase

Relative phase is the time delay between equivalent events (peaks, zero crossings, etc.) on two separate signals, and doesn't use the Keyphasor event. Figure 2-7 shows an example of a relative phase measurement. The two vibration signals have been filtered to the same frequency and represent the displacement vibration at different axial positions on a machine (but the same transducer orientation). Select one of the signals as a reference, and then select a convenient measurement point on it. Here, the positive peak is used. The equivalent point is located on the second signal, and the relative phase is calculated using Equation 2-1.

The result is, "Signal B lags signal A by 130°." It is important to note *which* signal leads (or lags) the other and by *how much*, or the description is not correct or complete. Normally, the reference signal is stated last. In this case, signal A was the reference signal, and signal B was measured relative to the reference.

For another example, suppose a relative phase measurement is made on the signals in Figure 2-8. Initially the "A" signal is selected as a reference. The relative phase is measured as "B lags A by 270°." The result can be restated as "B leads A by 90°." Either is correct.

In order to make a relative phase measurement, three conditions should be met. First, the two signals *must* have the same frequency, but it can be any frequency, not just integer multiples of running speed. If we attempt to measure the relative phase between signals with different frequencies, we will obtain different results depending on where we make the measurement, and the result will be meaningless.

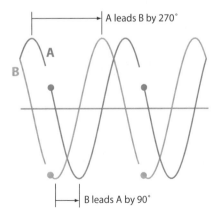

Figure 2-8. Equivalent measurements of relative phase. When signal A is used as a reference, B leads A by 90° (B lags A by 270°). When signal B is used as a reference, A leads B by 270° (A lags B by 90°). Each is correct, and the application determines which is appropriate.

Second, relative phase measurements are most often applied to vibration signals with the same units of measurement. If we want to compare the relative phase of the rotor vibration at different axial positions, we would typically compare two displacement, two velocity, or two acceleration signals. (Since the phase relationship of acceleration and velocity, and velocity and displacement are always 90° (see Figure 1-4), we could compare these signals by applying the right correction.)

Third, vibration transducers should have the same radial orientation if they are in different axial planes.

Relative phase measurements *can* be made between transducers with different orientations, as long as they are in the same plane, to determine the direction of precession of a rotor.

For example, Figure 2-9 shows an end view of a rotor shaft that is precessing in a circular orbit. The vibration signals from X and Y (coplanar) transducers are also shown with the Y signal above the X signal, the Bently Nevada display convention. The relative phase shows that X leads Y by 90°. (To determine the direction of precession, the relative phase relationship used must be the one that is less than 180°.) This means that the rotor high spot passes under the X transducer 90° before it passes under the Y transducer. This shows that the direction of precession of the rotor is X to Y.

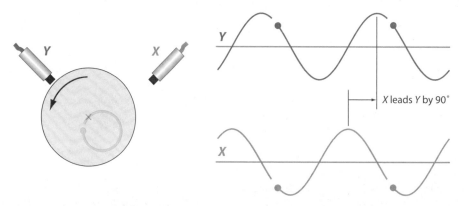

Figure 2-9. Relative phase and direction of precession. Two perpendicular probes in the same plane view a shaft that is moving in a 1X, circular orbit. To determine the direction of precession, choose the leading relative phase relationship that is less than 180°; here, X leads Y by 90°. This means that the rotor high spot passes next to the X probe before it passes next to the Y probe; thus, the direction of precession of the rotor is X to Y.

Differential Phase

Differential phase is a special application of relative phase measurement. It can be used to locate the source of a machine problem, such as fluid-induced instability. Several vibration measurements, filtered to the frequency of interest, are taken at different axial locations in a machine. Because the frequencies are the same, relative phase measurements can be made between the signals. The signal with the earliest phase will be from the transducer that is mounted closest to the source of the problem.

For this kind of measurement, all the transducers *must* have the same radial mounting orientation (for example, all must be vertical or all must be 90° R (right), etc.).

This technique can be used on vibration signals of any frequency, like those that result from fluid-induced instability. Differential phase measurements can be made between any two signals, as long as both signals are filtered to the same frequency.

Differential phase measurements must be used with caution. Significant phase changes can occur across nodal points that can produce misleading results. (A nodal point is an axial position where shaft vibration is zero or a minimum.) Phase delays may be more than 360°, which could reduce to seemingly small phase numbers.

Summary

Phase is a measure of the timing between two events. Phase measurement requires that the signals of interest have one dominant frequency component. For this reason, signals are usually filtered to a single frequency before phase measurements are made.

A Keyphasor event is used as the timing reference for absolute phase measurement. It is most commonly produced when a once-per-turn notch on the shaft passes by a Keyphasor transducer.

For absolute phase, the phase is measured from the Keyphasor event to the next positive peak of the vibration signal, and the result is expressed in degrees phase lag. Absolute phase can only be applied to a signal with a frequency that is an integer multiple of running speed (1X, 2X, ..., nX).

Relative phase compares the timing of equivalent events on two vibration signals, and either one can provide the reference event. The result is expressed as "Signal A leads (or lags) signal B by so many degrees." Relative phase measurement requires that the two signals have the same frequency, usually the same measurement units, and that the transducers are either in the same plane or in different planes with the same orientation.

Differential phase is a type of relative phase measurement where the signals from several transducers are compared. All the transducers must have the same mounting orientation and measure the same parameter. The vibration signal with the earliest phase typically comes from the transducer that is closest to the source of the vibration.

Chapter 3

Vibration Vectors

IN THE PRECEEDING CHAPTERS, WE DISCUSSED vibration signals and the measurement of phase. Most of the discussion involved the measurement of vibration signals that are single-frequency sine waves.

In order to make a meaningful phase measurement, a vibration signal must contain only one (or predominantly one) frequency. However, since typical machinery vibration signals contain several frequencies, the signal must first be filtered to a single frequency. Measurement of the amplitude and phase of the filtered signal produces a *filtered response*, *response vector*, or *vibration vector*. This vector is a powerful tool that provides the foundation for the detection of many different machine malfunctions and is vital information for balancing. The vibration vector is the underlying concept for all the Bode, polar, and amplitude-phase-time (APHT) data plots.

We will start with a discussion of the characteristics of unfiltered vibration, followed by a discussion of the vibration vector. Finally, we will discuss an important special case of the vibration vector called the *slow roll vector*.

Unfiltered Vibration

The raw (unfiltered) vibration signal from a transducer is sometimes called the *direct* vibration signal; theoretically, there is nothing in the signal path between the transducer and the instrumentation. In practice, some modification of the signal may occur (for example, an output from a monitor that includes signal processing), but if the circuitry provides no signal processing besides buffering (something that should always be verified), the output is assumed to be an exact copy of the original, unfiltered signal, including any dc offset.

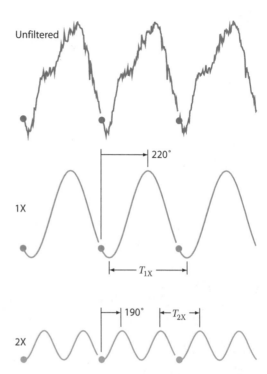

Figure 3-1. Unfiltered vibration signal with its 1X- and 2X-filtered vibration components. Accurate phase measurement requires that the signal be filtered to the desired frequency.

Thus, in general, the word *unfiltered* implies that no modification of the signal has taken place in the instrumentation, and that it contains all of the frequency components (with amplitude and phase intact) that exist in the incoming transducer signal. Figure 3-1 shows an unfiltered vibration signal and its 1X- and 2X-filtered frequency components. A number of other frequency components are contained in the unfiltered signal.

The amplitude of an unfiltered signal can be accurately measured in peak-to-peak or peak units (see Chapter 1); however, unless the unfiltered vibration signal is dominated by a single frequency, it is not possible to measure phase relationships accurately. Phase measurement requires a signal with a single frequency.

Also, since particular rotor behaviors or malfunctions may be associated with a specific frequency (for example, rotor unbalance), filtering of the vibration signal is normally required.

Filtering and the Vibration Vector

Filtering is a signal processing technique that, ideally, rejects all frequencies that are outside the bandpass region of the filter. The filter used most often on machinery vibration signals is the *bandpass* filter, which removes all signal content that is above and below the center (bandpass) frequency of the filter. The center frequency is usually set to either running speed (1X) or a multiple of running speed if a significant amount of machine vibration occurs at those frequencies (for example, a 5-vane pump impeller would produce five vane-pass events per revolution, so 5X-filtering might be desirable). Because the rotor speed changes, some filters automatically adjust the bandpass frequency to track running speed. Such a filter is called a *tracking filter* and is commonly used in rotating machinery applications.

After filtering, the vibration signal is close to a pure sine wave at the bandpass frequency, and the amplitude and phase of the filtered signal can be measured using the techniques discussed in the previous chapters.

The amplitude and phase of the filtered signal describe a *vibration vector*, which is plotted in the *transducer response (UV) plane* (Figure 3-2). A vector is a mathematical object that has both magnitude and direction. The magnitude of the vibration vector corresponds to the vibration amplitude (in whatever units are convenient, but usually μm pp or mil pp for shaft relative vibration). The direction of the vector corresponds to the absolute phase of the filtered vibration signal.

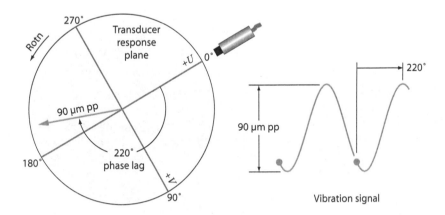

Figure 3-2. The vibration vector. The vector contains the amplitude and absolute phase information from the filtered vibration signal. It is plotted in the transducer response plane, where the *U* axis is aligned with the measurement transducer. The length of the vector represents the amplitude, and the angular position of the vector represents the absolute phase of the signal. The angular position is measured from the *U* axis in the direction *opposite* the direction of rotation of the shaft.

The *U axis* of the plane is aligned with the measurement axis of the transducer. In the figure, the transducer is mounted 30° from the horizontal. The *V axis* is always 90° from the *U* axis, in the direction opposite of shaft rotation. It is important to note that the *UV* axes are independent of any other machine coordinate system and are associated with *each transducer*. Each transducer has its own transducer response plane, and the measurement axis of the transducer is always aligned with the *U* axis of its response plane.

The length of the vibration vector is equal to the amplitude of the filtered vibration. The angle of the response vector relative to the *U* axis is the absolute phase lag, measured from the measurement axis in a direction *opposite* to the direction of rotation of the machine rotor (Figure 3-3). Thus, depending on the direction of rotation, the vector can plot in different places. Note that the positive *V* axis is always located at 90°, measured opposite the direction of rotation.

To plot a vibration vector, follow these steps:

1) Determine the angular orientation of the transducer relative to your machine viewpoint. This will define the direction of the *U* (measurement) axis.

2) Determine the direction of rotation of the rotor. The positive *V* axis will be located 90° from the *U* axis in a direction opposite to rotor rotation.

3) Use the absolute phase of the filtered vibration signal to locate the angular orientation of the vibration vector. Measure the angle from the *U* axis, opposite the direction of rotation, toward the direction of the *V* axis.

4) The length of the vibration vector is the amplitude of the filtered vibration signal. Typically, displacement units are µm pp or mil pp, velocity units are mm/s pk or in/s pk, and acceleration units are g pk.

Because the vibration vectors define the response of the machinery to a variety of factors, it is critical to document this data under a variety of operating conditions. On critical machinery, where transducers are installed at many locations, the vibration data from each transducer should be recorded over the entire operating speed range during startup and shutdown. 1X and 2X vectors are most commonly measured, but other frequency components should be measured if there is a forcing function (such as blade passage) that is at a harmonic of running speed.

Vibration vectors are also monitored while a machine is running at a constant speed. Changes in operating and load conditions can produce predictable changes in response vectors, but significant changes outside this envelope could indicate a change in the machine's health. Unexpected changes in vibration vectors are important for the early detection of machine internal problems, such as unbalance, rub, instabilities, and shaft cracks, and external problems, such as coupling failure, piping strain, and foundation deterioration.

The tip of the vibration vector defines a point in the transducer response plane. A plot of a set of these points corresponding to different machine conditions provides a powerful visual display of the response of the machine at that transducer location, whether the machine is starting up, at operating speed, or coasting down. The plot of a set of startup or shutdown vibration vector points is equivalent to a *polar plot* (See Chapter 7), one of the most informative plots available for diagnosing machinery condition. A set of such points at a steady operating speed (steady state) produces an *APHT plot*, and vibration vectors are monitored during machine operation in acceptance regions in these plots.

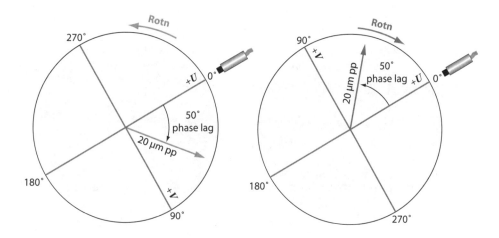

Figure 3-3. *V* axis orientation versus direction of shaft rotation. The +*V* axis is located 90° from the +*U* axis, against the direction of rotation of the shaft. Phase lag is always measured from *U* to *V*. The same vibration vector will plot differently, depending on the direction of rotation.

Working with Vibration Vectors

When working with vibration vectors, it is important to use a system of notation that is both convenient and complete. Commonly, vibration vectors are noted as

$$r = A \angle \Phi \tag{3-1}$$

where r is the displacement vibration vector, A is the vibration amplitude, $\angle$ identifies the value that follows as an angle, and Φ (Greek upper case phi) is the phase angle, usually expressed as positive phase lag. This is a *polar* representation of the vector. An equivalent *rectangular* representation is given by

$$r = u + jv \tag{3-2}$$

where j is the square root of -1, and

$$\begin{aligned} u &= A\cos\Phi \\ v &= A\sin\Phi \end{aligned} \tag{3-3}$$

The variables u and v are the rectangular coordinates of the vector in the transducer response plane. The u coordinate is measured along the U axis (the transducer measurement axis), and the v coordinate is measured along the V axis. (As we have already noted, U and V are *not* the same as the physical XY coordinate system used to describe the machine.) Vibration vectors are actually complex numbers, and the j term originates in complex number theory.

Conversion from rectangular form to polar form is performed using these expressions:

$$\begin{aligned} A &= \sqrt{u^2 + v^2} \\ \Phi &= \arctan 2\left(\frac{v}{u}\right) \end{aligned} \tag{3-4}$$

where arctan2 represents the arctangent2 function, which takes quadrants into account.

For example, the vibration vector in Figure 3-2 can be expressed in polar form as

$$r = 90 \ \mu\text{m pp} \ \angle 220° \ (3.5 \ \text{mil pp} \ \angle 220°)$$

and in rectangular form as

$$\boldsymbol{r} = -69\ \mu\mathrm{m\ pp} - j58\ \mu\mathrm{m\ pp} \quad (-2.7\ \mathrm{mil\ pp} - j2.3\ \mathrm{mil\ pp})$$

However, conversion in the opposite direction can lead to difficulty. If a simple arctangent function is used to calculate the phase lag angle, the result is

$$\Phi = \arctan\left(\frac{v}{u}\right) = \arctan\left(\frac{-58}{-69}\right) = 40°$$

which is *incorrect*. The situation is shown in Figure 3-4. Adding 180° produces the correct result: 220°. When using the standard arctangent function, it is a good idea to sketch the situation, carefully noting the signs of the coordinates, and verify the result. Engineering and scientific calculators use the arctangent2 function when converting from rectangular to polar coordinates, but they produce a result between ±180°. When the calculated result is negative, add 360° to produce a positive phase lag between 0° and 360°.

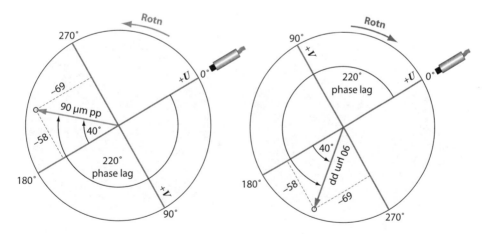

Figure 3-4. The arctangent function and rectangular to polar conversion. The same vector is plotted for different rotation directions, and the rectangular coordinates are shown. Use of the standard arctangent function yields a phase lag angle of 40°, which is incorrect; the true phase lag angle is 220°. When using the arctangent function, it is a good idea to sketch the situation to verify the calculated angle.

Vibration vectors often need to be added, subtracted, multiplied, and divided. Addition and subtraction of two vibration vectors can be done graphically, or the result can be easily calculated using the rectangular form. Multiplication and division are calculated most easily using the polar form.

Addition is done by adding the u components and v components separately and then combining the results to define a new vector. The units of measurement of the two vectors must be the same or the result will be meaningless.

Two vibration vectors, r_1 and r_2, can be added graphically to produce a resultant vector, r_3 (see Figure 3-5). To do this,

1) Plot r_1 in the transducer response plane with its tail at the origin.

2) Plot r_2 in with *its* tail at the origin.

3) Slide r_2 over (copy it) so that its tail is at the tip of r_1.

4) Draw a new vector from the origin to the tip of the copy of r_2. This vector is the resultant, r_3.

Figure 3-5. Graphic vector addition. To add r_1 and r_2, plot the two vectors in the transducer response plane. Copy r_2 so that the tail of r_2 is at the tip of r_1. The resultant, r_3, is the vector from the origin to the tip of r_2.

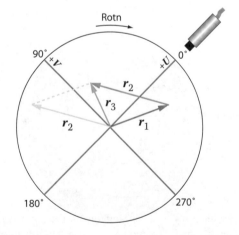

The graphical technique is the mathematical equivalent of adding the two vectors' u and v components:

$$r_3 = r_1 + r_2 = (u_1 + u_2) + j(v_1 + v_2) \tag{3-5}$$

Example
A gas turbine rotates in a Y to X direction at 7450 rpm. Data is taken from a casing velocity transducer (which provides absolute casing motion) and a shaft relative displacement transducer. Both transducers are mounted at 45° R. The 1X, integrated, casing vibration, r_c, is found to be 40 μm pp $\angle 35°$ (1.6 mil pp $\angle 35°$). The 1X, shaft relative vibration, r_{sr}, is measured as 30 μm pp $\angle 120°$ (1.2 mil pp $\angle 120°$). Find the 1X, shaft absolute vibration vector, r_s.

Solution
The shaft absolute vibration vector is found by adding the u and v components of the casing vibration and shaft relative vibration vectors (Figure 3-6). The transducer response plane is shown with the U axis aligned with the transducer's measurement axis. Because rotation is Y to X, the positive V axis is located 90° counterclockwise from the U axis, and the phase angle is measured in that direction.

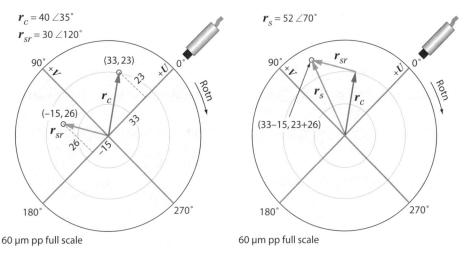

Figure 3-6. Addition of vibration vectors to find the shaft absolute vibration. Graphically add the casing absolute vibration vector, r_c, to the shaft relative vibration vector, r_{sr}, or add the u and v components of each vector.

1) Convert both measurements to rectangular form, using Equation 3-3:

$$r_c = (40 \ \mu m \ pp)\cos 35° + j(40 \ \mu m \ pp)\sin 35°$$
$$r_c = 33 \ \mu m \ pp + j23 \ \mu m \ pp$$

$$r_{sr} = (30 \ \mu m \ pp)\cos 120° + j(30 \ \mu m \ pp)\sin 120°$$
$$r_{sr} = -15 \ \mu m \ pp + j26 \ \mu m \ pp$$

2) Add the components to get the solution in rectangular form using Equation 3-5:

$$r_s = (33 - 15) \ \mu m \ pp + j(23 + 26) \ \mu m \ pp$$
$$r_s = 18 \ \mu m \ pp + j49 \ \mu m \ pp$$

3) Convert to polar form using Equation 3-4:

$$A = \sqrt{(18 \ \mu m \ pp)^2 + (49 \ \mu m \ pp)^2}$$
$$\Phi = \arctan 2 \left(\frac{49 \ \mu m \ pp}{18 \ \mu m \ pp} \right)$$

$$r_s = 52 \ \mu m \ pp \ \angle 70° \ (2.0 \ mil \ pp \ \angle 70°)$$

Subtraction is done by subtracting the u components and v components separately and then combining the results to define a new vector. Graphical subtraction is performed by adding the *negative* of one vector to the other. Again, the units of measurement of the two vectors must be the same or the result will be meaningless.

Two vibration vectors, r_1, and r_2, can be subtracted graphically to produce a resultant vector, r_3 (see Figure 3-7). To find $r_3 = r_1 - r_2$,

1) Plot r_1 in the transducer response plane with its tail at the origin.

2) Find the *negative* of r_2 by changing the phase angle by 180°. This is also equivalent to multiplying r_2 by −1.

3) Plot $-\boldsymbol{r}_2$ with *its* tail at the origin.

4) Copy $-\boldsymbol{r}_2$ so that its tail is at the tip of $\boldsymbol{r}_1$.

5) Draw a new vector from the origin to the tip of the copy of $-\boldsymbol{r}_2$. This vector is the resultant, $\boldsymbol{r}_3$.

The graphical technique is the mathematical equivalent of subtracting the two vectors' u and v components:

$$\boldsymbol{r}_3 = \boldsymbol{r}_1 - \boldsymbol{r}_2 = (u_1 - u_2) + j(v_1 - v_2) \qquad (3\text{-}6)$$

Multiplication of two vectors is performed most easily using the polar format; multiply the amplitudes and add the phase angles:

$$\boldsymbol{r}_3 = (A_1 \angle \Phi_1)(A_2 \angle \Phi_2) = (A_1 A_2) \angle (\Phi_1 + \Phi_2) \qquad (3\text{-}7)$$

Division is performed by dividing the amplitudes and subtracting the phase angles:

$$\boldsymbol{r}_3 = \frac{A_1 \angle \Phi_1}{A_2 \angle \Phi_2} = \left(\frac{A_1}{A_2}\right) \angle (\Phi_1 - \Phi_2) \qquad (3\text{-}8)$$

See the Appendix for examples of multiplication and division of vibration vectors.

Figure 3-7. Graphic vector subtraction. To subtract $\boldsymbol{r}_2$ from $\boldsymbol{r}_1$, plot $\boldsymbol{r}_1$ and $\boldsymbol{r}_2$ in the transducer response plane. Plot the *negative* of $\boldsymbol{r}_2$ and copy it so that the tail of $-\boldsymbol{r}_2$ is at the tip of $\boldsymbol{r}_1$. The resultant, $\boldsymbol{r}_3$, is the vector from the origin to the tip of $-\boldsymbol{r}_2$.

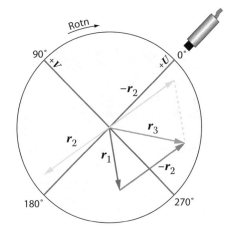

NOTE: For all vector operations, the phase lag angle should be expressed as a positive number between 0° and 360°. If the calculated phase lag is negative, add 360°. If the result is greater than 360°, subtract 360°.

Most scientific and engineering calculators can operate directly on complex numbers and don't require conversion between polar and rectangular forms.

This vector concept extends to more than just vibration measurement. The force due to unbalance is a rotating force vector that has a particular angular position when the Keyphasor event occurs. And Dynamic Stiffness, a very important concept in machinery behavior, is also expressed as a complex number, usually in rectangular form. These two vector entities, together with the vibration vector, are fundamental to understanding the dynamic behavior of machinery.

The Slow Roll Vector

The slow roll vector is an important application of vector subtraction. The slow roll vector is a constant, or slowly varying, component of the vibration vector that represents nondynamic action observed by a transducer. The slow roll vector will be different for each measurement transducer location. It originates in mechanical effects, such as a bowed rotor or coupling problem, or in mechanical or electrical runout, and it can distort and obscure the machine's dynamic response data (Figure 3-8). *Slow roll vector compensation* is the technique of subtracting the measured slow roll vector from the transducer vibration vector (Figure 3-9).

To measure the slow roll vector, we must be able to find an operating condition where the slow roll is the dominant component of the vibration signal. Since the 1X dynamic response due to unbalance tends to zero at low speeds, any 1X vibration measured at these low speeds is considered to be due to sources other than unbalance. Thus, slow roll vectors are measured in this speed range, which is called the *slow roll speed range*. One guideline (and it is *only* a guideline) is that the upper limit of the slow roll speed range is about 10% of the first balance resonance speed of the machine. The slow roll speed range is best identified using an uncompensated Bode plot (see Chapter 7) of a machine startup or shutdown.

While noise affects all transducers, slow roll data is usually obtained only from displacement transducers. Eddy current displacement transducers have a frequency response that extends to dc (zero speed), while velocity and acceleration transducers do not. Because of this, velocity and acceleration slow roll response generally cannot be measured, and vibration data from these transducers is not compensated.

Figure 3-8. The 1X slow roll vector. The 1X slow roll vector (red) adds to the 1X response vector due to unbalance (green). This can produce a vibration vector that is significantly different (blue) than the unbalance response vector. Slow roll vectors can be measured for any harmonic of running speed.

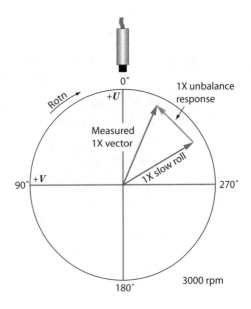

Figure 3-9. Slow roll vector compensation. To compensate for slow roll, subtract the slow roll vector from the vibration vector measured by the same transducer. The resultant is the slow-roll-compensated, dynamic response vector (green).

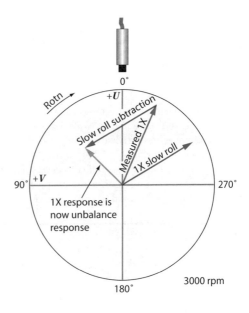

Slow Roll Vector Changes

The basic underlying assumption when using slow roll compensation is that, at running speed, the shaft probes view the same section of rotor surface that they view at slow roll. However, at each axial position on a shaft, the shaft surface is likely to produce a different slow roll vector.

Thermal growth can be one source of slow roll vector change. During a cold startup, rotors can grow axially relative to the machine casing; thus, probes may view a different section of shaft surface with a different slow roll vector (Figure 3-10). Because of this, all compensated transient startup data should be used with caution. Data from a hot shutdown is much less likely to have this problem.

Even after the machine reaches thermal equilibrium at running speed, slow roll data may be invalid. Machines with high operating thermal gradients, such as gas turbines or refrigeration compressors, can have different rates of axial rotor and casing growth. In this situation, cold slow roll vectors are questionable, and hot shutdown slow roll vectors are likely to be more reliable.

In general, it is better to compensate cold data with cold slow roll vectors and to compensate hot data with hot slow roll vectors.

Even when probes view the same section of shaft surface, slow roll vectors can change over a long period of time due to changes in rotor bow, changes in electrical runout, corrosion of the viewing surface, or developing machine problems. Changing slow roll vectors are often a sign that something significant is happening to the machine and should be investigated.

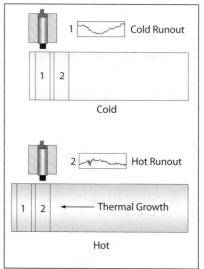

Figure 3-10. Rotor thermal growth and slow roll runout measurements. When the rotor is cold (blue) the probe views probe track 1. One revolution produces the slow roll waveform shown next to the probe. When the rotor is hot (red), it grows axially, and the probe now views track 2, which has a different slow roll runout. The cold slow roll measurement is not valid for the hot condition.

Summary

An unfiltered, or direct, vibration signal is unchanged from the original transducer vibration signal. It is assumed to contain all of the original frequency, amplitude, and phase content and the original dc offset, if any.

Filtering removes signal content. Many machinery vibration signals are bandpass filtered to a multiple of running speed, most often 1X. The filtered signal is a sine wave with a frequency equal to the bandpass frequency of the filter. After filtering, the amplitude and absolute phase of the signal can be measured.

A vibration vector is the combination of the amplitude and absolute phase of a filtered vibration signal. This vector is plotted in the transducer response plane. Because vibration vectors are complex numbers, they can be added, subtracted, multiplied, and divided.

The slow roll speed range of a machine is the range of speeds where the dynamic rotor response due to unbalance is insignificant compared to the slow roll vector; roughly, it is below 10% of the first balance resonance speed of a machine. The slow roll speed range is best identified using an uncompensated Bode plot.

Slow roll compensation is the subtraction of the slow roll vector from a vibration vector at the same measurement location. The resultant vibration vector will only reflect the dynamic response of the rotor.

Data Plots

Chapter 4

Timebase Plots

THE TIMEBASE PLOT IS THE MOST FUNDAMENTAL graphic presentation of machinery dynamic data. It shows how a single parameter (most often displacement, velocity, or acceleration, but also any other dynamic measurement) from a single transducer changes on a very short time scale, typically a fraction of a second. This is in contrast to trend plots, which display the value of a slowly changing parameter (for example, axial position) over a much longer time scale, typically hours to months.

A timebase plot represents a small slice of time in the vibration history of the machine. Usually, the amount of time involves only a few revolutions of the rotor. During this short length of time (about 17 ms for one revolution of a 3600 rpm machine), the overall behavior of the machine is not likely to change significantly. However, unfiltered timebase plots can clearly show a change in machine response if sudden events occur in the machine or if the machine is rapidly changing speed (such as an electric motor startup).

Timebase plots have several important uses. They have the advantage in being able to clearly display the unprocessed output from a single transducer. This allows us to look for noise on the signal or to detect the presence of multiple frequency components. An important use of a timebase plot is to identify the presence and timing of short term transient events.

Multiple timebase plots can allow us to establish timing relationships at different axial locations along the machine train. Or, the timebase plots from a pair of *XY* transducers can be used to determine the direction of precession of the rotor shaft.

To understand the timebase plot, we will discuss its structure and construction, followed by an explanation of the meaning of the Keyphasor mark.

We will then discuss slow roll compensation and a special application of the waveform compensation technique that can be used to produce a Not-1X timebase plot.

Finally, we will demonstrate how to obtain the large amount of information that exists in a timebase plot, such as the peak-to-peak amplitude, the filtered vibration frequency, the rotor speed, the nX amplitude and phase of a filtered signal, and the relative frequency of the filtered vibration signal versus running speed.

The Structure of a Timebase Plot

The timebase plot is a rectangular (Cartesian) plot of a parameter versus time (Figure 4-1). Time is on the horizontal axis, and elapsed time increases from left to right; events occurring later in time will be to the right of earlier events. Because of the time scales encountered in rotating machinery, the elapsed time is typically displayed in milliseconds (ms).

The measured parameter, converted from voltage to engineering units, is on the vertical axis. On Bently Nevada timebase plots, the data is approximately vertically centered in the plot, and the unit of measurement per vertical scale tick mark is identified (in the figure, this is 1 μm/div).

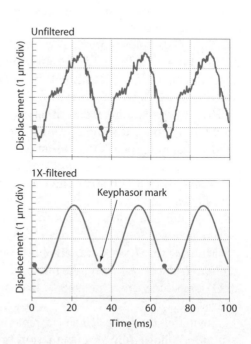

Figure 4-1. Unfiltered and filtered timebase plots. The plot shows the change in a measured parameter over time. Time, on the horizontal axis, increases from left to right. The vertical axis represents the measured parameter (in this case displacement), and the scale indication (1μm/div) refers to the small tick marks. Timebase plots can be unfiltered (top) or filtered (bottom, a 1X-filtered plot of the same data). The Keyphasor mark indicates the occurrence of a Keyphasor event.

The vertical position of a point on the timebase plot represents the instantaneous value of the measured parameter. For velocity and acceleration transducers, it represents the instantaneous value of velocity and acceleration relative to a point in free space; for displacement signals, the vertical position represents the instantaneous position relative to the probe tip.

Note that the terms peak (pk), peak-to-peak (pp), and root-mean-square (rms) are used to describe how *changes* in the parameter are measured and are not appropriate units for the vertical axis of a timebase plot. However, the signal can swing through a range that *can* be measured in peak-to-peak units. In the figure, the amplitude of the filtered signal (bottom) is about 6.0 μm (0.24 mil) pk, 12 μm (0.47 mil) pp, and 4.2 μm (0.17 mil) rms. All of these terms describe the same signal.

In unfiltered timebase plots, digitally sampled signal voltages are first divided by the transducer scale factor to convert them to equivalent engineering units. Then, the converted values are plotted on the timebase plot. The resulting waveform describes the instantaneous behavior of the measured parameter from one moment to the next.

Filtered timebase plots are constructed from the amplitude and phase of vibration vectors. The plot is synthesized by computing a sine wave with the correct frequency, amplitude, and phase (see Appendix 2 for details). This synthesis process assumes that conditions in the machine don't change significantly over the period of time represented by the synthesized waveform. This is usually, but not always, a correct assumption.

Computer-based timebase plots display a *digitally sampled waveform*. The sample rate determines the upper frequency limit of the signal that is displayed, and the length of time over which the waveform is sampled determines the low frequency limit. Low frequency signals will not be completely represented if the sample length is shorter than the period of the low frequency component. For these reasons, digitally sampled, unfiltered timebase plots are, inherently, both low- and high-pass filtered.

A timebase plot has several important differences from the timebase display on an oscilloscope: a basic oscilloscope displays voltage on the vertical axis, while a timebase plot displays engineering units, such as μm, mil, mm/s, g, etc.; the scope can display over a very long time frame; and there are subtle differences in the display and meaning of the Keyphasor mark.

The Keyphasor Mark

The blank/dot sequence on the timebase waveform is called a *Keyphasor mark*. The mark represents a timing event, the Keyphasor event, that occurs once per shaft revolution. The timing signal comes from a separate, Keyphasor transducer and is combined with the waveform so that the timing of the Keyphasor event can be seen clearly. *The time between two Keyphasor marks represents the period of one revolution of the shaft.*

On all Bently Nevada plots, the Keyphasor event is shown as a blank/dot sequence, and the dot represents the instant that the Keyphasor event occurs (see Figure 2-4). This is different than the Keyphasor mark on an oscilloscope, which may be a blank/bright or bright/blank sequence depending on the type of shaft mark and the type of oscilloscope used.

The Keyphasor mark on a timebase plot adds important additional information that will be discussed below. It can be used to measure rotative speed, the absolute phase of an nX frequency component (n is an integer), and the vibration frequency in orders of rotative speed.

Compensation of Timebase Plots

The primary objective of compensation is to remove unwanted signal content (noise) that is unrelated to the machine behavior that we want to observe. This noise, electrical and mechanical runout (glitch), bow, etc., can partially or completely obscure the dynamic information. Shaft scratches or other surface defects create a pattern of signal artifacts that repeats every revolution. It can be very useful to remove this noise to better reveal the important dynamic information. In Chapter 3 we discussed one type of compensation, slow roll compensation of vibration vectors. Most often, we wish to remove the effects of any 1X slow roll response that may be present in the signal so that we can see the 1X response due to unbalance.

Slow roll compensation is primarily applied to eddy current displacement transducer data because these transducers have a significant output at slow roll speeds. At these speeds, output from velocity and acceleration (seismic) transducers is extremely low, and there is usually no measurable slow roll signal. For this reason, slow roll compensation is rarely, if ever, performed on seismic transducer data.

Filtered timebase plots can be slow roll compensated using a 1X, 2X, or nX slow roll vector. The slow roll vector is subtracted from the original vibration vector, and the new, compensated vibration vector is used to synthesize the filtered waveform. The end result is a filtered timebase plot that is slow roll compensated.

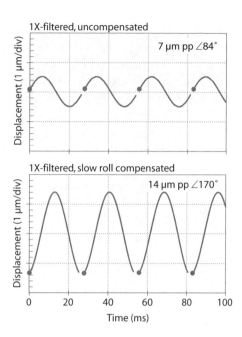

Figure 4-2. Slow roll compensation of filtered timebase plots. The top plot is a 1X-filtered, uncompensated plot. The bottom plot shows the same data after compensation with a slow roll vector. Note that, in this example, the amplitude is larger for the compensated plot and the absolute phase is significantly different. More often, slow roll compensation will result in a signal with lower amplitude.

Figure 4-2 shows plots of an uncompensated (top) and compensated (bottom) 1X-filtered waveform. The bottom plot has been compensated by subtracting the slow roll vector, 15 μm pp $\angle 17°$ (0.59 mil pp $\angle 17°$), from the uncompensated response vector, 7.0 μm pp $\angle 84°$ (0.28 mil pp $\angle 84°$). Note that the vibration amplitude of the compensated plot is *larger*, 14 μm pp $\angle 170°$ (0.55 mil pp $\angle 170°$). Subtraction of vectors can sometimes result in a larger vector, depending on the relative amplitudes and phases of the two vectors. In this example, the slow roll vector is significantly larger than the original vibration vector. Note also that the absolute phase is quite different between the two plots.

Another type of compensation, waveform compensation, can be applied to the unfiltered waveform. Unfiltered timebase waveforms consist of a sequence of digitally sampled values. One waveform, selected from the slow roll speed range, becomes the slow roll *waveform* sample. Each of the slow roll sample values can be subtracted from a corresponding value in the original waveform (the Keyphasor event can be used as a waveform timing reference). This method has the advantage of being able to remove most, if not all, of the slow roll component of the signal.

Waveform compensation will remove all components with frequencies up to the Nyquist sampling frequency limit (½ the sampling rate). Thus, 1X, 2X,..., nX (n an integer), and all subsynchronous and supersynchronous frequencies (to the Nyquist limit) will be removed from the vibration waveform, which includes many of the signal artifacts due to shaft surface defects. Figure 4-3 shows unfiltered timebase plots, with the same scale, from a machine before and after slow roll waveform compensation. Two things are immediately clear: the compensated plot has higher vibration amplitude and the waveform is much smoother. Most of the high frequency noise in the signal also existed in the slow roll signal; the waveform compensation removed it.

Unfiltered timebase waveforms can also be notch filtered by compensating with a synthesized, filtered waveform. The compensation waveform is reconstructed from a nX-filtered vibration vector that is sampled at the same time as the waveform to be compensated. The synthesized waveform is then subtracted from the vibration waveform of interest.

Using this technique, you can examine a vibration signal without the presence of *any* 1X vibration. A Not-1X waveform is created by subtracting the 1X-synthesized waveform from the original unfiltered waveform. The resultant waveform reveals any frequency information that may have been obscured by the 1X response. This can be helpful for identifying vibration characteristics associated with a variety of malfunctions.

Figure 4-4 shows an unfiltered timebase plot, with a combination of 1X and ½X vibration, (top), and the Not-1X version (bottom) of the same signal. Note that the ½X vibration, which is the dominant remaining component, is clearly visible.

Compensation is an art as well as a science. There are many variables that can change the compensation vector or waveform. It is possible, by using incorrect compensation, to produce plots that convey a wrong impression of machine behavior. Initially, it is always best to view data without any compensation. Then, when it is used, compensation should always be done with caution.

Information Contained in the Timebase Plot

The timebase plot has many features of a basic oscilloscope display. Before the widespread use of computerized data acquisition systems, the oscilloscope timebase display was a basic tool for machinery diagnosis. With the advent of the digital vector filter and the addition of the Keyphasor mark, the capabilities of the oscilloscope timebase display were extended. Now, computer-based data acquisition systems have evolved to the point where they *almost* provide a virtual oscilloscope.

Both oscilloscope timebase displays and computer-based timebase plots can be used to make a number of measurements. The following discussion applies primarily to timebase plots, but it can be extended to oscilloscope timebase displays.

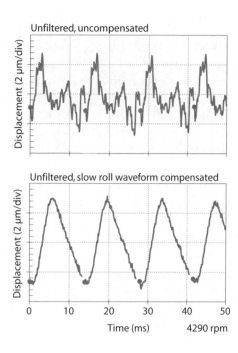

Figure 4-3. Waveform compensation of an unfiltered timebase plot. The top plot shows an unfiltered waveform from a machine running at 4290 rpm. The bottom plot shows the same data after waveform compensation using a slow roll waveform. The predominantly 1X vibration is clearly visible, and the waveform compensation has removed most of the noise in the signal. The noise was most likely due to glitch.

Figure 4-4. Vector compensation to produce Not-1X. The top plot shows an unfiltered waveform. A 1X vibration vector, measured at the same speed, is used to construct the 1X compensation waveform. The Not-1X plot (bottom) is the original signal with only the 1X content removed, and it shows predominantly 1/2X vibration.

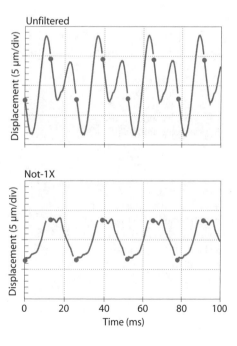

One additional word of caution should be mentioned: on oscilloscopes, a *division* usually means the space between major grid lines. On Bently Nevada plots, a division is usually the space between tick marks. This can and does cause confusion, and it is important to be sure which measurement system is being used.

Single timebase plots with Keyphasor marks can be used to measure the amplitude of unfiltered vibration; the rotor speed; the frequency, amplitude, and absolute phase of filtered vibration; and the relative frequency of filtered vibration versus rotor speed. Additionally, the shape of an unfiltered timebase signal can provide important clues to the behavior of machinery.

Multiple timebase plots can be used to measure the relative phase of two signals and, when the signals are from orthogonal displacement transducers, the direction of precession of the rotor.

Before continuing, it is important to recall that, for dynamic signals that conform to Bently Nevada standards, the positive peak of the timebase waveform represents the maximum positive value of the measurement parameter. The positive peak represents the maximum positive velocity for velocity transducers, the maximum positive acceleration for accelerometers, and the maximum positive pressure for dynamic pressure transducers.

For displacement signals, the positive peak of the timebase plot always represents the closest approach of the shaft to the transducer. For 1X vibration, the point on the shaft which is on the outside of the deflected shaft is called the *high spot*. Thus the positive peak in a 1X-filtered displacement signal represents the passage of the high spot next to the displacement transducer. See Chapter 2.

Figure 4-5. Measuring peak-to-peak amplitude on a timebase plot. The vertical scales have a 2 µm (0.08 mil)/div increment (scale factor). The red lines are drawn at the positive and negative peaks of the signal. The number of divisions between the lines times the scale factor is the peak-to-peak amplitude of the vibration signal.

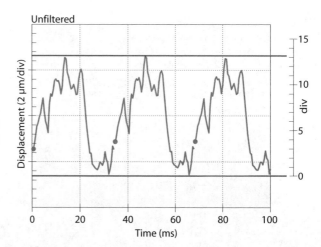

Perhaps the most basic measurement that can be made on a timebase plot of vibration is the *amplitude*. This measurement can be made on either filtered or unfiltered plots. To measure the peak-to-peak amplitude,

1. Draw horizontal lines that just touch the most positive and negative peaks of the signal.

2. Count the number of vertical divisions between the two lines (peak-to-peak).

3. Note the vertical scale factor (units per division) on the plot.

4. Calculate the peak-to-peak amplitude using Equation 4-1.

$$\text{pp amplitude} = (\text{number of div pp})\left(\frac{\text{units}}{\text{div}}\right) \qquad (4\text{-}1)$$

The peak amplitude is one-half of the peak-to-peak amplitude.

For example, Figure 4-5 shows an unfiltered displacement timebase plot that was captured during the shutdown of a 10 MW steam turbine generator set. The Keyphasor marks show that approximately three full revolutions of data are plotted. Red horizontal lines have been drawn that touch the maximum and minimum of the signal. The vertical scale factor is 2 μm/div.

To make measurement of the peak-to-peak amplitude easier, a duplicate scale has been placed at the right of the plot, aligned with the lower measurement line.

Following the procedure above, there are a little over 13 divisions between the two measurement lines. Applying Equation 4-1, the total change is

$$\text{pp amplitude} = (13 \text{ div pp})\left(\frac{2 \text{ μm}}{\text{div}}\right) = 26 \text{ μm pp } (1.0 \text{ mil pp})$$

Examination of the *shape* of the unfiltered waveform in the figure reveals that the vibration is predominantly 1X (one large cycle of vibration per Keyphasor event). Also, a low level of some higher order, probably harmonic, vibration is also present. Some of the noisy appearance of the waveform may be due to electrical or mechanical runout (glitch) in the shaft, which is more visible because of the relatively low level of 1X vibration that is present.

The Keyphasor dots can be used to measure the *rotor speed*, Ω (Greek upper case omega), of the machine:

1. Draw vertical lines through two successive Keyphasor dots.

2. Determine the elapsed time, Δt, (delta t) between the dots.

3. Calculate the rotor speed in rpm from the following formula.

$$\Omega \text{ (rpm)} = \left| \frac{1 \text{ rev}}{\Delta t \text{ (ms)}} \right| \left(\frac{1000 \text{ ms}}{\text{s}} \right) \left(\frac{60 \text{ s}}{\text{min}} \right) \tag{4-2}$$

For example, in Figure 4-6, red vertical lines have been drawn through adjacent Keyphasor dots. A measurement scale has been placed below the lines to help measure the elapsed time between Keyphasor events, which represents one revolution of the shaft. The time for one revolution is approximately 34 ms. Applying Equation 4-2,

$$\Omega = \left(\frac{1 \text{ rev}}{34 \text{ ms}} \right) \left(\frac{1000 \text{ ms}}{\text{s}} \right) \left(\frac{60 \text{ s}}{\text{min}} \right) = 1760 \text{ rpm}$$

Figure 4-6. Measuring rpm on a timebase plot. The time between successive Keyphasor marks represents the time for one revolution of the shaft. The reciprocal of this gives the number of revolutions per unit time, the rotor speed of the machine (see the text for details).

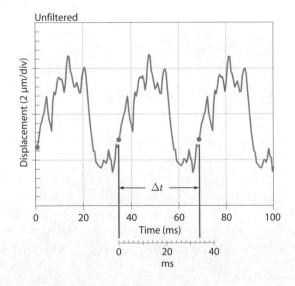

The *frequency* of a filtered vibration signal can be measured on a timebase plot. To measure frequency,

1.   Display a filtered timebase plot which shows at least one full cycle of vibration. For very low frequencies, this may require several revolutions worth of data. (An unfiltered plot can be used if the signal is dominated by one frequency.)

2.   Draw vertical lines through two equivalent points on the signal that are one cycle of vibration apart. For example, use zero crossings or peaks.

3.   Determine the elapsed time, which is the period, *T*, of the signal. (If and only if this is 1X vibration, it will be the same as the time between Keyphasor dots.)

4.   Calculate the frequency, *f*, of vibration using the following equation. This equation assumes that the period has been measured in milliseconds.

$$f \text{ (cpm)} = \left[\frac{1 \text{ cycle}}{T \text{ (ms/cycle)}} \right] \left(\frac{1000 \text{ ms}}{\text{s}} \right) \left(\frac{60 \text{ s}}{\text{min}} \right) \qquad (4\text{-}3)$$

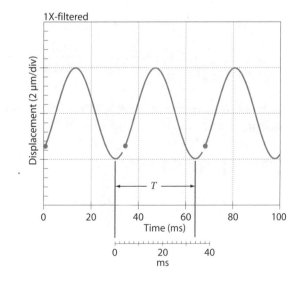

Figure 4-7. Measuring the frequency of a filtered signal. Locate two points on the waveform that are one cycle apart (in this case, the negative peaks). The time between these events is the period, *T*, of the signal. The frequency is the reciprocal of the period.

For example, in Figure 4-7, red vertical lines have been drawn through successive minima of the signal. A measurement scale has been placed below the lines to help measure the period of one cycle of vibration. This time is approximately 34 ms. Applying Equation 4-3, we can calculate the frequency, f:

$$f = \left(\frac{1 \text{ cycle}}{34 \text{ ms}}\right)\left(\frac{1000 \text{ ms}}{\text{s}}\right)\left(\frac{60 \text{ s}}{\text{min}}\right) = 1760 \text{ cpm}$$

The *amplitude* and *absolute phase* of a vibration vector can be measured from a filtered timebase plot. The peak-to-peak amplitude is found using the method discussed above. The absolute phase is defined as the phase lag from the Keyphasor event to the first positive peak of the filtered vibration waveform.

1. Draw vertical lines through a Keyphasor dot and the first positive peak after the Keyphasor dot.

2. Determine the elapsed time, Δt, between these two lines. The elapsed time is always less than the time for one complete cycle of vibration.

3. Determine the period, T, of one cycle of vibration, using the method described above.

4. Calculate the absolute phase, Φ, of the signal using Equation 4-4.

$$\Phi = \left|\frac{\Delta t \text{ (ms)}}{T \text{ (ms/cycle)}}\right|\left(\frac{360 \text{ deg}}{\text{cycle}}\right) \tag{4-4}$$

For example, in Figure 4-8, to find the peak-to-peak amplitude, draw two horizontal lines at the positive and negative peak of the signal. The distance between the two lines is a little over 10 divisions. Use Equation 4-1 to find the peak-to-peak amplitude, A:

$$A = (10 \text{ div pp})\left(\frac{2 \text{ } \mu m}{\text{div}}\right) = 20 \text{ } \mu m \text{ pp } (0.79 \text{ mil pp})$$

The peak amplitude is one-half of the peak-to-peak amplitude: 10 µm (0.39 mil) pk. Because this filtered signal is a sine wave, the rms amplitude is 0.707 times the peak amplitude, or 7.0 µm (0.28 mil) rms.

To measure the absolute phase, draw vertical lines through a Keyphasor dot and the first positive peak of the signal. The elapsed time, Δt, is 12.5 ms, and the period, T, which is the same as in Figure 4-7, is 34 ms. Use Equation 4-4 to determine absolute phase:

$$\Phi = \left(\frac{12.5 \text{ ms}}{34 \text{ ms/cycle}} \right) \left(\frac{360 \text{ deg}}{\text{cycle}} \right) = 130°$$

Thus, the 1X vibration vector, r, is

$$r = 20 \text{ µm pp} \angle 130° \ (0.79 \text{ mil pp} \angle 130°)$$

Because this is a 1X-filtered signal, each signal peak represents the passage of the rotor high spot next to the probe.

Figure 4-8. Measuring the peak-to-peak amplitude and absolute phase of a filtered signal. The absolute phase is defined as the elapsed time from a Keyphasor event to the first positive peak of the signal. It is stated as a fraction of a full cycle, expressed in degrees.

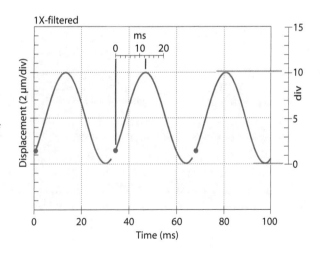

The *relative frequency*, in orders of running speed, is the ratio of the vibration frequency to the rotative speed. When a filtered timebase plot contains Keyphasor marks, the frequency of the filtered vibration signal can be compared to rotor speed:

1. Find the frequency, f, of the filtered vibration signal.

2. Find the rotor speed in the same units (Hz or cpm).

3. Divide the frequency of the vibration signal by the rotor speed.

4. Express the result in the form nX, where

$$n = \frac{f_{signal}}{f_{rotor}}$$ (4-5)

The n will be a number that represents the relative frequency in orders of running speed.

For example, in Figure 4-8, the frequency of vibration is equal to rotor speed; thus, n = 1, and the relative frequency is 1X. If there were two complete cycles of vibration per revolution of the shaft, the relative frequency would be 2X. Sub- and supersynchronous frequency ratios are possible, such as ½X, 0.43X, ⅔X, ³⁄₂X, or 1.6X.

A useful visual analysis is to examine the progression of Keyphasor marks across an unfiltered timebase plot. If the relative frequency is a sub- or super-harmonic of running speed (⅓X, ½X, 2X, 3X, etc.), then the Keyphasor dots will always be in the same relative place on the waveform, from one Keyphasor dot to the next. If the Keyphasor dots gradually shift position on the waveform, then the vibration frequency is a more complex ratio, such as ⅔X, ¾X, ⁴⁄₉X, ⁴⁄₃X, or a decimal fraction such as 0.47X or 0.36X.

Figure 4-9 compares two unfiltered timebase plots, each with eight revolutions of data. In the top plot, the waveform is dominated by ½X vibration (there are exactly two Keyphasor dots for each cycle of vibration). Note that the Keyphasor dots do not change position with time; every other Keyphasor dot occurs at the same relative place in the waveform. This fixed pattern indicates that the vibration frequency is a simple 1/n or n/1 ratio relative to running speed, where n is an integer.

In the bottom plot, the relative vibration frequency is *not* a sub- or super-harmonic of running speed; it is slightly less than ½X, close to 0.48X. For this case, every other Keyphasor event occurs at a slightly different place in the waveform; the Keyphasor dots plot at different vertical positions. This visual behavior is clear indication that the relative vibration frequency is not a simple integer relationship to running speed.

It is possible to see by inspection that the vibration frequency is slightly less than ½X. First, pick a Keyphasor dot as a starting reference. Next, move to the right to one complete cycle of vibration (the red line in the figure). In moving to the right, we pass two Keyphasor dots. The cycle of vibration is complete at the red circle. Therefore, there is less than one cycle of vibration for two revolutions of the shaft, for a ratio of less than 1:2 (less than ½X). Another way to determine the ratio is to note that the *period* of vibration is *longer* than the period for two shaft revolutions, therefore the *frequency* of the vibration is *less* than ½X.

Figure 4-9. Relative frequency and nonharmonic vibration. The unfiltered timebase (top) has one cycle of vibration for two Keyphasor marks (two revolutions of the shaft), and the Keyphasor marks do not change position with successive cycles (they are "locked"). Therefore the relative frequency of this vibration is exactly 1/2X. Keyphasor marks will remain locked whenever the vibration is a sub- or superharmonic of running speed, such as 1/3X, 1/2X, 1X, 2X, 3X, etc. The signal at the bottom has less than one cycle of vibration for two Keyphasor marks, and the vibration frequency is less than 1/2X (0.48X). The Keyphasor marks shift position from one cycle to the next. The pattern will eventually repeat if the relative frequency is an integer ratio, such as 2/3X, 3/4X, 4/3X, etc.

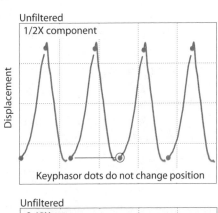

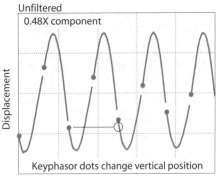

Time

X and Y timebase plots can be used to determine the *direction of precession* of a rotor shaft. Determination of the direction of precession is an application of relative phase (see Chapter 2). The plots must be constructed from data from two, coplanar, orthogonal displacement probes. By measuring the relative phase of the two waveforms, the direction of precession can be determined.

In Figure 4-10 a rotor shaft is observed by an XY pair of displacement probes. By Bently Nevada convention, the Y timebase plot is displayed above the X timebase plot. Use the positive peak of the X signal as a reference, and find the corresponding peak on the Y signal that is less than 180° out of phase. The relative phase shows that X leads Y by 90°. Thus, the rotor first passes the X probe and then passes the Y probe, showing that the precession of the shaft is X to Y.

Relative phase measurements can also be made between pairs of transducers in different axial locations, as long as the transducers have the same angular orientation. One application of this is to estimate the mode shape of the rotor by examining the timebase plots from several axially spaced transducers. The relative phase information in the plots can help establish a picture of how the rotor is deflecting along its length, including the approximate location of nodal points (Figure 4-11). This can provide useful information for balancing or for troubleshooting other machinery problems, such as coupling misalignment. See Chapter 12 for more information on mode identification.

Summary

The timebase plot is a rectangular plot of a vibration signal from a single transducer. Elapsed time is shown on the horizontal axis, with zero at the left edge of the plot. The vertical axis shows the instantaneous value of the measured parameter in engineering units (μm, mil, mm/s, g, etc.).

Timebase plots can present filtered or unfiltered vibration data. Filtered timebase plots are synthesized from vibration vectors using a mathematical sine function with the appropriate phase lag. Unfiltered timebase plots represent the digitally sampled waveform from the transducer.

Keyphasor events are indicated on the plot by a blank/dot sequence. The Keyphasor event, which occurs once per shaft revolution, is a timing event and is observed by a separate transducer.

Filtered timebase plots can be compensated with synthesized, filtered waveforms created from vibration vectors. Unfiltered timebase plots can be compensated with unfiltered waveforms (usually a slow roll waveform), or with a synthesized waveform from a vibration vector. If the vibration vector is measured at the same speed as the uncompensated vibration signal, then the resulting subtraction produces a Not-nX waveform, where nX represents the filtering frequency relative to running speed.

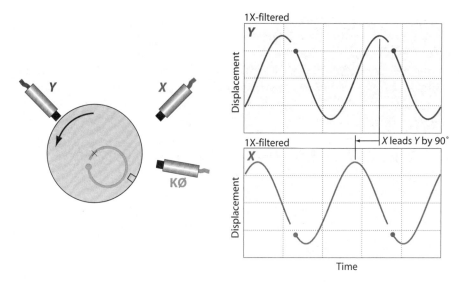

1X-filtered

Y

Displacement

1X-filtered

X

Displacement

X leads Y by 90°

Time

Figure 4-10. Direction of precession from *XY* timebase plots. As the shaft rotates, it will pass close to the *X* probe before it passes the *Y* probe. In the timebase plots, the positive peaks of the signals, which represent the passage of the rotor high spot nearest the probes, show that *X* leads *Y* by 90°. That means that the rotor is precessing in an *X* to *Y* sense, in the same direction as rotation; thus, the precession is forward.

Figure 4-11. The application of relative phase from probes in axially separated planes. 1X-filtered timebase plots from vertical probes near the bearings show that the relative phase differs by about 220°. The timebase plot on the right is repeated on the left plot for reference. The relative phase indicates that the rotor is approximately out of phase at opposite ends of the machine. A rigid body shape is shown; other deflection shapes are possible, and more probes are needed to confirm the shaft deflection shape.

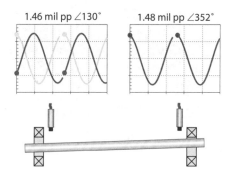

1.46 mil pp ∠130°   1.48 mil pp ∠352°

Timebase signals should first be viewed without any compensation. When necessary, compensation should be used with caution and should never be automatically applied to a signal.

Single timebase plots with Keyphasor marks can be used to measure the amplitude of unfiltered vibration; the rotor speed; the frequency, amplitude, and absolute phase of filtered vibration; and the relative frequency of filtered vibration versus rotor speed, in orders of running speed. The shape of an unfiltered timebase signal can provide important clues to the behavior of machinery. Timebase plots from *XY* probe pairs can be used to measure the direction of precession of the rotor, and timebase plots from probes at different axial locations can be compared to determine the mode shape of the rotor.

Chapter 5

The Orbit

I<small>N THE CHAPTER ON TIMEBASE PLOTS, WE SAW</small> how rotor dynamic motion along the measurement axis of a single transducer can be displayed as a time varying waveform. While the timebase plot can provide important and useful information, it is inherently limited to one dimension of rotor motion. Since, in any lateral plane along the rotor, the rotor moves in a two-dimensional path, or orbit, this one-dimensional picture provided by a single transducer is not adequate.

To measure this motion, a second transducer must be installed perpendicular to, and coplanar with, the first transducer. Only then will there be enough information to observe the complete motion of the rotor in that plane. This information could be presented on two, one-dimensional timebase plots, but it would be even better if we could display the two-dimensional dynamic motion of the rotor. That is the purpose of the orbit plot.

The orbit represents the path of the shaft centerline relative to a pair of orthogonal eddy current transducers. These transducers are usually mounted rigidly on the machine casing near a bearing; thus, the orbit typically represents the path of the shaft centerline relative to the bearing clearance of the machine. (Orbits can be constructed from casing vibration data, but this has limited application. This chapter will present orbits from shaft relative (displacement) probes.) Because of its ease of interpretation and extensive information content, the orbit, with Keyphasor mark, is probably the most powerful single plot format available to the machinery diagnostician.

In our discussion of the orbit, we will start with a description of how two timebase waveforms are used to create the orbit. We will discuss the information obtained when the Keyphasor mark is included on an orbit, and slow roll and Not-1X compensation of orbits. Finally, we will discuss the various kinds of information that can be obtained from an orbit.

The Construction of the Orbit

The orbit combines the timebase waveform data from two, perpendicular, coplanar transducers to create a single plot showing the two-dimensional dynamic motion of the shaft centerline (Figure 5-1). The orbit in the figure is unfiltered, but is predominantly 1X. The data comes from *XY* transducers, which observe the motion of the rotor. These transducers are mounted at 0° and 90° R (relative to the reference direction, "Up," also known as the orientation angle reference), but any transducer orientation is possible as long as the transducers are perpendicular to each other. The signals from the transducers can be displayed as two, independent timebase plots or can be combined to produce the orbit.

The Orbit plot format is a square, with identical horizontal and vertical scales and scale factors. A point on the orbit is defined by a pair of *X* and *Y* values, which are obtained from the timebase waveform data. A set of values from the sampled waveforms can create anything from a portion of the orbit to several orbits. The center of the orbit plot is defined by the average values of the *X* and *Y* timebase waveforms. A Keyphasor signal acts like a strobe: the dot shows the location of the shaft centerline when the Keyphasor event occurs. To complete the plot, a reference direction (for example, "Up" or "West"), the probe locations, and the direction of rotation are included on the plot.

Note that the direction of *rotation* cannot be determined from the orbit without additional information. The best way to determine the direction of rotation is to examine the machine. The direction of rotation may be visible to the eye, or it may be marked on the machine with an arrow. Another way is to use slow roll orbits (with caution!), which are almost always forward; thus, knowledge that the machine is at slow roll allows us to determine the direction of rotation by observing the direction of precession. The direction of *precession* can be determined by the blank/dot sequence on the plot. Be aware that crossed probe wiring or an active rotor malfunction that causes reverse precession at slow roll can render this method invalid.

Positive voltage or position changes on the timebase plot correspond to a motion component toward the transducer. On the orbit, this positive change always corresponds to motion toward a transducer, along its measurement axis, regardless of the transducer orientation. Since the orbit is much smaller than the transducer, the measurement is always made parallel to the transducer measurement axis.

In Figure 5-1, points 1 through 5 show the progression of the shaft centerline around its orbit. Point 1 shows the location of the shaft centerline (crosshairs) when the Keyphasor event occurs; that is, when the leading edge of the Keyphasor notch passes next to the Keyphasor probe (shown below the rotor).

Points 2 and 4 mark the farthest and closest approach to the *X* probe (the minimum and maximum peaks on the *X* timebase plot). Similarly, points 3 and 5 mark the farthest and closest approach to the *Y* probe (the minimum and maximum peaks on the *Y* timebase plot).

Often, several cycles of vibration are plotted on the orbit. In the figure, two cycles are shown in the timebase plots, which means that the orbit also has two cycles and, in this case, overwrites itself during the second cycle.

The positive peak of the timebase plot always represents the closest approach of the shaft to the associated transducer. For 1X vibration, the point on the shaft which is on the outside of the deflected shaft is called the high spot. The positive peak in a 1X-filtered displacement signal represents the passage of

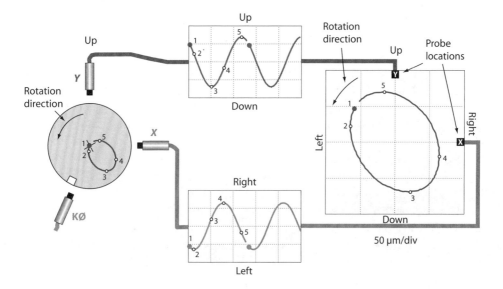

Figure 5-1. Construction of an orbit. *XY* transducers observe the vibration of a rotor shaft. A notch in the shaft (at a different axial location) is detected by a Keyphasor transducer. The vibration transducer signals produce two timebase plots (middle) which combine into an orbit plot (right). At position 1, when the Keyphasor probe detects the notch, the shaft centerline is located at the position of the Keyphasor dot. Positions 2 through 5 show the correlation of the orbit position and the timebase plot values. Two revolutions of data are shown in the timebase plots, but only one can be seen on the orbit because, in this case, the shaft follows the same path.

the high spot next to the displacement transducer, and this concept extends to the orbit. For a 1X-filtered, circular orbit, the orbit represents the path of the rotor high spot, as well as that of the shaft centerline.

Transducer mounting orientations are usually measured relative to the reference direction *for the machine*. For a horizontal machine, the reference direction is usually "Up." For vertical machines, the reference direction can be any convenient reference, for example, "North." Bently Nevada orbits are always plotted with the reference direction at the top of the plot. The actual transducer locations are indicated on the edge of the plot. This provides a uniform visual reference along the machine train, regardless of transducer mounting orientation. The orbit on the plot is oriented as an observer would see it when positioned with his head in the reference direction, looking along the axis of the machine in the viewpoint direction. (By Bently Nevada convention, this viewpoint is usually from the driver toward the driven machine.)

Figure 5-2 shows two examples of an orbit display with different transducer orientations. In both cases, the rotor orbit is the same, only the transducer mounting orientations are different. The orbit plots show the same orbit orientation relative to the "Up" reference. Note that the probe labels on the orbit plots show the actual probe mounting orientations.

At the bottom of the figure, equivalent oscilloscope orbits are shown. Because the *XY* axes of the oscilloscope on the right do not match the actual transducer locations, the oscilloscope must be physically rotated 45° CCW to display the orbit with the correct orientation. In this orientation, the horizontal and vertical oscilloscope axes are aligned with the actual transducer orientations. It is important to remember that, when viewing orbits on an oscilloscope, the XY axes of the oscilloscope must match the actual transducer mounting orientations, or the displayed orbit will be rotated and will not appear as it does on the machine.

Filtered orbit plots, like filtered timebase plots, are not constructed directly from waveform data. A filtered timebase waveform plot is constructed (synthesized) from a filtered vibration vector; a filtered orbit is constructed from the synthesized waveforms from a pair of vibration vectors. See Appendix 2 for details of this process.

The Keyphasor Mark

The blank/dot sequence on the orbit is called a Keyphasor mark. The mark represents a timing event, the Keyphasor event, that occurs once per shaft revolution. The timing signal comes from a separate (Keyphasor) transducer that is mounted at a different axial location. The timing signal is combined with the orbit so that the timing of the Keyphasor event can be seen clearly. The

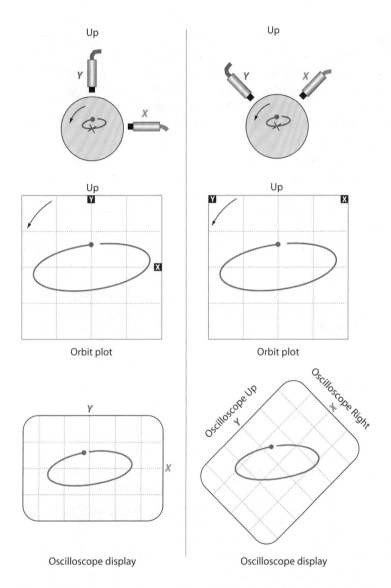

Figure 5-2. Probe orientation and the orbit plot. On the left side, the Y and X probes are mounted at 0° and 90° R, respectively. The orbit plot and oscilloscope display show the same view. On the right, the probes are mounted at 45° L and 45° R. The orbit plot is automatically rotated so that it is properly aligned with the "Up" reference direction. The oscilloscope, however, must be physically rotated 45° CCW to display the correct orbit orientation. Note that the Keyphasor marks on the orbit plots show the plot convention, where the dot marks the event; the bottom displays show the event at the beginning of the blank, one possible oscilloscope display.

Keyphasor mark on the orbit shows the location of the shaft centerline at the instant when the once-per-turn mark on the shaft passes next to the Keyphasor probe. On circular, 1X-filtered orbits, the Keyphasor dot marks the location of the rotor *high spot* at the instant of the Keyphasor event. The blank/dot sequence shows the direction of increasing time.

Figure 5-3 shows an orbiting rotor (the size of the orbit is greatly exaggerated) that is viewed by two orthogonal transducers. As the rotor rotates, the shaft centerline also moves (precesses) along a path which defines the orbit. A Keyphasor probe is installed to detect a once-per-turn mark on the shaft, in this case a notch. When the leading edge of the notch passes next to the Keyphasor probe (position 3 in the figure), the shaft centerline is located at the Keyphasor dot on the orbit. The Keyphasor signal is like a strobe that briefly illuminates the shaft as it travels in its orbit. Even though, in the figure, the rotor is on the opposite side of the orbit from the Keyphasor probe, the notch on the shaft is in a position to be sensed by the Keyphasor probe.

On all Bently Nevada plots, the Keyphasor event is shown as a blank/dot sequence (as shown in Figure 5-2 in the orbit plots), and the dot represents the instant that the Keyphasor event occurs. The Keyphasor mark on an oscilloscope, however, may be a blank/bright or bright/blank sequence depending on the type of shaft event and the type of oscilloscope used. Figure 5-2 (bottom) shows a blank/bright sequence; the beginning of the blank marks the event.

In timebase plots, the time between two Keyphasor marks represents one revolution of the shaft. In orbit plots, the rotor moves along the path between two Keyphasor marks during one revolution of the shaft. This path may be quite complicated. A Keyphasor mark will be plotted every time the rotor completes one revolution. If several revolutions of data are plotted on an orbit (Figure 5-4), several Keyphasor marks should be visible. However, in nX-filtered orbits, where n is an integer, successive Keyphasor marks will plot on top of each other. In the figure, the orbit on the right is an unfiltered orbit, but consists primarily of 1X vibration. The Keyphasor dots plot almost on top of each other.

The Keyphasor mark on an orbit plot adds important information. It can be used to determine the instantaneous direction of motion of the rotor and to estimate the absolute phase, the vibration frequency in orders of rotative speed, and, with multiple orbit plots, the mode shape of the rotor.

Compensation of Orbits

As we discussed in the chapter on timebase plots, the primary objective of compensation is to remove unwanted signal content (noise) that is unrelated to the machine behavior that we want to observe. Like timebase plots, both filtered and unfiltered orbits can be compensated.

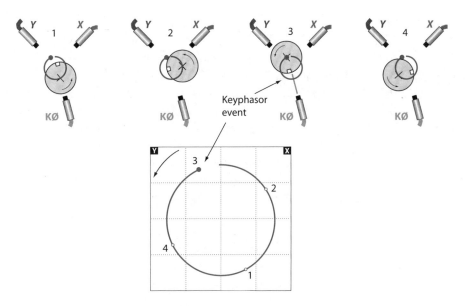

Figure 5-3. The motion of the shaft around a 1X, circular orbit. The Keyphasor event occurs at position 3, when the Keyphasor probe detects the notch. At that instant, the shaft center-line is located at the position of the Keyphasor dot in the orbit plot.

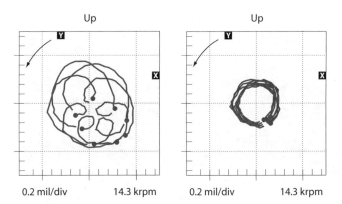

Figure 5-4. Two unfiltered orbits from a 14 ,300 rpm compressor. Each orbit plot shows eight revolutions of data. The Y probe is mounted at 22° L, and the *X* probe is mounted at 68° R. These directions are indicated by the small, black labels on the plot. The left plot shows multiple Keyphasor dots because of a subsynchronous frequency component due to a fluid-induced instability. The right orbit shows predominantly 1X behavior at a time when the instability is absent or very small. Note the clustering of Keyphasor dots into one group, indicating dominant 1X behavior.

Filtered orbit plots can be slow roll compensated using 1X, 2X, or nX slow roll vectors. While compensation of a timebase plot requires one slow roll vector, compensation of an orbit plot requires a pair of slow roll vectors. Each transducer has a slow roll vector that is subtracted from its original vibration vector; the resulting pair of compensated vibration vectors is used to synthesize the filtered orbit. The end result is a filtered orbit plot that is slow roll compensated.

Figure 5-5 shows plots of an uncompensated (left) and compensated (right) 1X-filtered orbit. The slow roll vectors are relatively large and in phase with the vibration, so that, after compensation, the orbit is significantly smaller. Also, the change in position of the Keyphasor dot shows that the phase of the orbit has significantly changed, moving the observed high spot location about 45° counterclockwise. This is a significant difference that is important for efficient and accurate balancing.

Another type of compensation, waveform compensation, can be applied to the unfiltered orbit. Each unfiltered timebase waveform used to construct an

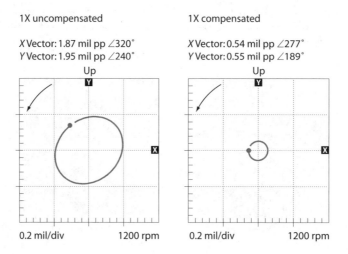

1X uncompensated

X Vector: 1.87 mil pp ∠320°
Y Vector: 1.95 mil pp ∠240°
Up

0.2 mil/div   1200 rpm

1X compensated

X Vector: 0.54 mil pp ∠277°
Y Vector: 0.55 mil pp ∠189°
Up

0.2 mil/div   1200 rpm

Figure 5-5. Slow roll vector compensation of a 1X-filtered orbit. The orbits are constructed from the pairs of vibration vectors shown above the plots. Slow roll vectors of *X* = 1.2 mil pp ∠324° and *Y* = 1.4 mil pp ∠231° are subtracted from the original vectors to produce the vectors used in the compensated plot. Note the significantly smaller size of the orbit and the change in position of the Keyphasor dot by more than 45° counterclockwise from the uncompensated position. This correction produces an orbit that displays only the dynamic response of the system and is very important for efficient and accurate balancing.

orbit consists of a sequence of digitally sampled values. For each transducer, a suitable slow roll waveform is selected from the slow roll speed range. Each of the slow roll sample values can be subtracted from its corresponding value in the original waveforms (the Keyphasor event is used as a waveform timing reference). This method has the advantage of removing most, if not all, of the slow roll component of the signal.

Waveform compensation will remove all components with frequencies up to the Nyquist sampling frequency limit (½ the sampling rate). Thus, 1X, 2X, ..., nX (n an integer), and all subsynchronous and supersynchronous frequencies (to the Nyquist limit), will be removed from the orbit. This includes most of the signal artifacts due to shaft surface defects.

Figure 5-6 shows how waveform compensation works. At the left, two uncompensated timebase plots from a steam turbine are combined to produce

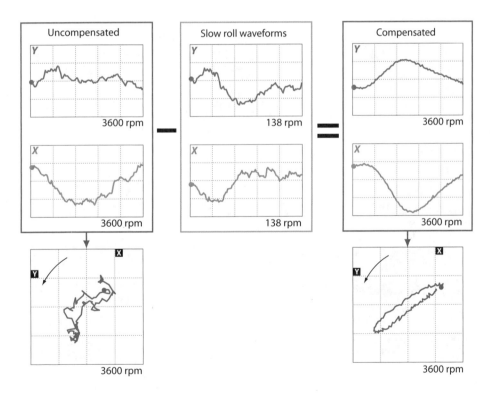

Figure 5-6. Slow roll waveform compensation of an orbit from a steam turbine. At left, two uncompensated waveforms are used to construct the uncompensated orbit. Two slow roll waveforms are subtracted from the original waveforms to produce the compensated waveforms and orbit at right, which are much clearer.

an uncompensated, and rather noisy, orbit. To compensate the orbit, slow roll waveforms are subtracted point-by-point from the original uncompensated waveforms. The result is a pair of compensated waveforms at the right, which produce the compensated orbit at bottom right. The shape of the orbit is much smoother, less noisy, and more indicative of the dynamic response of the rotor.

Unfiltered orbits can also be notch filtered by compensating both of the original waveforms with a synthesized, filtered waveform. Each compensation waveform is reconstructed from a nX-filtered vibration vector that is sampled at the same time as the original waveforms were sampled. The reconstructed, nX waveforms are then subtracted from the original vibration waveforms, and the two resulting waveforms are used to construct the Not-nX orbit.

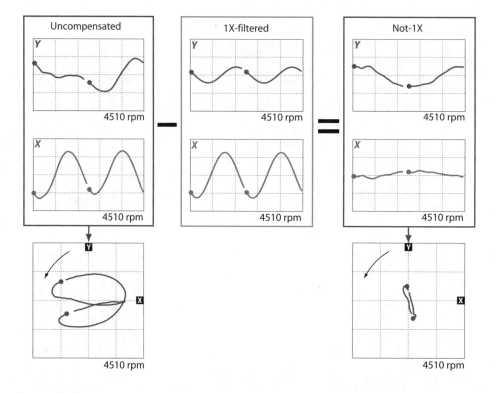

Figure 5-7. Not-1X compensation of an orbit. At left, two uncompensated waveforms are used to construct the uncompensated orbit. 1X waveforms, synthesized from vibration vectors at running speed, are subtracted from the originals to produce the Not-1X waveforms and orbit at right. These waveforms and orbit contain all frequencies except 1X. The remaining vibration is primarily 1/2X from a rub.

For example, using this technique, you can examine an orbit with all of the 1X vibration removed (Figure 5-7). A Not-1X orbit is created by subtracting two, synthesized 1X waveforms from the original unfiltered waveforms. The resultant orbit reveals any frequency information that may have been obscured by the 1X response. This can be helpful for identifying vibration characteristics associated with a variety of malfunctions. In the figure, note that the ½X vibration, which is the dominant remaining component, is clearly visible.

The warning about compensation mentioned in the last chapter is worth repeating here: compensation is an art as well as a science. There are many variables that can change the compensation vectors or waveforms. It is possible, by using incorrect compensation, to produce orbits that convey the wrong impression of machine behavior. Initially, it is always best to view data without any compensation. Then, when it is used, compensation should always be done with caution.

Information Contained in the Orbit

An orbit plot, especially with Keyphasor marks, is a powerful diagnostic tool. It can be used to measure the amplitude of filtered or unfiltered vibration in any radial direction; the relative frequency of filtered vibration versus rotor speed; the relative frequency of X versus Y unfiltered vibration; and the direction of precession. Using the orbit, the absolute phase of filtered vibration can be estimated. Additionally, the shape of an unfiltered or filtered orbit can provide important clues to the behavior of machinery, highlight significant changes in response that one-dimensional timebase plots cannot, and help identify where a problem may be occurring in relationship to the components of the machine.

Recall that timebase signals are plotted about a mean value and contain no dc information. These plots contain only dynamic (ac) information. Because the orbit is constructed from timebase plots, it also has no dc content. The orbit only displays the shaft motion relative to the average position; there is no information in the orbit about the average position of the rotor. To obtain the average shaft position, use the average shaft centerline plot (Chapter 6).

Multiple orbit plots can be created from the same location at *different* rotor speeds to show evolution of rotor vibration over speed; or, they can be created from different axial locations at the *same* speed to show the mode shape of the rotor.

Like the timebase plot, the orbit has many of the characteristics of a basic oscilloscope display. Both oscilloscope orbit displays and computer-based orbit plots can be used to make a number of measurements. The following discussion applies primarily to orbit plots, but it can be extended to oscilloscope orbit displays.

While many software packages have the ability to process and display this machinery vibration information, a machinery diagnostician should be able to analyze the information without using a computer, for two reasons. First, an oscilloscope, with an orbit display, may be the only instrument available. Second, it is always good to verify the numerical results that come out of a computer. A quick glance at the orbit plot can provide a useful sanity check on any other numerical results.

One of the most basic measurements that can be made on an orbit plot is the peak-to-peak *amplitude of vibration*. This measurement can be done on either filtered or unfiltered plots. To measure the peak-to-peak amplitude (Figure 5-8),

1. Select a transducer. In general, the amplitude will be different for each transducer. In the figure, the X transducer is chosen.

2. Draw a line (the measurement axis) from the transducer location (the X mark on the perimeter of the plot) through the center of the plot. The line must extend well beyond the limit of the orbit itself.

3. Construct two lines (3 and 4) that are perpendicular to the measurement axis and tangent to the orbit at the maximum and minimum peaks of vibration with respect to the transducer (the red circles).

4. Measure the distance between the two tangent lines in a direction parallel to the measurement axis (a plot scale has been added for convenience). Calculate the peak-to-peak amplitude using Equation 5-1:

$$\text{pp amplitude} = (\text{number of div pp})\left(\frac{\text{units}}{\text{div}}\right) \qquad (5\text{-}1)$$

The peak amplitude is one-half of the peak-to-peak amplitude.

In the figure, there are a just under 12 divisions between the two measurement lines. Applying Equation 5-1, the peak-to-peak amplitude of the orbit as viewed by the X probe is

$$\text{pp amplitude} = (12 \text{ div pp})\left(\frac{5\ \mu\text{m}}{\text{div}}\right) = 60\ \mu\text{m pp}\ (2.4 \text{ mil pp})$$

There are two key points to remember when using this technique. First, the peak-to-peak measurement must be made *parallel to the measurement axis of the probe*. Measuring simply vertically or horizontally, in this case, would produce a different and incorrect result.

Second, the peak-to-peak measurement is made between the *tangents* to the orbit that are also perpendicular to the measurement axis of the probe. Remember that the orbit is small compared to the transducer size, so that the measurement axis is always in the same direction. It will help to remember that, on the scale of the plot, the face of an eddy current transducer would be about 1 m (3 ft) in diameter!

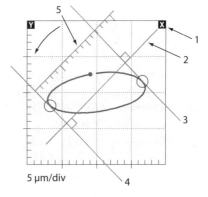

Figure 5-8. Measurement of peak-to-peak amplitude on an orbit. Here, the *X* transducer measurement axis is drawn together with perpendicular lines that are tangent to the maximum and minimum points on the orbit (with respect to the *X* transducer). A plot scale is drawn parallel to the measurement axis for convenience.

An orbit can be used to determine the *direction of precession* of the rotor. The Keyphasor mark on the orbit (the blank/dot sequence on Bently Nevada orbit plots), shows the direction of increasing time, which is the direction that the shaft is moving (the direction of precession). On oscilloscopes, however, the sequence can be a blank/bright or bright/blank, depending on the type of oscilloscope and whether a notch or projection is used as the Keyphasor mark on the shaft. When using an oscilloscope, it is always a good idea to verify the configuration of the event that is being used in your equipment by examining a timebase display.

Once the Keyphasor mark sequence is determined, it will show the direction of increasing time. This is the direction that the rotor moves in the orbit, regardless of the direction of rotation. The direction of precession can be compared to the direction of rotation to determine whether the precession is forward (precession direction same as rotation direction) or reverse (precession direction opposite rotation direction).

On complex orbits, the rotor may undergo forward precession over part of the orbit and reverse precession over another part of the same orbit. In the ½X orbits in Figure 5-9, note how inside loops maintain *forward* precession (left), while outside loops show *reverse* precession (right).

The filtered orbit can be used to estimate the *absolute phase* of the two component signals. Phase estimation will be most accurate for circular orbits, and less accurate for elliptical orbits (Figure 5-10). This is because, in a circular orbit, the shaft moves along the orbit with constant angular velocity (equal time intervals and equal angles between dots). In elliptical orbits, the orbital angular velocity is not constant (equal time intervals and *unequal angles* between dots). Because phase is a timing measurement, this angular velocity variation causes inaccuracies when trying to estimate the phase with respect to each transducer. On 1X orbits, it also causes the high spot on the shaft to oscillate as the rotor traverses an orbit. This effect, when combined with bending, actually produces 2X stress cycling in a shaft with a 1X, elliptical response.

This phase estimation technique is best used to quickly confirm the validity of phase data from some other source. Usually, a visual inspection of the orbit with a Keyphasor mark will provide a good cross-check of the data. *For accurate measurement of both absolute and relative phase, the timebase plot is a better choice.*

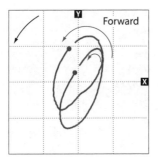 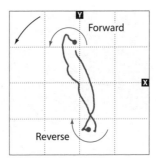

Figure 5-9. Direction of precession in orbits. In the orbit plot, the shaft moves from the blank toward the dot. The orbit plot on the left illustrates that an inside loop is always forward precession. At the top of the right orbit, the shaft moves in a counterclockwise (X to Y) direction, which is the same as the direction of rotation. Thus, the precession is forward. At the bottom of the right orbit, the path forms an outside loop, and the shaft moves for a short time in reverse precession.

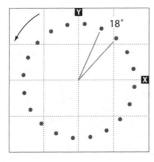 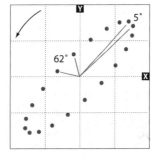

Figure 5-10. Shaft orbital angular velocity in circular and elliptical orbits. The orbit dots show the changes in position of the shaft centerline in equal time intervals. During each time interval, the shaft rotates 18°. In a circular orbit the shaft centerline has constant orbital angular velocity and moves through equal 18° increments in equal time intervals. In elliptical orbits, the shaft centerline has different orbital angular velocities in different parts of the orbit. In this example, the shaft orbital angular velocity varies from 5° to 62° per interval. This changing angular velocity makes it difficult to estimate phase from highly elliptical orbits.

To estimate the absolute phase of a signal (Figure 5-11),

1. Be sure that the orbit is filtered to a harmonic of running speed (1X, 2X, 3X, etc.). An unfiltered signal can be used to estimate the phase if the orbit is dominated by a single frequency. Select the desired transducer. In the figure, the Y transducer is selected.

2. Locate the Keyphasor mark on the orbit.

3. Determine the direction of precession. This will be the direction that the rotor is moving in the orbit and is indicated by the blank/dot sequence (red arrow).

4. Absolute phase is the fraction of the vibration cycle, in degrees, from the Keyphasor event to the first positive peak of the signal with respect to the selected transducer. On the orbit, this will be from the Keyphasor dot, in the direction of precession, to the point on the orbit that is closest to the transducer (the red circle in the figure).

5. Draw lines from the Keyphasor dot to the center of the orbit and from the closest approach point to the center of the orbit. The angle between these lines is the estimate of the absolute phase.

The *relative phase* of the two signals can also be estimated. The relative phase is the fraction of the vibration cycle between the point of closest approach to one probe and the closest approach to the other probe. For a circular, 1X orbit, this will be 90°. For an elliptical orbit, this number can range from nearly 0° to nearly 180°, depending on the orbit ellipticity and orientation (Figure 5-12). While the orbit can provide an estimate of the relative phase, the timebase plot is a better choice for accurate measurement.

Figure 5-11. Estimating absolute phase with respect to the Y transducer on a 1X-filtered orbit. The angle between the Keyphasor dot and the closest approach to the probe (red circle) is an estimate for the absolute phase of the Y transducer signal. Here, the measured angle is about 65°. Because the orbit is elliptical, the rotor shaft will be moving along this part of the path relatively quickly (see Figure 5-10) and will cover the angle in somewhat less time. Thus, the absolute phase will be less than 65°; it is actually about 60°.

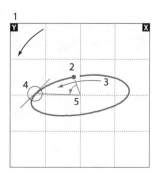

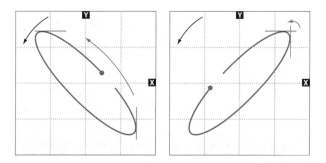

Figure 5-12. Estimating relative phase in orbits. Two 1X-filtered, highly elliptical orbits are shown. The positive peak of the X signal is shown with a green, vertical line, and the positive peak of the Y signal is shown with a blue, horizontal line. The relative phase, in this case, is the portion of the vibration cycle between maxima of the X and Y signals, measured in the direction of precession (blank to dot, increasing time). In the left plot, the relative phase is about 160°. In the right plot, the relative phase is about 20°. Because of timing issues with highly elliptical orbits, time-base plots are a better tool for determination of relative phase.

The unfiltered orbit can be used to determine the *relative frequency of vibration versus running speed*. This technique can be used for both supersynchronous or subsynchronous vibration and uses the Keyphasor marks that are generated once per turn of the rotor.

To determine the relative frequency versus running speed:

1. Plot an unfiltered orbit, and select a reference transducer.

2. Start at a Keyphasor dot on the orbit. Trace a path around the orbit, counting the number of complete cycles of vibration relative to the reference transducer, until you return to the original Keyphasor dot. This may require several revolutions worth of data.

3. Count the number of shaft revolutions that occur during the cycles of vibration.

4. Express the result in the form nX, where n is a fraction and is defined by

$$n = \frac{\text{number of cycles of vibration}}{\text{number of shaft revolutions}} \tag{5-2}$$

5. Reduce the order of the fraction to the lowest common denominator. For example, $\frac{2}{4}$X can be reduced to $\frac{1}{2}$X.

Figure 5-13 shows several examples of orbits with different frequency ratios. There are several items of note:

1. For integer ratios, the number of Keyphasor dots in the orbit is always equal to the denominator of the frequency ratio. Both the $\frac{1}{3}$X and $\frac{2}{3}$X orbits have three Keyphasor dots. Similarly, $\frac{1}{4}$X and $\frac{3}{4}$X would have four.

2. Frequency ratios with one in the numerator ($\frac{1}{3}$X, $\frac{1}{2}$X, 1X) have orbits with clearly defined blank regions before the Keyphasor dots.

3. Frequency ratios with an integer other than one in the numera-
    tor can have poorly defined or obscured blank regions. For
    example, in the 2X orbit, there are two complete cycles of vibra-
    tion for each revolution of the shaft. Thus, there will be one
    Keyphasor mark for every two cycles of vibration. If the orbit has
    no other frequency components, it will cover up the blank of the
    Keyphasor mark during the second cycle of vibration. Thus, at
    first glance, a 2X or 3X orbit will look very similar to a 1X orbit;
    however, the higher order orbits will paint over the blanks of the
    Keyphasor marks on an oscilloscope. Some software plotting
    packages have a special provision to avoid this.

Using these rules, it is possible, with a little practice, to determine simple
frequency ratios of vibration with a quick observation of an orbit.

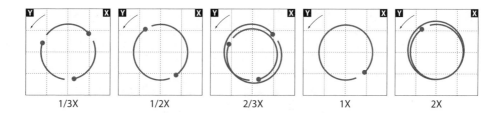

| 1/3X | 1/2X | 2/3X | 1X | 2X |

Figure 5-13. Vibration frequency relative to running speed. Several simulated, unfiltered orbits are
shown with different frequency ratios relative to running speed. The paths of the 2/3X and 2X
orbits are shown slightly offset to emphasize the path and Keyphasor dot behavior. The number
of vibration cycles yields the numerator of the frequency ratio, the number of Keyphasor dots
determines the denominator.

We have discussed this behavior for vibration at simple integer ratios. What if the vibration frequency is slightly less or more than an integer ratio? Each orbit in Figure 5-14 shows several revolutions of data. The middle orbit shows vibration that is exactly ½X, the orbit on the left shows vibration that is slightly below ½X, and the orbit on the right slightly above ½X.

When the frequency is an exact integer ratio, each Keyphasor dot plots in the same place every vibration cycle: the Keyphasor dots are said to be "locked."

When the frequency is slightly above or below a simple integer ratio, the Keyphasor dots will move slowly around the orbit. The direction that they move will depend on whether the vibration frequency is above or below the fractional ratio. How fast they move depends on how far the frequency is from the integer ratio.

When the frequency is slightly below a simple integer ratio (left orbit) the orbital motion of the rotor is slower, so the rotor completes less of the vibration cycle per revolution. The Keyphasor dot occurs a little earlier in the cycle and appears to move slowly around the orbit in a direction opposite to the direction of rotor precession.

When the frequency is slightly above a simple integer ratio (right orbit), the orbital motion of the rotor is slightly faster, so the rotor completes more of a cycle of vibration per revolution. Thus, the Keyphasor dot occurs a little later in the cycle and appears to move slowly around the orbit in the same direction as the direction of precession.

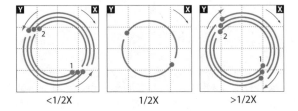

<1/2X   1/2X   >1/2X

Figure 5-14. Keyphasor dot behavior in unfiltered orbits. The direction of rotation in all three orbits is *Y* to *X* (clockwise), and the numbers show successive Keyphasor dots. In the left orbit, the dominant frequency of vibration is slightly less than 1/2X, and each successive Keyphasor dot plots in a new position located slightly against the direction of rotation. The middle orbit shows exactly 1/2X vibration; the Keyphasor dots are locked. The right orbit shows vibration that is slightly greater than 1/2X, and successive Keyphasor dots move in the same direction as the direction of rotation. The Keyphasor dot is acting like a strobe.

Because of the sensitivity of this visual effect, the orbit can be superior to the spectrum plot for determining whether vibration is an exact integer ratio of running speed. Spectrum plots have an inherent limit in resolution which is determined by the span and number of spectral lines. For example, a 400-line spectrum with a span of 500 Hz will have a resolution, or frequency bin width, of $500/400 = 1.25$ Hz $= 75$ cpm. If a machine is turning at 3600 rpm, ½X vibration has a frequency of 1800 cpm, and 0.49X vibration has a frequency of 1764 cpm. These frequencies differ by only 36 cpm, less than the spectral resolution. Thus, at this resolution, both frequencies would plot in the same spectral line, and it would require a much higher resolution spectrum to discriminate between these two frequencies.

Yet this frequency difference can be very important. Under the right conditions, rub can produce exactly ½X vibration. On the other hand, fluid-induced instability typically occurs at a subsynchronous frequency a little below ½X and is unlikely to occur at exactly ½X. Determining this seemingly small difference in frequency can be very important to properly diagnosing a machine malfunction. The orbit would clearly show locked Keyphasor dots for pure ½X vibration and Keyphasor dots moving against the direction of precession for vibration at slightly less than ½X.

The unfiltered orbit can be used to determine the *relative frequency of vibration* in the *X* direction compared to the frequency of vibration in the *Y* direction (Figure 5-15):

1.   Plot an unfiltered orbit.

2.   Start at a Keyphasor mark and move around the orbit. Note how many positive (or negative) peaks are encountered with respect to one of the transducers.

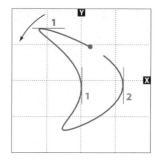

Figure 5-15. Frequency ratios from orbits. Start at the Keyphasor dot and move around the orbit. Count the number of positive peaks that occur in the *X* direction and in the *Y* direction. In this example, the *X* transducer sees two positive peaks (one is smaller than the other), and the *Y* transducer sees only one positive peak. The *X:Y* frequency ratio is 2:1.

3. Repeat this procedure with respect to the other transducer. The relative frequency can be stated as

$$f_X : f_Y \qquad\qquad (5\text{-}3)$$

or the reverse.

In the figure, two positive peaks are encountered in the X direction, and one positive peak is encountered in the Y direction. Thus the $X{:}Y$ frequency ratio is 2:1, and the components are 2X and 1X. (There is also a 1X component in the X direction, as revealed by the different horizontal positions of the two peaks.) As seen in this example, the shape of an unfiltered orbit can provide important information about the frequency content of machinery vibration.

Shape can also provide clues to the presence of excessive radial loads that may exist. High radial loads tend to push the rotor to high eccentricity ratios in a fluid-film hydrodynamic bearing. The oil film that supports the rotor produces very high spring stiffness at high eccentricity ratios. This stiffness is highest in the radial direction and lowest in the tangential direction. Figure 5-16 shows two unfiltered orbits from two different steam turbines with high radial loads. Note that the two machines turn in opposite directions (black arrows). Both orbits display remarkably similar shapes; in fact they are nearly identical when corrected for rotation direction. The arcs indicate the location of the bearing wall, and the red arrows indicate the likely direction of the applied radial load.

So far we have discussed measurements that can be performed on single

Figure 5-16. Effect of radial load on orbit shape. Orbits are shown from two different steam turbines with opposite rotation directions (black arrows). Both machines are experiencing high radial loads. The red arrows indicate the approximate direction of the applied radial load. The arcs represent the probable orientation of the bearing wall.

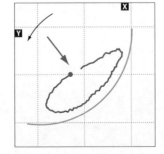
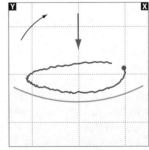

orbits. However, *multiple* orbits can greatly increase the power of the orbit plot. Multiple orbits can be created over speed, over position, over changing load, or over a changing machine process parameter. The changes that appear in multiple orbits help illuminate various aspects of machine behavior.

Multiple orbits over speed are created using data from a single measurement plane in the machine. During a startup or shutdown, at appropriate speed or time intervals, a data sample is taken that is used to create an orbit. Several such plots can be combined to show how rotor behavior evolves over speed.

Multiple orbits of this kind can be used to identify a balance resonance. Figure 5-17 shows a series of 1X-filtered, compensated orbits taken during the shutdown of a 75 MW steam turbine. Remember that the Keyphasor dot shows the position of the rotor high spot when the Keyphasor event occurs. As the machine passes through the resonance, the relationship between the unbalance location (the *heavy spot*) and the rotor response (the *high spot*) changes. The heavy spot location does not change (it is fixed in the shaft relative to the Keyphasor notch), but, during a shutdown, the high spot lags the heavy spot less and less as the machine passes through the resonance. The orbit shows these changes. First, as speed decreases, the high spot location (which is shown by the Keyphasor dot) typically moves around the orbit in the same direction as rotation. At the same time, the orbit size increases, reaches a maximum as the machine passes through the resonance, and decreases again below the resonance. Note also that the orientation of the orbit ellipse changes as the shaft goes through the resonance, due to the anisotropic stiffness (the stiffness is not the same in all radial directions, see Chapter 13) of the system. These effects are a result of the rotor system dynamic response to unbalance (see Chapter 11).

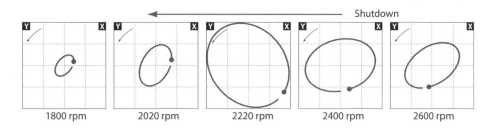

Shutdown

| 1800 rpm | 2020 rpm | 2220 rpm | 2400 rpm | 2600 rpm |

Figure 5-17. Multiple orbits over speed from a 75MW steam turbine generator. All orbits are plotted at the same scale from 1X-filtered shutdown data from the HP turbine bearing. The orbits show the machine passing through a balance resonance at around 2220 rpm. With decreasing speed, the Keyphasor dot on the orbit moves in the direction of decreasing phase lag (the direction of rotation).

Multiple orbits over position are created when the data is taken from several measurement planes at the same time. Because the unfiltered orbit shows the path of the shaft centerline, multiple orbits of this kind give us a three-dimensional picture of the motion of the rotor along the length of the machine train. This technique works best when machines are rigidly coupled; flexible couplings reduce the influence of machines on each other.

Figure 5-18 shows a series of 1X-filtered orbits from a 125 MW steam turbine generator set. The Keyphasor dots mark the location of the shaft in each plane at the instant the Keyphasor event occurs. These dots can be linked to obtain an estimate of the three-dimensional mode, or deflection, shape along the rotor.

Note that, on a simple orbit plot, we cannot do this for the remainder of the orbit. Shaft motion along the orbit occurs at different rates in different parts of the orbit. Without additional timing marks, we cannot say for certain where the shaft is at any particular time. The Keyphasor mark gives us the timing information for one particular point on each orbit. If we *can* access the individual digital sample points on the orbit, then we can connect simultaneous points on different orbits and obtain mode shape shape information for those points.

Note also that the deflection shape of the shaft is an estimate. Other, more complicated shapes are possible, and it would require more planes of measurement to be sure of the deflection shape at this speed. This is specifically the

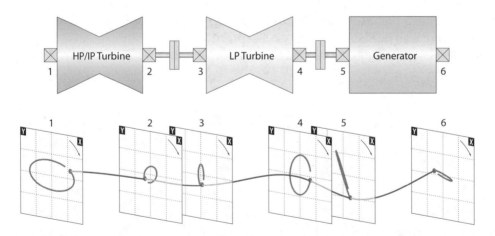

Figure 5-18. Multiple orbits over position from a 125 MW steam turbine generator set. A series of 1X-filtered orbits at the same scale were captured at the same moment in time. For each orbit, the Keyphasor dots show the location of the shaft when the Keyphasor event occurs. The Keyphasor dots can be linked (red curve) to obtain an estimate of the deflection shape of the rotor shaft.

objective of mode identification probes (see Chapter 12). However, this information can be combined with information from a good rotor system model to confirm the rotor deflection shape.

Knowledge of the rotor deflection shape can be helpful for interpolating the rotor vibration at midspan points well away from the measurement locations. This information can help identify possible locations where high vibration of the rotor might conflict with limited clearances in the machine.

Multiple orbits over changing operating conditions can be created with data from a single plane (or multiple planes). Changes in load or operating conditions often produce changes in vibration behavior. The information from multiple orbits can help clarify the cause of a machine problem.

Figure 5-19 shows a series of orbits that were obtained from a single plane on a gas pipeline compressor. As suction pressure was varied, vibration behavior changed dramatically, from normal, mostly 1X behavior to fluid-induced instability. This information was used to diagnose and develop a remedy for the problem.

Multiple orbits are important because they open up other dimensions, such as speed, time, load, or some other changing parameter. The additional information can be very helpful for detecting and diagnosing machinery problems.

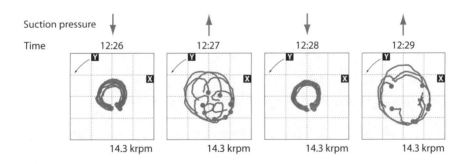

Figure 5-19. Multiple orbits over changing operating conditions from one bearing of a gas pipeline compressor. While the machine runs at 14 300 rpm at a constant discharge pressure, the orbits show that a fluid-induced instability occurred whenever the suction pressure was increased.

The Orbit/Timebase Plot

The orbit/timebase plot combines the orbit with the two timebase plots that are used to create it and provides the same choice of display characteristics: filtered, unfiltered, or compensated. Timebase plots are discussed in Chapter 4.

Bently Nevada orbit/timebase plots are created with the orbit on the left side of the plot. The Y timebase plot is displayed above the X timebase plot to the right of the orbit (Figure 5-20). The plot contains information on the direction of rotation, the plot scaling used in the orbit (the same as the vertical scale in the timebase plots), the speed, and the time scale on the timebase plots.

The figure is an example of how to use an orbit/timebase plot to locate a surface defect on a shaft. The plot shows slow roll data from a boiler feed pump motor. This orbit has a large amount of glitch, probably due to some shaft surface damage. Surface defects displayed in orbits typically show up as spikes that point in the general direction of the transducers. The timebase plots help clarify the timing relationships of the spikes and make it possible to determine the angular location of the surface damage. The spike in the Y plot occurs about 50 ms after the Keyphasor event. The period of one revolution is the time between successive Keyphasor events and is about 400 ms (actually 392 ms,

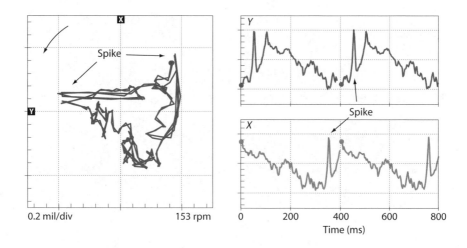

Figure 5-20. An orbit/timebase plot from the inboard bearing of a boiler feed pump motor. This plot shows two revolutions of slow roll data from probes mounted at 90° L and 0°. The timebase clearly shows the timing of one large positive-going noise spike, which shows up on the signals from both probes, 90° apart. Note that, on the Y timebase plot, the spike occurs about 50 ms after the Keyphasor event; thus, the location of this mark on the shaft can be determined. See the text for details.

based on the speed of 153 rpm). So, once the Keyphasor event occurs, the shaft turns approximately

$$\left(\frac{50 \text{ ms}}{400 \text{ ms/rev}}\right)(360°/\text{rev}) = 45°$$

until the defect is under the Y probe. To find the damaged spot, we would align the Keyphasor notch with the Keyphasor probe, and look 45° *against* rotation from the *Y* probe.

Remember that positive peaks on the waveform represent rotor passage next to the measuring probe and that the probe mounting locations are shown on the orbit plot. The Keyphasor marks provide an important guide for establishing the location on the orbit or timebase plots. The Keyphasor mark represents the same instant in time on all the plots.

This combination of plots allows us to correlate events on the orbit with their corresponding events on the timebase plots. The timebase plots act to provide a time scale that can help establish accurate timing of observed events on the orbit.

Summary

The orbit shows the path of the shaft centerline. It combines the one-dimensional timebase information from two, orthogonal, coplanar transducers into a two-dimensional plot of the lateral motion of the rotor shaft. Orbits can be unfiltered or filtered.

A Keyphasor mark on an orbit shows the location of the shaft when the once-per-turn Keyphasor mark on the shaft passes next to the Keyphasor transducer.

To remove slow roll runout from the orbit, unfiltered orbits can be waveform compensated, and filtered orbits can be vector compensated. Orbits can also be effectively notch filtered by compensating the unfiltered orbit with two synthesized, filtered waveforms. The end result is a Not-nX orbit.

Orbits can be used to measure the peak-to-peak amplitude of filtered or unfiltered vibration and the direction of precession of the rotor. Filtered orbits can be used to estimate the nX amplitude and phase.

Orbits are useful for various kinds of frequency analysis. The relative frequency content of *X* and *Y* signals can be determined. With the Keyphasor mark, the orbit can be used to determine frequencies of vibration relative to running speed. The Keyphasor marks are superior to a spectrum plot for establishing whether the frequency of vibration is an exact submultiple of running speed or not.

Orbit shape can yield information on the direction and relative magnitude of static radial loads. Also, different frequencies of vibration can produce characteristic and recognizable shapes in orbits.

Multiple orbits can be created over speed, axial position, or change in load or some other parameter. By adding another dimension, multiple orbits greatly increase the information available for machinery diagnosis.

Orbit/timebase plots are created from the combination of an orbit with the two XY timebase plots used to create it. The timebase plots are displayed to the right of the orbit with the Y plot over the X plot. Orbit/timebase plots can be used to establish timing relationships for features seen in the orbit.

Chapter 6

Average Shaft Centerline Plots

THE ORBIT, TIMEBASE, AND ORBIT/TIMEBASE PLOTS PRESENT dynamic (rapidly changing) shaft position data, but they do not show changes in the *average* shaft position, which is also an important characteristic of system response. These changes are caused by changes in the static radial load or changes in the stiffness characteristics of the rotor system. They routinely occur during start-ups or shutdowns and during steady state operation of the rotor system, over relatively short or long time spans. When a rotor system with fluid-film bearings changes speed, there are changes in the stiffness characteristics of the bearing, which cause a change in the average position of the shaft. Thus, changes in shaft position can provide very important diagnostic information.

The average shaft centerline plot provides this information. This plot is designed to show changes in the *average* position of the shaft; thus, the plot is effectively low-pass filtered and does not display rapidly changing (dynamic) data. However, when the information in the shaft centerline plot is combined with other information, such as known clearances, orbit dynamic behavior, and centerline plots from other bearings, we can obtain a more detailed picture of the motion of the shaft, its relationship to available clearances, and the static radial loads acting on the machine.

The average shaft centerline plot is most often used to display changes in shaft position versus speed, but it is also used to display changes in shaft position versus time, so the changes can be correlated to changing operating conditions. Because some malfunctions (misalignment, rub, and fluid-induced instability, to name a few) can produce noticeable changes in the centerline behavior, the shaft centerline plot is a very important tool for correlation with other plots when performing diagnostics.

In this chapter, we will discuss the construction of the shaft centerline plot and the addition of the bearing clearance circle. We will then define the position angle and the attitude angle and show how to obtain them from the plot. Then, we will show examples of how the shaft centerline typically behaves in machines with internally pressurized (hydrodynamic), fluid-film bearings. Finally, we will show how the combination of the shaft centerline plot, the bearing clearance circle, and the orbit can produce a very powerful and detailed picture of the dynamic response of the shaft.

The Construction of the Average Shaft Centerline Plot

In the Chapter 5, we saw how vibration signals from two orthogonal transducers are combined to produce an orbit. The orbit shows the dynamic motion of the shaft centerline *about* an average position and is constructed from the *ac* part of the vibration signals. The average shaft centerline plot shows changes in the average position of the shaft centerline in two dimensions and is constructed from the *dc* part of the vibration signals.

The dc information is contained in the *gap voltage* of the transducers. When the machine is operating, the voltage fluctuates continuously about an average value. For Bently Nevada 5 mm and 8 mm transducers, this corresponds to a physical gap in the range of 0.25 mm to 2.0 mm (10 mil to 90 mil). If the gap voltages from two orthogonal transducers are low-pass filtered, the results represent the average position of the shaft in the plane of the transducers.

This average position information from two, orthogonal, coplanar transducers is combined to produce a point on an *XY* (Cartesian) plot. The point represents the shaft, as if it were spinning without vibration, at a particular location inside the bearing clearance. When a set of this data is collected versus time or speed, the plot becomes an average shaft centerline plot.

An example of an average shaft centerline plot (Figure 6-1) shows the outboard compressor bearing data from the shutdown of a steam turbine compressor train. The plot has equal scaling in both horizontal and vertical directions and is square in shape. The reference direction ("Up" in the figure) and the direction of rotation (curved black arrow) are shown to aid the viewer in orienting the plot to the machine and interpreting the data. The data points (yellow) may be labeled with the speed of the machine or the sample time. Note that, unlike the orbit plot, the probe orientations (which in this example are 45° L and R from vertical) are not shown on the plot.

If the dimensions of a nearby bearing or seal are known, then a *clearance circle* (green) can be added to the shaft centerline plot. This is a circle (or an ellipse) that is the path traced out by the shaft centerline as the shaft walks around the bearing or seal, and it represents the available clearance. The diameter of the clearance circle is *not* the same as the bearing diameter; it is equal to the bearing diameter minus the shaft journal diameter, the *diametral clearance*. The position of the shaft within the clearance circle is often expressed as its eccentricity ratio (see the sidebar).

To the right of the plot are illustrations of the shaft position inside the bearing at speeds of 340 rpm and 6100 rpm (the bearing clearance is greatly exaggerated for clarity). The bottom figure shows the average position at the slow roll speed of 340 rpm, where the shaft rests close to the bottom of the bearing. The top figure shows the response of the shaft to the static forces and stiffnesses at operating speed. While the orbit may or may not have changed, there are many changes in static position which are important to documenting the response of the system.

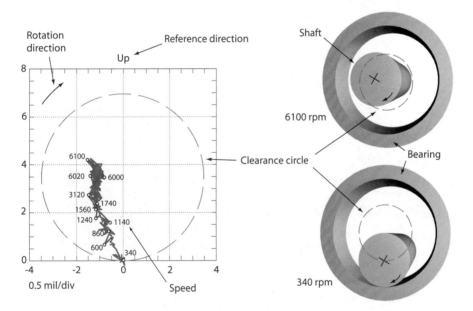

Figure 6-1. An average shaft centerline plot of a shutdown of a steam turbine compressor train (outboard compressor bearing) versus speed. The arrow shows rotation direction, and the 7.0 mil (180 μm) diameter clearance circle (green) shows the available diametral clearance of this plain, cylindrical bearing. The shaft position at slow roll is at the bottom center of the plot. The figures to the right show the position of the shaft (greatly reduced in size for clarity) relative to the bearing wall for the operating and slow roll speeds.

If the measurement plane is close to the bearing or seal, then the clearance circle, if it is accurately drawn, can show when the average shaft position is approaching or exceeding the limit of the available clearance. If the shaft centerline exceeds the available clearance, then it is a sign that something could be seriously wrong in the machine, such as a severe bearing wipe.

However, if the measurement plane is some distance away from the bearing or seal, shaft deflection can make the shaft position appear to exceed the limit of the clearance circle under normal operating conditions.

Figure 6-2 shows another variation of the shaft centerline plot from the outboard bearing of a 125 MW HP/IP turbine. The machine is running at a constant speed of 3600 rpm. The journal is shifted down and to the right as the applied load on the rotor changes. This can be the result of relatively high pressure on one side of the rotor due to unbalanced valve sequencing. It is also possible that this large change was caused by a change in alignment as the machine reached thermal equilibrium after the load change. Note that the plot has time labels, so that the data can be correlated with the operational changes.

No bearing clearance data was available, so no clearance circle has been drawn on this plot. Typical machines of this type have shaft diameters of about 300 mm (12 in). An approximate rule is that, for plain cylindrical bearings, bearing diametral clearance is typically between 0.1% to 0.15% of the shaft diameter. Thus, in this case, we would expect a diametral clearance of between 300 μm (12 mil) to 450 μm (18 mil). The shaft centerline plot shows two distinct clusters of positions that are about 20 mil (510 μm) apart. Thus, it is probable that the shaft is moving from one side of the bearing to the other during this load change.

Eccentricity Ratio

The radial position of a shaft is often described using the eccentricity ratio, ε (Greek lower case epsilon). The eccentricity ratio is defined as the ratio of the distance between the center of the shaft and the center of the bearing, r, to the available radial clearance, c:

$$\varepsilon = \frac{r}{c} \qquad (6\text{-}1)$$

When the shaft centerline contacts the clearance circle (equivalent to the shaft contacting the bearing or seal), the eccentricity ratio is one. When the centerline is in the middle of the clearance circle (equivalent to the shaft being centered in the bearing or seal), the eccentricity ratio is zero. Thus, the eccentricity ratio is, theoretically, always a number between zero and one.

Figure 6-2. A shaft centerline plot from the outboard bearing of a 125 MW steam turbine HP/IP unit. The machine is running at a constant speed of 3600 rpm while the load is being changed. The journal is being shifted down and to the right during the load change, possibly due to unbalanced valve sequencing or to thermal growth and changing alignment. The data is plotted versus time instead of rpm, which allows correlation of the shaft position with operational changes. See the text for more details.

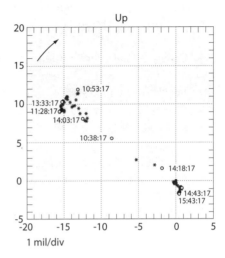

Information Contained in the Average Shaft Centerline Plot

The average shaft centerline plot can be used to infer a great deal about a machine's condition. It can be used to measure the shaft position angle and estimate the shaft attitude angle and load direction, and it can be used to monitor bearing wear, electrostatic erosion, and thermal effects. The startup and shutdown behavior of a shaft in a fluid-film bearing can be compared to theoretical and historical behavior; the change in shaft position with respect to the clearance circle is commonly used to deduce whether the shaft position change is appropriate for the expected operating condition and bearing geometry. Shaft position can be compared across bearings, couplings, and machines to detect potential misalignment or coupling problems. Finally, load or operating condition changes often result in shaft position changes; these can be examined for signs of abnormal behavior. The average shaft centerline plot is a powerful tool for machinery diagnostics, especially when used to correlate data from other plot formats and process data.

The shaft centerline plot can be used to measure the shaft *position angle*. This is the angle between the line through the shaft and bearing centers and an arbitrary reference direction. In horizontal machines, this reference direction is almost always down. The angle is measured from the reference direction, in the direction of rotation (Figure 6-3). To measure the shaft position angle,

1) Create a shaft centerline plot with an accurate clearance circle.

2) Verify that the starting point (reference gap voltage) is correct. This will usually be the low-speed point for a startup and is typically at the bottom of the plot for a horizontal machine.

3) Draw a line from the center of the clearance circle to the bottom center of the plot. This is the reference direction.

4) Draw a line from the center of the clearance circle through the average shaft centerline position for the rpm or time of concern.

5) Measure the angle from the reference direction to the line between centers, in the direction of rotation.

In the figure, the reference direction is down, and the shaft position angle is 80°.

The *attitude angle,* Ψ (Greek upper case Psi), is the angle between the applied load and the system's response to the load (Figure 6-4). The measurement of the attitude angle is similar to that of the position angle: from a reference to the line of centers, in the direction of rotation. The reference, though, is the *direction of the applied static radial load*, which can vary with operating condition. The static radial load is the vector sum of all radial loads, including gravity, that are acting on the rotor, and it can be in any direction.

Historically, the dominant radial load on a horizontal machine was considered to be gravity, and the attitude angle was thought to be the same as the position angle. However, we know today that large loads can act in other directions (for example, partial steam admission loads in a steam turbine, fluid-handling loads, gear mesh loads, or misalignment loads) and that they can be strong enough to move and even lift the rotor. Thus, the static radial load will include contributions from gravity and all other loads; the vector sum may point in a different direction than down. Figure 6-2 shows a clear example of how a massive steam turbine rotor can be moved to an unexpected position by a major change in load.

Unfortunately, it is difficult to know the exact direction or magnitude of the static radial load vector acting on the rotor shaft. However, the shape of a startup or shutdown average shaft centerline plot, combined with our knowledge of

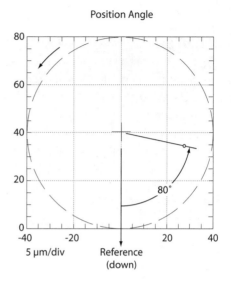

Position Angle

Figure 6-3. Measurement of the position angle. An operating shaft centerline position is shown (yellow dot) in relation to the clearance circle for the bearing. The reference direction (down) is identified, and a line is drawn from the bearing center through the shaft position. The angle is measured from the reference direction to the shaft position in the direction of rotation.

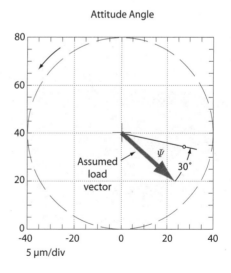

Attitude Angle

Figure 6-4. Measurement of the attitude angle, Ψ. The average shaft centerline plot shows the same shaft position (yellow dot) as in Figure 6-3. The assumed direction of the load vector has been identified. A line is drawn from the bearing center through the shaft position, and the angle is measured from the load vector to the shaft position in the direction of rotation.

how the shaft *should* move for the type of bearing installed, can give us a clue as to the load direction. Once the load direction is assumed, the attitude angle can be estimated.

In practice, an abnormal *position angle* provides an indication that the radial load has a different magnitude or direction than expected, or that the stiffness of the system has changed. When a direction for the load is assumed, it can lead to identifying the potential source of the change in the load.

In a machine with internally pressurized (hydrodynamic), fluid-film bearings and a static radial load, changes in rotor speed will usually produce a change in average shaft position. This happens because the stiffness of the bearing changes with rotor speed. Different bearing types and different static loads produce different behaviors over speed. The shaft centerline plot can be used to check on this behavior and to assess the changes in the magnitude and direction of the load.

Figure 6-5 shows average shaft centerline shutdown data from the outboard bearing of a horizontal compressor train. Note that the machine rotates in a *Y* to *X* (clockwise) direction. The large position angle and low eccentricity ratio at running speed are not normal for this type of bearing (plain cylindrical) in this service, and imply that the load may be pointed as shown (red) and have lower than normal magnitude. As the machine slows down, the shaft centerline shifts to a position that indicates that gravity (blue) is the dominant load on the shaft. The shaft position near the end of the shutdown is quite normal for a plain, cylindrical bearing (the hydrodynamic fluid wedge produces a force that moves the rotor up and to the left of center for this rotation direction).

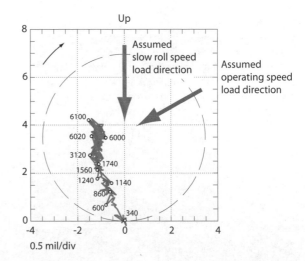

Figure 6-5. Shutdown behavior at a compressor outboard bearing. The machine is equipped with plain cylindrical bearings and rotates in a *Y* to *X* (clockwise) direction. The assumed load vectors for high speed (red) and slow roll (blue) operation show a dramatic change in loading of the bearing. See the text for details.

Calibrating the Clearance Circle

When the clearance circle is included on the plot, it implies that the plot provides an absolute measurement of shaft position. We now want to know the shaft centerline position relative to the clearance circle. What was a plot showing *relative changes* in position now becomes a plot of *absolute position*. Although we know the position of the shaft relative to the probe tip, we do not know the position of the probe tip relative to the bearing wall, so we must somehow calibrate our measurement. Calibration involves determining the *gap reference voltage* (dc) for both measurement transducers when the shaft is in contact with the bearing wall for at least one location (usually the bottom for horizontal machines). Once one point is known, the bearing clearance circle can be established, at least in theory. Instead of showing the position of the shaft relative to the probes, the plot will now show the correct position of the shaft relative to the clearance circle.

There are three ways to do this in practice. Each of these methods determines the values of the gap reference voltages for the measurement transducers.

1) Measure the location of the shaft with the machine stopped. In horizontal machines, the assumption is made that the shaft sits in the bottom center of the bearings when the machine is stopped. The gap voltages can be measured by data acquisition software, if it has that capability, or by hand with a voltmeter. Either way, the voltage values define the starting point of the shaft centerline plot.

2) Measure the gap voltages while a horizontal machine is at slow roll speed. The assumption is made that the hydrodynamic action of fluid-film bearings will not be strong enough to push the rotor significantly away from the bottom center of the bearings. Figure 6-1 uses this method.

3) Perform a *lift test*. The stopped rotor is physically moved around the bearing clearance. During this process, the maximum and minimum gap voltages for each transducer are recorded and related to the bearing clearance. When the rotor is released and returns to the equilibrium position, the equilibrium position gap voltages can be used with the clearance circle to define the actual rest position. *A lift test is not suitable for tilting pad bearings*, because measurements between pads, combined with pad movement, can give the false impression of greater diametral clearance.

Remember that machines may not have reached proper alignment until they are up and running and have reached equilibrium temperature. Ideally, these gap reference measurements should be taken while the machine is hot, because thermal growth may change the clearances. In practice, however, that cannot always be done; obviously, performing a lift test on a hot machine would take unusual talent.

Vertical machines are a special problem. Because there is no gravity available to move the shaft into a repeatable rest position, the shaft in these machines can stop in a different position every time the machine is stopped. If a vertical machine is critical to the process, the shaft can be moved to each side to define the range of gap voltages, the clearance circle, and one or more reference voltages.

At constant speed, changes in load will also produce a change in the attitude angle and, therefore, the position angle. Thus, changes in the position angle in a shaft centerline plot indicate changing loads. Some of these loads may be due to process changes, but misalignment can also produce significant load changes in a bearing.

The average shaft centerline plot is a powerful tool for detecting *changes in alignment* in machine trains. In a horizontal machine where the primary radial load is gravity with no gearing loads, normally loaded, plain cylindrical, hydrodynamic bearings will have a position angle of between 30° and 45°, and the shaft will normally operate at an eccentricity ratio of 0.6 to 0.8. Horizontal machines with tilting pad bearings will normally have a position angle of between 5° and

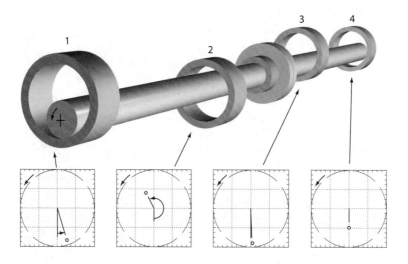

Figure 6-6. Shaft position plots for a misaligned machine train. The plots show the average shaft positions and position angles for the four bearings. Bearing 2 is low, bearing 3 is high, and the shafts are rigidly coupled. This particular combination of parallel and angular misalignment produces a load transfer from bearings 2 and 4 to bearings 1 and 3, where the shaft operates at a high eccentricity ratio. Bearing 2 is very lightly loaded, and the shaft position is in the upper half of the bearing. Note that the shaft position across the coupling is in opposite quadrants.

15° and an eccentricity ratio close to zero. Misaligned machines can cause a load transfer between bearings, and one or more bearings will carry more than their share of the radial load. This leaves other bearings relatively unloaded or, possibly, loaded in opposite directions (Figure 6-6).

When such misalignment exists, loads transmitted by the shaft can add to or subtract from the gravity load at each bearing, and the radial load vectors can change dramatically in magnitude and direction. Thus, as shown in the figure, the shaft position angle at operating speed can be very different for two adjacent bearings in a misaligned machine. See Chapter 20 for more information.

Other malfunctions can produce dramatic changes in shaft centerline position. Because a rub acts as a new bearing in the system, a rotor-to-stator rub can

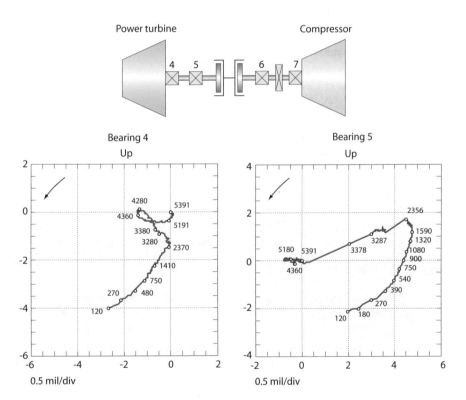

Figure 6-7. Shutdown of a gas turbine compressor with a locked gear coupling and a rub. The plots from bearings 4 and 5 on the power turbine show a dramatic shift in centerline position at about 4000 rpm. This occurs when the coupling unlocks and the rub ceases. The centerline behavior below 2300 rpm is normal. The coupling is between bearing 5 and 6.

result in a radial load transfer that can load or unload nearby bearings, depending on the orientation of the rub. This causes a change in position angle, which can be detected with the shaft centerline plot.

Also, as we have seen, the journal in a normally loaded, hydrodynamic bearing will operate at a high eccentricity ratio. Fluid-induced instability whirl or whip can cause a change in average shaft position, at the source of the instability, to a lower eccentricity ratio.

Thus, the average shaft centerline plot can reveal or help confirm serious machine problems. Figure 6-7 shows an example of the shaft centerline response due to a locked gear coupling between a low-pressure gas turbine and a compressor. The shaft centerline plots of the two turbine bearings, 4 and 5, are shown during shutdown of the machine. The high-speed operating position in bearing 5 is abnormal. As the machine slows to about 4000 rpm, the coupling unlocks, causing the shaft position to suddenly move to the right. The path of the shaft centerline appears normal from about 2300 rpm on down to slow roll. Note that bearing 4 also shows an abnormal path at the beginning of this shutdown. The shaft position was so extreme that it caused a rub in the machine until the coupling unlocked at about 4000 rpm.

The Complete Picture: Orbit Plus Average Shaft Centerline Position

A vibrating shaft has an *average position* and *dynamic motion* about that average position. The average shaft centerline plot displays only the average position; the orbit plot displays only the dynamic motion. Both pieces of information are needed to completely define the dynamic position of the shaft relative to the bearing in the measurement plane.

Figure 6-8 shows a sequence of shaft centerline plots from the shutdown of a steam turbine generator set. Each plot includes an orbit captured at the same speed as the position data (yellow dot) and displayed at the same scale. The clearance circle has been estimated.

The orbit begins a large amplitude, ½X vibration at 2580 rpm. From the shape of the orbit, it appears to contact the bearing boundary in two places: the lower right quadrant and the upper left quadrant. This was a violent, 18 mil pp (460 µm pp) vibration that was actually heard by nearby personnel. At 1727 rpm, the orbit has returned to a flattened, mostly 1X shape, which still shows some evidence of rub in the lower right quadrant. The combination of the orbit plus shaft centerline has produced a striking set of data that greatly clarifies what is happening to the machine, and the reason why!

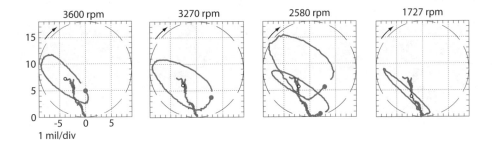

Figure 6-8. Orbits superimposed on shaft position plots taken during the shutdown of a steam turbine generator. The data from the HP/IP outboard bearing shows a violent 1/2X vibration at 2580 rpm, which causes contact with the bearing in the lower right and upper left quadrants.

Summary

The average shaft centerline plot is an *XY* plot of the average position of the shaft in the measurement plane. The circle drawn on the plot represents the diametral clearance of a nearby bearing or seal. The combination allows us to visualize the average position of the shaft relative to the available clearance during startup, shutdown, or over time.

The position angle on horizontal machines is measured from a vertical reference (usually down) to the line between centers of the bearing and shaft, in the direction of rotation.

The attitude angle is the angle between the applied load and the system's response to the load and is a key characteristic of the operating condition of the machine. Typically, the load is not known, and the attitude angle is estimated and used to work back from the average shaft position to the direction and magnitude of the load.

The average shaft centerline plot is useful for detecting and confirming the existence of many machine malfunctions, such as rub, fluid-induced instability, bearing wear or erosion, and misalignment.

The combination of the shaft centerline plot, the bearing clearance circle, and the orbit can produce a very powerful and complete picture of the static and dynamic response of the shaft relative to the bearing.

Chapter 7

Polar, Bode, and APHT Plots

IN CHAPTER 3 WE DISCUSSED THE CONCEPT of the *vibration vector*. This vector represents the amplitude and phase of a filtered vibration signal from a single transducer (usually a shaft relative, displacement transducer), where the phase is the absolute phase of the filtered signal measured relative to the Keyphasor event.

A vibration vector will sometimes change with machine speed. Changes in 1X-filtered vectors occur because of the way rotor systems respond to unbalance forces and changes in the Dynamic Stiffness. Harmonics of running speed (2X, 3X, etc.) can also change in response to changing conditions in the machine. As we will see in later chapters, these changing vibration vectors, combined with our knowledge of rotor dynamic response, are a major key to understanding the root cause of many rotor system malfunctions.

Because of the importance of vibration vectors in machinery diagnostics, several vector plot formats have been developed to present this information. Two of these, the polar plot and the Bode (pronounced BO dee) plot are designed for the presentation of startup and shutdown data. Another pair, the Amplitude-PHase-Time (APHT) plots, are very similar to polar and Bode plots and are designed for trending.

Polar and Bode plots present the same vector data. Because of the differences in format, the two plot types complement each other in ways that allow us to see some information more precisely than would be seen with either plot alone. The importance of vibration vectors to diagnosis, and the clarity of presentation of these plots, make the polar and Bode plot formats powerful and valuable tools for the machinery diagnostician.

Because of the similarity between the polar/Bode and APHT plot families, they will all be treated in this chapter. We will start with a description of the construction of polar and Bode plots. We will then discuss slow roll compensation, a very important technique for clarifying the dynamic information in these plots. Then we will discuss the large amount of information contained in these plots, such as the slow roll speed range, the slow roll vector, resonances (both rotor and structure) and resonance speeds, the Synchronous Amplification Factor (SAF), the heavy spot location, and mode shapes from multiple polar plots. Finally, we will discuss how to generate and use the APHT plots.

While polar and Bode plots can be created from velocity and acceleration data, they are most commonly used to present shaft relative, displacement vibration data. Consequently, this chapter will be limited to a discussion of displacement plots and their interpretation. See Chapter 16 for a discussion of the important differences in the appearance of polar plots created from velocity and acceleration data.

The Structure of Polar and Bode Plots

Polar and Bode plots present data from the startup or shutdown of a machine. During this transient process, vibration vectors (1X, 2X, 3X, etc.) are collected at small speed increments between the startup speed and operating speed of the machine. This can result in several hundred vibration vectors for each measurement point.

In Chapter 3 we showed how a vibration vector is plotted in the *transducer response plane* (Figure 7-1). The vector is drawn from the origin to the point (yellow dot) on the plane that represents the peak-to-peak amplitude of the filtered signal and its absolute phase lag angle. This phase lag is measured relative to the transducer measurement axis in the direction *opposite* to the direction of rotor rotation.

The polar plot is a straightforward extension of this concept. The plane of the polar plot is the same transducer response plane. In the polar plot, though, the arrow is omitted, and just the set of points (the locus of the response) is plotted, with a line connecting consecutive points (Figure 7-2).

For 1X data, the vibration vector represents the approximate location of the rotor *high spot* relative to the transducer when the Keyphasor event occurs. (Because we are describing a physical spot on the shaft, we will use the term high spot only for 1X response.) This is exactly true for 1X, circular orbits, and approximately true for 1X elliptical orbits. The Keyphasor acts like a strobe that illuminates the location of the high spot at the instant of the Keyphasor event. The 1X polar and Bode plots show how the high spot angular location and the vibration amplitude change with speed.

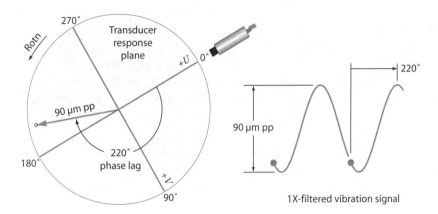

Figure 7-1. A vibration vector plotted in the transducer response plane. The 1X vector is 90 μm pp ∠220° (3.5 mil pp ∠220°). The zero degree reference is at the transducer angular location, and the phase lag increases in a direction opposite to the X to Y (CCW) rotation. See Chapter 3.

Figure 7-2. A 1X, uncompensated polar plot showing data from the shutdown of a 10MW, vintage-1938, steam turbine. The 0° mark is aligned with the transducer location, and the phase lag angles increase in the direction opposite to rotation. Speeds are shown for some of the points.

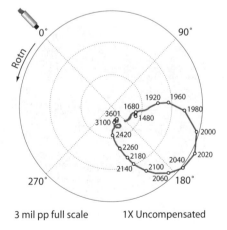

The polar plot is generated with data from a single transducer. The zero degree mark on the perimeter of the plot is aligned with the angular mounting location of the transducer, and the degrees increase in a direction *opposite* to rotation.

In the figure, these angles are marked at 90° intervals, but any convenient interval can be used. Speed labels are added to selected points (yellow). The direction of rotation, filtering used (usually 1X), and full scale range for amplitude are included as part of the documentation.

Because of the way rotor response typically changes near a resonance, most of the points on a polar plot tend to be crowded together close to the low and high-speed ends of the plot. While the polar plot can be zoomed to give more visibility in the low-speed range, the Bode plot, which includes a frequency scale, can be a better choice for examining data away from resonances.

The Bode plot (Figure 7-3) displays the same vibration vector data as the polar plot; the vibration amplitude and phase are plotted separately on two, rectangular plots with speed (or frequency) on the horizontal axes. The upper plot

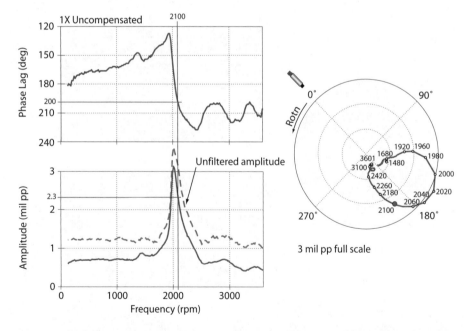

Figure 7-3. A 1X, uncompensated Bode plot and polar plot showing the same data (blue). The Bode plot is actually two plots; the phase plot is above the amplitude plot. All data is from a single transducer, oriented as shown by the 0° location on the polar plot. The unfiltered amplitude is shown in green on the Bode plot. A single point, shown in red on the polar plot, is marked with red lines on the Bode plot.

displays phase lag in degrees on the vertical axis, increasing from top to bottom rather than bottom to top (see Appendix 1). The lower plot displays the vibration amplitude on the vertical axis. The red vertical line in the Bode plot identifies the same values of amplitude and phase as the red point in the polar plot, but also explicitly identifies the rpm.

The unfiltered vibration amplitude can be plotted on the amplitude part of the Bode plot (green), which allows easy comparison between unfiltered and filtered data (phase cannot, generally, be measured for unfiltered vibration). Because the unfiltered data contains all frequencies in the vibration signal, the difference between the 1X amplitude and the unfiltered amplitude is the Not-1X vibration component in the signal. A difference as large as is shown in the figure warrants further investigation.

Slow Roll Compensation

As we discussed in Chapter 3, *slow roll compensation* removes slow roll runout from a filtered vibration signal so that (presumably) only the dynamic response remains. Compensation is most often applied to 1X data because of the importance of 1X dynamic information for balancing. The slow roll vector is a vibration vector that is measured in the slow roll speed range, a speed low enough that no significant dynamic vibration is taking place. The data from each transducer will have a different slow roll vector. Compensation is the process of subtracting an appropriate slow roll vector from a transducer's entire vector data set before plotting. The resulting, compensated vectors produce a *compensated* polar or Bode plot (Figures 7-2 and 7-3 are *uncompensated* plots).

An unstated assumption with slow roll compensation is that the slow roll vector remains valid for the entire set of startup or shutdown data and from one transient event to the next. All assumptions, including this one, should be regularly checked. See the sidebar in Chapter 3 for some reasons why slow roll vectors can change.

Subtraction of a vector from itself produces a vector with zero amplitude. Thus, compensated vector data should have zero amplitude at the speed of the slow roll vector. On a polar plot, that point should plot on the origin. On a Bode plot, the amplitude will go to zero at this speed.

This behavior allows us to easily cross-check a vector plot for correct compensation. *A slow roll compensated vector plot will have zero amplitude at the chosen compensation speed.* If, on a compensated plot, the amplitude does not go to zero at the speed of the slow roll vector, then either the slow roll vector is incorrect or it is not correctly subtracted.

How do you choose a slow roll vector? First, use an *uncompensated*, 1X Bode plot to identify the slow roll speed range. This range extends from the slowest running speed of the machine up to the speed where dynamic effects due to unbalance become apparent. Check both the amplitude and phase plot for the appearance of dynamic effects where the amplitude or phase begin to significantly change.

Next, from within the speed range, select a sample that is typical of the nearby data. Especially at low speeds and low amplitudes, the phase data can appear very noisy, due to the limitations of the instrumentation. Some visual smoothing may be necessary to identify values that are typical or atypical for the range.

There are times when the phase and amplitude in a Bode plot will start changing from the lowest speed in the database. When this happens, there may be no clearly defined slow roll speed range, and the only choice may be to select the slowest speed in the database that has useable data.

A slow roll speed range is identified on the Bode plot in Figure 7-4. At 120 rpm, the slow roll vector is 0.61 mil pp ∠180° (15 μm pp ∠180°). (This slow roll vector is somewhat atypical, but is not a bad data point. A better choice might have been one in the 200 to 400 rpm range.) The slow roll vector is subtracted

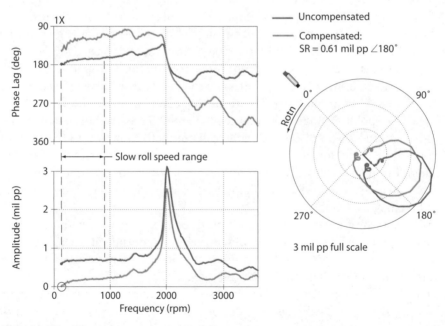

Figure 7-4. Bode and polar plots showing the effect of slow roll compensation. On the Bode plot, the slow roll vector (red dots on Bode plot and red arrow on polar plot) is taken from the uncompensated amplitude and phase data (blue) within the slow roll speed range. Compensation of a polar plot involves a simple shift in a direction opposite the slow roll vector. The amount of shift is equal to the amplitude of the slow roll vector.

from every data sample of the uncompensated data (blue) to produce the compensated data (green). The compensated phase plot is slightly noisier near the compensation speed, where the amplitude is low. Note that the zero amplitude point on the Bode amplitude plot (red circle) corresponds to the slow roll vector speed.

On the polar plot, slow roll compensation is equivalent to shifting the entire plot by the inverse of the slow roll vector (the small red arrow), or by moving the origin over to the slow roll sample point. This will place the compensation speed point at the origin of the polar plot, as seen in the figure. This technique allows polar plots to be easily compensated by inspection. Notice that the shape of the polar plot does not change. It is much more difficult to compensate a Bode plot by inspection.

Information Contained in Polar and Bode Plots

Polar and Bode plots are an important window to the dynamic behavior of rotor systems. They are used primarily for two purposes, balancing and the identification and analysis of resonances. Thus, it is difficult to discuss the use of polar and Bode plots without touching on some rotor dynamic theory, a large and complex topic that will be presented later in this book. Because of space limitations, the rotor dynamic discussion here will be very brief. Balancing, which is a complex subset of rotor dynamic theory, is covered in Chapter 16.

Basic rotor dynamic theory predicts that, for synchronous (1X) behavior, at speeds well below a resonance, the heavy spot (which represents concentrated rotor unbalance) and the high spot will be *in phase* (0° phase lag). Thus, low-speed vibration vectors (which represent the location of the high spot when the Keyphasor event occurs) will point in the direction of the heavy spot. At the resonance, the amplitude will reach a maximum, and the high spot will lag the heavy spot by about 90°. In other words, the vibration vector at resonance will point about 90° (measured in a direction opposite rotation) from the direction of the heavy spot. At speeds well above a resonance, the amplitude will decline to a constant value, and the high spot will lag the heavy spot by about 180°; the vibration vectors at high speed will point in the opposite direction from the heavy spot. See Chapter 11 for a detailed development of these principles.

These basic rotor behavior characteristics are used to extract information from polar and Bode plots. In the most common application, balancing, the 1X compensated plots are used to identify resonances, determine the mode shapes of the resonances, and identify the location of the heavy spot(s) for each mode. 1X, compensated polar and Bode plots can also be used to calculate the Synchronous Amplification Factor (SAF), a measure of the Quadrature Dynamic Stiffness of the rotor system.

Equally important, 1X and 2X plots, when combined with historical startup or shutdown data, can be used to detect changes in rotor system behavior that signal the presence of several types of malfunctions. 2X and higher-order polar and Bode plots can be used to identify the presence of, and changes in, resonances above running speed.

Vibration in machines always involves a system, which includes the rotor shaft, the bearing supports, the machine casing, any attached piping and auxiliary equipment, and the floor and foundation structure. All of the components of the system will participate in every vibration mode of the system, but some parts of the system will vibrate in some modes more than others.

Usually, we are interested in modes that involve large amounts of shaft vibration relative to the machine casing. These rotor modes are usually the most important for machinery management. Rotor resonances tend to produce large amplitudes of measured shaft relative vibration and are easily identified on Bode plots as a peak and on polar plots as a large loop (sometimes called a "polar circle"). However, it is important to remember that the machine casing, and consequently the observing probes, may also participate in the vibration. This is especially true for machines that have support structures with relatively low stiffness. Thus, the shaft relative vibration at resonances (and away from resonances, for that matter) may include significant contributions from casing vibration. This vibration can either add to or subtract from the shaft absolute vibration, depending on the phase relationship.

Modes can be excited where most of the vibration occurs in the piping system, other attachments, or the foundation and support structure. These modes (sometimes called *structural resonances*) can produce a relatively low amplitude vibration of the casing, and, by extension, the measurement probes. These modes do not usually involve a significant amount of rotor motion, but, because of casing motion relative to the rotor shaft, they appear as small, but occasionally large, loops on polar plots. It can be difficult to tell the difference between a mode where the rotor and casing are both significantly vibrating in phase and a mode which produces a small vibration in the casing only. Both modes will produce small loops. Casing transducers, by revealing the amount of casing vibration, can help resolve the difference (see Chapter 12).

A *balance resonance* has the following characteristics on a Bode plot:

1. An amplitude peak, and

2. A significant increase in phase lag at the frequency of the peak.

On a polar plot, rotor modes will produce large, curving loops or partial loops. Other modes will tend to produce small loops, as will the split balance resonances caused by anisotropic (unequal) support stiffness (see Chapter 13). Small system resonances are often more visible on a polar plot because they often appear as a distinctive small loop.

Figure 7-5 shows Bode and polar plots of a balance resonance and several other small resonances. A quick check shows that these are 1X, compensated plots.

On the Bode plot, the primary rotor (balance) resonance is identified by the peak that appears at just over 2000 rpm and the increasing phase lag with increasing speed. The balance resonance speed is at the speed of maximum amplitude.

The polar plot shows the same data as a large loop. The maximum amplitude of the loop locates the resonance at 2020 rpm. Simple rotor modeling predicts that the phase lag at resonance will change by about 90° from the low-

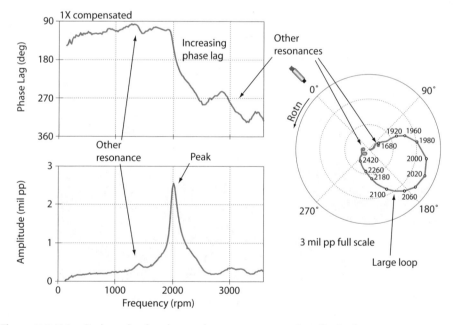

Figure 7-5. Using Bode and polar plots to detect a resonance. On a Bode plot, a rotor resonance is shown by a peak in amplitude at the same time as an increase in phase lag. On a polar plot, the same data appears as a loop in the plot, with phase lag increasing in a direction *opposite* to the direction of rotation. The important shaft relative rotor resonance occurs at 2020 rpm. Small loops on the polar plot correspond to the perturbations in the Bode phase and amplitude plots and are most likely other small system resonances.

speed phase lag. Thus, either the maximum amplitude or the 90° phase change can help locate the resonance. In the polar plot in the figure, the phase at the resonance peak (about 160°) lags the low-speed phase (about 110°) by 50°. This is significantly less than predicted by the simple model, but still provides a useful cross-check.

In the polar plot, there is a small loop at the low-speed end of the data and two small loops at the high-speed end of the data. These loops appear as phase and amplitude disturbances on the Bode plot. Most likely, these are small system resonances that have been excited by the rotor system unbalance response.

Note that, even though a simple rotor model predicts a 90° phase change at a balance resonance and a 180° phase change through a balance resonance, this does not always occur in practice. The identifying characteristic of any resonance is a peak in amplitude occurring at the same time as an increase in phase lag. In plant machinery, the total phase change through a resonance may be considerably more or less than 180°. This is true even for small resonances, which is evident if you view the small small loop on the polar plot as a miniature polar plot.

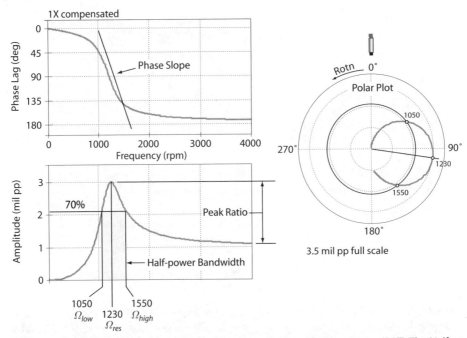

Figure 7-6. Four methods for measuring the Synchronous Amplification Factor (SAF). The Half-power Bandwidth method uses the 70% vibration amplitude points to locate the two speeds which define the half-power bandwidth. Divide the resonance speed by the bandwidth to obtain the SAF. See the example in the text.

The *Synchronous Amplification Factor* is a measure of how much 1X vibration is amplified when the system passes through a resonance. Systems with high effective damping tend to have a low SAF, and systems with low effective damping have a high SAF. There are four methods to measure the SAF (Figure 7-6), three using the Bode plot (Peak Ratio, Half-power Bandwidth, and Phase Slope), and one using the polar plot (a variation of the Half-power Bandwidth method).

The SAF is based on the dynamic response of rotor systems to a rotating unbalance force. Because of this, *all methods for measuring the SAF use 1X, compensated polar and Bode plots.* Slow roll compensation removes the part of the rotor response that is not due to unbalance. Because the Half-power Bandwidth method is so widely recognized, it will be described in detail here. See Appendix 4 for details of the other methods.

The Half-power Bandwidth method [1], endorsed by the American Petroleum Institute, is also known in the USA as the API method. The term "half-power" originated in ac electrical circuit theory; the half-power point corresponds to the −3 dB (0.707) point of the voltage response curve of an electrical oscillator (because power is proportional to the square of the voltage, −6 dB (0.5) power corresponds to −3 dB (0.707) voltage). Since simple electrical and mechanical oscillators are mathematically equivalent, the method can be applied to rotor systems and yield meaningful results.

The half-power points of the Bode plot, Ω_{low} and Ω_{high} in the figure, have a vibration amplitude of about 70% of the maximum balance resonance amplitude. Once these speeds have been identified, they define the half-power bandwidth (the blue region). These two rotor speeds (or frequencies) are used together with the speed of resonance, Ω_{res}, to calculate the SAF:

$$\text{SAF} = \frac{\Omega_{res}}{(\Omega_{high} - \Omega_{low})} \qquad (7\text{-}1)$$

Because the SAF is dimensionless, any consistent speed or frequency unit can be used.

Figure 7-6 shows Bode and polar plots that have been generated by a rotor model. Using the example in the figure, the SAF is found to be

$$\text{SAF} = \frac{1230}{(1550 - 1050)} = 2.5$$

A word of caution is appropriate here. All methods for measuring SAF are based on ideal, isotropic rotor behavior. Real rotor systems can (and usually do) have some degree of anisotropy in the support stiffness that causes the measurement of SAF using *any* method to be sensitive to the mounting angle of the measurement probes. Be sure to see Chapter 13 before applying any of the SAF measurement methods to data from your machine.

1X, compensated polar and Bode plots can be used to *locate the direction of the heavy spot* for balancing purposes, probably their most important use. As we have discussed, at speeds well below a resonance, the heavy spot and high spot will be in phase; the vibration vector will point in the direction of the heavy spot. This principle can be applied to each vibration mode of a machine.

Because of its format, the polar plot is almost always easier to use for this purpose. Figure 7-7 shows 1X, compensated Bode and polar plots from the same small steam turbine, with the direction of the low-speed vector (heavy spot) indicated in red. On the Bode plot, the direction of the low-speed vibration vec-

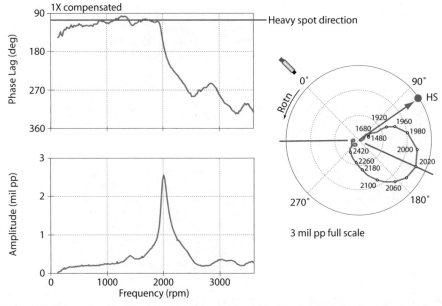

Figure 7-7. Heavy spot location using Bode and polar plots. The heavy spot direction is indicated by the red dot on the polar plot. At speeds well below the resonance, the phase on the compensated polar plot points toward the heavy spot. On the Bode plot, the phase just before the resonance change indicates the direction of the heavy spot. The resonance and the high-speed data are 90° and 180° from the heavy spot direction for an ideal rotor system. On the polar plot, the blue lines show the resonance and high-speed directions which deviate from the ideal.

tor is taken from a speed range just before the phase begins to change due to resonance. This provides a valuable cross-check on the polar plot interpretation.

When a Bode plot is not available, the 0°, 90°, and 180° relationships can be used on a polar plot to check the low-speed vector direction. In the figure, the blue lines show the phase lag at resonance (2020 rpm) and at well above resonance. Ideally, these lines should be 90° and 180° from the heavy spot. Anisotropic stiffness and other small resonances present in this machine distort these simple relationships (see Chapter 13). Even so, if the heavy spot locations indicated by the three construction lines were averaged, the error here would be within tens of degrees, adequate enough for balancing. For ideal rotor systems with isotropic stiffness, polar plots from *XY* transducers will look like identical circles and yield identical estimates of the heavy spot location. However, anisotropic stiffness will cause the polar plots to look significantly different (Figure 7-8) and produce different implied locations for the heavy spot. When balancing, whenever possible, compare both polar plots. The heavy spot locations can be averaged, or more sophisticated signal processing techniques can

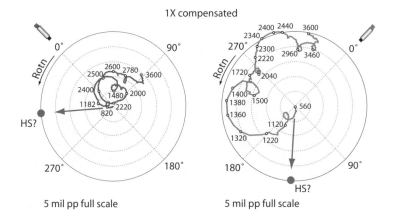

Figure 7-8. Polar plots from *XY* probes at the turbine bearing of a 10 MW steam turbine generator set with anisotropic stiffness. Both plots are to the same scale. The implied heavy spot (HS) locations (red), based on low-speed phase direction of each polar plot, are quite different for this system. The two locations can be averaged, or more sophisticated signal processing techniques can be applied (see Chapter 13 and Appendix 5).

be applied. These techniques include Virtual Probe Rotation or, even better, forward response vectors (see Chapter 13 and Appendix 5).

Each rotor resonance, or mode, will appear on a Bode plot as an amplitude peak, with an associated phase lag increase. On a polar plot, each mode will appear as a loop in the polar plot. Some modes tend to produce very small loops in a polar plot. Here we are discussing significant rotor modes of the system, which usually produce large loops on a polar plot.

Figure 7-9 shows data from an experimental machine with clearly defined first (blue) and second (red) modes. Note that the phase lag increases in a direction opposite to rotation for each mode. There is also a small mode at just over 1000 rpm (the small loop on the polar plot).

The rotor modes appear on this polar plot as two large loops. Each loop is an independent mode; each has a low speed, resonance, and high-speed section that has an approximate 0°, 90°, and 180° relationship, respectively, to the heavy spot *for that mode*. The first mode heavy spot is marked with a blue dot. The sec-

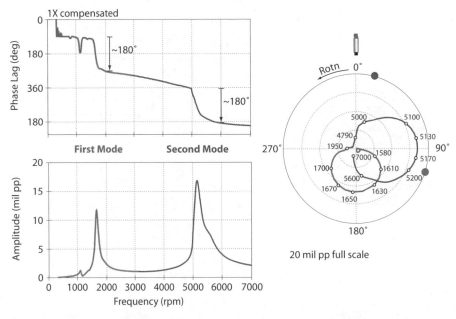

Figure 7-9. A two-mode response from an experimental machine. The first (blue) and the second (red) modes appear as peaks in the Bode plot at 1650 and 5150 rpm and as multiple loops in the polar plot. Each resonance has an associated phase lag of approximately 180°. The first mode heavy spot is marked with a blue dot, and the second mode heavy spot is shown with a red dot. There is also a smaller phase change associated with a small resonance at slightly over 1000 rpm.

ond mode appears to start at a point slightly away from the polar plot origin (where the color changes to red), where it adds to the residual response of the first mode. The start point of the second mode can be mentally shifted to the origin of the plot. When this is done, the second mode heavy spot at this transducer location is approximately at the red dot.

Polar plots from multiple planes of measurement can be used to *estimate the different mode shapes* of a machine. Figure 7-10 shows 1X, compensated polar plots from vertical transducers in two planes. The measurement planes are both inside the nodal points associated with the bearings.

In the polar plots, the first mode forms loops (blue) that have the same orientation in both planes. This data corresponds to the approximate mode shape in the top diagram. The shaft is bent into a simple curve, where each end of the shaft passes next to the measurement transducers at approximately the same time. Thus, this is called an *in-phase* mode.

The second mode loops (red) have the *opposite* orientation; the high spots are 180° from each other. The shaft is bent into an "S" shape, where the shaft passes a transducer at one end half a turn later than at the other end. This mode shape is an example of an *out-of-phase* mode.

Mode shape information like this is very important to balancing, because weight placement can influence several modes simultaneously or have little influence on a mode if the weight is close to a node. Knowledge of the mode shape is used to select the size of balancing weights and their axial distribution.

Measurement of modes can be tricky. The measured amplitude of vibration is determined by the motion of the rotor *and* the motion of the measurement probe. It is possible for the rotor and casing to have large amplitude, in-phase vibration in a particular mode, producing a relatively small shaft relative vibration signal that may look like a small system mode. Casing transducers can help identify such modes. The phase relationship of measured modes will also depend on the axial location of the measurement transducers relative to any nodal points in the rotor. In the first bowed mode at the top of the figure, if either transducer were moved to a location on the opposite side of the bearing, the nodal point near the bearing would produce a phase inversion in the polar plot. Knowledge of transducer axial location and the likely location of nodal points is important to establishing the correct mode shape of the rotor (see Chapter 12).

Specific machine speed points on polar plots from different axial positions in the machine can be linked to produce a gross estimate of the mode shape of the rotor. This method is similar in concept to linking Keyphasor dots on multiple orbits to obtain the rotor deflection shape. However, unlike the orbit, polar

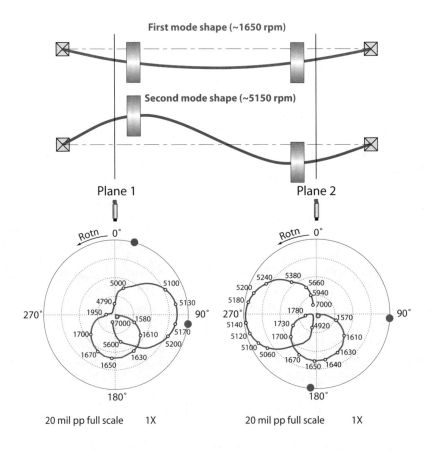

Figure 7-10. Polar plots from different measurement planes in a machine. Two distinct modes are visible: the first mode in blue and the second mode in red. The heavy spots for each mode are shown. Diagrams of the probable mode shapes for this machine are shown at the top. See the text for a complete discussion.

plots only provide an approximation of the direction and amplitude of the response. An unfiltered orbit displays the actual dynamic position of a rotor. A polar plot, however, is created from filtered, not unfiltered data, and it displays the vibration vector as measured by *only one transducer*. This produces a reasonably accurate estimate of the rotor position at the instant of the Keyphasor event *if and only if* the orbit is circular and predominantly 1X. However, most 1X orbits are elliptical, not circular. In the diagrams at the top of the figure, the pictures represent an approximation to the shape of the rotor at the moment of the Keyphasor event.

Finally, several possible mode shapes can have similar polar plots. We typically assume the simplest mode shape. Here, knowledge of the machine construction, together with knowledge of all lower modes, must be used to arrive at the probable mode shape. It is possible that the mode shape could be much more complicated. On a more complex machine, mode identification probes should be used to obtain more information at different planes in the machine, or existing measurements can be correlated with a good model of the rotor system.

Polar and Bode plots are used to display startup and shutdown data. It is very useful to maintain a history of these plots so that data from different startups and shutdowns can be compared. Slow roll vectors, resonance frequencies, and the shape of the response should be checked for signs of change. Changes in resonance frequencies imply changes in rotor system support stiffness. Any change is evidence of a changing machine condition and should be investigated for its significance.

APHT Plots

Amplitude-PHase-Time (APHT) plots are a variation of polar and Bode plots. The vibration vectors are plotted versus time (trended) rather than versus frequency. These plots are designed to be used for long term trending of vibration vectors while the machine runs at constant speed. Because of the possibility that the slow roll vector will change, APHT plots are not normally slow roll compensated. APHT plots can display any harmonic of running speed.

Vibration is a ratio of the applied force to the Dynamic Stiffness of the rotor system. Changes in vibration vectors mean that the applied force, the Dynamic Stiffness, or both have changed. Thus, a change in a vibration vector (either magnitude or direction) can provide early warning of a developing machine problem.

Figure 7-11 shows a set of 2X APHT plots from a vertical reactor-coolant pump. The data was trended while the pump was running at 1187 rpm. For the first two months of operation, the 2X vibration did not change significantly. Then, in late October, the 2X amplitude and phase lag began to change. The amplitude reached a maximum on 12 November, and, shortly after that, the phase lag increased dramatically. As the vibration decreased, the pump was shut down and inspected, possibly the first time a machine was stopped because of *lower* vibration. It was soon restarted, but stopped again a short time later. Upon inspection, the pump shaft was found to be cracked.

In this example, the 2X vector change revealed the underlying change in Dynamic Stiffness. An interesting aspect of this data is that the APHT plot looks very much like a classic startup or shutdown Bode plot of a machine going through a resonance, yet the machine operated at a constant speed during this entire period. Instead of the machine passing through a resonance with changing speed, *a resonance passed through twice operating speed* while the machine was at constant speed. This implies that either the rotor mass increased dramatically (unlikely) or the rotor system stiffness decreased dramatically. In fact, as the crack propagated through the shaft, the shaft bending stiffness decreased, lowering the natural frequency. As the natural frequency passed through twice running speed, it was excited by the asymmetric shaft stiffness due to the crack

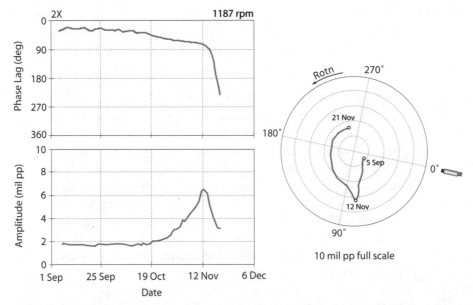

Figure 7-11. A set of 2X APHT plots of a vertical reactor-coolant pump with a developing shaft crack. The horizontal axis is time, and the pump is running at a constant speed during this entire period. The 2X vibration vector changes dramatically as a resonance passes through twice running speed. See the text for a complete discussion.

(see Chapter 23). In essence, the system changed from a condition where the natural frequency was above twice running speed to a condition where it was below twice running speed. Thus, twice running speed was initially *below* a natural frequency, and ended up *above* the natural frequency, producing the amplitude and phase changes characteristic of a resonance.

Acceptance Region Plots

As a historical database is developed for a machine, normal behavior can be defined. Machines in good health should have vibration vectors that are repeatable for similar conditions of speed and load. These vibration vectors should plot in the same general areas on a polar APHT plot, and boundaries can be defined that enclose such regions.

Such a plot is also called an *acceptance region plot*. Acceptance regions contain the normal behavior of the vibration vector being measured. These are usually 1X or 2X vectors, but they can be filtered to any order of running speed. Acceptance regions can be defined for different loads, speeds, etc.

Figure 7-12 shows an example of an acceptance region plot, with the region (red) of normal, historic behavior for this machine at this measurement point, operating speed, and operating conditions. The acceptance region is defined over a range of vibration amplitude from 75 to 110 μm pp (3.0 to 4.3 mil pp) and phase lag from 95° to 160°. This region might include typical behavior for a generator at different loads. Movement of the vibration vector out of the acceptance region constitutes abnormal behavior and should be investigated.

Figure 7-12. An acceptance region plot. The red boundary defines the region of normal behavior for the 1X vibration vector at this measurement point. The boundary is defined by the ranges of vibration amplitude and phase. Response outside the acceptance region constitutes abnormal behavior and should be investigated.

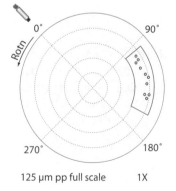

125 μm pp full scale   1X

Summary

Polar, Bode, APHT, and acceptance region plots are designed to display vector data. Polar and Bode plots are used for startup and shutdown (transient) data, APHT plots are used primarily for long term trending during steady state conditions, and acceptance region plots are used to identify response outside of normal, expected behavior.

Polar plots display the locus of a set of vibration vectors, in polar format. The phase angle is measured relative to the transducer location, in a direction opposite to rotation.

Bode plots display the same information in two, separate, rectangular plots: phase lag versus frequency is plotted above, and vibration amplitude versus frequency below.

APHT plots are similar to polar and Bode plots, except that the data is plotted against time instead of speed.

Polar and Bode plots are usually slow roll compensated, using a slow roll vector selected from the slow roll speed range. The uncompensated Bode plot is used to identify the slow roll speed range and a suitable slow roll vector.

Polar and Bode plots can be used to identify resonances and resonance frequencies. The Synchronous Amplification Factor (SAF) is most often measured from the Bode plot, although a polar plot can be used for this purpose.

The 1X polar plot is most often used to identify the location of the heavy spot for balancing purposes. Multiple plots from different axial locations can be used to identify the mode shapes for different resonances.

APHT plots are used for long term monitoring of nX vibration vectors. The polar APHT plot can be used to define regions based on typical vibration vector behavior. Such a plot is called an acceptance region plot and can be used with software alarms to detect significant changes in vibration vectors.

References

1. American Petroleum Institute, *Tutorial on the API Standard Paragraphs Covering Rotor Dynamics and Balancing: An Introduction to Lateral Critical and Train Torsional Analysis and Rotor Balancing*, API Publication 684 (Washington, D.C.: American Petroleum Institute, 1996), p. 3.

Chapter 8

Half and Full Spectrum Plots

IN PREVIOUS CHAPTERS, WE HAVE DISCUSSED the use of filtering to obtain vibration vectors. These vectors are filtered to multiples of running speed, 1X, 2X, 3X, etc., and provide us with information about the behavior of a machine at one of those particular frequencies. This information is presented to us as the amplitude and phase of the vibration at that frequency.

However, machines can vibrate at many different frequencies simultaneously. These frequencies can be related or unrelated to running speed and include both subsynchronous and supersynchronous frequencies. Since these frequencies are associated with the operating condition of the machine, the machinery diagnostician must have some way to determine the frequency content of a vibration signal in order to make an accurate diagnosis.

Vibration frequencies sometimes appear as a series of harmonics. The series consists of the lowest frequency in the series, called the *fundamental,* and a number of frequencies at integer multiples of the fundamental. In a typical series, the amplitude of higher order frequencies will decline rapidly. To avoid confusion, we will define a *harmonic* as any frequency that is an integer multiple of the fundamental. The *first harmonic* is the fundamental, the *second harmonic* has a frequency of twice the fundamental, the *third harmonic* has a frequency of three times the fundamental, etc. Often, the term *harmonics* will be used as a general term to indicate integer multiple frequencies that are above the fundamental.

The fundamental vibration frequency of a series can be any vibration frequency. Often, the fundamental is 1X, but it can also be any subsynchronous or supersynchronous frequency. For example, a series could be based on a fundamental at ½X and include 1X, ³⁄₂X, 2X, ⁵⁄₂X, etc. In this series, the ½X is the fundamental or first harmonic, 1X (= $\frac{2}{2}$X) is the second harmonic, $\frac{3}{2}$X is the third harmonic, etc. Such a series can be generated by a $\frac{1}{2}$X rub, as we will see later in this chapter.

While the timebase and orbit can be used to evaluate frequency information, the most convenient plot for this purpose is the *spectrum plot*. The spectrum plot is created from the signal of a single transducer. It is the basic display of a spectrum analyzer and has been a mainstay of machinery diagnostics for many years.

In the past few years, an important new tool, the *full spectrum plot*, has been developed that uses the signals from a pair of orthogonal, shaft relative, vibration transducers. The full spectrum plot compares to a conventional spectrum plot in the same way that the orbit plot compares to a timebase plot. The full spectrum plot contains much more information than the spectrum plot, including vibration precession direction and orbit ellipticity. It is so important for machinery diagnostics that we now refer to the conventional spectrum plot as the *half spectrum* plot.

Spectrum plots are used to identify the frequency components that are present in complex vibration signals and to trend changes in the amplitude of frequency components. These frequencies include running speed, multiples of running speed, line frequency electrical noise, gear mesh frequencies, gear defect frequencies, rolling element bearing frequencies, and vane and blade pass frequencies. Rotor system natural frequencies that are excited will also show up on the spectrum plot. Subsynchronous frequencies that are often associated with fluid-induced instability, compressor rotating stall, compressor surge, or rub, and supersynchronous frequencies that are often associated with rubs and shaft cracks can also be identified.

In this chapter, we will start with a discussion of the complex vibration signal, its frequency content, and how that information is displayed on the half spectrum plot. We will then discuss some technical aspects of spectrum signal processing, followed by the meaning of and the enhanced information content in the full spectrum plot.

After full spectrum, we will discuss plot formats that present spectrum data versus speed and versus time: the *spectrum cascade plot* for startup or shutdown data and the *spectrum waterfall plot*, which is used primarily for steady state trending. Both of these plots can be generated in half and full spectrum formats. These plots are similar in structure, but have important differences in their application.

The Half Spectrum Plot

Let's start with a machine operating at a constant speed. Because of a combination of unbalance and other effects, the machine is vibrating in a complicated way. The unfiltered vibration signal from a transducer on this machine will reveal all of the complexity of the machine vibration that falls within the bandwidth of the data collection system. A *filtered* signal from this transducer will be a sine wave at the filter frequency with some amplitude and phase.

Figure 8-1 shows a complex, timebase vibration signal (red) and a series of sine waves (blue) that add up to produce the timebase signal. Using the Fourier transform, the frequency, amplitude, and phase of these sine waves (called *components*) can be computed from a digital sample of the original timebase signal. The phase for each signal is measured with respect to the trigger signal that

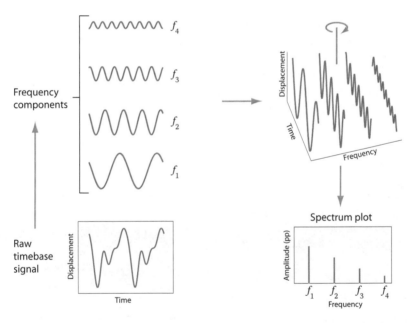

Figure 8-1. Time and frequency domain display of a complex signal. The Fourier transform applied to a complex, periodic, timebase signal (red) produces a set of harmonic sine waves, or *components*. The signal components are grouped at upper right by adding the third dimension, frequency. The plot is rotated to produce a two-dimensional plot of amplitude versus frequency, the half spectrum plot. The components now appear as a series of vertical lines, whose lengths represent the peak-to-peak amplitudes of the signal components. Because the timing (phase) information is lost, it is not possible to reconstruct the original waveform from the components of the spectrum plot.

starts the sampling process at time t_0. The Fourier transform output is equivalent to the output of a series of band-pass filters that have been set to integer multiples of the lowest frequency signal, f_1. (In practice, the lowest displayed frequency of a spectrum plot will usually be below the lowest measured vibration frequency.)

The component sine waves in the figure are plots of displacement versus time. If we also plot them versus frequency, we can create a three-dimensional plot (upper right). With this perspective, we can see each component's frequency, amplitude, and phase.

This plot is somewhat repetitious along the time axis. After all, we know these are sine waves; why continue repeating the same data over and over? If we rotate the plot so that the time axis disappears, we will see a two-dimensional plot of amplitude versus frequency (bottom right). Note that the component signals now appear as a series of vertical lines; each line represents a single frequency and its height is the amplitude of the signal. *This is a half spectrum plot.*

By hiding the time axis, we have obtained a relatively simple plot format that allows us to clearly see the frequencies and amplitudes of the component signals. Unfortunately, we have hidden an important piece of information, *the phase of the component signals*. Because of this, is not possible to reconstruct the original waveform from the component frequencies and amplitudes. This is a drawback of all types of spectrum plots.

The amplitude scale can be either linear or logarithmic. Logarithmic scaling is useful when there is a need to compare signals with both very large and very small amplitudes. This scaling will clearly display all signal components and the noise floor. However, when applied to rotating machinery work, logarithmic scaling makes it more difficult to quickly discriminate between significant and insignificant vibration components. Linear scaling has the advantage of showing the most significant components; weak, insignificant, and low-level noise components are greatly reduced in scale or eliminated. Because of its advantage for machinery work, linear scaling will be used for the spectrum plots in this book.

The frequency scale can be displayed in several frequency units. Most spectrum analyzers display the frequency in hertz (Hz). This is useful when comparing machine vibration frequencies to line frequencies, such as in induction motor or steam turbine generator diagnostics. Some software packages can display units of Hz, cpm, or orders of running speed. Cpm is a very convenient unit when working with machinery, because it is easy to compare a frequency in cpm to the running speed of the machine in rpm. Spectrum plots that are displayed in orders of running speed (1X, 2X, etc.) are also easy to interpret.

Technical Issues

While, on the surface, a spectrum plot appears simple to interpret, it is important to understand its limitations and to recognize bad or questionable data. The discussion here is a brief summary of the most important points.

The Fourier transform (and its computational cousin, the fast Fourier transform, or FFT) assumes that the unfiltered vibration signal has always been, and will always be, unchanged. In other words, the machine vibration state does not change, and the signal repeats in exactly the same way forever. This assumption is an adequate approximation for most machines that operate at a steady state speed or change speed slowly.

This assumption can break down badly for machines that experience suddenly changing vibration conditions (such as crushers or wood chippers) or for machines that accelerate (induction motors) or decelerate very rapidly. Spectrum plots under these circumstances can have significant errors in amplitude and frequency. Spectra of rapidly changing data can exhibit broadened spectral lines that are significantly shifted in frequency.

In practice, the fast Fourier transform (FFT) calculates the spectrum from a *sample record*, which contains a specific number of digital waveform samples. Because the sample record has a finite length, part of the algorithm involves extending its length by repeatedly wrapping the signal around on itself. Unless the number of cycles of the signal exactly matches the length of the sample record (which is improbable), there will be a discontinuity at the junction. This discontinuity introduces noise (*leakage*) into the spectrum, which broadens the frequency lines, reduces the calculated amplitudes, and increases the noise floor.

This problem is reduced by *windowing*. A window function applied to the sample record forces the signal to zero at the endpoints, typically in a gradual and smooth manner. This has the effect of eliminating the step discontinuity in the extended signal. Depending on the software, several types of windowing functions are available, each with its own advantages and disadvantages. Different windowing functions will result in different values of amplitude and frequency when applied to the same data. A Hanning window function is usually the best compromise for rotating machinery work, providing good amplitude and frequency resolution.

Figure 8-2 shows a vibration waveform, containing a mixture of 1X and ½X frequencies, and two examples of half spectrum plots. For the top spectrum plot (the middle plot in the figure), no windowing function was applied to the sample record. Note that the spectrum "lines" are not quite lines; instead, they have some finite width and widen at the bottom. A small noise floor is also visible. This is an example of leakage due to the discontinuity at the sample record end-

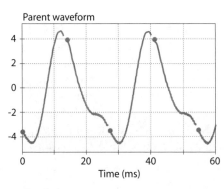

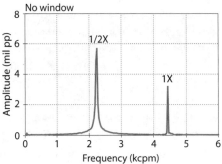

Figure 8-2. A timebase plot with two examples of half spectrum plots. For the middle plot, no windowing function was applied to the sample record. The spectrum "lines" are not quite lines; instead, they have some finite width and widen at the bottom. The bottom plot shows the spectrum calculated using a Hanning window. The 1/2X spectral line is narrower and higher, and the residual noise floor has virtually disappeared.

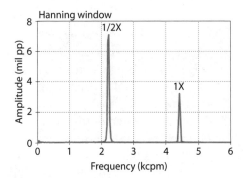

points and the limitations of digital sampling. The bottom plot shows the spectrum when a Hanning window is applied to the sample record. Note that the ½X spectral line is narrower and higher, and the residual noise floor has virtually disappeared.

A digitally calculated spectrum consists of discrete frequency *bins*, or *lines*, of finite width. The width of these lines, the *resolution* of the spectrum, is an important consideration. The maximum resolution of a spectrum is determined by the ratio of the spectrum *span* (the range of displayed frequencies) to the *number of spectrum lines* that are displayed:

$$\text{Resolution} = \frac{\text{Span}}{\text{Number of Lines}} \qquad (8\text{-}1)$$

The spectrum plot is a collection of these lines, arranged side by side. The width of each line is equal to the resolution of the spectrum. For example, a 400 line spectrum with a span of zero to 200 Hz will have a resolution of

$$\text{Resolution} = \frac{200 \text{ Hz}}{400 \text{ Lines}} = 0.5 \text{ Hz/Line}$$

Thus, each frequency line will, ideally, represent only the spectral energy in a 0.5 Hz (30 cpm) wide band from 0.25 Hz below to 0.25 Hz above the center frequency of the line. Accuracy in the displayed amplitude and frequency of a spectrum line will depend on where the actual vibration frequency is with respect to the center frequency and which window function is used.

The limited resolution of spectrum plots means that there is always an uncertainty associated with any frequency we wish to measure. In the example above, a frequency actually located at, for example, 99.75 Hz, is displayed at 100 Hz. A spectrum plot with poor resolution will have a corresponding large uncertainty in the measured frequency. Even good resolution spectra may not be able to discriminate between vibration frequencies of exactly ½X and 0.49X, an important distinction for malfunction diagnosis. Higher resolution (zoomed) spectra can help, but orbits with Keyphasor dots can sometimes be superior to spectrum plots for making this kind of discrimination (see Chapter 5).

Noise can be a problem in spectrum plots. The Fourier transform of a spike is a series of spectrum lines extending to very high frequency. Thus, anything that produces a sharp corner in the signal will produce a series of spectrum lines. Sharp corners can result from shaft rebound at a rub contact point or from an inadequate sampling frequency (causing a corner where a smooth transition really exists), among other things. Spikes or steps in the signal can originate from electrical noise problems or from scratches on the shaft. Spectrum plots are calculated from *uncompensated* waveforms, which may contain significant slow roll or glitch content. In general, the appearance of spectrum lines as a series of harmonics should be viewed with caution. Use timebase, orbit, or cascade plots (below) to validate the data.

The Full Spectrum

The half spectrum is a spectrum of a single timebase waveform. *The full spectrum is the spectrum of an orbit.* It is derived from the waveforms from two, orthogonal, shaft relative transducers, combined with knowledge of the direction of rotation. The information from the two transducers provides timing (phase) information that allows the full spectrum algorithm to determine the direction of precession at each frequency. Because the timing information is critical, the two waveforms must be sampled at the same time.

The full spectrum is calculated by performing an FFT on each transducer waveform. The results are then subjected to another transform that converts the data into two new spectra that represent frequencies of precession, one spectrum for X to Y precession and one for Y to X precession. The last step uses the direction of rotation information to determine which of the spectra represents *forward* and which represents *reverse* precession frequencies. When this process is completed, the two spectra are combined into a single plot, the full spectrum plot (Figure 8-3).

Figure 8-4 shows the relationships among timebase waveforms, half spectra, the orbit, and the full spectrum. The Y and X timebase waveforms and their half spectra are at the top. The two waveforms combine to produce the orbit at bottom left. The data used to generate the half spectra are further processed to produce the full spectrum at bottom right. Note that you cannot generate the full spectrum by combining the two half spectra.

In the full spectrum plot, the spectrum of forward precession frequencies is on the positive horizontal axis and the spectrum of reverse precession frequencies is on the negative horizontal axis. Thus, for each frequency, there are two possible spectrum lines, one forward, and one reverse. The relative length of the spectrum lines for each frequency indicates the shape and direction of precession of the orbit filtered to that frequency.

Figure 8-5 shows four, circular, 1X orbits, with different directions of precession, indicated by the blank/dot sequence, and different directions of rotor rotation, indicated by the arrow. To the right of each orbit is its full spectrum. Since each orbit is circular, there is only one line, which is the peak-to-peak amplitude

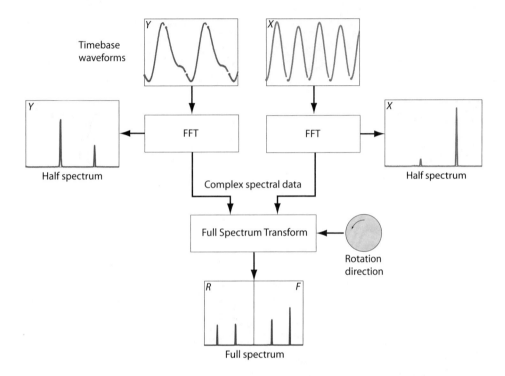

Figure 8-3. Calculation of the full spectrum. An FFT is performed on each waveform from an *XY* transducer pair. The complex spectral data is then subjected to another transform that generates two new spectra that represent the frequencies of precession: one spectrum for *X* to *Y* precession and one for *Y* to *X* precession. The direction of rotation is used to determine which of the spectra represents forward precession and which represents reverse precession frequencies.

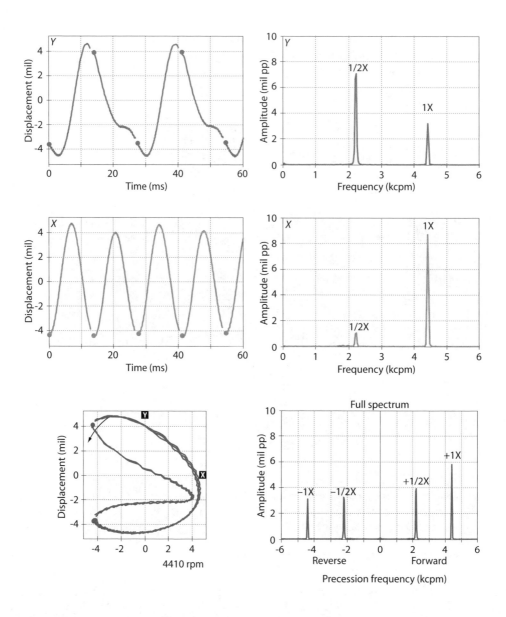

Figure 8-4. Timebase waveforms and their half spectra, the orbit and its full spectrum. The two waveforms combine to produce the orbit. The data that produces the two half spectra is processed to produce the full spectrum at bottom right, which is the spectrum of the orbit.

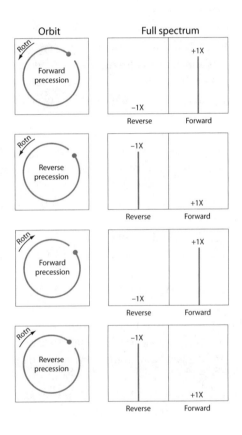

Figure 8-5. 1X, circular orbits and their full spectra. The spectrum line appears on the forward side of the plot for the two orbits that are undergoing forward precession. The spectrum line appears on the reverse side of the plot for the two orbits that are undergoing reverse precession. The relative direction of vibration precession, not just the direction of rotation, determines whether the line is forward or reverse.

of the orbit. Regardless of the direction of rotation, when the direction of precession is forward (in the direction of rotation), the line is on the positive axis, and when the direction of precession is reverse (opposite the direction of rotation) it is on the negative axis.

The path of these circular orbits is generated by a single, rotating vector. The vector length is the peak amplitude of the orbit (one-half the line height, which represents peak-to-peak amplitude). It rotates at the frequency of the line and in the direction of precession indicated by the line. As this vector rotates, the tip of the vector will trace out the path of the orbit. The full spectrum line defines this rotating, forward vector, and, consequently, the orbit. As with the half spectrum, there is no phase information in the full spectrum plot, so the Keyphasor dot location is arbitrary.

For the 1X, elliptical orbit in Figure 8-6, the direction of precession is X to Y, the same as the rotation direction, so the orbit is another example of forward precession. Its full spectrum shows a 1X, forward precession component and a smaller, 1X, negative precession component. The vectors a and b are defined by one-half the value of the positive and negative lines of the full spectrum and rotate in opposite directions. The sum of the vectors a and b generate the path of the orbit. Because they rotate in opposite directions, they will alternately add to and subtract from each other twice per revolution, defining the semimajor and semiminor axes of the elliptical orbit. (The sum and difference of the full spectrum line heights are peak-to-peak values and would define the major and minor axes).

Thus, the full spectrum lines represent the forward and reverse vectors that define the orbit. Note that the orientation of the orbit ellipse shown in the figure is arbitrary. The full spectrum contains information about size, ellipticity, and direction of precession, but, because there is no phase information, there is no information about *orientation*. An orbit with *any* orientation, but possessing the same ellipticity, size, and direction of precession, will have the same full spectrum. Thus, the full spectrum is independent of transducer orientation. This is different from half spectrum, which does depend on the transducer orientation.

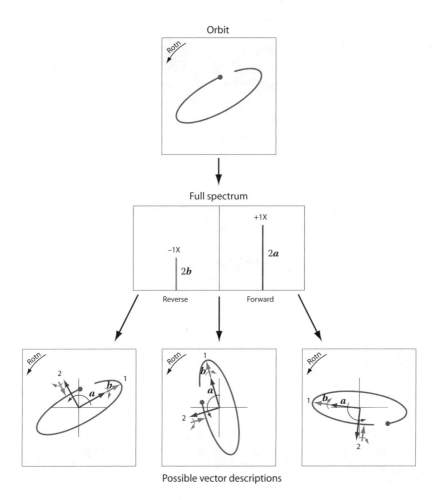

Figure 8-6. Forward and reverse vector construction of a 1X, elliptical orbit. The full spectrum of an orbit shows a 1X, forward precession component and a smaller, 1X, reverse precession component. The sum of the lengths of the two full spectrum lines is equal to the length (peak-to-peak) of the major axis of the elliptical orbit (1). The difference between the lengths of the two full spectrum lines is equal to the length (peak-to-peak) of the minor axis of the elliptical orbit (2). The orbit is generated by the sum of two, counterrotating vectors with lengths equal to half the spectrum line length. Because of the lack of phase information in the full spectrum, there is not enough information to uniquely reconstruct the original orbit.

Figure 8-7 shows the progression of 1X orbit shapes from forward circular through line to reverse circular and the associated full spectra. The relative size of the forward and reverse line heights correlate with the shape and precession direction of the orbit:

1. A single component, whether forward or reverse, means a circular orbit.

2. The largest component determines the direction of precession.

3. The smaller the difference between the components, the more elliptical the orbit.

4. Equal components mean a line orbit.

Complicated orbits will have forward and reverse components at many frequencies. Each pair of components represents a set of vectors that rotate in forward and reverse directions at a specific frequency. The most complex orbit can always be described by set of such vectors and full spectrum lines. The lines in the full spectrum represent the precessional structure of the orbit. Each pair of forward and reverse precession frequency components describes an *orbital component*, a suborbit (circular, elliptical, or line) with a particular precession frequency and direction. The entire orbit can be expressed as the sum of its orbital components in the same way that a timebase waveform can be expressed as the sum of its sine wave components.

Figure 8-8 shows a complex orbit from a steam turbine with a ½X rub. The orbit contains ½X, 1X, and some higher order vibration frequencies. The full spectrum helps clarify the complexity. Note that the 1X spectral line pair shows that the 1X component is largest, forward, and mildly elliptical. The ½X line pair shows that this component is nearly a line orbit. Also, there is 2X vibration present that is also a line orbit. Some small ³⁄₂X, the third harmonic of the ½X fundamental, is also visible.

At first glance, the full spectrum might seem abstract. What is significant about pairs of vectors with forward and reverse precession? It lets us easily identify key orbit characteristics that might otherwise be obscured. Precession direction and ellipticity provide insight into the state of health of a machine. More importantly, some rotor system malfunctions can have characteristic signatures on a full spectrum plot that are *not available* on half spectrum plots. These char-

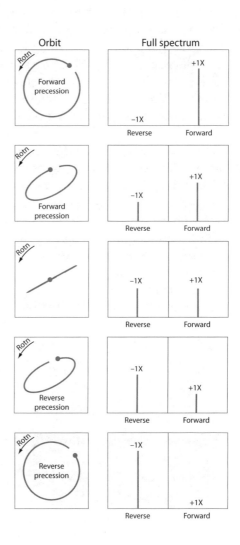

Figure 8-7. Circular and elliptical 1X orbits with their full spectra. The direction of precession of the orbit is indicated by the dominant line of the forward and reverse components. The ellipticity is determined by the relative size of the forward and reverse components. Note that when the orbits are circular, there is only one spectrum line, and when the orbit is a line, the spectrum components are equal.

acteristics can be used to discriminate between different malfunctions that produce vibration with similar frequencies.

An example is discrimination between a ½X rub and fluid-induced instability. Fluid-induced instability almost always appears as a predominantly forward, nearly circular, subsynchronous vibration, usually at a frequency below ½X. Compare the half and full spectrum plots (Figure 8-9) of a ½X rub (red data) to a fluid-induced instability (blue data). Note the similarity in appearance of the half spectrum plots (top). The frequencies of the subsynchronous lines (in orders of machine speed) are very close. It would be very difficult to discriminate between these two malfunctions given only half spectrum plots.

Compare the full spectrum plots (middle). There is a clear difference in the relative size of the forward and reverse subsynchronous components. The plot for the rub (left) shows that the subsynchronous component is extremely elliptical. The full spectrum plot for the instability (right) shows that the subsynchronous vibration is clearly forward and nearly circular. The forward, circular, subsynchronous behavior is typical of fluid-induced instability and atypical of rub. The additional information on the full spectrum plot, which may not be immediately obvious on the orbits (bottom), clearly reveals a difference in behavior that is valuable for diagnostics.

Full spectrum is a new tool. Once its relationship to the orbit is understood, half spectrum plots appear limited by comparison. The effort made to master this important new format will be rewarded by an enhanced understanding of machinery behavior.

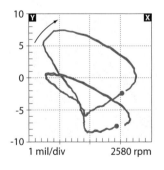
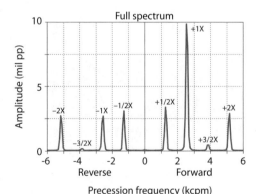

Figure 8-8. An orbit and full spectrum from a steam turbine with a 1/2X rub. The full spectrum helps clarify the complex orbit, which is a sum of 1/2X, 1X, and some higher order vibration. The 1X component orbit is the largest, forward, and mildly elliptical. The 1/2X and 2X orbits are nearly line orbits. A small 3/2X component is also visible and is the third harmonic of the 1/2X fundamental.

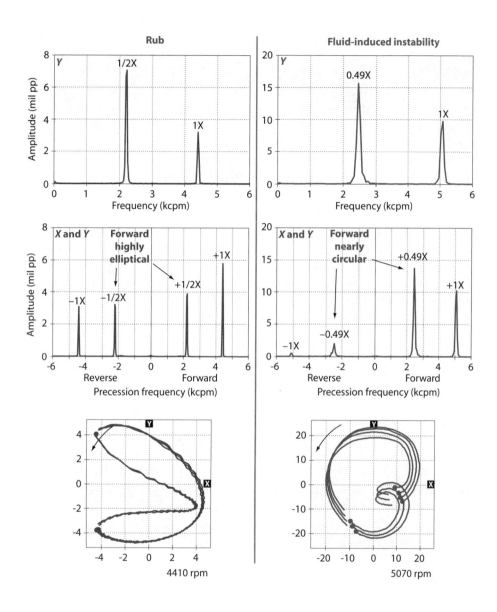

Figure 8-9. Half and full spectrum display of a 1/2X rub (red data) and a fluid-induced instability (blue data). Note the similarity in appearance of the two half spectrum plots (top). The full spectrum plots clearly reveal the difference in the subsynchronous vibration: the rub orbit is extremely elliptical; the fluid-induced instability orbit is forward and nearly circular. The unfiltered orbits are shown for comparison.

Spectrum Cascade Plots

During a startup or shutdown, spectra can be taken at different speeds. These spectra can be displayed by adding a third dimension to the spectrum plot, rotor speed. The spectra are positioned in the order of increasing speed with the lowest speed spectrum in front. Such a plot is called a spectrum cascade plot, or, more simply, a cascade plot. A cascade plot can be constructed with a series of half spectra or with a series of full spectra. The full spectrum cascade plot is preferred because of its higher information content.

The full spectrum cascade plot in Figure 8-10 shows the startup of a machine with a rub. As with the full spectrum plot, the horizontal axis represents precession frequency. The vertical scale to the right is for amplitude, which is measured from the baseline of each spectrum. The vertical scale to the left is for the third dimension, rotor speed. Each spectrum is placed on the plot so that its baseline corresponds to the rotor speed at which the sample was taken.

Three primary relationships should be examined when viewing a cascade plot. First is the *diagonal* relationship; vibration frequencies that change with, or *track*, running speed. Order lines, which are drawn diagonally from the origin (zero speed, zero frequency), are the most typical diagonal relationship (these are not available when the frequency axis is in orders of running speed). The ±1X order lines show the points on the spectra where the vibration or precession frequency is equal to running speed. The ±2X order lines identify frequencies equal to twice running speed, the ±½X lines identify frequencies equal to one-half running speed, etc.

Order lines quickly establish important tracking frequency relationships. The most obvious are the 1X order lines. Vibration on these lines is typically caused by a combination of runout, shaft bow, and unbalance. Normally, the +1X vibration component will be higher than the −1X component because unbalance usually produces forward orbits. The figure shows two probable balance resonances, which appear as peaks in amplitude. Because of the lack of phase information on the spectrum plot, suspected resonances should always be confirmed on a Bode or polar plot.

Remember that rapid machine accelerations and decelerations may cause smearing and offset of frequencies in the spectra. A good check is to verify that the 1X vibration is aligned with the 1X order line. Any significant offset implies that all frequencies for that spectrum sample have been shifted.

The second key relationship is horizontal. Horizontal relationships exist for different frequencies at the same speed (in the same spectrum). One example of this relationship is the integer multiples (harmonics) of forcing frequencies produced by nonlinearities and asymmetries in rotor systems. The primary forcing frequency, 1X due to unbalance, can produce harmonics at 1X, 2X, 3X, etc.

Another example is the sum and difference frequencies (sidebands) produced when one signal modulates another.

Harmonics can also be generated by rubs. Anything in a machine that causes a sudden change in direction of the shaft will produce harmonics in the spectrum. The sharper the turn, the richer the harmonic spectrum. Subsynchronous vibration frequencies can also produce harmonics; for example, a ½X rub can produce harmonics at 1X, ³⁄₂X, 2X, ⁵⁄₂X, etc (Figure 8-8). Scratches on shafts cause sudden changes in displacement signals that result in harmonics. These signals also track running speed and stay constant in amplitude over a wide speed range.

Horizontal relationships can involve more than harmonics. The ½X vibration in Figure 8-10 is caused by a rub that is the result of high amplitude response in the second balance resonance. The horizontal relationship is important because of the correlation of the ½X vibration with the resonance, and it is marked with the horizontal ellipse.

The third key relationship is vertical. Vertical relationships exist for things that happen at the same frequency over different speeds (multiple spectra).

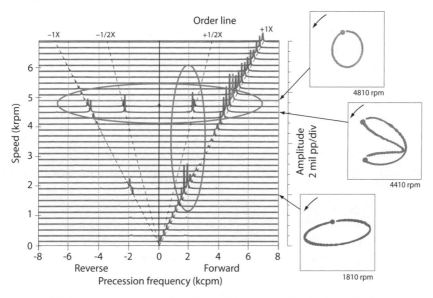

Figure 8-10. A full spectrum cascade plot of a machine startup. The horizontal axis represents precession frequency, the amplitude scale is to the right, and the rotor speed scale is on the left. Order lines, drawn diagonally from the origin, highlight diagonal, tracking relationships: vibration frequencies that are proportional to running speed. The horizontal and vertical relationships associated with the machine resonances and a rub are marked with ellipses. See the text for a full discussion.

Many rotor system natural frequencies remain constant over speed and appear on cascade plots as a series of lines on different spectra, arranged vertically. As a machine changes speed, if the 1X forcing function coincides with (crosses on a cascade plot) a natural frequency of the rotor, a resonance will occur. If there are harmonics, the harmonic vibration is also available to excite any resonance. Thus, if 2X vibration coincides with a natural frequency, then it will excite that natural frequency as it passes through. The resonance will show on the 2X order line as a peak of amplitude that will be vertically aligned with the peak of amplitude on the 1X line. See Figure 23-7 for an example.

Similarly, 3X, 4X, etc., vibration (for example, that produced by a blade- or vane-pass mechanism) can also excite a resonance. These vertical relationships can be important for malfunction diagnosis.

In the figure, the vertical ellipse shows the nearly vertical relationship between the rub vibration frequency and the first balance resonance frequency of this machine. The offset in frequency is predictable, because the rotor system has been stiffened by the rub contact, moving the rotor system natural frequency higher.

The full spectrum cascade plot is a good tool to use when a significant amount of Not-1X activity is detected. The components of the Not-1X vibration can be quickly identified by using this plot, which will aid in identifying the source of the vibration.

Unbalance response will usually produce negligible vibration at slow roll speeds. Because spectrum plots are generated from uncompensated data, a large slow roll runout will produce significant vibration along the 1X order line down to very low speeds, and it can be easily recognized. Figure 8-10 shows this behavior. Note that the +1X vibration is clearly visible at slow roll speed; this machine had a significant rotor bow.

Shaft scratches can produce a rich harmonic spectrum. Because the parent waveforms are uncompensated, the scratch spectrum will appear in all of the spectra on the cascade plot. This behavior makes it fairly easy to recognize. If the same set of harmonics are visible at all speeds, then they are probably due to one or more shaft scratches. Multiple scratches can appear as a mixture of forward and reverse harmonics on a full spectrum, depending on the number of scratches and their spacing on the shaft.

Spectrum Waterfall Plots

While spectrum cascade plots are designed to display multiple spectra versus speed, from transient, startup or shutdown data, spectrum waterfall plots are designed to display multiple spectra versus time, usually during constant speed operation. Waterfall plots substitute time for rotor speed on the third axis (although rotor speed may change). The horizontal and vertical relationships of the cascade plots are maintained, but the diagonal relationships are, typically, distorted; order lines may not be straight.

Waterfall plots are commonly used to examine how machine vibration changes with a change in an operating parameter. The full spectrum waterfall plot in Figure 8-11 shows the response of a compressor with a center seal instability problem. As suction pressure varied, vibration behavior changed dramatically, from normal, mostly 1X behavior, to fluid-induced instability, and back again. Orbits are shown for different suction pressure conditions. Note that the full spectrum clearly shows that the subsynchronous vibration is predominantly forward at that frequency; this is a strong indicator that the problem is a fluid-induced instability.

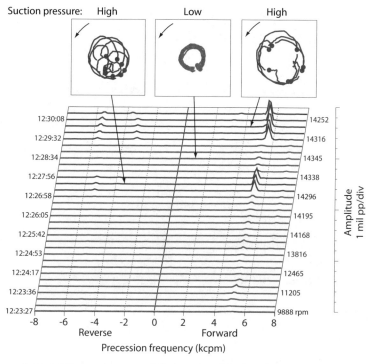

Figure 8-11. A full spectrum waterfall plot. Waterfall plots display spectra with respect to time, while the machine speed is either constant or changing. It is an excellent plot for correlating response to operating parameters. The running speed is displayed on the right side of the plot, and the amplitude scale is at the extreme right. In this example, a pipeline compressor has an instability that appears when suction pressure is high (red). Significant full spectrums are identified with their orbits.

At times, machines will be started, run for a short time, and then shut down. This is an ideal application for a waterfall plot. The waterfall plot can provide good visibility of these three different regions on one plot. Figure 8-12 shows a full spectrum waterfall of the startup, steady state, and shutdown of an induction motor with an electrical noise problem. In the startup region (red), the very high amplitude set of lines at ±60 Hz is line frequency noise. The ±1X motor rotor vibration appears on the diagonal as the motor accelerates. When the motor reaches the operating speed of around 3590 rpm, electrical power is reduced, and the 1X rotor response and 60 Hz line frequency noise combine into a single line (green region). When power is cut around 11:29, the ±60 Hz noise component disappears suddenly, leaving the ±1X coastdown vibration (blue). The APHT plot from this machine showed a periodic ripple in amplitude and phase caused by the beat frequency between the 60 Hz (3600 cpm) line noise and the 1X rotor frequency at 3590 cpm. This waterfall plot proved that the problem in the data was noise-related and not rotor-related.

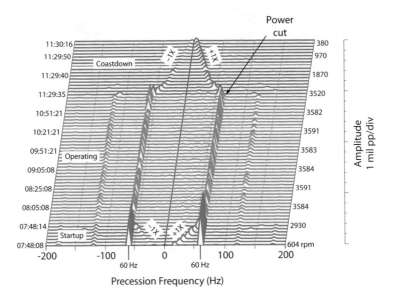

Figure 8-12. A full spectrum waterfall of an induction motor with an electrical noise problem. The very high amplitude lines at ±60 Hz in the startup region (red) are line frequency noise. When the motor reaches the operating speed of around 3590 rpm (green), electrical power is reduced, and the ±1X lines become a mixture of 1X rotor response and 60 Hz line noise. When power is cut at around 11:29, the 60 Hz lines disappear suddenly, leaving the 1X, coastdown vibration (blue).

Summary

The conventional, or half spectrum plot displays amplitude of vibration on the vertical axis versus frequency of vibration on the horizontal axis. It is constructed using the sampled timebase waveform from a single transducer.

Spectrum plots can be used to identify the frequencies of running speed, harmonics of running speed, sub- and supersynchronous vibration frequencies, gear mesh frequencies, gear defect frequencies, rolling element bearing defect frequencies, vane and blade pass frequencies, sidebands, glitch, and line frequency noise.

The full spectrum uses the waveforms from an orthogonal pair of vibration transducers (usually shaft relative). The full spectrum displays frequency and direction of precession on the horizontal axis. Forward precession frequencies are displayed to the right of the origin and reverse precession frequencies are displayed to the left of the origin.

The full spectrum is the spectrum of an orbit, and the forward and reverse frequency component pairs represent orbit components (filtered orbits). The ratio of the amplitudes of full spectrum component pairs gives information about the ellipticity and direction of precession of the components, important characteristics for malfunction diagnosis. However, there is no information about the orientation of the orbit.

Spectrum cascade plots are sets of spectra that are collected during the startup or shutdown of a machine. Cascade plots can be constructed from either half spectra, or full spectra. Cascade plots have important information associated with vertical, horizontal, and diagonal relationships.

Waterfall plots are collections of spectra obtained, usually, during steady state operating conditions and plotted versus time. They also can use either half spectra or full spectra.

The spectrum plot is a powerful tool when carefully applied. Because of its wide availability, there is a temptation to use the spectrum plot to the exclusion of other plot formats. But the spectrum, however powerful, is not a substitute for the information that can only be obtained in other plots: the filtered amplitude and phase in polar and Bode plots, the shaft position information in average shaft centerline plots, the shape and frequency information in the orbit, and the waveform information in the timebase plot. All of this information is needed for comprehensive machinery management.

Chapter 9

Trend and XY Plots

IN CHAPTER 7 WE DISCUSSED THE Amplitude-PHase-Time (APHT) plots, a form of polar and Bode plots, which are used for trending vector data. Besides vector data, there are many other parameters that we would like to trend: vibration levels, position data, process data, or any other parameter that can be useful for machine condition monitoring. The trend plot shows changes in and the rate of change of parameters that may signal a developing or impending problem in a machine. This information can be used to set limits or thresholds for action.

We may also wish to examine how any of these variables change with respect to others. Such correlation is the heart of a good diagnostics methodology. No single variable or plot type can reveal everything about a machine. Data is usually correlated with many other pieces of information to arrive at a diagnosis. This kind of correlation is often done with multiple trend plots, where several variables are plotted against the same time scale. Correlation can also be done with XY plots, where two parameters are plotted against each other.

This chapter will deal with the construction and uses of the trend plot and provide several examples. We will briefly discuss problems that can arise when the data sample rate is too low. Finally, we will discuss XY plots, a special type of trend plot used for correlation of two parameters.

Trend Plots

The trend plot is a rectangular or polar plot on which the value of a measured parameter is plotted versus time. Trend plots can be used to display any kind of data versus time: direct vibration, nX amplitude, nX phase (the APHT plot is a trend plot that displays both), gap voltage (radial or thrust position), rotor speed, and process variables, such as pressure, temperature, flow, or power. Trend plots are used to detect changes in these important parameters. They are used for both long and short term monitoring of machinery in all types of service and are, typically, an example of a *steady state* (constant speed) plot.

The data for a trend plot can be collected by computer or by hand. Figure 9-1 shows a trend plot of *hand-logged* gap voltage from a fluid-film bearing at the discharge end of a refrigeration compressor. Due to improper grounding, electrostatic discharge gradually eroded 280 μm (11 mil) of the bearing, allowing the rotor shaft to slowly move into the babbitt. The trend plot alerted the operators to the fact that something was wrong, and they scheduled a shutdown in time to prevent serious damage. This is an example of how a very simple data set provided valuable information that saved the plant from an expensive failure.

Even though a trend plot may look like a continuous history, it is not. Parameters are assumed to be slowly changing, so the data to be trended is sampled at intervals that depend on the importance of the machinery and the data. If a sudden change in behavior of the parameter occurs between samples, the data will be missed.

Some data values may fluctuate periodically. For example, 1X amplitude and phase may change periodically due to a thermal rub. The period of change for this kind of malfunction can be on the order of minutes to hours. Amplitude and phase modulation can occur in induction motors, due to uneven air gap, at twice the slip frequency; the period here is usually a fraction of a second. If the sampling frequency is less than twice the frequency of interest (does not satisfy the Nyquist criterion), then the frequency of the changes in the trend plot will be incorrect, an effect known as aliasing.

The trend plot from an induction motor (Figure 9-2) looks like, at first glance, a timebase plot. However, it is a trend of unfiltered, peak-to-peak vibration that is changing periodically. This motor, which drives a boiler feed pump, has an uneven air gap problem. The vibration amplitude is modulated at a beat frequency equal to twice the slip frequency of the motor.

The data in blue was sampled very rapidly, at about 10 samples per second. This produced a high resolution trend plot. The data in red is a portion of another trend plot from about two hours earlier, when the motor was experiencing the same problem. The sample rate was one sample every 10 seconds, a factor of 100 slower. Note that the frequency of the change of the red is much lower, the result of aliasing. This would not be obvious unless the data taken at the higher sample rate was available. The observed modulation frequency is much lower than the true modulation frequency. Parameters which change periodically like this are relatively rare, but this example demonstrates how the sample rate can produce a misleading picture of machine behavior. This effect can also happen

Figure 9-1. A trend of hand-logged gap voltage from a fluid-film bearing at the discharge end of a refrigeration compressor. Due to improper grounding, electrostatic discharge gradually eroded 280 μm (11 mil) of the bearing, allowing the rotor shaft to slowly move into the babbitt. The trend plot provided early warning of the problem and identified the rate of change, allowing a scheduled shutdown. This particular machine problem was also discussed by Eisenmann in reference [1].

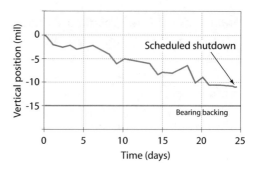

Figure 9-2. Aliasing in a trend plot. This is not a timebase plot! This boiler feed pump motor has an uneven air gap. The vibration amplitude is modulated at a beat frequency equal to twice the slip frequency of the motor. The data in blue was sampled at about 10 samples per second. The data in red is a portion of a trend plot that was sampled about two hours earlier, at one sample every 10 seconds, a factor of 100 slower. When the two trends are compared, it is clear that the red data is aliased; the sample rate was not fast enough to accurately capture the changes in the vibration.

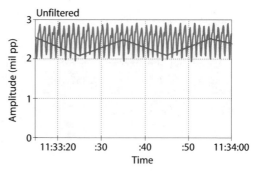

when, to increase the trend interval on the horizontal axis, the database of sampled data is decimated (samples are thrown out).

Multiple parameters can also be displayed on the same plot, or on several plots with the same time scale, to correlate changes that occur in a machine. Figure 9-3 shows a trend plot of a compressor with a center seal instability problem. Both 1X (blue) and unfiltered (red) vibration amplitude are shown on the same plot and to the same scale. While the machine was running at full speed, the suction pressure was varied, and a fluid-induced instability appeared or disappeared depending on the level of suction pressure. Note that the 1X vibration amplitude *decreased* when the unfiltered vibration *increased*. This can happen when high amplitude, Not-1X vibration moves the rotor to a region where the Dynamic Stiffness is different, changing the 1X response. A plot of the actual

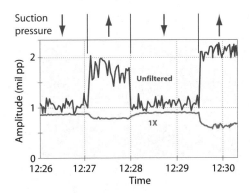

Figure 9-3. A trend plot of a compressor with a center-seal instability problem. Both 1X (blue) and unfiltered (red) vibration amplitudes are shown on the same plot, at the same scale. While the machine was running at full speed, the suction pressure varied; a fluid-induced instability appeared and disappeared, depending on the level of suction pressure. Note that the 1X vibration decreased when the unfiltered vibration increased (see text for further explanation).

pressure data, which was unavailable, would highlight the correlation of the variables.

Figure 9-4 shows trend data from a 30,000 hp, synchronous electric motor driving an axial flow air compressor. The plot shows vibration amplitude from a displacement probe (blue, right scale) and a velocity transducer (green, left scale). This motor had a weak foundation system that slowly loosened, allowing the vibration amplitude, measured by both transducers, to slowly increase. When sets of chock wedges were installed and the foundation bolts retightened around 30 August, the vibration dropped sharply, followed by another slow rise. Near the end of the record, the machine was shut down, and the foundation was completely overhauled. The motor itself was found to have problems, and the unit was replaced. After restarting, the vibration returned to very low levels.

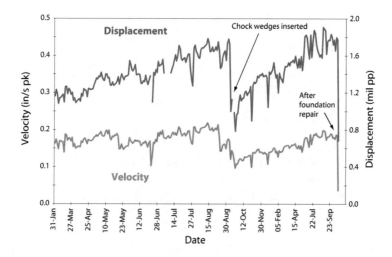

Figure 9-4. Trend data from a 30,000 hp, synchronous electric motor driving an axial flow air compressor. The plot shows vibration amplitude from a displacement probe (blue, right scale) and a velocity transducer (green, left scale). This motor had a weak foundation system that slowly loosened. The vibration amplitude slowly increased on both transducers until around 30 August, when sets of chock wedges were installed and foundation bolts retightened. The vibration shows a sharp drop, followed by a slow rise. Near the end of the record, the machine was shut down, and the foundation was completely overhauled.

XY Plots

Where the trend plot displays one or more parameters versus time, the XY plot (not to be confused with *XY* axes or *XY* transducers) can be used to display any two parameters versus each other. Correlations between the parameters will show a diagonal relationship. A complete lack of correlation will show either a horizontal or vertical relationship.

Figure 9-5 shows an XY plot of vibration amplitude versus gap voltage from a 125 MW steam turbine generator, HP/IP unit running at 3600 rpm. The plot starts at point 1 when the machine undergoes a load change. Between points 1 and 2 (red), the plot clearly shows a correlation between changing shaft position (measured by the gap voltage) and 1X vibration amplitude. As the shaft moves (blue) to point 3 during the next three hours, the vibration decreases while the gap voltage remains approximately constant. It is possible that a gravity bow may be working itself out or the measurement probe may be viewing a different section of the shaft as the machine reaches thermal equilibrium. The shaft takes only about 35 minutes to move from point 3 to point 4 (green), most likely in response to another load change.

Figure 9-5. An XY plot of 1X vibration amplitude versus gap voltage from a 125 MW steam turbine generator, HP/IP unit running at 3600 rpm. The plot clearly shows (red) the correlation between changing shaft position (measured by the gap voltage) and an increase in1X vibration amplitude when the load changes. As the shaft moves to point 3 during the next three hours, the vibration decreases while the gap voltage remains approximately constant (no correlation). After that, the shaft takes only about 35 minutes to move to point 4 (green), most likely in response to another load change.

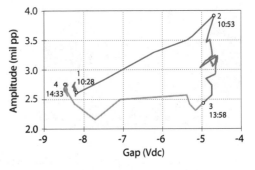

Summary

The trend plot is a rectangular or polar plot of a measured parameter versus time. Trend plots can be used to display any kind of data versus time: direct vibration, nX amplitude, nX phase, gap voltage, rotor speed, and process variables, such as pressure, temperature, flow, or power. Data can be correlated by plotting several variables on the same time scale.

Trended data is sampled at periodic intervals, and it is assumed to be slowly changing. If data values can change periodically, the sampling frequency must be at least twice the frequency of change (the Nyquist criterion). If not, the data will be aliased; the displayed behavior of the trend data will not be correct.

The XY plot can be used to display any two parameters against each other. Correlations between the parameters will show a diagonal relationship. A complete lack of correlation will show either a horizontal or vertical relationship.

References

1. Eisenmann, Robert C., Sr., and Eisenmann, Robert C., Jr., *Machinery Malfunction Diagnosis and Correction* (Upper Saddle River: Prentice-Hall, Inc., 1998), pp. 751-758.

The Static and Dynamic Response
of Rotor Systems

Chapter 10

The Rotor System Model

Rotor systems are subjected to many kinds of forces. Forces can act in radial and axial directions, and torques and moments can act in angular directions. These forces can be *static*, or unchanging in direction and time, or they can be *dynamic*, where they can change in magnitude or direction with time.

Static forces acting on the rotor system produce static deflections of rotor system elements. For example, a static radial load applied to the midspan of a rotor shaft will cause the shaft to deflect in a direction away from the applied load. Or, when a torque is applied to the shaft of an operating machine, the shaft will twist to some extent in response to the torque.

Dynamic forces acting on the rotor system produce vibration (Chapter 1). Vibration can appear in the form of radial, axial, and torsional vibration. Usually, we measure radial vibration in machinery because radial vibration is the most common vibration problem. Axial vibration is less frequently encountered but can produce machine problems. Torsional vibration is very difficult to measure and tends to be overlooked. Both torsional and axial vibration can produce radial vibration through cross-coupling mechanisms that exist in machinery. Unbalance is the most common example of a dynamic force (the force direction rapidly rotates) that produces radial vibration.

How do dynamic forces act on the rotor system to produce vibration? Somehow, the rotor system acts as an energy conversion mechanism that changes an applied force into observed vibration. The rotor system can be viewed as a very complicated "black box" that takes dynamic force as an input and produces vibration as an output (Figure 10-1). If we can understand the nature of this black box, we should be able to understand how forces produce vibration. We should also be able, by observing the vibration and knowing the workings of the black box, to deduce something about the forces that produce the vibration.

We can try to guess the contents of the black box by shaking it using a technique called *perturbation* and observing the behavior of the system. This is the same technique some people use when trying to guess the contents of a wrapped gift. They shake the gift and evaluate the weight, balance, and sound. When applied to rotor systems, the shaking applies a known force to the rotor system, and the vibration response to the force is measured.

We can also try to estimate the contents of the black box by developing a mathematical *model* of the rotor system. A good model will allow us to relate observed vibration to the forces that act on the system. This will allow us to detect, identify, and correct potential problems in the rotor system.

A good model will also give us the ability to *predict* how changes in forces will affect vibration. This is the key to effective balancing technique. Imagine trying to balance a complex machine by merely guessing how much weight to add and where to place it. Without a systematic approach based on knowledge of rotor behavior, accurate balancing would be virtually impossible. A model gives us the foundation for a systematic, efficient, and effective balancing technique.

In this chapter we will develop a simple model of a rotor system. The primary result of the model, *Dynamic Stiffness*, is the solution to the mystery inside the black box. It is a fundamental and important concept for understanding rotor behavior, it provides a powerful tool for malfunction diagnosis, and it is the key to successful balancing.

In developing this model, there is no way to avoid the mathematics of differential equations and complex numbers. We will make every effort to keep the mathematics as simple and clear as possible. Those who do not have the mathematical background should be able to skip the math and still understand the concepts. The math is there for those who wonder where it all comes from.

We will focus on the development of a rotor system model based on radial vibration. The basic concepts that we will develop here can be easily extended to axial and torsional vibration.

Figure 10-1. The rotor system as a "black box." The system converts dynamic input forces to output vibration.

Dynamic force → Rotor system → Vibration

Introduction to Modeling

Everyone has seen scale models of aircraft. A model airplane mimics important features of the real thing. When viewed from different directions, a well-built model airplane can look very much like the real thing, but it includes only certain features of the full-sized airplane. However, even though it looks the same, a model airplane does not behave in all ways as a real airplane; if it does not have a working engine, it cannot fly. In fact, all models are simplifications designed to represent particular features, and they will not function properly when pushed beyond the limits of their applicability.

Our rotor system model is a *mathematical* representation that is designed to mimic certain important features of the real rotor system. The rotor model is an attempt to describe the function of the black box that transforms dynamic forces into vibration.

Because it is only a model, it will have limited applicability. The limits of the model are stated in the *assumptions* used to derive the model. Assumptions almost always involve simplifications that make the solution of the model easier. Applying a model beyond the limits expressed in the assumptions will usually lead to error. Sometimes the error can be tolerated, sometimes not. Often the amount of error is unknown.

Most real rotor systems are very complex machines. We cannot, given the current state of computers and mathematics, construct a model that duplicates the behavior of these machines in every detail. We *can* construct complicated computer models that do a good job of mimicking some aspects of complex behavior, but the results of such models tend to be very narrowly focused and are difficult to generalize.

Simple equations can be more easily understood and interpreted. The benefit of the simple approach is clarity and, we hope, an intuitive understanding of basic rotor system behavior. Because of this, we will develop a model that will yield some relatively simple algebraic equations. The price we pay for this simplicity is that the model may not have the capability to accurately represent the behavior of complex systems. We must always keep in mind that a simple model will be limited in its application. In essence, we will trade detail for insight.

The model we are going to develop is a variation of an early rotor model, often called the *Jeffcott rotor*, developed by Henry Jeffcott [1] in 1919. Our model extends the Jeffcott model by including the effects of fluid circulation around the rotor and by using complex number notation to simplify the mathematics. It is necessary to include fluid circulation effects if we want our model to predict the rotor response in machines with fluid-film bearings, seals, and other areas where fluid is in circumferential motion. Our model will be a slight simplification of the model presented by Bently and Muszynska in reference [2].

Here are some basic definitions of terms that will be used in the derivation and discussion of our model and throughout the book:

The *rotor system* includes all parts of the machine that are involved with vibration. This includes the shaft with any attached disks, the bearings that support the shaft, the structures that support the bearings, the machine casing, the foundation system, coupled machines, and attached piping systems or unsecured cabling. The rotor system can also include all of the plant equipment that is involved in the process in which the machine is imbedded. When working with simple models it is easy to forget that real rotor systems include all of these components.

The *rotor* is the rotating shaft assembly that is supported by bearings. The rotor may be rigidly coupled to other rotors in other machines, effectively forming a large, extended rotor.

The *stator* is the stationary part of the machine that contains the rotor. The rotor rotates in and is supported by bearings in the stator. The purpose of bearings is to eliminate friction while preventing unwanted contact between the rotor and the stator.

Forces that act on the machine will be divided into internal and external forces. *Internal forces* are those that appear from the machine's interaction with parts of itself. Support forces in bearings, forces resulting from shaft deflection, and forces due to interaction of the rotor with the surrounding fluid are examples of internal forces. *External forces* are forces that are applied to the rotor system and produce some sort of perturbation, or disturbance of the system, such as impact forces due to rotor-stator contact, static radial loads, or deliberately induced perturbation forces. Even though rotating unbalance is generated internally, it will be treated as an external force.

The term *synchronous* refers to anything that is rotating at the same frequency as the rotor. Unbalance is an example of a synchronous rotating force. The term 1X is used to describe a synchronous frequency (–1X is also considered to be a synchronous frequency).

The term *nonsynchronous* refers to any frequency other than synchronous. A nonsynchronous frequency may be either *supersynchronous* (higher than running speed) or *subsynchronous* (lower than running speed).

A rotor system *parameter* is a property of the system that affects system response. Mass, stiffness, and damping are examples of rotor system parameters.

The term *isotropic* describes the properties of a system that are radially symmetric. For example, isotropic stiffness means that the stiffness of the system is the same in all radial directions (Figure 10-2). The term isotropic is distinct from the term *symmetric*, which implies a geometric (shape) symmetry.

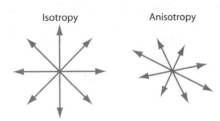

Figure 10-2. Isotropic and anisotropic systems. A system property is *isotropic* if it is the same in all radial directions. A system property is *anisotropic* if it has different values in different radial directions.

A system property is *anisotropic* if it has different values in different radial directions. Fluid-film bearing stiffness is isotropic when journals operate at low eccentricity ratios and anisotropic at high eccentricity ratios, where the stiffness in the radial direction is typically much higher than the stiffness in the tangential direction. On the other hand, rolling element bearing stiffness is usually isotropic.

Modeling of physical systems usually follows a structured process:

1. *State the assumptions that will be used.* These usually involve simplifications that allow easier solution of the problem, but limit the application of the model. These limits must be kept in mind when applying the model to the real world.

2. *Define a coordinate system.* The rotor system moves in space, and there must be a measurement system to describe the motion.

3. *Describe the forces that act on the system.* Forces are modeled as physical elements which depend on displacements, velocities, or accelerations. For example, a rolling element bearing support force can be described as a spring element where the force is proportional to the displacement of the spring.

4. *Develop a free body diagram.* This diagram contains the rotor mass (or masses) and all of the forces acting on it (or them).

5. *Derive the equation of motion.* This is the differential equation that combines the forces and mass elements with a physical law that describes how the system must behave.

6. *Solve the equation of motion.* The result will be an expression that describes the position of the system over time.

7. *Compare the predicted behavior to the observed behavior of the machine.* Theoretical behavior is compared to the results of experiments.

8. *Adjust the model if the description is not adequate.*

Assumptions

The assumptions define the limitations of our model. They make the model easier to solve at the expense of detail in the final results.

1. *The rotor system will have one degree of freedom in the complex plane* (1-CDOF). One degree of freedom implies that there is one, independent, lateral position measurement variable (*r*, which will be complex), no angular deflection, and one differential equation to describe the system. This will produce a model capable of only one forward mode, or resonance.

2. *The rotor system parameters will be isotropic.* This will allow us to use a more compact mathematical description for the model. The effects of anisotropy will be discussed in Chapter 13.

3. *Gyroscopic effects will be ignored.* Gyroscopic effects can cause a speed-dependent shift in rotor system natural frequencies. This can be very important for overhung rotor systems, but we can ignore gyroscopic effects and still gain a good understanding of basic behavior.

4. *The rotor system will have significant fluid interaction.* All the fluid interaction will be in an annular region; that is, a fluid-film bearing, seal, impeller, or any other part of the rotor that is equivalent to a cylinder rotating within a fluid-filled cylinder.

5. *Damping will be viscous and due only to fluid interaction.* There will be no other source of damping in the system. This reduces the number of parameters in the equation and simplifies the mathematics.

6. *The model will be linear.* This is a difficult term to define briefly. A useful definition is that a system is linear if a multiplication of the input by a constant factor produces a multiplication of the output by the same factor. For example, if we multiply the unbalance by a factor of two, then the vibration of the machine will increase by a factor of two. Also, if a linear system is subjected to a dynamic input at a particular frequency, only that frequency will appear as an output. While machines can and do behave in nonlinear ways, nonlinear mathematics can be very difficult to solve algebraically. Fortunately, most machinery behavior is approximately linear, and the linear models approximate real machine behavior well enough to be quite useful. (That's good, because balancing techniques depend on linear behavior.)

7. *A fluid will completely surround the rotor.* Fluid-film bearings will be *fully lubricated (360°, or 2π).* While normal hydrodynamic bearings operate in a partially lubricated *(180°, or π)* condition, misalignment can unload the bearing, resulting in a transition to full lubrication and fluid-induced instability. Also, seals are designed to operate concentrically with the rotor; thus, they operate, by design, in a fully "lubricated" condition. For these reasons, the fully lubricated assumption is both realistic and necessary to adequately describe fluid-induced instability problems.

8. *A nonsynchronous, rotating, external force will be applied to the rotor system.* We will see that rotating unbalance is a special case of this general nonsynchronous force.

The Coordinate System and Position Vector

Figure 10-3 shows a basic physical description of the rotor system. The rotor can be described as a single, concentrated, perfectly balanced rotor mass, M, located in the center of a fully lubricated, fluid-film bearing that is fixed in place. A massless shaft is supported at the left end by an infinitely stiff bearing that provides only lateral constraint (no angular constraint). Thus, all of the rotor mass is concentrated in the disk and is supported by the bearing. The only stiffness element in the system is associated with the fluid bearing (which can also represent a seal). The rotor rotates at an angular speed, Ω, in rad/s, in a counterclockwise (X to Y) direction, as shown in the section view. The bearing clearance is greatly exaggerated for clarity.

Note that, even though this description implies that the rotor mass and shaft can pivot in the small bearing, the rotor is assumed to be constrained to move only in the plane of the bearing with no angular deflection. The most accurate graphical description of the model would eliminate the shaft and small bearing altogether, leaving only the rotor mass and the fluid-film bearing.

Figure 10-4 shows the coordinate system for the measurement of the lateral motion of the rotor mass. The X and Y axes represent the real and imaginary axes of the complex plane. The terms real and imaginary come from the mathematics of complex numbers. *Both of these directions are quite real, and nothing about the rotor position is imaginary.* The origin of the coordinate system is the equilibrium position of the rotor when no external forces are applied to the rotor, and, in our model, it is located at the exact center of the fluid-film bearing.

The *rotor position vector*, r, represents the position of the center of the rotor relative to the equilibrium position. It is defined in the rectangular complex plane as

$$r = x + jy \tag{10-1}$$

where x is the position of the rotor in the X direction, y is the position in the Y direction, and

$$j = \sqrt{-1} \tag{10-2}$$

The length, or magnitude, of r is A, where

$$A = |r| = \sqrt{x^2 + y^2} \tag{10-3}$$

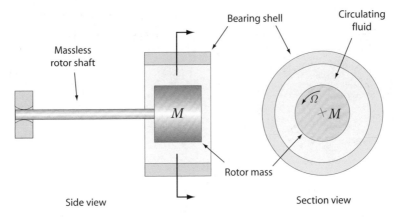

Figure 10-3. The basic, physical rotor system. The rotor is a single, concentrated mass, M, located in the center of a fluid-film bearing. The shaft provides no support for the rotor mass; all of the mass is supported by the bearing. All of the stiffness in the system is assumed to be located in the fluid bearing (which can also represent a seal, if desired). The rotor rotates counterclockwise (X to Y) at an angular speed, Ω, in rad/s, as shown in the section view.

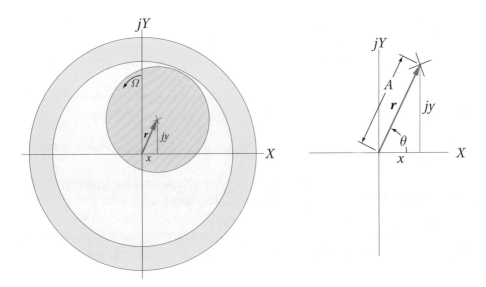

Figure 10-4. End view of the rotor and its coordinate system. At left, the rotor is deflected from the center of the system. The detailed view at right shows the response more clearly. The X axis and the Y axis are the coordinate axes of the complex plane. See the text for details.

The angular position of $\boldsymbol{r}$ is measured as a positive angle in a counterclockwise direction from the positive X axis. This angle, θ (Greek lower case theta), is given by

$$\theta = \arctan\left(\frac{y}{x}\right) \qquad (10\text{-}4)$$

Also,

$$x = A\cos\theta$$
$$y = A\sin\theta \qquad (10\text{-}5)$$

Notice the similarity between this position vector notation and the vibration vector notation in Chapter 3. The two are very closely related; in fact, the solution of the model's equation of motion will yield vibration vectors.

Leonhard Euler (1707-1783) showed that the position vector can be described using an exponential notation, which is very compact:

$$\boldsymbol{r} = x + jy = Ae^{j\theta} \qquad (10\text{-}6)$$

where $e = 2.71828...$ is the base of natural logarithms.

The elements in front of the exponential function (in this case, A, but there will be other elements) define the *length*, or amplitude (magnitude) of the vector, $\boldsymbol{r}$. The exponential function defines the *angle* of $\boldsymbol{r}$.

If $\boldsymbol{r}$ rotates around the origin with constant, nonsynchronous circular frequency, ω (in rad/s), then the angle, θ, becomes a function of time:

$$\theta = \omega t + \alpha \qquad (10\text{-}7)$$

where α (Greek lower case alpha) is the *absolute phase* angle at time $t = 0$, when the Keyphasor event occurs, and $\boldsymbol{r}$ is located at an angle α with the horizontal axis. The Keyphasor event acts like a strobe, momentarily illuminating the rotating vector at the angle α. If we substitute Equation 10-7 into Equation 10-6 we obtain a general expression for $\boldsymbol{r}$ that will be very useful for our purposes:

$$\boldsymbol{r} = Ae^{j(\omega t + \alpha)} \qquad (10\text{-}8)$$

Equation 10-8 describes a position vector that rotates; the tip of the vector and the center of the rotor precess about the origin in a circular orbit. We obtain the velocity (the rate of change of position) by differentiating the position with respect to time, assuming constant amplitude, A, and constant angular velocity, ω:

$$\boldsymbol{v} = \frac{d\boldsymbol{r}}{dt} = \dot{\boldsymbol{r}} = j\omega A e^{j(\omega t + \alpha)} \qquad (10\text{-}9)$$

We differentiate once more to obtain the acceleration,

$$\boldsymbol{a} = \frac{d\boldsymbol{v}}{dt} = \ddot{\boldsymbol{r}} = -\omega^2 A e^{j(\omega t + \alpha)} \qquad (10\text{-}10)$$

A few words about j are in order. Whenever j appears outside the exponential, it basically means "change phase by 90° in the leading direction." In Equation 10-9, j orients the velocity vector 90° ahead of the precessing position vector. This makes sense if you realize that, as $\boldsymbol{r}$ precesses in an X to Y direction, the instantaneous velocity of the tip of $\boldsymbol{r}$ points (for circular motion) 90° from $\boldsymbol{r}$ in the direction of precession.

Note also that in Equation 10-9, the amplitude of the velocity, ωA, is proportional to the circular frequency, ω.

In the acceleration expression in Equation 10-10, the negative sign indicates that the direction of acceleration is *opposite* to the direction of $\boldsymbol{r}$. The negative sign is the product of $j \cdot j$ ($j^2 = -1$), so acceleration must lead displacement by $90° + 90° = 180°$. The amplitude of the acceleration is proportional to ω^2.

Finally, note that the *mathematical* angle measurement convention is that for positive ω, $\boldsymbol{r}$ precesses in a counterclockwise (X to Y) direction, and the measured angle is positive. This is opposite of the Bently Nevada instrumentation convention, where phase *lag* is measured as a positive number in a direction *opposite* to precession (see Appendix 1). This difference is very important when trying to relate the results of the model to measured vibration.

Lambda (λ): A Model of Fluid Circulation

Whenever a viscous fluid is contained in the annular region between two, concentric cylinders which are rotating at different angular velocities, the fluid will be dragged into relative motion. This motion can have a complicated behavior. What we need is a simple way of quantifying this behavior. λ (Greek lower case lambda) is a model of fluid circulation that reduces this complexity to a single parameter. Though our discussion of λ will focus on fluid-film bearings, keep in mind that these concepts can be applied to any similar physical situation, such as seals or pump impellers.

Imagine two, infinite flat plates separated by a fluid-filled gap (Figure 10-5). The upper plate moves with a constant linear velocity, v, and the lower plate has zero velocity. Because of friction, the linear velocity of the fluid next to the surface of the moving plate will be v, while the velocity of the fluid next to the surface of the stationary plate will be zero. The velocities in the fluid will form a linear *velocity profile* as the velocity smoothly changes from one surface to the other. The average linear velocity of the fluid (red) must be somewhere between zero and v, and, for this situation, it is $0.5v$.

Now imagine wrapping the two plates into two, concentric, infinitely long cylinders, as shown at the bottom of the figure. This is similar to a rotor operating inside a fluid-film bearing. The fluid is trapped in the annular region between the cylinders, the inner cylinder rotates at some *angular* velocity, Ω, and the outer cylinder remains motionless. As with the flat plates, the fluid next to the surfaces of the cylinders must have the surface velocity of the cylinders.

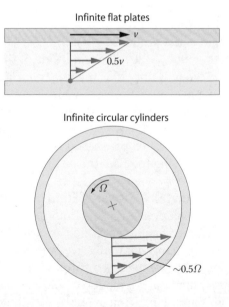

Figure 10-5. Viscous fluid flow between infinite flat plates and infinite circular cylinders. At top, the upper gray plate moves with a constant linear velocity, v, and the lower plate has zero velocity. Because of adhesion of the fluid, the linear velocity of the fluid immediately next to the surface of the moving plate will be v. The fluid next to the surface of the stationary plate will have zero velocity. The average linear velocity (red) of the fluid for this situation is $0.5v$. Now, imagine wrapping the two plates into two concentric, infinitely long cylinders, containing the fluid in the annular region between the cylinders (right). The inner cylinder rotates at some *angular* velocity, Ω; the outer cylinder remains motionless. As with the flat plates, the fluid next to the surface of the inner cylinder will have angular velocity Ω, and the fluid next to the surface of the outer cylinder will have zero angular velocity. For these *infinitely long* cylinders, the average angular velocity will be almost 0.5Ω.

The angular velocity of the fluid next to the inner cylinder is Ω, and the angular velocity of the fluid next to the surface of the outer cylinder is zero. The fluid in the annular region will have an average angular velocity between zero and Ω. For these *infinitely long* cylinders, the average angular velocity will be almost 0.5Ω.

Real journals and bearings are not infinitely long. In real bearings, the fluid is lost due to end leakage and has to be replaced. This is usually accomplished by radially injecting makeup fluid into the bearing through one or more ports. If the ports are radial, then when this fluid first enters the bearing, it will have zero angular velocity. The new fluid gradually undergoes angular acceleration due to the shearing action of the moving fluid that is already in the bearing. But, at the same time, because of the pressure differential between the injection point and the end of the bearing, the fluid starts moving axially. As a result, the fluid path traces out a spiral (Figure 10-6) and may be ejected before it reaches the angular velocity seen in the infinite cylinder. For this reason, the average fluid angular velocity in typical, fully flooded, hydrodynamic bearings is typically lower than 0.5Ω.

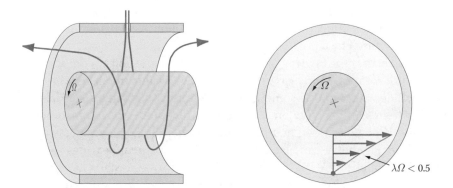

Figure 10-6. Fluid flow in a journal bearing. Fluid is injected into the bearing through one or more ports. When this fluid first enters the bearing, it has zero angular velocity. This fluid gradually undergoes angular acceleration due to the shearing action of the moving fluid that is already in the bearing. Because of the pressure gradient between the inlet port and the end of the bearing, the fluid traces out a spiral path to the end of the bearing. It may not reach the circumferential, angular velocity it would reach in an infinite cylinder. The average fluid angular velocity is $\lambda\Omega$.

If the fluid average angular velocity is v_{avg}, then we define λ as the ratio of the average angular velocity to the angular velocity of rotor rotation:

$$\lambda = \frac{v_{avg}}{\Omega} \qquad (10\text{-}11)$$

Thus, the fluid circumferential average velocity is

$$v_{avg} = \lambda\Omega \qquad (10\text{-}12)$$

λ is called the *Fluid Circumferential Average Velocity Ratio*. It is a dimensionless measure of the fluid circulation around the rotor and is a powerful tool for understanding rotor interaction with fluid-film bearings and seals. Typical values of λ for a *fully flooded*, hydrodynamic bearing with only radial injection of fluid are between 0.35 and 0.49. Hydrostatic bearings, because of their higher injection pressures and decreased exit time (less circumferential flow), can have values of λ less than 0.1.

If the injected fluid has a tangential angular velocity component, it will affect the value of λ. If the fluid enters the bearing or seal with an angular velocity component in the direction of rotor rotation (a condition called *preswirl*), then λ can have values considerably greater than 0.5. This can happen when fluid is preswirled by a previous stage in the machine.

If fluid enters the bearing or seal with an angular velocity component opposite to rotor rotation (*antiswirl*), then λ can have a value much less than 0.5, even approaching zero. Fluid is sometimes deliberately injected tangentially against rotation (*antiswirl injection*) in order to control a fluid-induced instability problem. This will be discussed in more detail in Chapter 22.

Bearing geometry can also affect λ. Plain cylindrical bearings tend to have the highest values of λ: $0.43 < \lambda < 0.49$. Many bearing designs have been developed to break up circumferential flow and reduce λ. Examples include tilting pad, lemon bore, pressure dam, multi-lobe, and elliptical bearings. Eccentricity ratio also affects λ, and this will be discussed later in this chapter.

For the purposes of modeling, λ will be assumed to be constant.

Fluid-film Bearing Forces and Stiffnesses

We have discussed how a cylinder rotating inside another, fluid-filled cylinder can set the fluid into motion. This is a good model for a plain, cylindrical, journal bearing or seal.

Assume the rotor is rotating at angular velocity Ω in a counterclockwise (X to Y) direction. When the journal is perfectly centered in the bearing (eccentricity ratio, $\varepsilon = 0$), the only forces acting on the shaft are shearing forces associated with the fluid. The journal acts like a pump, moving the fluid around the annular clearance in the bearing.

When the rotor is centered in the bearing, the radial clearance is the same all around the circumference of the bearing. However, if a static load is applied to the rotor, the rotor is displaced from the center. Now, the moving fluid encounters a reduction in available clearance and must slow down. The deceleration of this fluid results in an increase in the local pressure in the fluid (Figure 10-7). Some of the fluid escapes axially, but the fluid near the axial center of the bearing cannot. The fluid produces a circumferential *pressure wedge* that pushes on the rotor and moves it to the side. The rotor moves until the force pro-

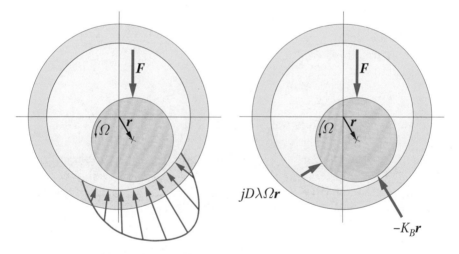

Figure 10-7. The forces in a fluid-film bearing. A static force, **F**, is applied to the rotor, which is rotating with angular velocity Ω. The rotor moves until, at position **r**, the force produced by the pressure in the oil wedge exactly cancels the force that is applied to the rotor. The pressure wedge forces can be resolved into two component vectors, a *radial* component that points in the opposite direction of **r**, toward the center of the bearing, and a *tangential* component that acts through the center of the rotor and points 90° from **r** in the direction of rotation. The sum of these two forces is equal and opposite to the applied force vector.

duced by the pressure wedge exactly opposes the force applied to the rotor. The position vector, r, extends from the center of the bearing (the equilibrium position and origin of the coordinate system) to the center of the rotor and is not precessing for this static load example. This pressure wedge is the primary means of rotor support in hydrodynamic journal bearings.

The force due to the pressure wedge can be resolved into two components (Figure 10-7, right), a *radial* component that points in the opposite direction of r toward the center of the bearing, and a *tangential* component that points 90° from r in the direction of rotation. Both forces are assumed to act through the center of the rotor. The vector sum of these two forces is equal and opposite to the applied force vector.

These two force components behave like forces due to springs. The radial force component, F_B, can be modeled as

$$F_B = -K_B r \qquad (10\text{-}13)$$

where K_B is the bearing spring stiffness constant in N/m or lb/in. F_B is proportional to the displacement and the stiffness, and the minus sign indicates that it points in the opposite direction of r. Such a force is also known as a *restoring force*, because it always acts in the direction of the original position, attempting to restore the system to equilibrium.

The tangential force component can be modeled as

$$F_T = jD\lambda\Omega r \qquad (10\text{-}14)$$

where D is the damping constant of the bearing. The j indicates that the direction of F_T is 90° leading relative to r (in the direction of rotation, Ω). In the figure, F_T is rotated 90° from r in an X to Y direction (the rotation direction of the rotor). If the rotor were rotating in a Y to X direction, then F_T would point in the opposite direction. The term $jD\lambda\Omega$ is called the *tangential stiffness*. See the Appendix for a discussion of the origin of this expression.

The tangential stiffness is proportional to the fluid damping. More importantly, it is proportional to the average fluid angular velocity, $\lambda\Omega$. Thus, the strength of the tangential force depends on both the rotor speed and λ; it will get stronger with increasing rotor speed and increasing λ.

Other Sources of Spring Stiffness

Besides fluid bearings, many other elements of the rotor system behave like springs. The shaft acts like a beam that is supported at two points by bearings. When a force is applied to the shaft, it will deflect, producing a restoring force directed toward the applied force. Shafts can be relatively flexible, such as in aeroderivative gas turbines, or very stiff, such as in electric motors. Because the shaft acts like a beam, beam deflection equations can be used to estimate its stiffness.

Some bearings can act like a pure spring, with little or no tangential stiffness. Rolling element bearings and low-speed bushings (such as oil-impregnated bronze bearings) are examples. Also, hydrostatic bearings, because of their high spring stiffness and low λ, have relatively low tangential stiffness.

Seals also contribute spring and tangential stiffness to the rotor system. Sometimes this stiffness can be significant when seals are located closer to the midspan of the rotor. Floating seals that become locked can produce drastic increases in rotor system stiffness.

All bearings are supported in structures that can deflect under load. Thus, bearing support pedestals and the foundation system also contribute spring stiffness to the rotor system.

In our development of the rotor model, all sources of spring stiffness in the rotor system (including the bearing spring stiffness) are combined to produce the effective *spring stiffness*, K. This constant is formed from the series/parallel combination of the various different spring stiffnesses. We will use an equivalent spring force vector, $\boldsymbol{F}_S$, to describe the spring force:

$$\boldsymbol{F}_S = -K\boldsymbol{r} \qquad (10\text{-}15)$$

Like the bearing spring force, $\boldsymbol{F}_S$ is proportional to K, and the minus sign indicates that it always points in the opposite direction of $\boldsymbol{r}$ (Figure 10-8).

Figure 10-8. The spring force. The rotor is displaced to an arbitrary position, $\boldsymbol{r}$, from the original position. The spring force is always directed back toward this original position and is proportional to both the magnitude of the displacement and the spring stiffness, K. K contains all spring stiffness contributions in the rotor system: shaft, bearing spring stiffness, bearing support stiffness, and foundation stiffness.

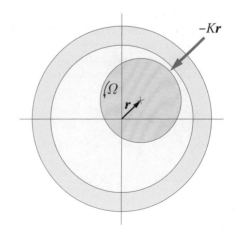

The Damping Force

All rotor systems have internal forces that cause the dissipation of energy. Friction is an example of a dissipative force. Friction forces can result from contact of the rotor with the stator, the movement of attached parts on the rotor, or from internal friction in the rotor material itself (also called *hysteretic damping*). All of these friction forces will be assumed to be small.

The damping force is generated when a viscous fluid is sheared between two surfaces in relative motion or when the fluid passes through a small orifice. An example is the force that is generated in an automobile shock absorber. The shock absorber has a piston that forces trapped fluid through an orifice, converting mechanical energy into heat in the working fluid.

Another example is a boat being propelled through the water. If the engine stops, the viscosity of the water will dissipate the kinetic energy of the boat, and it will come to a stop. The forces acting here are a combination of shearing and pressure drag.

Similar damping forces occur in a fluid-film bearing when the rotor precesses in the bearing. Put simply, the damping forces occur through a combination of shearing of the fluid and pressure drag. The amount of damping force

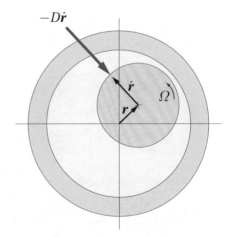

Figure 10-9. The damping force. The rotor has an instantaneous velocity vector, $\dot{r}$. The damping force is proportional to the both the viscous damping constant, D, and the magnitude of the velocity, and it acts in a direction opposite to the velocity vector.

generated is related to the velocity of the journal in the bearing. Additional damping can come from rotor interaction with the working fluid that surrounds it. Note that pressure drag effects are not, in a strict sense, equivalent to viscous drag. However, for simplicity, we will lump pressure drag effects into our description of the damping force that is based on viscous drag.

The damping force vector, F_D, is modeled by

$$F_D = -D\dot{r} \qquad (10\text{-}16)$$

The damping force is proportional to the damping constant, D, and acts in a direction opposite to the instantaneous velocity vector, $\dot{r}$ (Figure 10-9).

The magnitude of the damping force depends on both the damping *and* the velocity; if the velocity is very small, then the damping force will also be small. This can happen in rotor systems when a nodal point is located inside a fluid-film bearing. The small vibration at that location will produce a relatively small damping force. Conversely, if a mode shape produces a large amount of vibration inside a fluid-film bearing, then the damping force produced will be relatively large. These variations in damping force are related to the concept of *modal damping* which will be discussed in Chapter 12.

The Perturbation Force

A *perturbation* is a disturbance to a system. Perturbation forces are external forces that disturb the rotor from its equilibrium position. These forces can be static, or they can be dynamic. *Static* perturbation forces have constant magnitude and direction and produce static deflections or changes in rotor position. They include gravity loads in horizontal machines, fluid reaction loads in pumps, unequal steam admission loads in steam turbines, other process loads, or a combination of these. Misalignment can cause static radial loads to appear because of load transfer among bearings. Casing deformation and piping strain can shift bearing supports, leading to misalignment and the appearance of static radial loads. *Dynamic* perturbation forces periodically change in magnitude or direction, or both, and they produce a dynamic rotor system response that appears as vibration. Unbalance is an example of a rotating, synchronous perturbation force.

Many sources of nonsynchronous perturbation exist in rotor systems. Rotating stall in compressors can produce a subsynchronous, rotating perturbation force. Rotor asymmetries (such as produced by a shaft crack), coupling problems, and vane pass can cause supersynchronous perturbation. Impacting and cavitation can also produce nonsynchronous perturbations of the rotor system.

In order to produce a generalized dynamic vibration response from the rotor model, we must include some mechanism that will produce a controllable, non-synchronous perturbation. The *perturbator* shown in Figure 10-10 is a small unbalance mass (the *heavy spot*) "attached" to the rotor so that it is free to rotate independently (it could be attached to the outer ring of a rolling element bearing installed on the rotor). The perturbator can be rotated at any nonsynchronous frequency, ω. The unbalance mass, m, is located a distance, r_u, from the center of the rotor. A Keyphasor mark on this perturbator triggers once per revolution of the *perturbator*, not the rotor. At the moment of the Keyphasor event, the unbalance mass and the perturbation force are located at an angle δ with the positive X axis. The Keyphasor event acts like a strobe, momentarily illuminating the rotating perturbation force vector at the angle δ (Greek lower case delta). (For the purposes of modeling, this *absolute phase angle* is measured in the mathematical sense, counterclockwise from the positive horizontal axis, not in the instrumentation sense.) The resulting perturbation force vector, $\mathbf{F}_p$, is

$$\mathbf{F}_p = mr_u\omega^2 e^{j(\omega t+\delta)} \qquad (10\text{-}17)$$

$\mathbf{F}_p$ is a nonsynchronous, rotating unbalance force vector. The magnitude of $\mathbf{F}_p$ is proportional to the square of the perturbation frequency, ω, and at any time, t, it points radially outward in the direction given by $\omega t + \delta$.

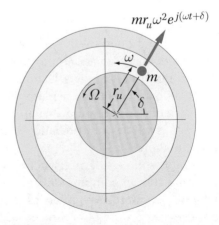

Figure 10-10. The perturbation force. A small unbalance mass, m (the *heavy spot*), is installed on a perturbator at a distance r_u from the center of the rotor. The perturbator rotates independently of the rotor at a nonsynchronous frequency, ω. (A Keyphasor mark on the perturbator enables speed and phase measurement.) At the Keyphasor event, the unbalance mass is located at an angle, δ, with the positive X axis. The perturbation force has a magnitude $mr_u\omega^2$.

The Free Body Diagram

Now that we have defined the forces acting on the rotor system, we can construct the free body diagram. This is a simple diagram that shows the rotor mass and the entire system of forces acting on it.

Figure 10-11 shows the free body diagram. The rotor with concentrated mass, M, rotates at a speed, Ω, in an X to Y direction, and it is displaced from the equilibrium position to a position, r. At that position, the rotor is moving at an arbitrary, instantaneous velocity, $\dot{r}$.

All forces acting on the rotor are assumed to act through the center of mass of the rotor. The spring stiffness force, F_S, points back toward the equilibrium position. The tangential stiffness force, F_T, points 90° from r in the direction of rotation. The damping force, F_D, points in a direction opposite to the instantaneous velocity vector, $\dot{r}$. The rotating perturbation force, F_p, is shown at angular position δ the instant the Keyphasor event occurs.

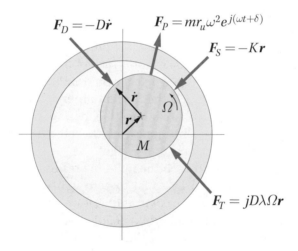

Figure 10-11. The free body diagram. The rotor with concentrated mass, M, rotates at a speed, Ω, in an X to Y direction. It is displaced from the equilibrium position to a position, r, where it moves at velocity, $\dot{r}$. All forces acting on the rotor are assumed to act through the center of mass of the rotor. The spring stiffness force, F_S, points back toward the original position. The tangential stiffness force, F_T, points 90° from r in the direction of rotation (leading). The damping force, F_D, points in a direction opposite to the instantaneous velocity vector, $\dot{r}$. The rotating perturbation force, F_p, is shown at angular position δ, the instant the Keyphasor event occurs.

The Equation of Motion

The rotor must obey physical laws in response to the forces acting on it. We apply Newton's Second Law: *The sum of the forces acting on a body is equal to the mass of the body times the acceleration of the body*:

$$F_S + F_T + F_D + F_P = M\ddot{r} \qquad (10\text{-}18)$$

Substituting the expressions for the forces, and being careful to keep track of the signs, we obtain

$$-Kr + jD\lambda\Omega r - D\dot{r} + mr_u\omega^2 e^{j(\omega t + \delta)} = M\ddot{r} \qquad (10\text{-}19)$$

Rearranging, we obtain the equation of motion in the standard form of a differential equation,

$$M\ddot{r} + D\dot{r} + (K - jD\lambda\Omega)r = mr_u\omega^2 e^{j(\omega t + \delta)} \qquad (10\text{-}20)$$

This is a second order, linear, differential equation with constant coefficients. The appearance of this equation differs from a standard mechanical (or electronic) oscillator equation because of the presence of the tangential stiffness term, $jD\lambda\Omega$. This term is what makes rotor system behavior so interesting, and it this term that is ultimately responsible for fluid-induced instability. If there is no fluid circulation, λ is zero, and the tangential term disappears, making the form of this expression identical to the equation for a simple oscillator. Note that the rotor system *internal* elements appear on the left side of the equation, and the applied, *external* force appears on the right.

If there were no forcing term on the right, the resulting equation (called the *homogeneous equation*) would be equal to zero and would describe the free (unforced) behavior of the system. For example, if we moved the rotor system to some position away from the equilibrium position and suddenly released it, the resulting rotor motion would follow the rules defined by the homogeneous equation. Free vibration will be discussed in Chapter 14.

The equation of motion is a set of rules that governs the behavior of the rotor system. The acceleration, the velocity, and the displacement of this rotor system must be related to the applied force by this equation. However, the equation of motion tells us very little about the vibration behavior of the system. We would like to know how this rotor system behaves over time, or what the amplitude and phase relationships are between the force and response. We now need to convert the set of rules into something more useful. This conversion process is called the *solution* of the equation of motion.

Solution of the Equation of Motion

To solve Equation 10-20, we must find a displacement function that, when differentiated (converted to velocity and acceleration) and substituted into the equation, makes the equation true. Since this is a linear system, perturbation at a frequency ω must produce a vibration at the same frequency ω. We will assume that the amplitude of vibration will have some nonzero value and that the absolute phase of the vibration response will be different from the phase of the perturbation force, δ.

Fortunately, the solution of this type of differential equation is well known. We assume a solution of the form,

$$\boldsymbol{r} = Ae^{j(\omega t + \alpha)} \tag{10-21}$$

where A is the length of the rotating displacement response, or vibration vector (the zero-to-peak amplitude of vibration), and α is the phase, or angle, of the response vector when the Keyphasor event occurs at $t = 0$.

We differentiate Equation 10-21 to find the velocity and acceleration. This has already been done in Equations 10-9 and 10-10. The displacement, velocity, and acceleration terms are substituted into Equation 10-20, and, after some algebra, we obtain

$$Ae^{j\omega t}e^{j\alpha} = \frac{mr_u\omega^2 e^{j\omega t}e^{j\delta}}{\left[K - M\omega^2 + jD(\omega - \lambda\Omega)\right]} \tag{10-22}$$

In this form, the expression on the left side of the equation represents the rotating response vector. The terms in the numerator of the expression on the right represent the rotating force vector. Note that each exponential term has been separated into a time term and a phase term. The time terms are responsible for the *rotation* of the vectors; the phase terms convey information about the *absolute phase* of the force and response vectors. Because the time terms are identical on both sides of the equation, we can eliminate them:

$$Ae^{j\alpha} = \frac{mr_u\omega^2 e^{j\delta}}{\left[K - M\omega^2 + jD(\omega - \lambda\Omega)\right]} \tag{10-23}$$

This equation describes the amplitudes and absolute phases of the vectors at the moment that the Keyphasor event occurs (Figure 10-12). In the figure, the response vector is shown lagging the force vector, but we will see below that the response vector can lead the force vector under some circumstances. The denominator of Equation 10-23 is called the *nonsynchronous Dynamic Stiffness*.

In its simplest form, Equation 10-23 states the following:

$$\text{Vibration} = \frac{\text{Force}}{\text{Dynamic Stiffness}}$$

Vibration is the ratio of the applied force to the Dynamic Stiffness. Whenever we measure vibration (for example using a vibration monitor), we are actually measuring the value of this ratio. Thus, *a change in vibration can be caused by either a change in force or a change in the Dynamic Stiffness or both*. This is an important machinery diagnostics concept. Because all of these elements are vector quantities, change can appear as either a change in amplitude or phase.

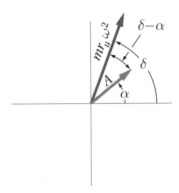

Figure 10-12. Force and vibration response vectors. The two vectors, which rotate with angular frequency ω, are shown frozen at the moment of the Keyphasor event. The force vector is shown leading the response vector (the response lags the force), but the opposite can be true.

Nonsynchronous Dynamic Stiffness

The nonsynchronous Dynamic Stiffness, K_N, is

$$K_N = K - M\omega^2 + jD(\omega - \lambda\Omega) \tag{10-24}$$

Dynamic Stiffness is a complex quantity that consists of two parts, the *Direct Dynamic Stiffness*,

$$K_D = K - M\omega^2 \tag{10-25}$$

and the *Quadrature Dynamic Stiffness*,

$$K_Q = jD(\omega - \lambda\Omega) \tag{10-26}$$

Direct Dynamic Stiffness acts *in line with* the applied force; Quadrature Dynamic Stiffness, because of the *j*, acts *at 90° to* the applied force.

Dynamic Stiffness is a very important result of the model. It is a function of the perturbation frequency, ω, and contains all of the rotor parameters in our model, including the rotor speed, Ω. *Dynamic Stiffness is the black box that transforms the dynamic input force to the output vibration of the rotor system.* It is a major key to understanding machine behavior, and it will be discussed in detail in Chapter 11.

Amplitude and Phase of the Vibration Response

Equation 10-23 can be manipulated into expressions for the amplitude and phase. First, let

$$F = mr_u\omega^2 \tag{10-27}$$

Multiply and divide the right side of Equation 10-23 by the complex conjugate of the denominator to eliminate the *j* terms in the denominator:

$$Ae^{j\alpha} = \frac{Fe^{j\delta}}{K_D + jK_Q}\left(\frac{K_D - jK_Q}{K_D - jK_Q}\right) \tag{10-28}$$

Now, multiply through and combine the exponential terms on the left,

$$\frac{A}{F}e^{j(\alpha-\delta)} = \left(\frac{K_D}{K_D^2 + K_Q^2} - j\frac{K_Q}{K_D^2 + K_Q^2} \right) \tag{10-29}$$

We now have an expression that mixes exponential and rectangular notation. The exponential form on the left already separates the amplitude and phase. The amplitude of the rectangular part is found by taking the square root of the sum of the squares of the direct and quadrature parts:

$$\frac{A}{F} = \sqrt{\frac{K_D^2}{\left(K_D^2 + K_Q^2\right)^2} + \frac{K_Q^2}{\left(K_D^2 + K_Q^2\right)^2}} \tag{10-30}$$

which reduces to

$$A = \frac{F}{\sqrt{K_D^2 + K_Q^2}} \tag{10-31}$$

Dynamic Stiffness controls the difference in absolute phase (the *relative phase*) between the force (the heavy spot) and the vibration response, $\delta - \alpha$. This change is found by taking the arctangent of the ratio of the quadrature and the direct parts of Equation 10-29:

$$\delta - \alpha = \arctan\left(\frac{K_Q}{K_D}\right) \tag{10-32}$$

Solving for α, the absolute phase angle of the vibration response,

$$\alpha = \delta - \arctan\left(\frac{K_Q}{K_D}\right) \tag{10-33}$$

Thus, α differs from the location of the heavy spot, δ (the phase angle of the forcing function) by the effect of the Dynamic Stiffness. The negative sign indicates that when K_Q and K_D are positive, the rotor vibration vector *lags* the heavy spot.

The Attitude Angle: Rotor Response to a Static Radial Load

A good test of the model is to see how the rotor responds to the application of a static radial load. We will replace the rotating unbalance with a static load, F. We assume that the load is applied vertically downward while the rotor is rotating at some speed, Ω. F is not rotating, so this is a special case of a non-synchronous perturbation force where the frequency, ω, is zero. Thus, the components of the Dynamic Stiffness become

$$\begin{aligned} K_D &= K \\ K_Q &= -D\lambda\Omega \end{aligned} \qquad (10\text{-}34)$$

Note that, for this static load case, the Direct Dynamic Stiffness is identical to the spring stiffness, and the Quadrature Dynamic Stiffness is identical (except for the sign) to the tangential stiffness. Substituting these elements into Equation 10-33 gives us the predicted response phase angle,

$$\alpha = \delta + \arctan\left(\frac{D\lambda\Omega}{K}\right) \qquad (10\text{-}35)$$

where we have passed the negative sign through the arctangent function.

This result is illustrated in Figure 10-13. The positive sign in Equation 10-35 indicates that the change in rotor position angle will also be positive, producing a change in position in a phase *lead* direction. This is exactly what we expect for

Figure 10-13. Rotor response to a static radial load. The downward acting force, F, produces a response, r, that acts in a leading direction. Because r leads F, the phase angle, α, of r, is larger than the phase angle, δ, of F. The difference between the phase angles, $\alpha - \delta$, is Ψ, the attitude angle.

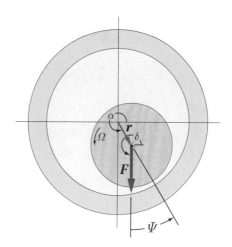

a rotating, statically loaded journal in a fluid-film bearing. The pressure wedge forces the shaft to an equilibrium position, which is in the direction of rotation. The amount of the phase lead will depend on the relative strength of the tangential and spring stiffnesses.

Note that this situation is identical to the basic definition of the *attitude angle* that was defined in Chapter 6. Thus, the attitude angle, Ψ, is defined by the model as

$$\Psi = \arctan\left(\frac{D\lambda\Omega}{K}\right) \tag{10-36}$$

Synchronous Rotor Response

A good definition of synchronous is *at the frequency of rotor rotation.* If we lock our nonsynchronous perturbation force to the rotor, it will rotate at the rotor speed and become a synchronous perturbation, where $\omega = \Omega$. If we substitute Ω for ω in Equation 10-23, we obtain an expression describing the synchronous rotor response to unbalance,

$$Ae^{j\alpha} = \frac{mr_u\Omega^2e^{j\delta}}{\left[K - M\Omega^2 + jD(1-\lambda)\Omega\right]} \tag{10-37}$$

Because we are now modeling synchronous (1X) behavior, δ represents the location of the *heavy spot*, the unbalance in the rotor; the vibration response absolute phase, α, represents the *high spot* of the rotor.

We can see that synchronous rotor response is actually a special case of general, nonsynchronous rotor response; however, it is the most important from a practical point of view. Ordinary, unbalance-induced 1X rotor vibration is a synchronous response. The rotor behavior described by Equation 10-37 will be thoroughly explored in the next chapter.

Synchronous Dynamic Stiffness

The denominator of Equation 10-37 is called the *synchronous Dynamic Stiffness*:

$$\boldsymbol{K}_S = K - M\Omega^2 + jD(1-\lambda)\Omega \tag{10-38}$$

The synchronous Direct and Quadrature Dynamic Stiffnesses are given by

$$K_D = K - M\Omega^2$$
$$K_Q = D(1-\lambda)\Omega$$

(10-39)

The Direct Dynamic Stiffness is identical in form to the nonsynchronous case in Equation 10-25, but the Quadrature Dynamic Stiffness has a different form than Equation 10-26. These differences will be discussed in the next chapter.

Predicted Rotor Vibration

We have already examined the predicted behavior of the model to a static load, and we have found that it produces a reasonable result. We will now examine the predicted rotor vibration response for both nonsynchronous and synchronous perturbation over a wide range of perturbation frequencies.

First, we will look at rotor system behavior for a system with low (subcritical) damping. A system like this is also referred to as an *underdamped* system. Low damping means that the Quadrature Dynamic Stiffness term, which depends on damping, is also low; this is a typical condition for most rotating machinery. The parameters used in the model are summarized in Table 10-1.

Table 10-1. Model parameters

Parameter	Low K_Q	High K_Q
D	52.7 x 10^3 N · s/m (301 lb · s/in)	1.58 x 10^6 N · s/m (9.02 x 10^3 lb · s/in)
Ω	900 rpm	1500 rpm
M	1000 kg (5.7 lb · s^2/in)	same
K	25.0 x 10^6 N/m (143 x 10^3 lb/in)	same
λ	0.48	same
m_{ru}	0.01 kg · m (13.9 oz · in)	same
δ	45°	same

With two minor differences (zero-to-peak amplitude and the mathematical phase convention), the model output is equivalent to a set of startup or shutdown 1X vibration vectors taken from a single transducer. In this simulation, since all angles are measured relative to horizontal right, the vibration transducer is mounted at horizontal right. The rotating heavy spot of the perturbator is located at 45° from the transducer, in the direction of rotation, when the Keyphasor event occurs.

Figure 10-14 shows the Bode and polar plots of the predicted behavior of the model. For the nonsynchronous perturbation, *the rotor is operated at a constant speed, Ω, of 900 rpm*. The perturbation frequency, ω, is swept from zero to 4000 cpm, and the model produces vibration vectors that are filtered to the *perturbation* frequency.

For the synchronous case, the perturbation frequency is set equal to the rotor speed (the unbalance heavy spot is now the perturbator), the *rotor speed* is varied from zero to 4000 rpm, and the model produces response vectors that are filtered to *rotor* speed. Thus, the horizontal axes represent cpm for nonsynchronous perturbation and rpm for synchronous perturbation.

The phase produced by the model is in mathematical form, where phase lead is positive and phase lag is negative. However, the phase in the plots in the figure is presented using the instrumentation convention, where phase lag is positive, increasing downward. Phase is measured relative to the positive X-axis of the system (the location of the transducer).

The amplitude produced by the model is zero-to-peak. On the plots, the amplitude has been doubled to produce peak-to-peak to conform to the instrumentation measurement convention for displacement vibration.

Note that, at frequencies near zero, the nonsynchronous response phase leads the heavy spot location slightly. However, *at zero speed the synchronous response phase (the high spot) is equal to the heavy spot location.* This is an important finding with application to balancing.

A resonance amplitude peak is clearly visible and is accompanied by a significant increase in phase lag. For this low damping case, it can be shown that the nonsynchronous resonance occurs near

$$\omega = \sqrt{\frac{K}{M}} \qquad (10\text{-}40)$$

Equation 10-40 is also called the *undamped natural frequency*, or, less accurately, the *natural frequency* of the system. This is sometimes referred to as the *mechanical resonance*.

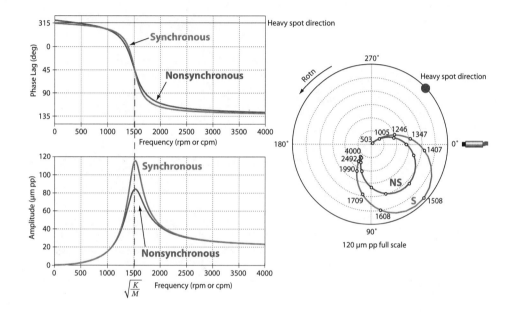

Figure 10-14. Bode and polar plots of predicted rotor vibration for low Quadrature Dynamic Stiffness. Both nonsynchronous (blue) and synchronous (green) perturbation results are shown. The heavy spot direction is shown in red. To make the results consistent with what would be measured on a machine, the amplitude of the model has been doubled to produce peak-to-peak, and the phase is shown in the instrumentation convention, where phase lag is positive downward. Phase is measured relative to the positive *X*-axis of the system.

The synchronous resonance occurs near

$$\Omega = \sqrt{\frac{K}{M}} \qquad (10\text{-}41)$$

A commonly used term in the industry for a synchronous balance resonance is a *critical*, or *critical speed*, but the term *balance resonance* is preferred when speaking of a synchronous resonance due to unbalance. At this frequency, the phase of the response lags the heavy spot location by 90°.

When damping increases to a *supercritical* (*overdamped*) value, the predicted vibration changes dramatically. Figure 10-15 shows plots for both nonsynchronous (blue) and synchronous (green) perturbation. For the nonsynchronous case, the rotor speed, Ω, was set to 1500 rpm.

At low speed, the nonsynchronous response phase leads the heavy spot by about 80°. *This is the attitude angle of the system.* Using the parameters in Table 10-1 and Equation 10-36, it is calculated as 78°.

Because the system is overdamped, there is no synchronous resonance. However, there is a nonsynchronous resonance near

$$\omega = \lambda \Omega \qquad (10\text{-}42)$$

This resonance is sometimes referred to as the *fluid-induced resonance*. At this perturbation frequency, the phase of nonsynchronous vibration is equal to the heavy spot location.

Both the mechanical resonance and the fluid-induced resonance are different manifestations of the same thing. Recall that our model is only capable of one resonance. The *frequency* of this resonance depends on whether the system is underdamped or overdamped, and on whether the perturbation is nonsynchronous or synchronous. The fluid-induced resonance is only visible when

1. The rotor system is *overdamped*, and

2. The rotor system is subjected to a *nonsynchronous* perturbation.

Both conditions must be true. Because operating machines are typically underdamped and subjected primarily to synchronous perturbation due to unbalance, the fluid-induced resonance will never be visible under normal operation. For a typical machine, the resonance will occur at the balance resonance speed given by Equation 10-41.

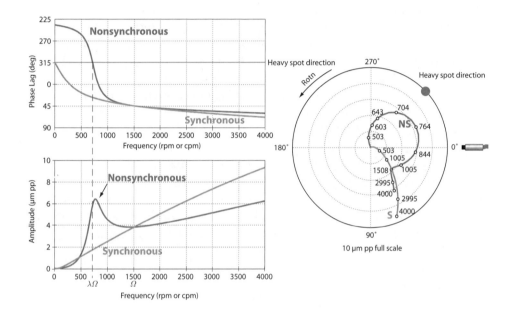

Figure 10-15. Bode and polar plots of predicted rotor vibration for high Quadrature Dynamic Stiffness. Both nonsynchronous (blue) and synchronous (green) perturbation results are shown. The heavy spot location is shown in red. The amplitude of the model has been doubled to produce peak-to-peak, and the phase is shown in the instrumentation convention, where phase lag is positive downward. Phase is measured relative to the positive *X*-axis of the system. The low-speed nonsynchronous phase lead relative to the heavy spot represents the attitude angle of the system.

Nonlinearities

Two basic assumptions used in the derivation of the model are that the system is linear and that the rotor system parameters are constant. Rotor shaft and bearing support stiffnesses are, for the most part, independent of rotor position. Fluid-film bearing and seal parameters are approximately constant at low eccentricity ratios; however, they can change rapidly at high eccentricity ratios.

The typical behavior of spring stiffness, damping, and λ versus eccentricity ratio is shown in Figure 10-16. Spring stiffness is approximately constant at low eccentricity and increases dramatically near the bearing surface. Damping also increases near the bearing surface, while λ decreases. The decrease in λ is reasonable when you consider that fluid circulation is restricted as the rotor approaches the limits of available clearance. Also, hydrodynamic bearings will usually transition to partial lubrication at a high eccentricity ratio, drastically reducing λ.

In spite of the fact that these parameters are not constant (and the resulting differential equation is nonlinear), rotor behavior does not usually deviate far from linear behavior, and our simple model remains useful. After all, most rotor systems run in fluid-film bearings at moderately high eccentricity ratios, and the behavior of most systems is predictable enough to allow balancing using techniques derived from a linear model. Rotor behavior is approximately linear when viewed in a small region around the equilibrium position (which can be at high eccentricity under static radial load). Usually, vibration in rotor systems is small enough to satisfy this approximation.

Nonlinearities can appear from other sources. Rub contact near the midspan of a rotor is a constraint that significantly increases K, either momentarily or continuously. Looseness in support systems can produce intermittent or continuous decreases in K. Much of diagnostic methodology involves correlating changes in system behavior with changes in K. The nonlinearities produced by some malfunctions feed through our linear model in a way that we can usefully interpret.

Vibration signal waveform distortion is evidence of the presence of nonlinearities. Ideal, linear rotor system vibration response to unbalance will produce a single, sinusoidal signal. Nonlinearities produce deviations from sinusoidal waveforms that result in more complicated orbits and harmonic series in spectrums.

The Benefits and Limitations of the Simple Model

The model that we have presented has several major benefits; it is solvable in an analytical form that is relatively easy to understand, and the equations that come from the model provide good insight into the basics of rotor behavior. We

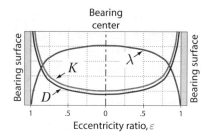

Figure 10-16. Qualitative plots of fluid-film bearing parameters versus journal eccentricity ratio. Stiffness, K, and damping, D, are minimum when the journal is at the center of the bearing, and they are approximately constant for low eccentricity ratios. As the journal nears the bearing surface, stiffness and damping increase dramatically. λ behaves in the opposite way. When the journal is at the center of the bearing, λ is maximum. As the journal nears the wall, the fluid flow is increasingly restricted, until λ nears zero at the wall.

will use this insight to examine synchronous rotor behavior in more detail in the next chapter.

As we have mentioned, vibration is a ratio, and changes in Dynamic Stiffness produce changes in vibration. Dynamic Stiffness is a function of the rotor parameters of mass, stiffness, damping, lambda, and rotor speed. By relating vibration behavior to changes in rotor system parameters, the model provides a conceptual link between observed vibration behavior and root cause malfunctions. This is a major advantage of this modeling approach when compared to matrix coefficient methods. The basic relationships between simple rotor parameters and malfunctions will be exploited throughout this book to solve practical machinery problems.

The model provides an excellent description of the lowest mode of a rotor system and can provide some information about higher system modes. However, accurate treatment of multiple modes requires a more complicated model with additional degrees of freedom.

Extending the Simple Model

The simple, isotropic model provides an excellent description of the lowest mode of a rotor system. However, it does not adequately describe the behavior of rotor systems with anisotropic stiffness or with multiple modes. In this section, we will present examples of a single mass, anisotropic rotor model with two *real* degrees of freedom (2-RDOF), and a two mass, two-mode, isotropic model with two *complex* degrees of freedom (2-CDOF). Readers can skip this section with no loss of continuity.

The anisotropic rotor model is similar to the 1-CDOF model that we have been discussing in this chapter; the rotor is modeled as a lumped mass with significant fluid interaction. There are two primary differences:

1. The displacement is measured using two, independent, *real* variables, x and y (two degrees of freedom). The complex plane used for the simple model is not used (although complex notation *will* be used to simplify the mathematics of the solution process).

2. The rotor parameters are different (anisotropic) in the X and Y directions. In general, any parameter can be anisotropic, but in this discussion, we will only treat the spring stiffness (K_x and K_y) as anisotropic; all other parameters will be assumed to be isotropic.

The rotor free body diagram of the anisotropic system (Figure 10-17) is similar to that for the isotropic system (Figure 10-11), with two exceptions: the force components are now shown aligned with the measurement axes and the tangential stiffness terms appear without the j that is used in the complex plane.

The tangential stiffness terms cause a response at right angles to the displacement. Imagine that the rotor, which is rotating here in an X to Y direction, is deflected a distance x in the positive X direction. Because of the fluid circulating around the rotor, a pressure wedge will form that will push the rotor up, in the positive Y direction. Thus, the tangential force in the Y direction is $+D\lambda\Omega x$.

Similarly, if the rotor deflects a distance y in the positive Y direction, the pressure wedge will try to push the rotor to the left, in the *negative* X direction. Thus, the tangential force in the X direction is $-D\lambda\Omega y$.

The tangential force terms *cross couple* the X and Y responses. As long as the tangential force term is nonzero, any deflection in one direction will create a force that produces a response in the other direction.

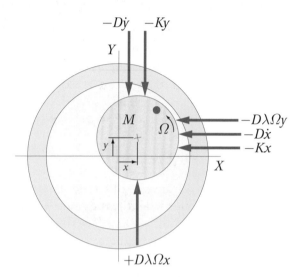

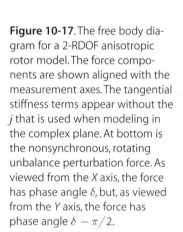

Figure 10-17. The free body diagram for a 2-RDOF anisotropic rotor model. The force components are shown aligned with the measurement axes. The tangential stiffness terms appear without the *j* that is used when modeling in the complex plane. At bottom is the nonsynchronous, rotating unbalance perturbation force. As viewed from the *X* axis, the force has phase angle δ, but, as viewed from the *Y* axis, the force has phase angle $\delta - \pi/2$.

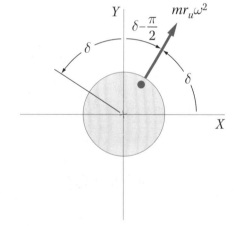

The perturbation force is also expressed in terms of X and Y components:

$$F_x = mr_u\omega^2 \cos(\omega t + \delta)$$
$$F_y = mr_u\omega^2 \sin(\omega t + \delta)$$

(10-43)

However, even though we are modeling the system with real numbers, it is mathematically simpler to use complex notation and take the real part of the result. Then, the perturbation force can be expressed as

$$\mathbf{F}_x = mr_u\omega^2 e^{j(\omega t + \delta)}$$
$$\mathbf{F}_y = mr_u\omega^2 e^{j\left(\omega t + \delta - \frac{\pi}{2}\right)}$$

(10-44)

where the $\pi/2$ is the angular difference between the two coordinate system axes. These two expressions identify the same rotating unbalance vector, which is referenced to each coordinate axis (see the figure).

The 2-RDOF system requires two differential equations in $\mathbf{x}$ and $\mathbf{y}$:

$$M\ddot{\mathbf{x}} + D\dot{\mathbf{x}} + K_x\mathbf{x} + D\lambda\Omega\mathbf{y} = mr_u\omega^2 e^{j(\omega t + \delta)}$$
$$M\ddot{\mathbf{y}} + D\dot{\mathbf{y}} + K_y\mathbf{y} - D\lambda\Omega\mathbf{x} = mr_u\omega^2 e^{j\left(\omega t + \delta - \frac{\pi}{2}\right)}$$

(10-45)

We assume two solutions of the form:

$$\mathbf{x} = A e^{j(\omega t + \alpha)}$$
$$\mathbf{y} = B e^{j(\omega t + \beta)}$$

(10-46)

where A and B are the amplitudes of the rotating response vectors, and α and β are the phases. The solutions will provide a set of rotating response vectors, each of which is measured relative to its own axis. The instantaneous physical position of the rotor is formed from the combination of the *real part* of these vectors:

$$x(t) = \text{Re}\left[A e^{j(\omega t + \alpha)}\right]$$
$$y(t) = \text{Re}\left[B e^{j(\omega t + \beta)}\right]$$

(10-47)

Solution of the system of equations 10-45 leads to

$$Ae^{j\alpha} = mr_u\omega^2 e^{j\delta} \left[\frac{K_y - M\omega^2 + jD(\omega + \lambda\Omega)}{(K_x - M\omega^2 + jD\omega)(K_y - M\omega^2 + jD\omega) + (D\lambda\Omega)^2} \right]$$

$$Be^{j\beta} = mr_u\omega^2 e^{j\left(\delta - \frac{\pi}{2}\right)} \left[\frac{K_x - M\omega^2 + jD(\omega + \lambda\Omega)}{(K_x - M\omega^2 + jD\omega)(K_y - M\omega^2 + jD\omega) + (D\lambda\Omega)^2} \right]$$

$$(10\text{-}48)$$

For each vector, the amplitude is found by taking the absolute value of the expression; the phase of the response is the arctangent of the ratio of the imaginary part to the real part,

$$\alpha = \delta + \arctan\left[\frac{\mathrm{Im}\left(Ae^{j\alpha}\right)}{\mathrm{Re}\left(Ae^{j\alpha}\right)}\right] \qquad (10\text{-}49)$$

The 2-RDOF, anisotropic model (in scalar form) can be converted to the simple, isotropic model quite easily, a procedure that validates the anisotropic modeling of the tangential force. We make the system isotropic by setting $K_x = K_y = K$. Equations 10-45 are modified to use the perturbation forces of Equations 10-43, and the y equation is multiplied by j:

$$M\ddot{x} + D\dot{x} + Kx + D\lambda\Omega y = mr_u\omega^2\cos(\omega t + \delta)$$
$$j(M\ddot{y} + D\dot{y} + Ky - D\lambda\Omega x) = j(mr_u\omega^2\sin(\omega t + \delta)) \qquad (10\text{-}50)$$

When the equations are added, we obtain

$$M(\ddot{x} + j\ddot{y}) + D(\dot{x} + j\dot{y}) + K(x + jy) - jD\lambda\Omega(x + jy)$$
$$= mr_u\omega^2\left[\cos(\omega t + \delta) + j\sin(\omega t + \delta)\right] \qquad (10\text{-}51)$$

This reduces to

$$M\ddot{r} + D\dot{r} + (K - jD\lambda\Omega)r = mr_u\omega^2 e^{j(\omega t + \delta)} \qquad (10\text{-}52)$$

which is identical to Equation 10-20, the equation of motion for the simple, isotropic model.

In the two-mode, isotropic system, the rotor is modeled with a complex displacement vector in each of two, axially separated, complex planes (two complex degrees of freedom, or 2-CDOF). There are many ways a system like this can be modeled; what follows here is only one possibility.

The rotor is separated into two, lumped masses, M_1 and M_2 (Figure 10-18, top). A midspan mass, M_1, is connected through a shaft spring element, K_1, to a stiff bearing at left. The mass experiences some damping, D_1. The mass is also connected through a shaft spring element, K_2, to a journal mass, M_2, at right. The journal operates in a fluid-film bearing with damping, D_B, bearing stiffness, K_B, and λ. The resulting free body diagrams are shown at the bottom.

As in the anisotropic model, a two degree of freedom system requires two differential equations, this time in two, independent, complex displacement vectors, r_1, and r_2:

$$M_1\ddot{r}_1 + D_1\dot{r}_1 + (K_1 + K_2)r_1 - K_2r_2 = m_1 r_{u1}\omega^2 e^{j(\omega t + \delta_1)}$$
$$M_2\ddot{r}_2 + D_B\dot{r}_2 + (K_2 + K_B - jD_B\lambda\Omega)r_2 - K_2r_1 = m_2 r_{u2}\omega^2 e^{j(\omega t + \delta_2)}$$

$$(10\text{-}53)$$

Note that there are two, independent unbalance masses, each with its own mass, radius, and phase angle. We assume a solution of the form

$$r_1 = A_1 e^{j(\omega t + \alpha_1)}$$
$$r_2 = A_2 e^{j(\omega t + \alpha_2)}$$

$$(10\text{-}54)$$

The solution is, again, two expressions:

$$A_1 e^{j\alpha_1} = \frac{m_1 r_{u1}\omega^2 e^{j\delta_1}(K_2 + K_B - M_2\omega^2 + jD_B(\omega - \lambda\Omega)) + m_2 r_{u2}\omega^2 e^{j\delta_2}K_2}{(K_1 + K_2 - M_1\omega^2 + jD_1\omega)(K_2 + K_B - M_2\omega^2 + jD_B(\omega - \lambda\Omega)) - K_2^2}$$

$$A_2 e^{j\alpha_2} = \frac{m_2 r_{u2}\omega^2 e^{j\delta_2}(K_1 + K_2 - M_1\omega^2 + jD_1\omega) + m_1 r_{u1}\omega^2 e^{j\delta_1}K_2}{(K_1 + K_2 - M_1\omega^2 + jD_1\omega)(K_2 + K_B - M_2\omega^2 + jD_B(\omega - \lambda\Omega)) - K_2^2}$$

$$(10\text{-}55)$$

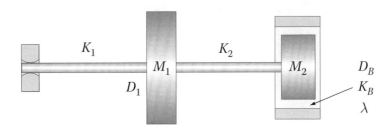

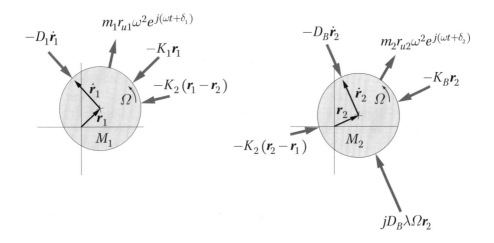

Figure 10-18. 2-CDOF rotor model and free body diagrams. The rotor is separated into two, lumped masses, M_1 and M_2. The midspan mass, M_1, is connected through a shaft spring element, K_1, to a stiff bearing at left. The mass also experiences some damping, D_1. The mass is also connected through a shaft spring element, K_2, to a journal mass, M_2, at right. The journal operates in a fluid-film bearing with damping, D_B, bearing stiffness, K_B, and λ. The free body diagrams show the forces acting on the rotor masses, including two, independent unbalance forces.

As with the anisotropic example, the amplitude is found by taking the absolute value of the expressions. The phase is found using these expressions:

$$\alpha_1 = \delta_1 + \arctan\left[\frac{\mathrm{Im}\left(A_1 e^{j\alpha_1}\right)}{\mathrm{Re}\left(A_1 e^{j\alpha_1}\right)}\right]$$

$$\alpha_2 = \delta_2 + \arctan\left[\frac{\mathrm{Im}\left(A_2 e^{j\alpha_2}\right)}{\mathrm{Re}\left(A_2 e^{j\alpha_2}\right)}\right] \qquad (10\text{-}56)$$

Summary

Lambda (λ), the Fluid Circumferential Average Velocity Ratio, is a nondimensional number that represents the average angular velocity of the circulating fluid as a fraction of the angular velocity of the rotor.

Using assumptions of a single, complex degree of freedom; isotropic parameters; no gyroscopic effects; significant fluid interaction; and linear behavior, a set of forces were defined that act on the rotor system. These forces are the spring force, the tangential force due to a pressure wedge in fluid-film bearings and seals, the damping force, and an external perturbation force.

The forces were combined in a free body diagram, and used with Newton's Second Law to obtain the differential equation of motion.

The solution of the equation of motion provided the rotor system Dynamic Stiffness, an important result. Dynamic Stiffness is the "black box" that relates input force to output vibration. The general, nonsynchronous Dynamic Stiffness was found to be

$$\boldsymbol{K}_N = K - M\omega^2 + jD(\omega - \lambda\Omega)$$

The response of the rotor to a static radial load led to an expression for the attitude angle of the rotor in terms of rotor parameters. The attitude angle was found to be equal to the arctangent of the tangential stiffness divided by the spring stiffness.

By setting the nonsynchronous perturbation frequency, ω, equal to the rotor speed, Ω, an expression for synchronous rotor vibration response was obtained. Synchronous rotor response, which is the most commonly observed mode of operation of machinery, was found to be a special case of the general, nonsynchronous model.

The model behavior over frequency or speed was explored. The model clearly shows a resonance, coupled with a 180° phase change in the lagging direction. The frequency of the resonance depends on the spring stiffness and mass of the system, the type of perturbation used (nonsynchronous or synchronous), and, for nonsynchronous response, on the Quadrature Dynamic Stiffness of the system. For underdamped rotor systems, the resonance occurs near the undamped natural frequency,

$$\omega = \sqrt{\frac{K}{M}}$$

References

1. Jeffcott, H. H., "The Lateral Vibration of Loaded Shafts in the Neighbourhood of a Whirling Speed.—The Effect of Want of Balance," *Philosophical Magazine* 6, 37 (1919): pp. 304-314.
2. Muszynska, A, "One Lateral Mode Isotropic Rotor Response to Nonsynchronous Excitation," *Proceedings of the Course on Rotor Dynamics and Vibration in Turbomachinery*, von Karman Institute for Fluid Dynamics, Belgium (September 1992): pp. 21-25.

Chapter 11

Dynamic Stiffness and Rotor Behavior

The concept of dynamic stiffness is an important result of the rotor model that was developed in the last chapter. Vibration was found to be the ratio of the applied dynamic force to the Dynamic Stiffness of the rotor system. Thus, a change in vibration is caused by either a change in the applied force or a change in the Dynamic Stiffness. By understanding how Dynamic Stiffness affects vibration, we can understand why rotor systems behave the way they do. This understanding will lay the foundation for balancing and the malfunction diagnosis of rotating machinery.

In this chapter we will explore Dynamic Stiffness in more detail. We will start with a discussion of the physical meaning of the components of Dynamic Stiffness. Then, we will show how the rotor parameters of mass, spring stiffness, damping, and lambda (λ) can be extracted from plots of Dynamic Stiffness versus frequency. Concentrating on synchronous rotor behavior, we will show how Dynamic Stiffness controls rotor response over the entire speed range of a machine and how it is responsible for the phenomenon of resonance. Finally, we will show how changes in Dynamic Stiffness produce changes in vibration in rotating machinery.

What Is Dynamic Stiffness?

Physically, Dynamic Stiffness combines the static effects of spring and tangential stiffnesses with the dynamic effects of mass and damping. We will discuss the physical meaning of this shortly. First, recall that the nonsynchronous frequency (of both perturbation and vibration), ω, is completely independent of the rotative speed, Ω. The equation for the generalized, *nonsynchronous* Dynamic Stiffness is

$$\boldsymbol{K}_N = K - M\omega^2 + jD(\omega - \lambda\Omega) \tag{11-1}$$

This can be broken into the nonsynchronous *Direct Dynamic Stiffness,*

$$K_D = K - M\omega^2 \tag{11-2}$$

and the nonsynchronous *Quadrature Dynamic Stiffness,*

$$K_Q = jD(\omega - \lambda\Omega) \tag{11-3}$$

The Direct Dynamic Stiffness acts along the line of the applied static or dynamic force. The *j* term indicates that the Quadrature Dynamic Stiffness acts at 90° (in *quadrature*) to the instantaneous direction of the applied force.

When Equation 11-1 is written as

$$\boldsymbol{K}_N = K - M\omega^2 + jD\omega - jD\lambda\Omega \tag{11-4}$$

the stiffness terms can be easily related to the internal and external rotor system forces.

K, the spring stiffness of the rotor system, is a combination of the shaft stiffness, the fluid-film bearing stiffness, the bearing support stiffness, and the foundation stiffness. This term behaves like the stiffness of a simple spring; when a force is applied to the rotor system, the rotor deflects and the spring is compressed, producing an opposing force (Figure 11-1, middle). Simple spring stiffness always acts in a direction opposite to the direction of the applied force; thus, the *K* in the Dynamic Stiffness is *positive,* showing that it will oppose the applied force. Positive springs are stabilizing in the sense that the force produced by the spring pushes in a direction back toward the original position.

The second term, $-M\omega^2$, is the *mass stiffness.* It is a dynamic term that appears because of the inertia of the rotor. Imagine a mass that is vibrating back and forth about the equilibrium position in a simple system (Figure 11-1, bottom). Whenever the mass moves beyond the equilibrium position, the spring force acts to decelerate the mass. However, the inertia of the mass creates an effective force that acts in the direction of motion of the mass, opposite to the spring stiffness force. Thus, the mass stiffness is *negative,* and acts to reduce the spring stiffness of the system. Negative springs are potentially destabilizing in the sense that the force tends to push an object farther away from the equilibrium position.

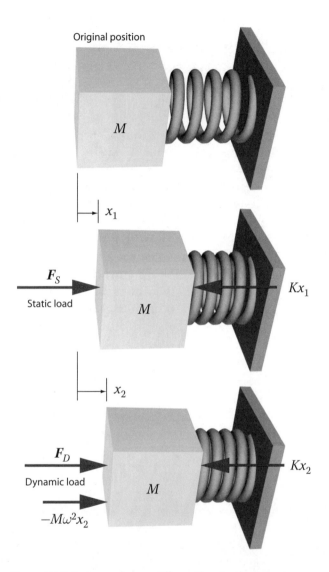

Figure 11-1. Spring and mass stiffness. The simple spring/mass system is shown with no applied force, a static force, and a dynamic force. When a static force is applied (middle), the positive spring stiffness, K, produces a force proportional to the displacement that opposes the applied force. When a dynamic force is applied (bottom), the inertia of the mass is directed away from the original position, increasing the displacement. This inertia effect is equivalent to a negative stiffness, called the mass stiffness, $-M\omega^2$.

The third term, $jD\omega$, originates in the damping force and is called the *damping stiffness*. The j indicates that the damping stiffness acts at 90° to the direction of the applied force. The fact that it is *positive* indicates that the damping stiffness acts to stabilize the rotor system. Like the mass stiffness, the damping stiffness is a dynamic stiffness, and it only appears when the rotor centerline has nonzero velocity.

The last term, $-jD\lambda\Omega$, comes from the tangential force of the fluid-film pressure wedge in the bearing or seal. The j indicates that this *tangential stiffness* term also acts at 90° to the direction of the applied force vector. Recall that the tangential stiffness shown in the last chapter (Equation 10-14) was *positive*. In the Dynamic Stiffness, the tangential stiffness term becomes *negative*, indicating that it acts like a negative spring. Here the negative spring acts to reduce the stabilizing damping stiffness. The tangential stiffness term is a function of the fluid circumferential average angular velocity, $\lambda\Omega$. As the rotor speed increases, fluid circulation increases, and the potentially destabilizing (negative) tangential stiffness gets larger. When the rotor speed is high enough, this term can neutralize the damping stiffness and trigger fluid-induced instability (Chapter 22).

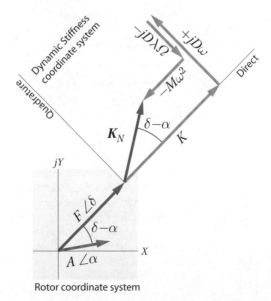

Figure 11-2. Nonsynchronous Dynamic Stiffness vector diagram. The Direct axis of the Dynamic Stiffness is in the direction of the applied force vector, and the Quadrature axis is 90° to the Direct axis. The four Dynamic Stiffness terms produce a resultant vector, the nonsynchronous Dynamic Stiffness vector, K_N. The angle between the applied force and the Dynamic Stiffness vector is the same as the angle between the rotating force and the vibration response vector.

The Quadrature Dynamic Stiffness is responsible for the smooth resonance transition of phase lag values between 0° and 180°. This can be seen in the vector diagram of the nonsynchronous Dynamic Stiffness (Figure 11-2). The Direct axis of the Dynamic Stiffness is aligned with the applied force vector, and the four Dynamic Stiffness terms add up to the nonsynchronous Dynamic Stiffness vector. The angle between the direction of the applied force vector and the Dynamic Stiffness vector is the same angle as the difference between the rotating force vector and the vibration response vector. (The angles appear in the opposite sense because the Dynamic Stiffness is in the denominator of the rotor response equation, Equation 10-23. See also Equation 3-8.) If both quadrature stiffness terms were zero, only the direct stiffness terms would remain, the Dynamic Stiffness vector angle would be 0° or 180° (depending on which term was larger), and the rotor vibration vector would be always be aligned with or opposite to the applied force vector.

When a static radial load is applied to the rotating rotor, the perturbation frequency, ω, is zero, and the nonsynchronous Dynamic Stiffness reduces to only the first and last terms, $K - jD\lambda\Omega$.

Figure 11-3. Synchronous Dynamic Stiffness vector diagram. The Quadrature Dynamic Stiffness consists of only one term and appears as a single vector. Like the nonsynchronous vector diagram, the angle of the synchronous Dynamic Stiffness vector is the same as the angle between the heavy spot direction and the vibration response vector (high spot).

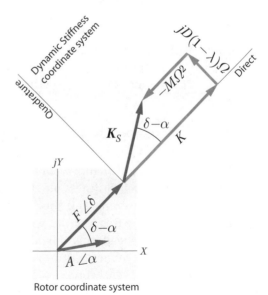

The *synchronous* Dynamic Stiffness is obtained from the nonsynchronous Dynamic Stiffness by setting $\omega = \Omega$:

$$\boldsymbol{K}_S = K - M\Omega^2 + jD(1-\lambda)\Omega \qquad (11\text{-}5)$$

The synchronous Dynamic Stiffness is most important for everyday machine applications, because machines vibrate primarily in response to rotating unbalance, a form of synchronous perturbation.

The physical meaning of the synchronous Direct Dynamic Stiffness is similar to the meaning of the nonsynchronous Direct Dynamic Stiffness. However, the Quadrature Dynamic Stiffness term in Equation 11-5 is different. Because Ω is common to both quadrature terms, it is factored out.

Figure 11-3 shows a typical synchronous Dynamic Stiffness vector diagram. Note that the Quadrature Dynamic Stiffness now consists of only one term and appears as a single vector. Like the nonsynchronous vector diagram, the angle of the synchronous Dynamic Stiffness vector is the same as the difference between the heavy spot direction and the vibration response vector (high spot).

We will discuss the behavior of $\boldsymbol{K}_S$ and its relationship to rotor behavior in detail in a later section.

Rotor Parameters and Dynamic Stiffness

Both nonsynchronous and synchronous Dynamic Stiffness can be plotted as functions of frequency (Figure 11-4). Dynamic Stiffness is plotted in two separate plots, with direct stiffness above and quadrature stiffness below. Both nonsynchronous (N) and synchronous (S) data are shown. The horizontal axis represents perturbation frequency, ω, in cpm for the nonsynchronous case, and rotor speed, Ω, in rpm for the synchronous case. Rotor speed for the nonsynchronous perturbation is 900 rpm. In the Direct Dynamic Stiffness plot, the nonsynchronous and synchronous cases plot on the same line. Below the Dynamic Stiffness plots are Bode plots of the corresponding rotor responses.

The Dynamic Stiffness plots can be used to obtain the rotor parameters. The figure was created using the same model and rotor parameters as in Chapter 10 (Table 10-1), and the key points are marked in red.

The Direct Dynamic Stiffness plot (top) is a parabola. At zero frequency, the mass stiffness term is zero, and the Direct Dynamic Stiffness is equal to the spring stiffness, K. The frequency at which the Direct Dynamic Stiffness is zero yields the resonance speed (this will be discussed below).

The Quadrature Dynamic Stiffness plots (second from top) are different for nonsynchronous and synchronous perturbation. Both plots are straight lines, but with different slopes and different Y intercepts.

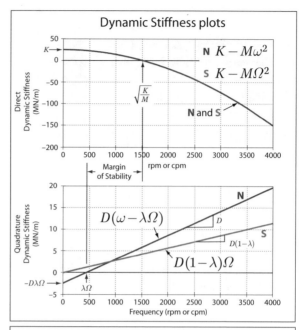

Figure 11-4. Bode and Dynamic Stiffness plots for synchronous (S) and nonsynchronous (N) data. Direct Dynamic Stiffness is the same for both synchronous and nonsynchronous cases. Rotor speed for the nonsynchronous perturbation is 900 rpm. See Table 10-1 for a complete list of rotor parameters. The Dynamic Stiffness plot can be used to obtain the rotor parameters of the basic model. See the text for a full description.

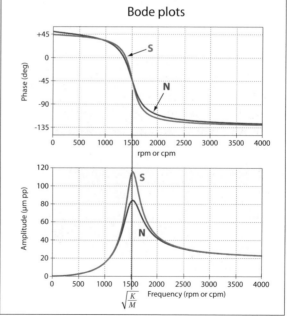

The nonsynchronous Quadrature Dynamic Stiffness (blue) has a negative Y intercept. The absolute value of this intercept is the tangential stiffness, $D\lambda\Omega$, of the rotor system. The stiffness then increases and becomes zero when the perturbation frequency, ω, is equal to $\lambda\Omega$. The slope of the line is equal to the damping, D. There is enough information in this plot to obtain D and λ. Thus, the direct and quadrature components of the nonsynchronous Dynamic Stiffness can provide all of the rotor parameters of our model: K, M, D, λ, and Ω.

The nonsynchronous plots also define the *Margin of Stability*, the frequency range between the zero values of the Direct Dynamic Stiffness and the nonsynchronous Quadrature Dynamic Stiffness. Rotor stability will be discussed in detail in Chapters 14 and 22. For now, we state that, if both the Direct and Quadrature Dynamic Stiffnesses become zero at the same nonsynchronous frequency, ω, then the Dynamic Stiffness of the rotor system will vanish. This zero in the denominator of the rotor response equation would result in a (theoretically) infinite response amplitude, a condition called instability.

The Y intercept of the synchronous Quadrature Dynamic Stiffness is at the origin $(0,0)$, and the slope is damping modified by fluid circulation. This is less than the slope of the nonsynchronous stiffness, which is D. Thus, we can define the *effective damping* (or *observed damping*), D_E, of the synchronous rotor system as

$$D_E = D(1-\lambda) \tag{11-6}$$

Because λ is usually a positive number less than 0.5, the effective damping for synchronous behavior is usually less than the actual damping constant, D. We have already mentioned that the tangential stiffness term is negative, which acts to oppose the stabilizing damping stiffness term. One effect of this negative stiffness is to reduce the effective damping of the system.

This makes sense if we imagine a rotor in a forward, circular orbit. Physically, the damping force acts to remove energy from the system. Force times velocity equals power, and the damping force produces *negative* power because the direction of the damping force is *opposite* the centerline velocity. At the same time, the tangential force acts in the *same* direction as rotor motion and pushes on the rotor. This is *positive* power, and this power input to the system partially cancels out the power loss due to the damping force. Thus, because of fluid circulation and the pressure wedge, the effective damping of the system is lower.

Synchronous Rotor Behavior

The primary source of vibration in rotor systems is due to unbalance. Unbalance produces a synchronous (1X) response in all rotating machinery and is the most commonly observed behavior. Because of its importance, we will concentrate on synchronous rotor behavior.

Synchronous rotor response can be divided into three, general, speed-related regions: well below resonance (which we will call "low speed"), resonance, and well above resonance ("high speed"). In each region, a different term of the synchronous Dynamic Stiffness controls the response of the rotor system. In our discussion, we will use the synchronous rotor model that was developed in the last chapter, in which the 1X response vector, *r*, is defined by

$$r = Ae^{j\alpha} = \frac{mr_u\Omega^2 e^{j\delta}}{K - M\Omega^2 + jD(1-\lambda)\Omega} \tag{11-7}$$

where, when the Keyphasor event occurs, the rotating unbalance dynamic force (the *heavy spot*), has magnitude $mr_u\Omega^2$ and is located at angular position δ, and the response vector (the *high spot*) has zero-to-peak amplitude A and is located at angle α. A simpler form of this expression can be made by substituting the angle notation (Chapter 3) for the exponential functions:

$$r = A \angle\alpha = \frac{mr_u\Omega^2 \angle\delta}{K - M\Omega^2 + jD(1-\lambda)\Omega} \tag{11-8}$$

Synchronous Behavior Below Resonance

Figure 11-5 shows plots of synchronous Direct and Quadrature Dynamic Stiffness (top) and Bode and polar plots of the 1X rotor vibration predicted by the model. At the right of the dynamic stiffness plots are the synchronous Dynamic Stiffness vector diagrams for low-speed, resonance, and high-speed conditions. The orientation of the Direct Dynamic Stiffness axis corresponds to the heavy spot location, 315°.

In the low-speed range (green), several things are apparent:

1. The rotor high spot (vibration response vector) is in the same direction as the heavy spot. This is approximately true over the low-speed range and is exactly true in the limit of zero rotor speed. The heavy spot and high spot are said to be *in phase*.

2. The vibration amplitude increases as the square of the rotor speed.

3. The synchronous Quadrature Dynamic Stiffness is close to zero.

4. The Direct Dynamic Stiffness equals K at zero speed.

The high spot/heavy spot relationship is an important key to balancing. Part of the balancing problem involves determining the direction of the rotor heavy spot. Either the Bode or the polar plot can be used to do this, although the polar plot is much easier to interpret.

At very low speeds, Ω is small, and the Dynamic Stiffness is dominated by the spring stiffness, K. Because of this, the mass stiffness and quadrature stiffness terms can be neglected, and Equation 11-8 becomes

Below resonance:
$$r = A \angle \alpha = \frac{mr_u \Omega^2 \angle \delta}{K} \tag{11-9}$$

Because the mass and quadrature stiffness terms are neglected, there is no phase change, and the response is in the same direction as the applied force, $\alpha = \delta$. Thus, the high spot and the heavy spot are in the same direction.

Synchronous Behavior At The Balance Resonance

Several aspects of the balance resonance region (red) are important:

1. The amplitude of vibration reaches a peak, and, *at the same time,*

2. The phase of the response lags the heavy spot by 90°. This occurs in the Bode plot where the phase slope is steepest and in the polar plot close to the maximum amplitude of the polar loop.

3. The *Direct* Dynamic Stiffness becomes zero. This can be seen on the direct stiffness plot and in the Dynamic Stiffness vector diagram.

4. The Quadrature Dynamic Stiffness is the only stiffness element available to restrain the rotor.

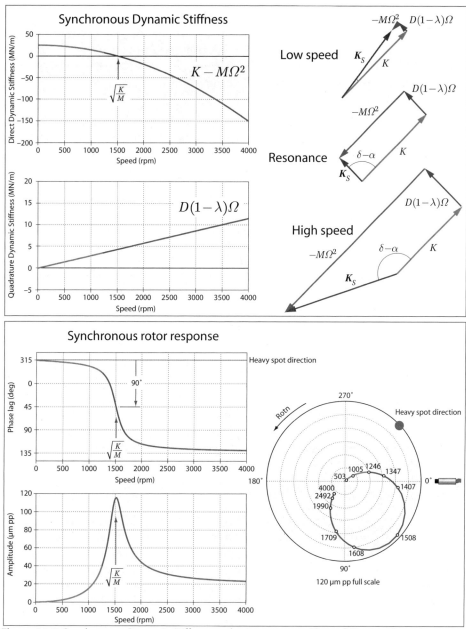

Figure 11-5. Synchronous Dynamic Stiffness and rotor response. Plots of direct and quadrature components of synchronous Dynamic Stiffness (top) are compared to Bode and polar plots of the same 1X rotor response (bottom). Dynamic Stiffness vector diagrams (right) are shown for three operating conditions: low speed, resonance, and high speed. See the text for a full description.

The zero crossing of the direct stiffness is near the speed of the resonance peak. This is typical for a machine with a moderate Synchronous Amplification Factor. The only way the direct stiffness can become zero is for the spring stiffness and the mass stiffness to cancel each other. Let Ω_{res} be the speed at the zero crossing of the direct stiffness. Then, for this condition,

$$K - M\Omega_{res}^2 = 0 \qquad (11\text{-}10)$$

which leads to this important relationship:

$$\Omega_{res} = \sqrt{\frac{K}{M}} \qquad (11\text{-}11)$$

This expression is referred to as the rotor system *balance resonance speed, resonance speed*, or *critical speed*. Because resonance occurs when the perturbation frequency is equal to the rotor system natural frequency, this expression is also called the *natural frequency*. More accurately, it is the *undamped natural frequency*, which ignores the effects of damping. For most rotor systems, damping is relatively small, and the damped natural frequency (the natural frequency) is close to and a little below the undamped natural frequency.

This expression is one of the most powerful tools in rotating machinery diagnostics. It shows that the balance resonance speed is determined by the spring stiffness and mass of the rotor system. Changes in the balance resonance can be caused by many rotor system malfunctions. Changes in spring stiffness are usually responsible for significant changes in the resonance speed (mass does not usually change). For example, spring stiffness can increase because of a rub or severe misalignment, or it can decrease because of a weakening foundation or a developing shaft crack.

This expression can be used to solve problems such as piping resonance. For example, say a machine has high amplitude piping vibration when the machine is at running speed. One solution to the problem is to move the resonance of the piping away from running speed. This could be done two ways: add mass to the piping system, which would *lower* the resonance, or add stiffness (bracing), to *increase* the resonance frequency to above running speed. The last choice is probably the best one, because the resonance will be moved completely away from the operating speed range of the machine.

Note that, in the Bode plot, the actual peak of the resonance occurs at a slightly higher speed than that given by Equation 11-11. This is because the rotating unbalance force increases with the square of the rotor speed. As the rotor passes Ω_{res}, the force temporarily increases more rapidly than the Dynamic Stiffness, and so overcomes the natural tendency for the vibration amplitude to decrease. The higher the quadrature stiffness of the system, which flattens the response and slows its decline, the more the peak is shifted to the right. Because this effect is usually small and not important to rotating machinery malfunction diagnosis, we will ignore it.

At the resonance, the Direct Dynamic Stiffness is zero, and the rotor response equation becomes

At resonance: $$\boldsymbol{r} = A \angle \alpha = \frac{mr_u\Omega^2 \angle \delta}{jD(1-\lambda)\Omega} \qquad (11\text{-}12)$$

The only remaining stiffness term at resonance is the Quadrature Dynamic Stiffness, and a major component is the effective damping, $D(1-\lambda)$. The j in the denominator is equivalent to subtracting 90°; thus, at resonance, the high spot *lags* the heavy spot by 90°.

The magnitude of the quadrature stiffness at resonance determines the magnitude of the vibration response. Because the quadrature stiffness is in the denominator, a smaller value results in a higher amplitude peak, and vice versa (low quadrature stiffness produces a high, narrow peak and high quadrature stiffness produces a low, broad peak). The quadrature stiffness expression shows that damping, fluid circulation, and rotor speed all play a part in the behavior of the rotor at resonance.

The effective damping applies only to *synchronous* rotor response. For the machinery operator, a primary concern during startup and shutdown is whether or not the machine can get through a resonance without an internal rub, and the effective damping controls the peak vibration amplitude.

When a machine is running at steady state, away from a resonance, nonsynchronous dynamic forces may exist in the machine that act to excite the natural frequency associated with the resonance. In this case, the *nonsynchronous* rules apply, and the full damping is available to limit machine response.

Synchronous Behavior Above Resonance

The rotor behavior at high speed (blue) shows two important relationships:

1.   The amplitude of vibration approaches a constant, nonzero value.

2.   The high spot lags the heavy spot by 180°.

At high speed, the mass stiffness term dominates the Dynamic Stiffness. The Ω^2 term becomes so large that the other stiffness terms can be neglected. Then, the rotor response equation becomes

$$r = A \angle \alpha = \frac{m r_u \Omega^2 \angle \delta}{-M\Omega^2} \qquad (11\text{-}13)$$

The speed terms cancel, and the equation reduces to

Above resonance: $$r = A \angle \alpha = -\frac{m r_u}{M} \angle \delta \qquad (11\text{-}14)$$

Thus, at speeds well above the balance resonance, the amplitude of vibration is constant and independent of rotor speed. It can be shown that the zero-to-peak amplitude in this equation is equal to the distance from the geometric center of the system to the mass center of the system. Thus, above resonance the rotor system rotates about its *mass center*.

The minus sign indicates that the high spot direction, α, is opposite the heavy spot direction, δ. In other words, the high spot lags the heavy spot by 180°.

How Changes In Dynamic Stiffness Affect Vibration

When the Dynamic Stiffness of a machine changes, the vibration of that machine will change. Dynamic Stiffness contains all of the rotor parameters, M, D, K, λ, and Ω, and each of these parameters may affect the vibration, depending on what region the machine is operating in. For a machine operating at steady state, the most likely parameter to change is the spring stiffness, K. This is because K is a combination of so many stiffness elements: shaft stiffness, fluid-film bearing or seal stiffness, bearing support stiffness, and foundation stiffness. Changes in any of these components can change K, and change the vibration in the low-speed or resonance regions. The change can be in amplitude, phase, or both. Interestingly enough, an *increase* in K does not always cause vibration to decrease, or vice versa. What actually happens will depend on where the machine is operating relative to the balance resonance.

The Bode plots of Figure 11-6 show the vibration response of a rotor system to changes in K. In all plots, the original rotor response curves are green. On the left, K has increased, shifting the resonance to a higher speed (red curves). On the right, K has *decreased*, shifting the resonance to a lower speed. In each plot, four operating speeds and the associated change in vibration at those speeds are shown.

For example, imagine a machine that was operating at speed Ω_3. After several months of operation, the foundation deteriorated, reducing the system spring stiffness, K, as shown in the Bode plot on the right. As K decreased, the resonance frequency decreased, moving the resonance peak to the left. This causes the amplitude and phase to change from the initial values (1) to the modified values (2). Thus, the reduction in stiffness produced a decrease in vibration amplitude and an increase in phase lag.

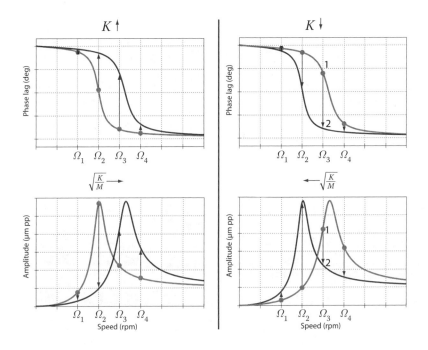

Figure 11-6. Changes in spring stiffness versus changes in vibration. In all plots, the original rotor response curves are green. On the left, K has *increased*, causing the resonance to shift to a higher speed (red curves). On the right, K has *decreased*, shifting the resonance to a lower speed. In each plot, four operating speeds are shown. The arrows show how the vibration amplitude and phase would change if the machine continued to operate at that speed.

A change in stiffness can also produce a change in nX vibration (Figure 11-7). The 2X APHT plot (left) from a vertical reactor-coolant pump shows data that was trended while the pump was running at 1187 rpm. Because of a shaft crack, the 2X vibration began to change dramatically, producing what looks like a resonance on 12 November.

The right half of the figure shows a set of Bode plots generated by the rotor model, with a resonance frequency near twice the running speed of the pump. The plots show the effect of decreasing spring stiffness, K, on the resonance. The initial operating condition is shown in green, and the final, low stiffness operat-

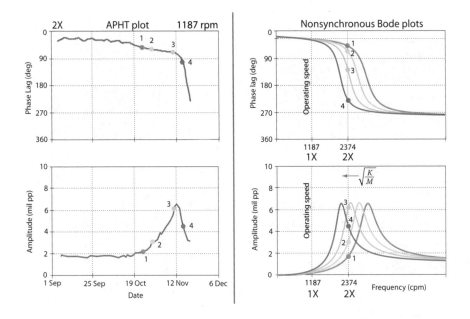

Figure 11-7. 2X APHT plot and modeled rotor response. The 2X APHT plot on the left is from a vertical reactor-coolant pump. The data was trended while the pump was running at 1187 rpm. The nonsynchronous Bode plot on the right, generated by the rotor model, simulates the rotor response when the rotor speed, Ω, is 1187 rpm. Initially, it has a resonance above twice the pump speed (green). As spring stiffness, K, decreases, the resonance frequency shifts to a lower frequency, passing through the 2X frequency. The final, low stiffness operating condition is shown in red. The 2X amplitude and phase (colored dots) change as the system natural frequency passes through twice operating speed.

ing condition is shown in red. The 1X and 2X pump frequencies are shown. In the amplitude plot, the 2X amplitude changes (colored dots) as the system resonance frequency passes through twice operating speed. The amplitude peaks and then declines, just as the APHT data shows. The Bode phase plot is not as good a fit to the APHT plot data, but it does predict that the 2X phase lag will increase as the rotor system natural frequency decreases.

Summary

Dynamic Stiffness consists of the static spring and tangential stiffnesses of the rotor system combined with the dynamic effects of mass and damping.

Two general types of Dynamic Stiffness exist. Nonsynchronous Dynamic Stiffness, the most general form, controls the rotor response to an applied dynamic force at any frequency, independent of rotor speed. Synchronous Dynamic Stiffness, a special case of nonsynchronous Dynamic Stiffness, controls the rotor response to a synchronous (1X) force, such as unbalance.

Dynamic Stiffness can be separated into Direct Dynamic Stiffness, which acts along the line of the applied force vector, and Quadrature Dynamic Stiffness, which acts along a line oriented at 90° to the applied force vector.

The components of Dynamic Stiffness are related to the forces that act on the rotor and the inertia of the rotor itself. Dynamic Stiffness contains spring stiffness, mass stiffness, damping stiffness, and tangential stiffness.

Synchronous Dynamic Stiffness terms are associated with the rotor response in three speed ranges: below, at, and above a balance resonance.

1. At speeds well below a resonance, spring stiffness dominates, and the rotor high spot is in phase with the heavy spot. Vibration amplitude increases as the square of the rotor speed.

2. At the resonance speed, Direct Dynamic Stiffness goes to zero, and only Quadrature Dynamic Stiffness remains. Rotor amplitude peaks, and the high spot lags the heavy spot by 90°.

3. At speeds well above a resonance, mass stiffness dominates, the vibration amplitude becomes constant, and the high spot lags the heavy spot by 180°. The rotor system turns about its mass center.

Changes in Dynamic Stiffness produce changes in the amplitude or phase (or both) of vibration. How vibration changes depends on where the rotor system is operating relative to a resonance.

Chapter 12

Modes of Vibration

The rotor model we developed in chapter 10 provides a good description of basic rotor behavior. In Chapter 11, we used the model to understand the basic principles of synchronous rotor behavior below, at, and above a resonance. Because the model has only one mass, it is limited to describing a system with only one, lateral, natural frequency, one forward resonance, and no gyroscopic effects.

While our model has single, *lumped* parameters of mass, stiffness, damping, and lambda (λ), real machines have *continuous* distributions of parameters (and often several sources of λ, from different bearings and seals), and larger and higher-speed machines often exhibit several resonances during startup and shutdown. These distributed systems are theoretically capable of an infinite number of resonances. In practice, we are primarily interested in only the lowest few resonances that the machine will encounter on the way up to or down from operating speed or that exist at some integer multiple of running speed.

When a rotor system encounters a resonance, the system vibration will be amplified. For large, distributed systems, the vibration amplitude and phase will be different at different axial positions along the rotor. Also, the machine casing will participate in the vibration in some complicated way. The total system vibration will affect rotor-to-stator clearances along the rotor, possibly leading to internal rubs on seals or blade tips.

This complicated, vibration deflection shape of the rotor system is commonly called the *mode shape* of the system. The mode shape describes the axial distribution of vibration amplitude and phase along the rotor system, and it changes with rotor speed. It is a function of the mass, stiffness, damping, and λ

distribution along the rotor, combined with the distribution of unbalance along the rotor.

In this chapter we will discuss of the concept of natural frequencies and free vibration mode shapes and show that the forced mode shape is the sum of several free vibration mode shapes, each of which is excited to varying degrees by the unbalance distribution of the system. We will show how rotor system mode shapes are influenced by the relative stiffness of the shaft and bearings, and we will introduce the concept of modal parameters. Finally, we will discuss some different techniques for estimating the mode shape of a rotor system using vibration data.

Mode Shapes

All mechanical systems have natural frequencies of vibration. These natural frequencies can be excited by momentarily disturbing the system from its equilibrium position. If the system is underdamped, it will vibrate at one or more natural frequencies until the initial input energy decays away. Because the system is not forced continuously, this kind of vibration is called *free vibration*.

Our rotor model is capable of only one natural frequency, ω_n, which, for low damping, is approximately

$$\omega_n = \sqrt{\frac{K}{M}} \tag{12-1}$$

As the number of masses in the system increases, so do the number of natural frequencies. A natural frequency is also called a *mode*, or *natural mode* of the system. Each natural frequency is associated with a particular vibration pattern, called a *mode shape*, and each mode shape is independent of all the other mode shapes of the system.

Figure 12-1 shows an example of the mode shapes of a simple, two mass, linear system. Because the system has two lumped masses, it is capable of two independent free vibration modes. The lowest mode of this system is an *in-phase* mode (left, blue), where both masses move in the same direction at the same time. Note that the amplitudes of the motion are different. The second mode (red), occurs at a higher frequency and is an *out-of-phase* mode, where the masses move in opposite directions. The frequencies of the modes and the relative amplitudes of vibration of the masses depend on the values of the mass and stiffness elements of the system.

Our 1-Complex-Degree-of-Freedom (1-CDOF) rotor model has only one moving element, the rotor. We can extend that concept to view the rotor and

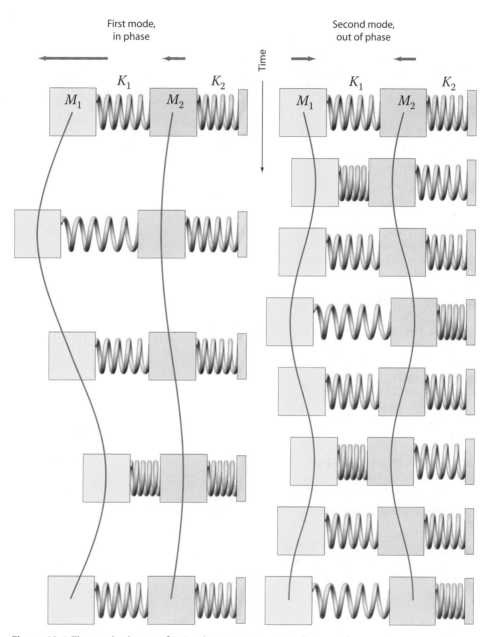

Figure 12-1. The mode shapes of a simple, two mass system. Because there are two masses, the system is capable of two, independent, free vibration modes. The lowest mode of this system is an in-phase mode (blue), where both masses move in the same direction at the same time. Note that the amplitudes of the motion are different. The second mode (red) occurs at a higher frequency and is an out-of-phase mode, where the masses move in opposite directions.

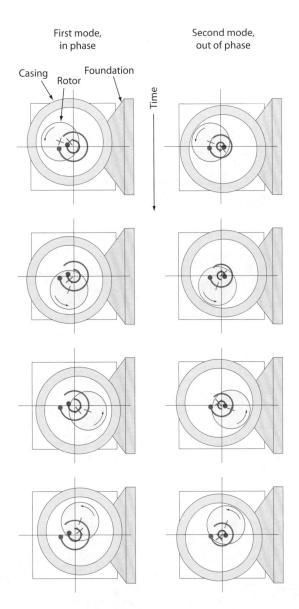

Figure 12-2. End view of a rotor system with two modes. The system is assumed to behave like two, lumped masses. The casing is shown in light red, and the rotor in light blue, and their circular orbits, measured in the inertial frame represented by the black axis lines, are shown in red and blue. The foundation is assumed to have some compliance that allows motion of the casing. In the left column, the rotor and casing move in orbits in an approximately in-phase relationship (top to bottom). In the second column, a second mode is shown where the rotor and casing move in an approximately out-of-phase mode. Note that, for the second mode, the rotor vibration amplitude is smaller than for the first mode, but the shaft relative motion of the rotor is larger.

casing as a 2-CDOF system, where the rotor and casing are treated as lumped masses. Like the system in Figure 12-1, this two mass system is also capable of two free vibration modes. But, instead of being constrained to motion in a line, both parts are capable of two-dimensional, independent, planar motion that, for an isotropic system, involves circular orbits.

Figure 12-2 shows and end view of this rotor system. The casing is shown in light red, and the rotor in light blue. The black lines represent the axes of the inertial reference frame. The foundation is assumed to allow motion of the casing. In the left column, the rotor and casing move in an approximately in-phase relationship. Both the rotor and casing move in circular orbits (red for the casing, blue for the rotor) about the inertial center of the system. For this mode, the rotor and casing are deflected from the inertial center in approximately the same direction at the same time, producing an *in-phase* mode. In the second column, a second mode shape is shown where the rotor and casing move in an approximately *out-of-phase* mode. Note that, for this second mode, the shaft relative motion of the rotor is larger.

Real rotor systems are *continuous* systems. Instead of lumped masses and springs, these systems have continuous distributions of mass and stiffness and possess many natural frequencies. Figure 12-3 shows the first three mode shapes of the simplest example of a continuous system, a string which is clamped at both ends. The diagrams show only the extreme positions that the string reaches during its vibration. When vibrating at a natural frequency in free vibration, the string can vibrate only in a particular, natural mode shape. The top mode shape in the figure corresponds to the lowest natural frequency, and the middle and bottom mode shapes correspond to successively higher natural frequencies.

Figure 12-3. The first three mode shapes of a freely vibrating string with clamped ends. When vibrating at a natural frequency in free vibration, the string can vibrate only in a particular, natural mode shape. The first mode shape (top) in the figure corresponds to the lowest natural frequency; the middle and bottom mode shapes correspond to successively higher frequencies.

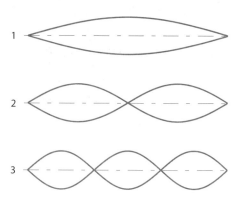

Rotor systems combine the characteristics of a continuous system (the rotor itself) and a lumped system, where the rotor and casing can behave like large lumped masses. In addition, lightweight, relatively flexible machine casings can deform in their own set of mode shapes.

Because of this complexity, the term mode shape can be somewhat confusing. It is fairly easy to imagine a rotating, flexible rotor that deflects in some complicated, three-dimensional shape like a piece of wet spaghetti. We will refer to this as a *rotor mode shape*. However, vibration modes involve the *simultaneous* vibration of all coupled components in the system: rotor, casing, foundation, attached piping, etc. The rotor and casing vibrate at the same time because the rotor and casing are coupled to each other through the bearing stiffness and damping. The casing can transmit vibration to the rest of the extended system, and it can transmit vibration to the rotor. The term mode shape can refer to the complicated pattern of rotor, casing, foundation, and piping system vibration. We will refer to this as the *system mode shape*. The rotor mode shape is part of the overall system mode shape, and each rotor and casing mode shape is associated with a natural frequency that includes the entire system.

When a rotor vibrates, it moves (precesses) in an orbit. The precession of the rotor produces a set of rotating reaction forces in the bearings. These forces are transmitted to the casing, and the casing responds dynamically to the rotating forces. Thus, the casing can move in an orbit in response to the rotor vibration, and rotor and casing mode shapes are a complicated, axially distributed set of rotor and casing orbits.

Rotor mode shapes are strongly influenced by the ratio of the shaft bending stiffness to the combination of bearing, casing mass, and casing support stiffnesses. If the stiffness ratio is low (relatively high support stiffness), then the bearings and casing will strongly constrain the rotor motion at the bearings, and most of the motion of vibration will occur through bending of the shaft. Rotors that experience bending modes, such as those in aeroderivative gas turbines and boiler feed pumps, are called *flexible rotors*. On the other hand, if the stiffness ratio is high (relatively high rotor stiffness), then the rotor is likely to exhibit *rigid* behavior, and the rotor natural modes will be *rigid body modes*. In this case, bending of the rotor will be relatively small compared to the motion of the rotor in the bearings (although there will be some rotor bending). A large electric motor rotor supported in fluid-film bearings is an example of a rigid rotor.

Figure 12-4 shows typical lowest rotor mode shapes for cases of high and low stiffness ratios. A high ratio of rotor stiffness to support stiffness tends to produce rigid body modes (left), while a low ratio tends to produce flexible rotor bending modes (right). The first modes (top) are essentially in phase, as shown by the Keyphasor dots on the orbit, while the second modes are out of phase.

Note the phase inversion across the nodal point (the point of minimum vibration amplitude). Machines with fluid-film bearings can have rigid body behavior in the very lowest modes and transition to flexible rotor behavior at higher modes.

Rotor mode shapes are also influenced by the distribution of stiffness and mass along the rotor shaft. Many rotor shafts have different section diameters or wall thicknesses at different axial locations. This produces variations in the local bending stiffness of the shaft. Disks and impellers with different masses are placed at different axial locations, resulting in an uneven axial mass distribution along the shaft.

These factors combine to affect the rotor mode shapes. Sections of the rotor with low local bending stiffness will bend more than the sections with higher stiffness. At the lowest modes, mass concentrations tend to produce larger deflections near the mass because it is harder for the shaft to constrain the inertia of the mass. At higher modes, the inertia of the mass produces high local mass stiffness and can result in very low vibration levels close to the mass concentration.

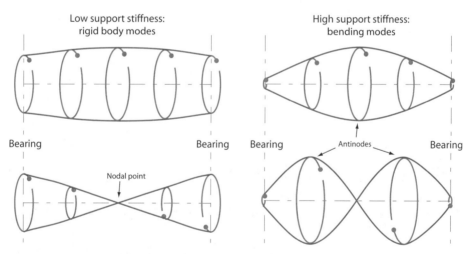

Figure 12-4. Typical lowest two rotor mode shapes for cases of high and low stiffness ratios. A high ratio of rotor stiffness to support stiffness tends to produce rigid body modes (left), while a low stiffness ratio tends to produce flexible rotor bending modes (right). Both first modes (top) are in-phase modes, as shown by the orbit Keyphasor dots, while both second modes are out-of-phase modes. Machines with fluid-film bearings can have rigid body behavior in the very lowest modes and transition to flexible rotor behavior at higher modes. A minimum of vibration is called a node, or nodal point; a maximum of vibration is called an antinode. Note the phase inversion that occurs across the nodal point.

Figure 12-5. Typical rotor mode shapes for three common rotor configurations. For each configuration the modes are shown with the lowest at top. The top group shows rigid and bending modes for typical single overhung rotors. When shaft stiffness is relatively high, the rigid mode will appear. More flexible rotors will show the first and second bending modes.

The double overhung configuration, capable of two rigid body modes. Here, the order of appearance of the rigid modes depends on the relative strength of the system angular rotor support stiffness to the lateral bearing stiffness. This is largely determined by the bearing spacing. Systems with relatively closely spaced bearings will experience a pivotal mode first. When bearings are widely spaced, angular stiffness is high, and the first rigid body mode will be cylindrical.

The most common rotor configuration, where most of the rotor mass is between the bearing centers. The first mode is a cylindrical or pivotal rigid body mode; which occurs first will depend on the bearing spacing, angular/lateral stiffness ratio, and the mass distribution. First and second bending modes follow one or both pivotal modes.

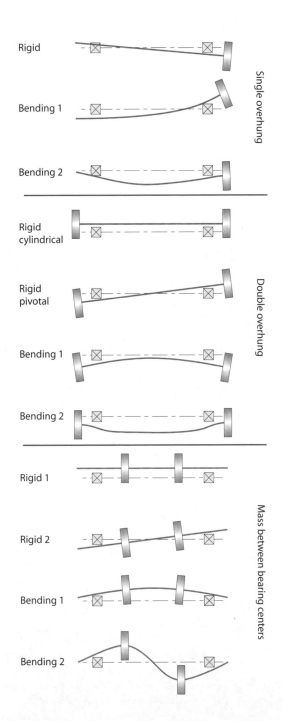

Figure 12-5 shows several rotor mode shapes for three common machine configurations. For each group, the modes are shown with the lowest mode at top. The first group shows rigid and bending modes for typical, single overhung rotors, such as a single-stage pump. The rigid and first bending mode are very similar; which form will appear depends on the ratio of shaft stiffness to bearing stiffness. When shaft stiffness is relatively high, the rigid mode will appear. More flexible rotors will show the first and second bending modes. If the rotor disk has a relatively high polar moment of inertia, gyroscopic effects at higher speeds will tend to resist bending in the area of the disk, forcing the disk to the near vertical orientation shown in the figure.

The double overhung configuration is capable of two rigid body modes. Here, the order of appearance of the rigid modes depends on the relative strength of the system *angular* rotor support stiffness versus the lateral bearing stiffness. This is largely determined by the bearing spacing. Systems with relatively closely spaced bearings will have relatively low angular stiffness and will experience a pivotal mode first. When bearings are widely spaced, angular stiffness is high, and the first rigid body mode will be cylindrical.

The last group shows typical mode shapes for the most common rotor configuration, where most of the rotor mass is concentrated between the bearing centers. The first mode is a cylindrical or pivotal rigid body mode; again, which occurs first will depend on the bearing spacing, angular/lateral stiffness ratio, and the mass distribution. First and second bending modes follow one or both pivotal modes.

Because of the relatively large rotor vibration amplitude in bearings during rigid body modes, damping forces can be very high, and these modes may not be visible on a polar or Bode plot during startup or shutdown.

Some points along the rotor mode shape have relatively high vibration, while others have little or no vibration. A location with no significant vibration is called a *node*, or *nodal point* (see also Figure 12-4). Locations where the vibration amplitude is maximum are called *antinodes*.

Nodal points are important because the vibration on either side of a nodal point will have a large phase difference, often 180°. If we fail to detect a nodal point, our perception of the mode shape of the system may be incorrect.

Antinodes are important because they are regions of high vibration amplitude. Because, for flexible rotor modes, bearings usually constrain nearby rotor vibration, relatively high vibration tends to occur near the midspan of the rotor. This has the potential to produce rubs that can damage seals, blade tips, or impellers. For these reasons, it is desirable to know the *forced mode shape* of the rotor

Forced Mode Shapes and Multimode Response

Up to this point we've discussed free vibration. However, operating rotor systems are subjected to *forced vibration*. Subsynchronous forcing can be caused by aerodynamic instabilities in compressors (rotating stall) or by fluid-induced instabilities associated with fluid-film bearings or seals. Supersynchronous forcing can be caused by compressor or turbine blades passing a close clearance, or pump vanes passing a cutwater. Rotors with cross-section asymmetries have a bending stiffness that depends on angular orientation. Asymmetry can be by design, such as in generators and motors, or the result of a shaft crack. When such a rotor is subjected to a static radial load when rotating, the asymmetry can produce supersynchronous forcing, most often 2X. Coupling problems can also produce 2X forcing.

Rotor-to-stator rub can produce impacting, a special situation where a periodic impulsive force (the rub contact) produces free vibration that decays until the next contact. Rub impacting can produce subsynchronous vibration, but, more often, a rub will produce a mild, once-per-turn impact that modifies the rotor stiffness in the area of the rub and the 1X unbalance response of the system.

The most common form of excitation of the rotor is rotating unbalance. The axial distribution of rotating unbalance produces an axially distributed force system that is available to excite natural frequencies. This force system has a shape (magnitude and angular orientation as a function of axial position) that is similar in concept to a mode shape. The degree of excitation of any natural mode depends on how well the unbalance distribution fits the particular natural mode shape. A good unbalance fit will produce a relatively large excitation of a natural mode, a balance resonance. A poor unbalance fit will result in little or no excitation of a mode (Figure 12-6), and little or no resonance. This characteristic is often deliberately exploited to balance one mode while not changing the unbalance state of another mode (Chapter 16).

The concept of an unbalance force distribution that matches a natural mode can be extended to include all of the excitation sources we have discussed. Any forcing function in the rotor system is available to excite system natural frequencies when the frequencies coincide. As with unbalance, the degree of excitation of a system mode will depend on the magnitude, orientation, and distribution of the source. The discussion that follows, while oriented toward unbalance excitation, applies to all sources of excitation in the system.

When the rotor speed equals a natural frequency of the rotor and the unbalance distribution approximately fits that natural mode shape, then that mode will be strongly excited, producing a balance resonance. The forced mode shape of the system will be dominated by that natural mode shape. As the rotor speed increases above the resonance speed, the amplitude of vibration will decline toward a residual level. If the unbalance distribution is a good fit to the next higher natural mode shape, then, as the machine accelerates, the next mode will become more strongly excited.

At a typical operating speed away from a resonance, the forced mode shape of the rotor will contain simultaneous contributions from several of the natural modes. The actual forced rotor mode shape will depend on the fit and magnitude of the unbalance distribution to each mode, and on the amplification of each mode at the particular speed. The complex interplay between unbalance distribution shape, natural mode shape, and resonance amplification produces a forced rotor mode shape that can continually change with speed.

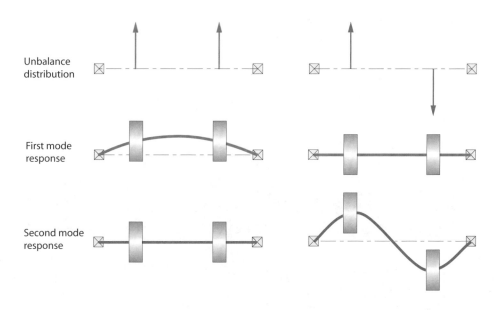

Unbalance distribution

First mode response

Second mode response

Figure 12-6. Unbalance distribution and mode excitation. The rotor shown has two modes: in phase and out of phase. The in-phase unbalance distribution (left) excites the first mode, but, since it does not fit the second mode, it does not excite the second mode. The out-of-phase unbalance distribution (right) fits the second mode, but not the first.

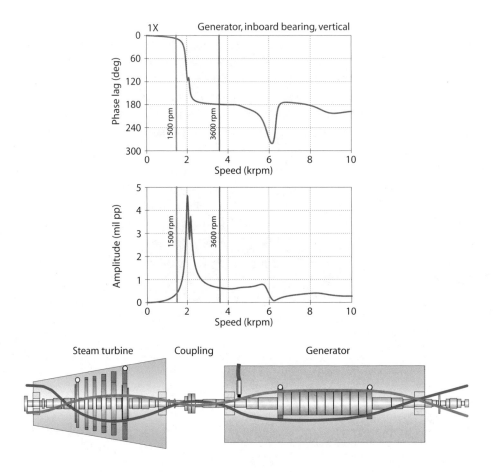

Figure 12-7. Two forced mode shapes of a steam turbine generator set predicted by a sophisticated rotor modeling program. The four equal unbalance masses were placed at 0° with respect to the vertical transducer (yellow dots). The Bode plot shows the 1X vibration response at the generator inboard bearing. The rotor mode shapes link the 1X orbit Keyphasor dot locations at 1500 rpm (green) and 3600 rpm (red).

Figure 12-7 shows the predicted behavior of a steam turbine generator set. The unbalance was the same magnitude at all four locations (yellow dots), and all masses were placed at 0° relative to the measurement transducer. The Bode plot, generated by a sophisticated rotor modeling program, shows the synchronous vibration response to this unbalance distribution. The rotor mode shapes at 1500 rpm (green) and 3600 rpm (red) are determined by the 1X orbit Keyphasor dots at each location.

It is interesting that this complicated system still follows the behavior predicted by our simple rotor model. At 1500 rpm, the machine operates below the first balance resonance, and the phase of the generator response (top) is close to the location of the heavy spots. The steam turbine and generator rotor mode shape (green) deflects toward the heavy spots.

At 3600 rpm, the machine operates between the first and second modes, where the phase of the generator response lags the heavy spot by about 180°. The rotor mode shape (red) shows that both the turbine and generator rotors are deflected away from the heavy spots.

Mode shapes are often three-dimensional; these mode shapes, though, are almost completely in the plane of the paper.

Modal Parameters

Rotor system behavior involving multiple modes is quite complex. The mathematical expressions necessary to accurately describe such behavior are well beyond the scope of this book. Instead, we would like to develop a more intuitive approach, which will allow us to extend the simple concepts we have already developed to the more complicated multimode rotor behavior we observe.

We have stated that the natural frequency of a one mode system is approximately given by Equation 12-1:

$$\omega_n = \sqrt{\frac{K}{M}}$$

where K is the combination of shaft spring stiffness, fluid-film bearing spring stiffness, and support spring stiffness, and M is the rotor mass.

We want to apply this simple expression to the natural frequencies of higher modes of the system. In the development of the simple model in Chapter 10, we assumed that the rotor parameters of mass, stiffness, damping, and λ were constant. Obviously, to obtain a higher natural frequency from this equation, either K must become larger or M must become smaller. We will show how both of these things happen.

In a fluid-film bearing, the spring stiffness, damping, and λ are nonlinear functions of eccentricity ratio. Thus, static radial load (which affects the average eccentricity ratio) and rotor speed (which affects the amplitude of vibration and the dynamic eccentricity ratio) produce changes in K and D, and in λ, which change the effective damping of the system.

More important than these eccentricity-related effects, though, is the mode shape of the shaft, which directly influences the effective stiffness, damping, and mass of the rotor itself.

A simple, vibrating, mechanical system involves the continuous cycling of energy between the potential energy of a spring and the kinetic energy of a moving mass. When the velocity of the mass is zero, all the energy of the system is stored in the compressed spring in the form of potential energy. When the velocity of the mass is maximum, at the equilibrium point, all the energy of the system is stored as kinetic energy of the mass, and the potential energy of the spring is zero. It is the ratio of these energy storage elements, K and M, that determines the natural frequency of the system.

When viewed from the side, a rotor can be viewed as a more complicated, vibrating, mechanical system. The energy in the system is traded between the potential energy of shaft deflection (the spring) and the kinetic energy of shaft motion. The mode shape of the shaft influences how much deflection is available for energy storage.

From the side, a deflected rotor shaft looks very much like a simple beam. At the top of Figure 12-8, the rotor behaves like a beam that is supported at the ends, which corresponds to a typical, first bending mode. According to beam theory, a beam that is supported in this way will have an effective stiffness in response to a static deflection force applied at midspan that is inversely proportional to the length cubed.

In the second case, the beam has the same shape as a typical, s-shaped, bending mode. This is equivalent to the beam having a pinned joint at the midspan nodal point, which prevents any deflection there. The beam is now similar to two beams with one-half the total length. A force applied to the one-quarter point will produce a deflection, but the perceived stiffness of the beam will be much larger than for the first mode shape. Thus, the effective stiffness of the rotor is much higher in the second mode than in the first mode. We use the term *modal stiffness* to describe the effective stiffness of a system in dynamic motion. The modal stiffness of a rotor will be different for each rotor mode.

The only rotor mass that is available to store kinetic energy is mass that is available to vibrate. The rotor mass near the center of the beam span (top) can move the most. Nearer the ends, the amount of motion decreases until the beam is constrained at the endpoints. At the bottom, the rotor mass near the center nodal point is also unable to move. The total moving mass for this mode must be less than the moving mass for the first mode. Thus, the effective mass of the rotor is lower for the second mode than for the first mode. We use the term *modal mass* to describe the effective dynamic mass of the system. The modal mass will be different for each mode, and, except when an entire rotor moves rigidly (a rigid body translational mode), the modal mass of the rotor will be less than the static weight of the rotor.

In our example, the second mode modal stiffness is *higher* than the first mode modal stiffness, and the second mode modal mass is *lower* than the first mode modal mass. Thus the ratio of K to M must be higher for the second mode, and Equation 12-1 will yield a higher natural frequency, which is exactly what we observe.

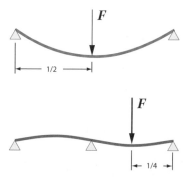

Figure 12-8. Modal stiffness of a rotor. At top, the rotor behaves like a beam that is simply supported at the ends with a static deflection force applied at midspan; this shape corresponds to a typical first bending mode. At bottom, the rotor behaves like a beam having an additional pinned joint at the midspan with a force applied to the one-quarter point. This second mode is a typical, s-shaped, bending mode. The beam now behaves like two beams with one-half the total length and a perceived stiffness much larger than for the first mode shape. The effective stiffness of the rotor is much higher in the second mode than in the first mode.

In most rotor systems, the primary source of damping is the fluid-film bearing. The damping force depends on the velocity of the rotor centerline in the lubricating fluid. If a rotor has a mode shape that produces a large amplitude of vibration, A, in a bearing, then the vibration velocity amplitude, $v = A\Omega$, will be high and the damping force, $Dv = DA\Omega$ will also be relatively large. This is the case for rigid body modes; the relatively stiff rotor has large amplitude vibration in the bearings (Figure 12-9). For this reason, rigid body modes often have high Quadrature Dynamic Stiffness and low Synchronous Amplification Factors. In many cases, the very lowest rigid body modes are overdamped, and a balance resonance does not appear at all.

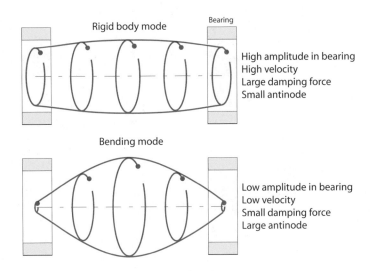

Figure 12-9. Modal damping in rotor systems. Most of the damping force originates in fluid-film bearings and is proportional to the lateral velocity of the rotor in the bearing. All bearings in this diagram are assumed to have the same damping constant, D. Rigid body modes produce large amplitudes in the bearings and large damping forces. Bending modes tend to produce smaller amplitudes in the bearings and smaller damping forces. Modal damping describes the effective damping available to the system and will vary with different mode shapes.

On the other hand, flexible rotor modes tend to have nodal points that are located relatively close to bearings. This results in lower vibration amplitudes in the bearings, which produces low vibration velocity and a low damping force. Such modes tend to have lower Quadrature Dynamic Stiffness and higher Synchronous Amplification Factors, with higher vibration at the antinodes.

We use the term *modal damping* to describe the actual damping force available to the system. The modal damping depends on the actual damping of the bearings and seals combined with the mode shape.

This qualitative discussion shows how modal stiffness, modal mass, and modal damping depend on mode shape. The rotor modal parameters combine with bearing parameters, which change with eccentricity ratio, to produce overall modal parameters. Thus, each mode of a rotor system can be viewed as having a different set of modal parameters that are associated with each natural frequency. The variations in modal damping will produce a different Synchronous Amplification Factor for each mode.

The Measurement of Mode Shape

Measurement of rotor mode shape involves determining the three-dimensional, dynamic deflection shape of the rotor at any point in time. A complete description of instantaneous rotor position would require unfiltered orbits and average shaft centerline position data. However, for the purpose of defining rotor dynamic behavior, we are usually concerned with defining only 1X rotor behavior versus speed. For that reason, the discussion that follows is concentrated on the measurement of 1X mode shape.

In principle, a set of axially spaced, shaft relative transducers can be used to determine the rotor mode shape over the entire operating speed range of the machine. This can be combined with data from casing transducers to establish the system mode shapes. This can done fairly easily with 1X polar plots or more accurately with 1X orbits.

1X polar plots provide the easiest approach to estimating the mode shape. This technique is commonly used in balancing and works best when orbits are circular. However, when the system has a significant degree of anisotropy, which produces elliptical orbits (Chapter 13), polar plots can produce misleading results.

The polar plot technique uses data from a single transducer per measurement plane to display the startup or shutdown data at points along the length of the rotor. The plots have the same full scale range and are positioned in a way that represents the axial location on the machine. Points at the same rotor speed are linked by a curve, which estimates the mode shape.

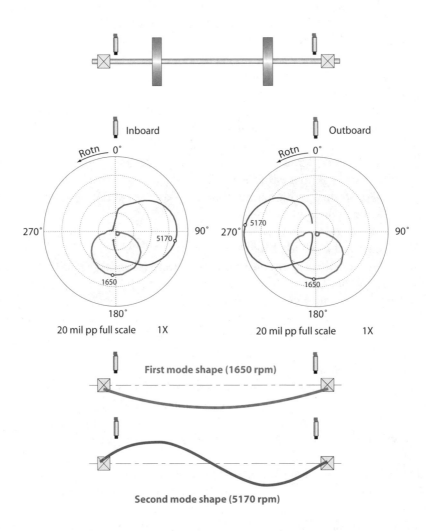

Figure 12-10. Using polar plots to estimate the rotor mode shapes. A two bearing rotor has shaft relative probes mounted just inboard of the bearings. The 1X polar plots show two balance resonances, at 1650 rpm and 5170 rpm, in the startup data. The estimated mode shapes are shown at the bottom.

The polar plots in Figure 12-10 show 1X startup data from a two bearing rotor with shaft relative probes mounted just inboard of the bearings. Balance resonances are observed at 1650 rpm and 5170 rpm. The estimated mode shapes are shown at the bottom.

If the rotor orbits are circular, then the point on the polar plot will accurately represent the location of the rotor (when adjusted for the peak-to-peak amplitude of the polar plot) when the Keyphasor event occurs. The generated mode shape curve would be equivalent to linking the Keyphasor dots (the location of the rotor when the Keyphasor event occurs) of a series of circular orbits.

If the orbits are *not* circular, but elliptical, then the amplitude and phase values on the polar plot may not identify the correct location of the Keyphasor dots on the orbits. Figure 12-11 shows two polar plots from the same measurement plane. This steam turbine generator has highly elliptical orbits, and the two polar plots look very different. There is a large disagreement as to the location of the rotor between the *Y* probe data (left) and the *X* probe data.

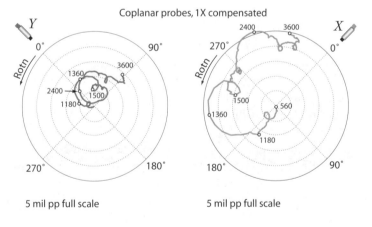

Figure 12-11. Polar plots showing anisotropic behavior. The polar plots are from *XY* probes mounted in the same plane. The polar plots show different measured behavior, due to highly elliptical orbits, which makes it difficult to estimate mode shapes. See Chapter 13 for an explanation of what causes this behavior.

The mode shape is more accurately determined using 1X orbits (Figure 12-12), which require two transducers at each measurement plane. Filtered orbits are constructed for each measurement plane, the orbits are plotted at the same scale, and the Keyphasor dots are connected.

If the orbits are digitally sampled, and all the waveform samples are synchronized, then individual mode shapes can be constructed for each sample time (individual point) in the sampled waveforms. For example, if 128 X and Y waveform samples were taken for each revolution, then X and Y sample 99 defines a point on the orbit. This point can be linked to sample 99 points on other orbits, defining the rotor mode shape. The collection of the mode shapes for all the samples defines the three-dimensional envelope formed by the orbits.

Mode Identification Probes

Accurate determination of the rotor and casing mode shapes would require a large set of XY shaft relative and casing transducers spaced along the axis of the machine. In practice, such a large set of shaft relative transducers cannot be installed because of physical limitations. It is not physically possible (and not economically acceptable) to install large numbers of shaft relative transducers in extremely high-pressure or high-temperature regions, or where transducers would interfere with process fluid flow paths. Because of these considerations, shaft relative transducers are usually mounted near bearings, where access, temperature, and interference with the process are not a factor.

Thus, mode shapes must be *interpolated* between a small set of measurement points. Usually, this interpolation includes places far away from the actual measurement points. This is unfortunate, because often our primary objective is to determine the clearance between the rotor and stator at the midspan of the rotor, exactly the area of highest uncertainty.

On large, critical machinery, modern management practice dictates the installation of XY shaft relative transducers at each fluid-film bearing. Unfortunately, this set of transducers will not always provide enough information to measure complicated, higher-order mode shapes when nodal points exist in the interior of a machine; often, more than one possible mode shape can fit the data. Additional probes, called *mode identification probes*, can be installed on both sides of each bearing, to provide more information.

The problem often occurs when nodal points exist at a location outside the bearing. Figure 12-13 (top) shows a machine with transducers installed on the inboard sides of the two bearings; the actual mode shape is shown in black. In this situation, a nodal point occurs inboard of the left probe. More than one possible mode shape (middle) could fit the observed data from these probes. When additional probes are installed outboard of the bearings, the additional infor-

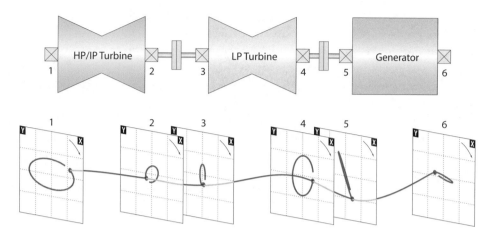

Figure 12-12. Estimation of rotor mode shape using multiple orbits. The 1X orbits were measured at the same rotor speed and plotted at the same scale. The Keyphasor dots show the 1X location of the rotor when the Keyphasor event occurs. The dots are connected to estimate the forced, 1X, rotor mode shape.

Figure 12-13. Mode identification probes help identify mode shapes. A machine has transducers installed on the inboard sides of the bearings. The actual mode shape is shown in black (top). More than one possible mode shape (middle) could fit the observed data from these probes. When additional probes are installed outboard of the bearings (bottom), the additional information helps identify the actual mode shape and the nodal point that occurs inboard of the left probe.

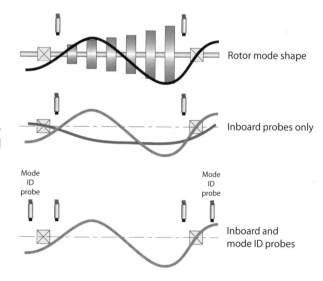

mation helps identify the actual mode shape. For very complex mode shapes, even this probe configuration may not provide enough information to unambiguously define the mode shape.

The best technique for mode shape estimation is to use advanced rotor modeling software in combination with vibration measurements. A model of the rotor system is constructed using accurate shaft and rotor disk dimensions and material properties, and the program calculates the theoretical mode shape based on known physical laws. When combined with actual measurement data, the software can automatically optimize bearing parameters to provide an accurate mode shape of the rotor. The time is coming when such software will be able to use real time vibration measurements to provide accurate rotor mode shape information.

Summary

A rotor mode shape is the rotor's three-dimensional, dynamic deflection shape, which changes with axial position.

A system mode shape includes information about the relative motion of the rotor, casing, piping system, and any other part of the coupled system.

The rotor system can exhibit free vibration at one or many natural frequencies. Each natural frequency, or mode, has its own characteristic mode shape that is different from the mode shapes at other natural frequencies.

A free vibration mode can be forced, or excited, by the distributed unbalance of the system. An unbalance distribution will have its own characteristic three-dimensional shape, with both amplitude and phase as a function of axial position. If the unbalance distribution shape is a good fit to the rotor mode shape, then that mode will be strongly excited, producing a balance resonance when the rotor speed is near the natural frequency.

Rotor system forced vibration includes contributions from many free vibration modes. Each mode is excited to some extent by the unbalance distribution, and the resulting rotor response is the sum of the contributions of the individual forced modes.

Each mode can be characterized by a set of modal parameters. The square root of the ratio of modal mass to modal stiffness determines the natural frequency for that mode. The modal damping determines the Synchronous Amplification Factor for the mode. Modal mass, stiffness, and damping derive from the mode shape of the rotor.

Mode shape can be estimated using polar plots from different axial locations or from orbits at these locations. Nodal points can make determination of the mode shape difficult. Mode identification probes are used to provide more information about nodal points near bearings.

Chapter 13

Anisotropic Stiffness

The rotor model that we developed in chapter 10 is isotropic, produces only circular, 1X orbits, and predicts one forward balance resonance. The model also serves as a basis for defining the Synchronous Amplification Factor.

An important result of the synchronous rotor model is that, at low speed, the heavy spot and high spot are approximately in phase. This allows us to use polar and Bode plots to identify the angular location of the heavy spot for balancing. This capability depends on the assumptions used in the model, which include single mode behavior and isotropic parameters of mass, stiffness, damping, and lambda.

However, in real operating machinery, multi mode behavior, in combination with fluid-film bearings, can sometimes produce a larger than expected phase lag near a bearing. This effect will be discussed in Chapter 16.

A more common problem is that 1X orbits are elliptical, and the orientation of the ellipse usually changes with speed. Elliptical orbits produce shaft center-line velocity variations that affect the interpretation of phase, leading to a breakdown of the assumed heavy/high spot relationship used in balancing. Also, because of this ellipticity, measurement of vibration amplitude depends on the orientation of the orbit relative to the measurement probe.

Many machines that produce highly elliptical orbits have closely spaced resonances that have a similar mode shape, called *split resonances*. In between these split resonances, over a short speed range, the rotor may even travel in a reverse, unbalance-driven, 1X orbit.

These effects are a result of *anisotropic stiffness* in rotor systems. In this chapter, we will discuss how anisotropic stiffness influences rotor system behavior, with an emphasis on measured vibration amplitude and heavy spot location.

We will start with a discussion of the meaning of anisotropic stiffness and the physical reasons why it is common in machinery. We will then discuss how anisotropic stiffness manifests itself in rotor behavior, show how, for anisotropic systems, measured vibration amplitude and phase depend on probe mounting orientation, and how this behavior can lead to ambiguity as to the location of the heavy spot.

Finally, we will present two signal processing techniques that improve the vibration measurements of anisotropic systems: virtual probe rotation and forward and reverse vector transformation.

Anisotropic Stiffness

For the purposes of this discussion, a parameter, such as mass, stiffness, damping, or λ (lambda), is *isotropic* if it has the same value when measured in all radial directions. A parameter is *anisotropic* if it has *different* values when measured in different radial directions (Figure 13-1). Because mass distributions, shafts, bearings, and support structures are not perfectly symmetric, all rotor parameters exhibit some degree of anisotropy.

Uneven mass distributions on rotor casings and support structures contribute to anisotropic modal mass in rotor systems. External piping can cause different observed modal casing mass along the axis of the piping compared to directions perpendicular to the piping. Rotor mass (and stiffness) can also be anisotropic due to shape asymmetry, which is common in electric motors, wind turbines, and generators. However, these asymmetries, because of rotor rotation, typically manifest themselves as higher-order *excitation* of the rotor system, particularly in the presence of a side load. A stationary observer sees an average value of rotating rotor mass, so we will assume all rotor parameters to be stationary in this sense.

Most rotor systems have relatively low Quadrature Dynamic Stiffness. Thus, damping and λ anisotropy will be assumed to have a relatively small effect on rotor response, and the tangential stiffness, $D\lambda\Omega$, will be assumed to be relatively isotropic.

However, anisotropic spring stiffness is common in rotating machinery and has a strong effect on rotor system response. Figure 13-2 shows an end view of a typical, horizontally split machine and the stiffness contributions of various components, including the piping, fluid film, and support structure. Note that the *XY* vibration measurement probes are mounted at ±45° from the vertical, to avoid the split line. This is a common mounting orientation that has important implications for vibration measurement of anisotropic systems.

The method of mounting the casing to the foundation can also produce anisotropic stiffness characteristics. Angular stiffness about the long axis of the

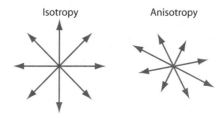

Figure 13-1. Isotropic and anisotropic systems. A system property is *isotropic* if it is the same in all radial directions. A system property is *anisotropic* if it has different values in different radial directions.

Figure 13-2. Sources of anisotropic stiffness in machinery. *XY* shaft relative vibration measurement probes are mounted at ±45° from the vertical to avoid the split line in a typical, horizontally split machine. Bearing supports, foundation, and piping attachments can all produce anisotropic stiffness effects. The fluid-film bearing is strongly anisotropic at high eccentricity ratios; the journal sees a higher spring stiffness in the radial direction (along the line connecting bearing and shaft centers) than in the tangential direction. The various contributions are assumed to combine to produce horizontally weak and vertically strong stiffnesses.

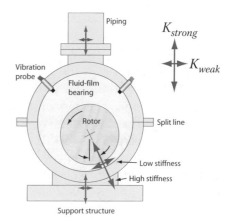

machine can be significantly lower than vertical stiffness; this can appear as a relatively weak horizontal stiffness.

The stiffness of the casing and support is influenced by the stiffness of the piping system and its attachments, and, typically, it will be different in the horizontal and vertical directions.

Most importantly, a typical rotor is supported in fluid-film bearings. Remember that the rotor model was developed with the assumption that the rotor was operating, fully lubricated, in the center of the bearing. In this region of the bearing, the spring stiffness is essentially isotropic. Lightly loaded, plain cylindrical fluid-film bearings operate at low eccentricity ratios and can have large attitude angles, sometimes reaching 90° or more. Also, externally pressurized (hydrostatic) bearings normally operate in a fully lubricated condition at very low eccentricity ratios; these bearings are essentially isotropic in behavior.

However, normally loaded, internally pressurized (hydrodynamic), plain cylindrical bearings operate in a partially lubricated condition at moderately high eccentricity ratios. At high eccentricity ratios, because of the action of the hydrodynamic fluid wedge, the journal sees anisotropic spring stiffness. (Imagine it much smaller than the bearing; if it were sitting in the bottom of the bearing, it couldn't move as freely down as it could move left to right.) The anisotropic stiffness resolves itself into a strong and a weak axis. The strong axis is approximately at the position angle of the rotor, acting in a radial direction, and the weak axis is at 90° in the tangential direction. (Be careful here. We are talking about variations in the *spring stiffness* in the radial and tangential directions, not about *tangential stiffness*, which we assume to be isotropic.) In a horizontal machine, a properly aligned, gravity-loaded rotor with plain, cylindrical, fluid-film bearings, will operate in the bearing at an attitude angle of a few tens of degrees. For tilting pad bearings, this is typically less than fifteen degrees. Thus, the orientation of the strong spring stiffness in the radial direction and weak spring stiffness in the tangential direction will be approximately vertical and horizontal, and the horizontal spring stiffness will be lower than the vertical spring stiffness.

In an anisotropic system, the radial spring stiffness distribution can be a complicated function of angle. In this chapter, we will assume that the spring stiffness distribution has an elliptical shape (like that in Figure 13-1) and can be resolved into strong and weak *stiffness axes* that are perpendicular to each other. The orientation of these axes can be in any direction, but because of the machine characteristics we have discussed, we will assume they are approximately horizontal (weak) and vertical (strong). We will call the weak spring stiffness K_{weak} and the strong spring stiffness K_{strong}.

During the following discussion, remember that this stiffness orientation is an *assumption* based on gravity loading of the rotor. Some machines may have a radial load vector that points in some other direction (for example, a gearbox), and the rotor may operate with a large position angle. In this case, the stiffness axes may be oriented in some other direction than horizontal and vertical.

As we discussed in the last chapter, different modes of vibration have different modal parameters. By extension, the degree of anisotropy may change from mode to mode. Thus, a rotor system with a relatively low degree of anisotropic stiffness in the first mode may have a higher degree in the second mode, or vice versa. Anisotropy may also change with axial position. We will primarily discuss rotor response from the perspective of a single mode.

Split Resonances

A *split resonance* consists of two balance resonances that have a similar mode shape, but are separated in frequency. Split resonances are a direct result of anisotropic spring stiffness. Recall that, for low damping, a balance resonance will occur when the rotor speed, Ω, is equal to the natural frequency of the rotor system,

$$\Omega_{res} = \sqrt{\frac{K}{M}} \tag{13-1}$$

where K is the spring stiffness of the rotor system and M is the mass of the rotor.

In our system with anisotropic spring stiffness, two values of spring stiffness exist, K_{weak} in the horizontal direction, and K_{strong} in the vertical direction. Thus, the system can produce two resonances, one associated with the horizontal spring and one associated with the vertical spring. The first resonance, associated with the weak spring, will occur near

$$\Omega_1 = \sqrt{\frac{K_{weak}}{M}} \tag{13-2}$$

and the second, associated with the strong spring, will occur near

$$\Omega_2 = \sqrt{\frac{K_{strong}}{M}} \tag{13-3}$$

If the stiffness axes are oriented horizontally and vertically, and the Quadrature Dynamic Stiffness of the system is low, then the rotor motion in the first resonance will have a large horizontal component, and in the second resonance, a large vertical component.

The response due to a typical split resonance is shown in Figure 13-3. This data, from a rotor system model with anisotropic stiffness (horizontal weak and vertical strong), shows the rotor response as it would be measured by a probe mounted at 45° L. Note that two, distinct resonance peaks can be seen in the Bode plot. The phase lag increases through the horizontal split resonance, then *decreases* as the system approaches the vertical split resonance, but increases again as the system goes through the vertical split. On the polar plot, there is a clear internal loop, which corresponds to the amplitude and phase changes between the split resonances. Orbits are shown for key rpm points.

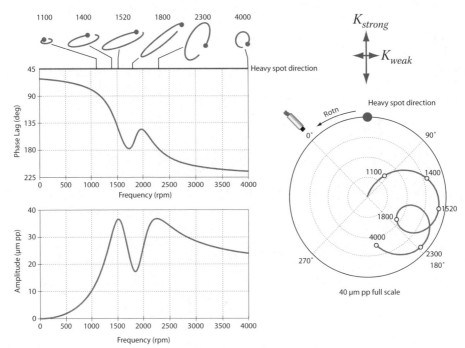

Figure 13-3. A typical split resonance. This data is from a rotor system model with anisotropic stiffness (horizontal weak and vertical strong) and shows the rotor response as it would be measured by a probe mounted at 45° L. Two, distinct resonance peaks can be seen in the Bode plot. The phase lag increases through the first of the resonances, then *decreases* as the system approaches the second resonance. Phase lag then increases again through the second resonance. On the polar plot, an internal loop is visible that corresponds to the amplitude and phase changes between the split resonances.

The amplitude behavior can be explained by examining the orbits from the perspective of the measurement transducer (Figure 13-4). The distance between the tangent lines represents the peak-to-peak amplitude as it would be seen by the measurement probe at 45° L. At low speed (1100 rpm), the anisotropic spring stiffness dominates the response; the orbit is elliptical, with the major axis nearly horizontal, due to K_{weak}. As speed increases, the orbit rotates and elongates, and the probe sees a maximum peak-to-peak amplitude near 1520 rpm. As the rotor system accelerates above this speed, the major axis of the orbit continues to increase, but the orbit axis rotates in such a way that the peak-to-peak amplitude actually declines (1800 rpm). At this speed, the major axis of the elliptical orbit is nearly perpendicular to the measurement probe. As the rotor speed approaches 2300 rpm, the orbit axis rotates farther, producing another increase in measured peak-to-peak amplitude. This corresponds to the second resonance

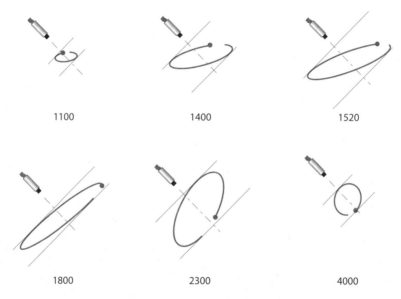

1100   1400   1520

1800   2300   4000

Figure 13-4. Orbits and measured amplitude for the anisotropic system of Figure 13-3. The peak-to-peak amplitudes are seen by the measurement probe at 45° L. At low speed (1100 rpm), the orbit is elliptical with the major axis nearly horizontal. As speed increases, the orbit rotates and elongates, and the probe sees a maximum amplitude near 1520 rpm. As the rotor speed continues to increase, the major axis of the orbit increases, but the axis rotates in such a way that the probe measurement actually decreases (1800 rpm). At 2300 rpm, the orbit axis has rotated and the aspect ratio of the axes has changed, producing another increase in measured amplitude, which corresponds to the second resonance peak. As the rotor reaches 4000 rpm, the system is above the split resonance, and mass stiffness begins to dominate the response. Because mass stiffness is isotropic, the orbit becomes more circular.

peak of the split. At 4000 rpm, the system is well above the split resonance, and the mass stiffness in the model dominates the response. Because mass stiffness is isotropic, the orbit becomes nearly circular. (If the next rotor system mode has anisotropic spring stiffness, then orbits will become elliptical when the second mode begins to dominate the rotor response.)

The appearance of split resonances can vary from a slightly broadened, single resonance peak to clearly separated resonance peaks. The separation will depend on the degree of anisotropy in the spring stiffnesses, the amount of Quadrature Dynamic Stiffness, and the viewpoint, or angular orientation, of the probe. Low quadrature stiffness will tend to create clearly separated peaks; high quadrature stiffness will tend to smooth the peaks together. The small polar plot loop will also change appearance; clearly separated peaks produce a well defined small loop, while, on a high quadrature stiffness machine, the small loop may only appear as a small bump. As we will see shortly, probes misaligned from the stiffness axes will tend to highlight split resonances, and those aligned with the stiffness axes will tend to obscure the split.

Measured Rotor Behavior and Anisotropic Stiffness

There are significant differences in the observed behavior of systems with anisotropic spring stiffness compared to isotropic systems: elliptical orbits, disagreement between high spot and heavy spot location at low speeds, and the presence of split resonances. Also, in anisotropic systems, data becomes dependent on the orientation of the measurement probes: there are differences in the appearance of Bode and polar plots, in the observed Synchronous Amplification Factors, and in the measured vibration amplitudes. Probe mounting orientation becomes an important factor for anisotropic systems.

Transducers (probes) are usually mounted in mutually perpendicular, XY pairs in each measurement plane of a critical machine. The probes can be mounted at 45° L and 45° R (typical for horizontal machines), 0° and 90° R, or any other desired orientation. These probes generate timebase signals that are combined to produce an orbit (Chapter 5). Each transducer signal can be used to create a separate nX Bode or polar plot of a machine startup or shutdown.

There is a tendency to use the vector data from only one probe for analysis. For isotropic behavior, this is acceptable, but isotropic behavior is rare in machinery with fluid-film bearings. For anisotropic behavior, the use of data from only one probe can lead to a serious misunderstanding of machine behavior.

Imagine a rotor system that is producing circular, 1X orbits. Because of the symmetry, the 1X vector from a single probe could be used to reconstruct the original orbit. However, if a rotor system is producing elliptical orbits, it is not possible to reconstruct the orbit with vector data from a single probe. Vibration vectors are required from an *XY* pair to reconstruct a 1X, elliptical orbit.

Similarly, a complete picture of anisotropic, nX rotor behavior versus speed requires data from two probes: two polar or two Bode plots. A single plot will not convey an adequate description of the vibration behavior of an anisotropic machine.

Table 13-1 summarizes the important differences in observed behavior between isotropic and anisotropic rotor systems.

Table 13-1. Isotropic versus anisotropic rotor behavior.

Isotropic	Anisotropic
Circular 1X orbits	Elliptical 1X orbits, possibly reverse between splits
No split resonances	Resonances can be split
Measured vibration not viewpoint dependent	Measured response changes with probe orientation
1X polar plots look circular	Polar plots may not be circular, and a small loop may appear
X and *Y* polar plots look the same	*X* and *Y* polar plots are different
Low-speed heavy /high spot are aligned	Low-speed heavy/high spot are aligned only under special circumstances
Single mode SAF matches theory	SAF is viewpoint dependent

Because orbits are circular in an isotropic system, measured vibration amplitude and phase behavior will *not* depend on the probe mounting orientation, and, consequently, polar plots from *XY* transducers will look identical (Figure 13-5). In isotropic systems, the polar plot of the rotor response through a balance resonance will have a circular shape.

Isotropic, single mode rotor system behavior matches the ideal behavior used to define the Synchronous Amplification Factor (SAF). Thus, the SAF measured on a single mode isotropic system will be a good match to theory and will also be independent of probe mounting orientation. However, SAF measurement can become troublesome even for *isotropic* systems when closely spaced modes can interact and distort the SAF measurement.

In anisotropic systems, 1X orbits can vary from nearly circular, for mildly anisotropic stiffness, to extremely elliptical, line orbits. In systems with low quadrature stiffness, orbits can also exhibit reverse precession between split resonances.

At speeds well below a resonance, rotor response is quasi-static, and the Dynamic Stiffness is dominated by spring stiffness (Chapter 11). The relatively weak spring of the anisotropic stiffness allows more rotor deflection in the direction of the weak stiffness axis; thus, the major axis of the low-speed, elliptical orbit will be approximately aligned with the weak stiffness axis.

Anisotropic spring stiffness can produce split resonances. The visibility of the split will depend on the degree of anisotropy of the spring stiffness (the separation of the two resonances), the Quadrature Dynamic Stiffness of the system, and the orientation of the viewing probes. Relatively high quadrature stiffness will tend to broaden resonance amplitude peaks and blend them together, especially if the degree of anisotropy (and separation) is low. For this reason, split resonance peaks may not be clearly separated on polar and Bode plots.

If a measurement probe is not aligned with the axis of the elliptical orbit, then a phase measurement anomaly will exist, producing an error in the inferred heavy spot location. The data from an *XY* pair will disagree on the implied location of the heavy spot. This will be discussed in more detail below.

Anisotropic stiffness can produce significant differences in measured 1X vibration response (both amplitude and phase) between *X* and *Y* probes in the same plane. This difference is largest when orbits are highly elliptical and disappears when orbits are circular. Figure 13-6 shows the effect of probe mounting angle (viewpoint) on the measurement of vibration amplitude of an elliptical orbit. In the elliptical orbit at left, the *Y* probe sees a much smaller vibration amplitude than the *X* probe. In the circular orbit, both probes measure the same amplitude.

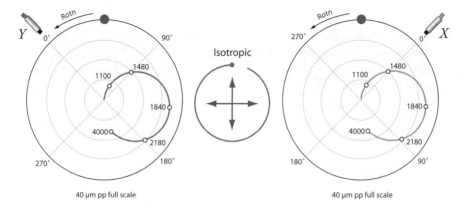

Figure 13-5. *Y* and *X* polar plots of an isotropic system. The heavy spot direction (red dot) is up for both plots. The appearance of the plots does not depend on probe orientation; the plots are identical, and all orbits are circular. In each case, the low-speed response vectors point toward the heavy spot. The low-speed orbit shows that the high spot (Keyphasor event) is in the same direction as the heavy spot.

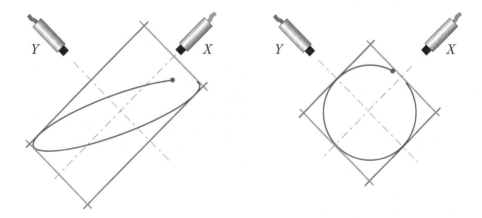

Figure 13-6. Probe viewpoint and amplitude measurement. For the elliptical orbit, the measured amplitudes depend on the probe and orbit orientation. For the circular orbit, both probes measure the same amplitude no matter what the orientation.

Because of the dependence of vibration measurement on probe and orbit axis alignment, polar and Bode plots of data from X and Y probes can have a very different visual appearance. As the orientation of an elliptical orbit changes through resonances, measured vibration amplitude and phase will change in a very different manner than for the circular orbit predicted by the simple, isotropic model.

Figure 13-7 shows 1X polar plots of XY transducer vector data produced by an anisotropic rotor system model. The orientation of the stiffness axes is shown in red, along with a low-speed orbit. The Y plot, which has the same scale as the X plot, has a smaller maximum amplitude and contains a small loop that looks like a structural resonance, while the X plot shows a much larger amplitude at the resonance and no signs of a loop.

The loop in the Y plot is *not due to a structural resonance*. The model used to generate these plots is not capable of producing a structural resonance. The loop is purely an artifact of the anisotropic rotor system response and the probe viewpoint. This implies that many of the small loops seen on polar plots are not structural resonances at all, but are due to anisotropic stiffness. Later, we will see examples of machine data that show nearly identical behavior.

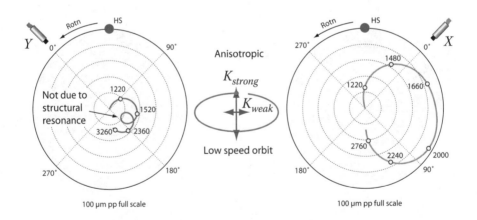

Figure 13-7. 1X polar plots from a rotor system model with anisotropic spring stiffness. The orientation of the anisotropic stiffness axes are shown in red inside a low-speed orbit. The Y plot, which has the same scale as the X plot, shows a relatively small maximum amplitude with a small loop that looks like a structural resonance, while the X plot shows a much larger amplitude at the resonance and no signs of a loop. The "structural" loop in the Y plot is not a structural resonance at all; it is purely an artifact of the anisotropic rotor system response and the probe viewpoint.

What Causes Reverse Orbits?

Rotating unbalance produces a purely forward perturbation of a rotor system. How can a reverse orbit be generated by forward perturbation?

The key is the split resonance, which can be thought of as a pair of resonances that occur in perpendicular directions. Assume that these directions are horizontal (X, the direction of the weak stiffness) and vertical (Y, the direction of the strong stiffness), that the system is viewed by two probes mounted horizontally and vertically, and that the rotor rotates in an X to Y direction.

During each resonance, the phase lag increases from 0° to about 180° relative to the heavy spot. When a split resonance is well separated, and the quadrature stiffness of the system is low, then it is possible for the horizontal resonance to move through most of the phase change before the phase lag of the second resonance changes significantly.

In the figure, the X response (green) changes phase and crosses the Y phase curve (blue). The crossover point produces a line orbit. In the speed range where the

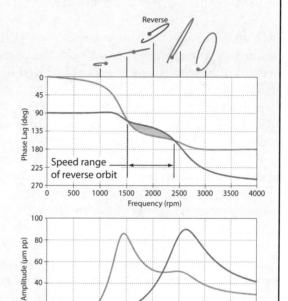

X phase is below the Y phase curve (red shading), the orbit is reverse. As the Y phase lag increases with the second resonance, the Y phase curve recrosses the X phase, producing a line orbit at the crossing speed. At higher speeds, the orbit is once again elliptical forward.

When the rotor operates at a speed in the yellow range, the horizontal component of vibration will be approximately out of phase with the heavy spot, while the vertical component will be approximately in phase. This phase relationship produces a reverse orbit. Instead of the rotor orbiting in an X to Y direction (bottom), the rotor now moves in a $-X$ to Y direction, which is equivalent to Y to X.

When the rotor speed increases further, the rotor passes through the vertical resonance, which causes the phase lag of the Y vibration to change by 180°. This produces a $-X$ to $-Y$ direction of precession, which is equivalent to X to Y, or forward.

Note that these phase boundaries only apply when the probes are aligned with the anisotropic stiffness axes of the system.

Probe Mounting Orientation and Measured Response

In isotropic systems, at speeds well below a resonance, the heavy spot and high spot are in phase. This behavior allows the heavy spot to be easily located on the polar plot. However, as we have discussed, in anisotropic systems the low-speed response of X and Y polar plots can be significantly different, making unique identification of the heavy spot direction more difficult.

The XY Bode and polar plots in Figure 13-8 were generated from a rotor model with anisotropic stiffness, where the weak stiffness axis is horizontal and the strong stiffness axis is vertical. The rotor response is the same for all plots; only the probe orientations are different. In the top plots, the probes are misaligned from the stiffness axes; in the bottom plots, they are aligned with the stiffness axes. The SAF is measured two ways for each resonance peak on the Bode plot: the Half-power Bandwidth method and the Peak Ratio method (in parentheses).

The top configuration is a typical stiffness orientation and probe mounting location for horizontal machines with fluid-film bearings. The plots show that the high spot at low speed is not aligned with the actual heavy spot location (the red dot). There is a large difference in the SAF values for the various peaks and for the different methods, and there appear to be three distinct resonance frequencies.

Figure 13-8. Probe orientation versus stiffness axes. All of the plots show the rotor response from the same anisotropic system, where the weak stiffness is oriented in the horizontal direction, and the strong stiffness is vertical. In the top plots, the probes are mounted at 45° L and 45° R and misaligned from the stiffness axes. The Bode plots show that the low-speed high spot is not the same for each probe. The SAF is shown for each resonance peak on the Bode plot in two ways, the Half-power Bandwidth method and the Peak Ratio method (in parentheses). There is a large discrepancy between the SAF values measured for the various peaks and by different methods. The bottom plots show the same machine response, but measured by an XY probe pair aligned with the stiffness axes. The low-speed response phase agrees with the location of the heavy spot.

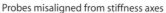
Probes misaligned from stiffness axes

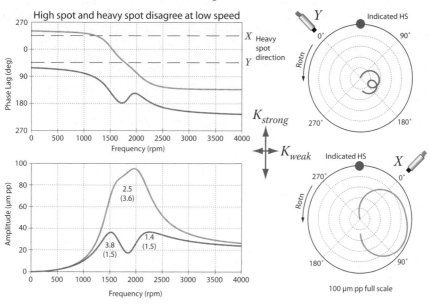

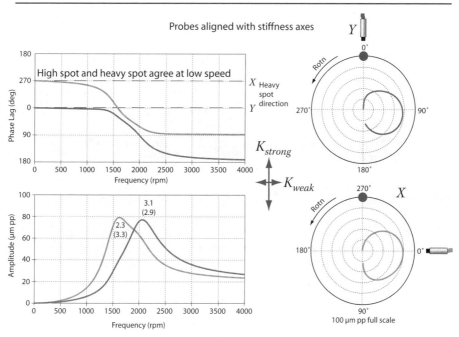

100 μm pp full scale

The bottom plots show the same machine response, but measured by an *XY* probe pair mounted at 0° and 90° R; thus, *the probes are now aligned with the stiffness axes*. The only difference between the upper and the lower plots is the orientation of the probes, yet the two sets of plots are very different. When the probes are aligned with the stiffness axes, the response (high spot) phase at low speed agrees with the location of the heavy spot. The polar loops are more similar to each other, and the small loop has disappeared. The calculated SAFs are still different from each other, but within the range of values obtained when the probes were at ±45°. The different resonance frequencies have condensed into two, closer to what we would expect from the strong/weak anisotropic stiffness model.

The heavy spot/high spot anomaly is related to the ellipticity of the orbit and the mounting orientation of the probes. In 1X circular orbits, both the rotor rotation and the orbital precession of the shaft centerline (high spot) have constant angular velocity; thus, the high spot maintains a constant angular relationship with the heavy spot. However, in elliptical orbits the centerline velocity changes, and the relationship is not constant. At low speed, the velocity variations in elliptical orbits can cause the high spot to go in and out of sync with the heavy spot. They are in sync only at the locations of the major and minor axes. If the probes are located at these points, then the phase of the vibration not only identifies the high spot, but also, at low speed, the heavy spot (Franklin and Bently [1]).

At low speed the orbit major axis will be approximately aligned with the weak stiffness axis. Thus, if the probes are aligned with the stiffness axes (0° and 90° R in this example), they will also be aligned with the orbit major or minor axis at low speed, and the inferred heavy spot location for each probe will be the same and will be correct.

However, if the probes are mounted at some other angle (for example, 45° L and 45° R), then a phase measurement anomaly will exist, which is evident by the fact that the phase measurement for each probe will not locate the high spot in the same location; this would incorrectly indicate that there are two heavy spots

When making phase measurements with a single probe, we tend to make the unconscious assumption that the high/heavy spot relationship is constant, but this is only true of a isotropic system with circular orbits. Imagine the machinery diagnostician who views only the polar plot for the *Y* probe at the top of Figure 13-8. The conclusion might be that this machine's vibration was not high enough to worry about. A very different perspective appears when *both* the *X* and *Y* plots are viewed at the same time, and when the probes are aligned with the stiffness axes!

Thus, we arrive at some important findings for systems with anisotropic stiffness:

1. *At low speed*, the high spot direction will point toward the heavy spot *only if* the measurement probes are aligned with the low-speed orbit axes (which, at low speed, are aligned with the spring stiffness axes).

2. Measured vibration amplitudes will seldom equal the major axis of the orbit, because the orbit, typically, is not aligned with the measurement axes.

3. SAF measurements will be different, depending on the degree of anisotropy of the system and the probe orientation, and results using different calculation methods will differ from each other.

4. When *XY* probe data is available, polar and Bode plots should *always* be viewed in pairs.

Anisotropic stiffness is common in machinery. Because of the way many horizontal machines with fluid-film bearings are constructed, stiffness axes tend to be near vertical (strong) and horizontal (weak). Since probes are often mounted at ±45° to avoid split lines, the amplitude and phase measurement anomalies we have discussed are common.

While it is often not physically possible to mount probes at 0° and 90° R, other factors in the machine (such as process loads or misalignment) may cause the shaft position angle to be different from what we expect, causing the stiffness axes to be oriented at some other angle. Ideally, we would like to adjust our view of the rotor response to any angle we choose and to have another method for accurate determination of the heavy spot location. There are two methods we will discuss: Virtual Probe Rotation, and transformation to Forward and Reverse components.

Virtual Probe Rotation

In an ideal world, we would like to be able to install a set of probes at any arbitrary angle. While we cannot always do that physically (or economically), we *can* take a pair of *XY* probes and rotate them mathematically to any angle we choose. We do this by modifying the original data set as a function of the angle we want to rotate the probes, creating data from a set of *virtual probes*. For each sample speed in a database, the original pair of vibration vectors are transformed to produce a set of vibration vectors equivalent to what would be seen by probes mounted at the new orientation. See Appendix 5 for more details.

The technique can be used to create a set of virtual probes that are aligned with the axes of the low-speed, 1X, elliptical orbit. When this condition is satisfied, the high spot at low speed will be aligned with the heavy spot, and the X and Y plots will agree as to the direction of the heavy spot.

The polar plots in Figure 13-9 show the effect of virtual probe rotation on 1X shutdown data from a small, 10 MW, steam turbine generator set. The data is from the inboard bearing of the steam turbine. This is a horizontal machine with plain, cylindrical fluid-film bearings and with probes mounted at ±45° from vertical. It is likely that the primary radial load on the rotor is gravity.

The original data (top) was taken from the physical, XY, vibration probes. The Y plot (left) has significantly lower vibration amplitude over the entire speed range, and there is a large internal loop. Compare these plots to the those obtained from the anisotropic rotor model in Figure 13-8. The overall pattern is very similar. Also note that, in Figure 13-9, the indicated heavy spot locations (red dots) disagree.

The lower sets of plots show the data after it has been transformed 30° clockwise to a set of virtual probes located at 15° L (Y_R) and 75° R (X_R). This rotation angle was chosen to provide agreement between the indicated heavy spot locations of each rotated probe.

The low-speed, 600 rpm orbit shows that the orbit major axis is oriented slightly more than 15° from the horizontal. At this speed, the orbit is approximately aligned with the weak and strong spring stiffness axes. Given the probable radial load direction (down), the rotation direction (X to Y), and the fluid-film bearing, it is likely that the minor axis of the orbit is oriented close to the position angle (and attitude angle) of the rotor in the bearing. This suggests that the dominant source of anisotropic stiffness is the fluid-film hydrodynamic bearing.

Once the virtual vibration vectors are found, it may be necessary to determine the physical location on the rotor that corresponds to a virtual vibration vector. On polar plots, positive phase lag is always measured relative to the location of the measurement transducer (real or virtual) in a direction opposite to rotation. To *physically* locate a vector on a machine, adjust the virtual phase by the amount of the virtual rotation angle, but in the opposite direction. For example, if you rotate the probes *against* the direction of rotation (which would *reduce* the phase lag at a given physical location), *add* the rotation angle to the virtual phase to obtain the location relative to the physical probe.

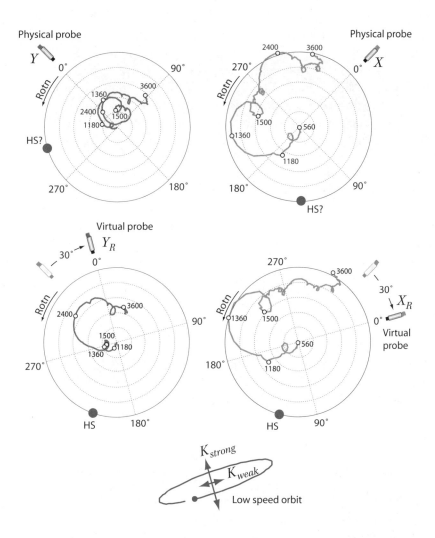

Figure 13-9. Virtual probe rotation. The polar plots show 1X shutdown data from a small, 10 MW, steam turbine generator set. It is a horizontal machine with plain, cylindrical, fluid-film bearings and with probes mounted at ±45° from vertical. The top set of polar plots shows the original data created from the physical, *XY*, vibration probes. The indicated heavy spot locations (red dots) disagree. The bottom set of plots shows the same data after it has been transformed 30° clockwise to a set of virtual probes, $X_R Y_R$, located at 15° L and 75° R. After rotation, there is good agreement as to the indicated location of the heavy spot. The low-speed, 600 rpm orbit is approximately aligned with the weak and strong spring stiffness axes and is aligned with the virtual probe angle.

Figure 13-10 is an example from a gas turbine generator set, showing 1X shutdown data from the outboard bearing on the generator. This machine is also horizontal, with fluid-film bearings, and has probes mounted at ±45° from the vertical. The physical *XY* polar plots (top) display an overall pattern very similar to the steam turbine data in Figure 13-9. The virtual probes (bottom) have been rotated 28° against rotation from the physical probes. The heavy spot locations now show good agreement, and the axes of the low-speed, 1X, elliptical orbit are in line with the polar plot axes, similar to the previous example. The virtual probes are now aligned with the spring stiffness axes, which are controlled by the fluid-film bearing.

When *XY* polar plots agree on the location of the heavy spot, the probes are aligned with the major and minor axes of the low-speed orbit, and the polar plot and orbit axes are aligned with the anisotropic spring stiffness axes of the machine. These two examples, combined with the predicted behavior shown in Figure 13-8, provide strong evidence that the primary source of anisotropic stiffness in a typical machine is the fluid-film bearing.

When balancing is what you need to accomplish, there is a much more efficient method of locating the heavy spot: the forward response vector.

Forward and Reverse Vectors

In Chapter 8 we showed that filtered orbits can be represented as the sum of a forward and reverse rotating vector and that the amplitudes of these vectors appear as frequency lines in a full spectrum plot. The full spectrum is created using a transform of *X* and *Y* data that preserves the phase information. When applied to startup or shutdown data, forward and reverse Bode and polar plots can be created.

Research [1] has shown that *the forward response maintains the correct heavy spot/high spot relationship with the dynamic unbalance force* acting on the rotor. This means that, at low speed, the forward response vector will identify the direction of the heavy spot.

When the system spring stiffness is completely isotropic, the reverse response disappears. This agrees with our understanding of orbit shape and full spectrum. A forward, 1X circular orbit will have a full spectrum consisting of only a single, forward frequency component at the 1X frequency. The shape of the orbit can be described by this rotating vector.

Anisotropic rotor systems produce elliptical orbits and, by extension, forward and reverse vibration vectors that are the components of the elliptical orbits. The magnitude of the reverse component is related to the degree of ellipticity of the orbit.

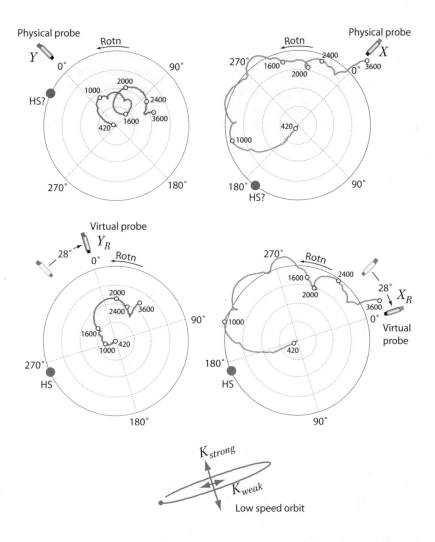

Figure 13-10. Virtual probe rotation of data from a gas turbine generator set. This is also a horizontal, fluid-film bearing machine with probes mounted at ±45° from the vertical. The physical, *XY*, polar plots are shown at top, and the overall pattern is very similar to the steam turbine data in Figure 13-9. At the bottom, virtual probes have been created 28° clockwise from the physical probes. The heavy spot locations now show good agreement, and the low-speed, 1X, elliptical orbit is aligned with the polar plot axes, similar to the previous example. The virtual probes are aligned with the spring stiffness axes, which are controlled by the fluid-film bearing.

In Figure 13-11, the data used to generate the polar plots (top) has been transformed to show the forward and reverse response polar plots (bottom). The bottom plots are labeled with direction of precession, not rotation. The phase markings on each plot are in degrees lag relative to the direction of precession (forward or reverse), using a coordinate system based on the X probe. Because the forward and reverse responses are derived from the data from two probes, they are completely independent of the mounting orientation of the physical probes.

The low-speed part of the forward plot (left) points toward the heavy spot, and this direction agrees with that found using virtual probe rotation in Figure 13-10. For any speed, the sum of the forward and reverse vectors, which contain both amplitude and phase information, will completely reconstruct the original orbit.

Summary

Anisotropic spring stiffness results when the support stiffness seen by the rotor mass is not the same in all radial directions.

It is common in horizontal machines with fluid-film bearings. While bearing support, casing, and foundation asymmetries can contribute to anisotropic stiffness, the primary source appears to be the unequal fluid-film spring stiffness in the radial and tangential directions when the rotor operates off center in the bearing.

Isotropic systems produce circular, 1X-filtered orbits; anisotropic stiffness produces elliptical, 1X orbits. Because of orbit ellipticity, measured 1X vibration amplitude will depend on the angular mounting location of the measurement probe. Also, the high spot, as it moves along the orbit, does not maintain a fixed relationship with the heavy spot; the phase doesn't always accurately locate the heavy spot.

Vector data from an XY probe pair observing an anisotropic system produces pairs of 1X polar and Bode plots that do not look alike. There are differences in measured amplitude, SAF, and phase when the probes are not aligned with the stiffness axes. The polar plots may show small loops that are not due to structural resonances.

Virtual Probe Rotation transforms the 1X vector data from a physical pair of XY probes to what it would look like from a set of virtual probes mounted at any desired angle. If the virtual probes are aligned with the anisotropic stiffness axes of the system, then the low-speed phase data will point toward the heavy spot.

Forward vibration vectors from XY probe data eliminate the phase measurement anomaly produced by elliptical orbits. Therefore, the low-speed part of a forward polar plot will point toward the heavy spot, a benefit when balancing.

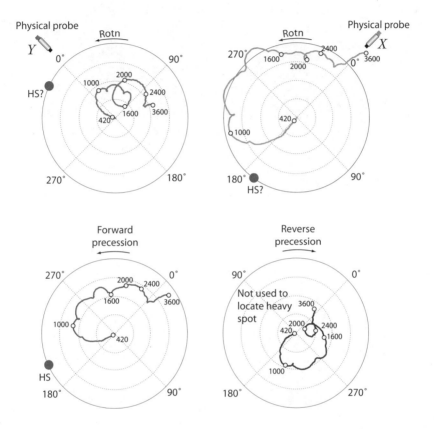

Figure 13-11. Forward and reverse transform polar plots. The polar plots (bottom) show the forward (left) and reverse (right) response of the data in Figure 13-10 in a coordinate system based on the X probe. The plots are labeled with direction of precession, not rotation. The phase markings on the plots are in degrees lag relative to the direction of precession. The low-speed phase of the forward plot points toward the heavy spot, and this direction agrees with that found using virtual probe rotation. The reverse response shows the amplitude and phase of the reverse vector for each speed. For any speed, the sum of the forward and reverse vectors will reconstruct the original orbit, including its orientation. The low-speed phase of the reverse polar plot does not, typically, point in the direction of the heavy spot.

This is a more efficient and accurate method than probe rotation for determining heavy spot location. The forward vectors are related to the isotropic stiffness behavior of the system and are calculated using the same transform used for a full spectrum.

References

1. Franklin, W., and Bently, D. E., "Balancing Nonsymmetrically Supported Rotors Using Complex Variable Filtering," *Proceedings of the Twenty-First Annual Meeting, Vibration Institute*, Willowbrook, Illinois (June 1997): pp. 67-72.

Chapter 14

Rotor Stability Analysis: The Root Locus

Until now, we have primarily discussed various aspects of forced vibration in rotor systems. The model we developed in Chapter 10 was solved to determine the *steady state* behavior of a rotor system. Steady state behavior describes how a rotor system responds to a continuous perturbation over a long period of time.

However, all vibrating systems also exhibit *transient* behavior, which describes how they respond to brief disturbances over relatively short time spans. An example of transient behavior is the motion of a pendulum after being displaced from its rest position. Transient vibration always involves the *free vibration* of a system at one or more natural frequencies. This differs from steady state vibration, which depends on the presence of a continuous forcing function and (for linear systems) takes place at a frequency equal to the frequency of the perturbation; for example, 1X vibration response due to unbalance. At any time, a complete description of the vibration of a system will include the sum of both steady state and transient vibration.

Transient disturbances in rotor systems are usually small, but they can occasionally become significant. Examples of small disturbances are the periodic impulses caused by blade passage across a small gap, the forces due to meshing gear teeth, or disturbances due to turbulent fluid flow. Rub impact is an example of a larger disturbance. All disturbances excite the free vibration of a rotor at one or more natural frequencies.

In stable rotor systems, transient vibration dies out over time as the damping force gradually removes the energy associated with the free vibration of the system. However, an unstable rotor system can respond to a disturbance with a dramatic increase in vibration, causing vibration levels to exceed allowable limits. Thus, the analysis of the stability of rotor systems involves the analysis of transient vibration.

When an instability does appear, it is important to be able to recognize it and to know how to eliminate it. In this chapter we will develop a powerful analytical tool, root locus, that can be used to reveal many general aspects of rotor behavior and help analyze rotor stability problems in particular. This chapter will present some basic analytical tools and concentrate on the data presentation of the root locus plot. See Chapter 22 for a discussion of the underlying physical causes and the diagnostic symptoms of fluid-induced instability.

We will use the simple rotor model we developed in Chapter 10 to explore the transient behavior of rotor systems. Our rotor model has a tangential stiffness term that mimics the effect of rotor interaction with a surrounding, circulating fluid. This fluid circulation can trigger instability in the rotor system. Though our discussion will concentrate on this *fluid-induced instability*, the basic analytical principles can be extended to any other type of instability.

We will start with a discussion of stability of both linear and nonlinear systems, followed by a transient analysis of our linear model. We will obtain results from this model, called roots or eigenvalues, that describe the free vibration of the system versus time, and we will show how these results can be used to determine the speed at which a rotor system goes unstable.

We will show how the free vibration behavior of a rotor system changes with rotor speed and how the information can be displayed in a convenient form on a special plot, called a root locus plot. We will show how to extract a large amount of useful information from this plot.

We will show how the root locus plot is related to (and superior to) the logarithmic decrement, which is commonly used to express the results of stability analysis. We will also compare the root locus plot to the Campbell diagram, which is used to show natural frequency relationships in rotor systems.

Finally, we will show how to use the root locus plot to perform stability analysis of rotating machinery.

What is Stability?

Stability is a broad term that can be interpreted in different ways. A good, general definition of stability is that *a mechanical system is stable if, when it is disturbed from its equilibrium condition, it eventually returns to that equilibrium condition.* A system is *unstable* if, *when it is disturbed, it tends to move away from the original equilibrium condition.*

We can think of a stable system as one that is easy to control and behaves in a predictable manner. A stable system may or may not vibrate; either way it behaves as we expect it to. An unstable system will behave in a way that is unpredictable and very difficult to control, and may even go completely out of control. A simple example of an unstable system is a broomstick balanced vertically on your hand. It is possible to balance it, but it is difficult and requires continuous adjustments of your hand position. If you stop repositioning your hand, the broomstick will go out of control and fall over.

When disturbed, a stable system with relatively high damping will slowly return to the equilibrium position. A stable system that has relatively low damping will oscillate (vibrate) around the equilibrium position for some time, as the vibration energy is slowly dissipated. This vibration will always occur at a natural frequency (or frequencies) of the system. (This is the essence of the term *natural frequency*. The disturbed system, if left alone, vibrates at this frequency.)

A ball at the bottom of a concave vessel filled with a viscous fluid (Figure 14-1, left and center), is an example of a very simple, stable system. The ball, due to the force of gravity, is in static equilibrium at the bottom of the vessel. If it is moved from the bottom and released, the force of gravity will move it back toward the equilibrium position, as shown in the timebase plots. If the fluid has low viscosity (air), the ball will move rapidly back to the equilibrium position, overshoot, climb partway up the other side, and oscillate with decreasing amplitude until it comes to rest at the bottom. If the fluid has high viscosity (thick oil), the ball will move slowly back to the bottom and come to rest, without overshooting.

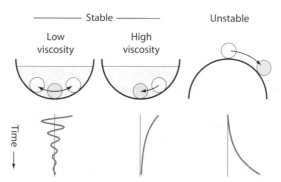

Figure 14-1. Stable and unstable systems. At left, a ball in the bottom of a concave vessel, filled with a viscous fluid, is a stable system. When the ball is moved from the bottom and released, the force of gravity will attempt to move it back to the equilibrium position. If the fluid has low viscosity (air), the ball will move rapidly back to the bottom, overshoot, and oscillate back and forth with decreasing amplitude until it comes to rest at the bottom. If the fluid has high viscosity (thick oil), the ball will move slowly back to the bottom and come to rest without oscillating. At right, the ball at equilibrium at the top of a convex surface is an unstable system. If it is disturbed, the ball will move away from the equilibrium position and never return.

A ball in equilibrium at the top of an convex surface (Figure 14-1, right), is an example of a nonvibrating, unstable system. If it is disturbed, the ball will move away from the equilibrium position and, because of the shape of the surface, will never return.

Many mechanical systems vibrate when disturbed from equilibrium. A stable, linear (in the sense of our linear rotor model) system with low damping, when disturbed from equilibrium, will vibrate with decreasing amplitude. The vibration amplitude of an *unstable*, linear system will increase *forever*. This is impossible in a real, physical system. In real systems, either nonlinear effects come into play that prevent the system vibration from exceeding a certain level, or the system destroys itself. Because of these effects, unstable, nonlinear systems may eventually reach a new, stable, operating condition that is different from the original one.

Rotor systems usually vibrate in a steady state condition (for example, a circular, 1X orbit) about a static equilibrium position. While moving in the orbit, a stable machine is in *dynamic equilibrium*; if it is subjected to some temporary disturbing force, it will eventually return to the original, dynamic equilibrium position.

However, when a rotor system with a surrounding, circulating fluid (for example, in a fluid-film bearing or seal) is at or above a particular speed, any disturbance will trigger a *fluid-induced instability*. This speed is called the *Threshold of Instability*. The machine will temporarily become unstable, and a subsynchronous vibration (at a rotor system natural frequency) will begin and rapidly increase in amplitude. As the vibration amplitude begins to increase, the machine will still behave in a linear way (that is, the spring stiffness is approximately constant). However, as the dynamic rotor position nears the surface of a fluid-film bearing or seal, the spring stiffness will increase dramatically (a nonlinearity), producing a stabilizing restraining force. The rotor will evolve into a new, stable operating condition, characterized by higher amplitude, forward, subsynchronous vibration (Figure 14-2). According to our general definition of stability, the machine is stable in this new orbit.

The unstable orbit in the figure shows a mixture of subsynchronous and 1X vibration; the measurement probe was located near the midspan of the rotor some distance from the source of the instability, a fluid-film bearing. High amplitude vibration is very undesirable and potentially damaging; thus, even though, technically, the new operating condition is stable, the machine may be unstable from a *practical* point of view. Thus, a practical definition of instability is *an undesireable level of subsynchronous vibration*.

Fluid-induced instability is an example of a self-excited vibration, where the energy of the circulating fluid is converted into the energy of vibration. Like all

Figure 14-2. Stability and practical instability in a rotor system. Rotor systems usually operate in dynamic equilibrium about a static equilibrium position (for example, a 1X orbit, left). When disturbed, a stable machine will eventually return to the original, dynamic equilibrium condition. Above the Threshold of Instability, any disturbance will trigger what is called *fluid-induced instability*: the rotor will evolve into a new, stable dynamic equilibrium, dominated by higher amplitude, subsynchronous vibration (right). The orbit shows a mixture of 1X and 0.48X vibration. According to our general definition of stability, the machine is stable in this new orbit, but the higher amplitude vibration may be undesirable and potentially damaging; thus, the machine is unstable from a practical point of view.

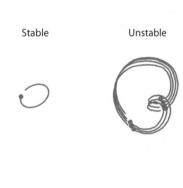

Stable   Unstable

self-excited vibration, the frequency of the instability vibration occurs at a natural frequency of the system, with a mode shape associated with that natural frequency. The amplitude of the measured vibration is affected by three conditions: how much the vibration increases before the system restabilizes, the mode shape of the vibration, and where the measurement probe is in relationship to the source and the mode shape. The highest amplitudes of the subsynchronous instability vibration will be physically located at the antinodes for the mode shape associated with the instability natural frequency. This could be, and often is, some distance away from the *source* of the instability.

Accurate stability analysis of rotor systems requires models based on nonlinear mathematics, but these models are difficult to solve analytically. This is why our rotor model was developed using a linear model. However, rotor behavior below, at, and immediately after crossing the Threshold of Instability is essentially linear in behavior, and we can use the linear model to understand the basic mechanism that leads to instability. We will see that adjustment of the linear model can explain the nonlinear effects that prevent the vibration from growing forever.

Stability and Dynamic Stiffness

Imagine a rotor that has been disturbed from a static equilibrium position. The spring force, $-K\mathbf{r}$, tries to push the rotor back toward the equilibrium position (see Chapter 10). However, the tangential force, $+jD\lambda\Omega\mathbf{r}$, pushes the rotor in a direction 90° from the displacement and prevents the rotor from returning directly to equilibrium. The tangential force is proportional to the rotor speed, Ω, becoming stronger as rotor speed increases, and it acts against the stabilizing damping force; ultimately it can destabilize the rotor system. Because the tangential force is the effect of the fluid circulating around the rotor, we call this form of instability fluid-induced instability.

This destabilizing effect is related to a loss of Dynamic Stiffness in the rotor system. We have shown that rotor vibration is the ratio of the applied force to the Dynamic Stiffness of the system. The Dynamic Stiffness acts to restrain the motion in a way that is similar to a spring (Chapter 11). If the Dynamic Stiffness were to disappear, there would be no constraint to rotor motion, and, when disturbed, the rotor would move away from the equilibrium position forever. This meets the general definition of instability. Thus, we can see that when the Dynamic Stiffness becomes zero, the rotor system becomes unstable.

The nonsynchronous Dynamic Stiffness is

$$\boldsymbol{K}_N = K - M\omega^2 + jD(\omega - \lambda\Omega) \qquad (14\text{-}1)$$

Dynamic Stiffness is a complex quantity, containing both direct and quadrature parts. For the Dynamic Stiffness to equal zero, both the direct and quadrature parts must be zero, *simultaneously*. Thus, the Direct Dynamic Stiffness is zero,

$$K - M\omega^2 = 0 \qquad (14\text{-}2)$$

and the Quadrature Dynamic Stiffness is zero:

$$jD(\omega - \lambda\Omega) = 0 \qquad (14\text{-}3)$$

For this last expression to be true, the term in parentheses must be to equal zero:

$$\omega - \lambda\Omega = 0 \qquad (14\text{-}4)$$

Because Equations 14-2 and 14-4 are equal to zero, they are equal to each other. We can find the rotor speed that satisfies this system of equations. Eliminating ω, and solving for Ω, we find the *Threshold of Instability*, Ω_{th}, to be

Threshold of Instability $\qquad \Omega_{th} = \dfrac{1}{\lambda}\sqrt{\dfrac{K}{M}} \qquad (14\text{-}5)$

This is the rotor speed at or above which the rotor system will be unstable. *This expression is a very powerful diagnostic tool, and it is the key to understanding how to prevent and cure fluid-induced instability problems in rotor systems.*

This expression combines the Fluid Circumferential Average Velocity Ratio, λ, with the undamped natural frequency of the rotor system,

$$\omega_n = \sqrt{\dfrac{K}{M}} \qquad (14\text{-}6)$$

For plain, cylindrical, hydrodynamic bearings (internally pressurized bearings) that become fully lubricated, λ is typically less than 0.5. Thus, the reciprocal of λ in Equation 14-5 is typically greater than 2. This tells us that a typical rotor system must operate at more than twice a natural frequency to trigger fluid-induced instability. For systems with multiple modes, the rotor system will encounter the lowest natural frequency first. Instability is almost always associated with the lowest mode of a rotor system.

To ensure rotor stability, all that is required is to raise Ω_{th} above the highest operating speed of the rotor. This can be done by reducing fluid circulation, which decreases λ, or by increasing the spring stiffness, K. Externally pressurized (hydrostatic) bearings, tilting pad bearings, and other bearings of noncircular geometry accomplish one of both of these objectives. This will be discussed in more detail in Chapter 22.

For now, we will move on to another form of stability analysis that can be extended to more complex rotor systems.

Stability Analysis

Stability analysis requires the development of a mathematical model of the rotor system. The level of required detail in the model depends on the complexity of the machine being considered and the likely instability mechanism. Models can range from simple, lumped mass systems, to more complicated, multiple lumped mass systems, to very complicated, finite element models. Here, for clarity of understanding, we will use the same rotor model that was developed in Chapter 10.

We start with the equation of motion of the rotor model,

$$M\ddot{r} + D\dot{r} + (K - jD\lambda\Omega)r = 0 \qquad (14\text{-}7)$$

where the perturbation force on the right side is zero, because we want to concentrate on the free vibration behavior of the rotor. This form of the equation of motion is called the *homogeneous* equation of the system.

We will assume a solution to this equation that is similar to the one we used in Chapter 10:

$$r = Re^{st} \qquad (14\text{-}8)$$

where R is an arbitrary, constant displacement vector. We know that the position will change in some way with time, t, but, since we don't know how it will change, we will use a general variable, s.

To solve Equation 14-7 we need expressions for the velocity and acceleration:

$$\dot{r} = sRe^{st}$$
$$\ddot{r} = s^2Re^{st} \qquad (14\text{-}9)$$

Substituting these expressions into 14-7, and collecting terms, we obtain

$$\left[Ms^2 + Ds + (K - jD\lambda\Omega)\right]Re^{st} = 0 \qquad (14\text{-}10)$$

For this expression to be true, either the term in square brackets must be zero or the initial displacement, R, must be zero. If R is zero, then the system is resting at equilibrium, which is a valid, but not very interesting case. We want to examine the case where R is not zero, which requires that

$$Ms^2 + Ds + K - jD\lambda\Omega = 0 \qquad (14\text{-}11)$$

This is an important relationship known as the *characteristic equation* of the system. It is a quadratic (second order) polynomial in s. The values of s that satisfy this equation are called the *roots* of the equation. When both λ and Ω are nonzero, solution of this equation will yield two complex roots of the form

$$\begin{aligned} s_1 &= \gamma_1 + j\omega_d \\ s_2 &= \gamma_2 - j\omega_d \end{aligned} \qquad (14\text{-}12)$$

where γ_1 (Greek lower case gamma), γ_2, and ω_d are complicated functions of M, D, K, λ, and Ω (see Appendix 6). γ is called the *growth/decay rate* and has units of 1/s; ω_d is the *damped natural frequency* and has units of rad/s. The meaning of these terms will be discussed shortly.

The roots are also known as the *characteristic values*, *eigenvalues*, and, in control theory, *poles* of the system. If we substitute these two solutions into Equation 14-8, we obtain two expressions:

$$\begin{aligned} r_1 &= (R_1 e^{\gamma_1 t}) e^{j\omega_d t} \\ r_2 &= (R_2 e^{\gamma_2 t}) e^{-j\omega_d t} \end{aligned} \qquad (14\text{-}13)$$

where the complex arguments of the exponential function have been separated into amplitude and frequency components. R_1 and R_2 are constant vectors that depend on the conditions at the beginning of free vibration.

The complete, free vibration response of the rotor is given by the sum of r_1 and r_2,

$$r = r_1 + r_2 \qquad (14\text{-}14)$$

where r_1 and r_2 are a pair of forward and reverse rotating vectors whose frequency of rotation is the damped natural frequency, ω_d. Because the frequency of r_1 is positive, it represents *forward precession*. The frequency of r_2 is negative and represents *reverse precession* at the same frequency.

The amplitudes of r_1 and r_2 are given by the expressions in parentheses. At time t_0, the initial amplitudes, as a result of a disturbance, are R_1 and R_2. Once

Everyday Eigenvalues

Roots, characteristic values, poles, and eigenvalues are different names for the same thing: a set of complex numbers that describe the free vibration behavior of an electrical, mechanical, or electromechanical system. An eigenvalue has two parts, γ and ω_d, where γ controls the rate of decay or growth of free vibration, and ω_d is the frequency of free vibration.

You can directly observe eigenvalues in many places in everyday life. Any mechanical system that vibrates when disturbed reveals one or more of its eigenvalues. Here are several examples.

Example 1. Place a flexible meter stick (yardstick) on a table so that half extends beyond the edge of the table. With one hand, hold the meter stick firmly against the table. With the other hand, push down the free end and release it suddenly. The free end of the meter stick will vibrate, and the vibration amplitude will decrease over time. The vibration frequency is the damped natural frequency, ω_d. The rate at which the vibration decays is related to γ. Here γ is negative because the vibration decays.

Example 2. Pull a simple pendulum to the side and release it suddenly. The displacement is the disturbance to the system. The oscillation frequency of the pendulum is ω_d,

and the rate that the oscillation amplitude decreases is related to γ. In most pendulums, the vibration amplitude will decrease very slowly, indicating a very small, negative value of γ.

Example 3. Push down on the bumper of a car and release it suddenly. The car will move toward the equilibrium position. A car with worn shocks will overshoot the equilibrium position and vibrate for several cycles at ω_d. Shocks in good condition have a large negative γ, and the suspension will move to the equilibrium position without any overshoot or oscillation, an example of critical or supercritical damping. For this last case, the value of ω_d would be zero.

These examples illustrate eigenvalues of nonrotating systems. Rotor systems with fluid interaction have more complicated free vibration behavior; when rotating, instead of vibrating back and forth in a line, they tend to vibrate in spirals or ellipses. The amount of vibration at different axial locations will depend on the particular mode shape (Chapter 12). In spite of this complexity, the basic principles remain the same; when disturbed, the rotor system vibrates according to the rules set by the eigenvalues: free vibration at a damped natural frequency, ω_d, and decay or growth at a rate determined by γ.

disturbed, the rotor begins to precess in an orbit, and the amplitudes change with time as functions of γ_1 and γ_2. If a γ is negative, then the exponential will become smaller with time, and the amplitude of vibration will decrease; the more negative, the faster the decay in amplitude. If a γ is positive, then the exponential function will become larger (grow) with time, and the amplitude of vibration will increase forever. For this reason, we call γ the *growth/decay rate*, because the magnitude and sign control how fast the vibration amplitude increases or decreases over time.

Figure 14-3 shows how the growth/decay rate controls the amplitude over time. Timebase plots show the free vibration behavior of a rotor system as it would be measured by a single transducer. At left, the system is displaced to an initial position, R, and then released. (Here, R appears as a scalar amplitude.) The system begins to vibrate at the damped natural frequency, ω_d, with a period of $2\pi/\omega_d$. Because $\gamma < 0$, the amplitude decays at a rate determined by the exponential function, the amplitude envelope (red). The middle plot shows behavior at the Threshold of Instability, where $\gamma = 0$. For this case, the exponential function is always equal to one, so the amplitude does not change. At right, $\gamma > 0$, and the amplitude grows with time.

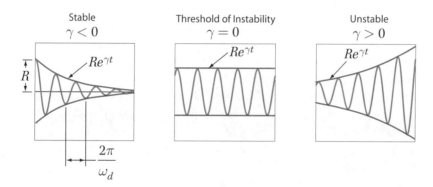

Figure 14-3. How the growth/decay rate controls the amplitude of vibration. Timebase plots show the free vibration behavior of a rotor system measured by a single transducer. At left, the system is displaced to an initial, scalar position, R, and then released. The system begins to vibrate at the damped natural frequency, ω_d, with a period of $2\pi/\omega_d$. Because $\gamma < 0$, the amplitude decays (red envelope) at a rate determined by the exponential function. The middle plot shows behavior at the Threshold of Instability, where $\gamma = 0$. Because the exponential function is always equal to one, the amplitude does not change. At right, $\gamma > 0$, and the amplitude grows with time.

Thus, γ gives us a *mathematical* definition of stability:

1. $\gamma < 0$: the system is *stable*. The vibration associated with a disturbance to the system will die out and the system will return to the original equilibrium position.

2. $\gamma = 0$: the system is operating at the Threshold of Instability. If the system is disturbed, then the vibration will be a steady state vibration that neither increases nor decreases with time.

3. $\gamma > 0$: the system is *unstable*. Once disturbed, if *any* $\gamma > 0$, then the vibration will, theoretically, increase forever.

The two rotating vectors, r_1 and r_2, of Equation 14-14 combine to describe the free vibration behavior of the rotor (Figure 14-4) as a function of γ, starting from some initial displacement (green dot). The set of orbits on the left represent typical behavior for a stable system. Both the forward (top) and reverse (middle) orbit decay in opposite directions in circular spirals, but the reverse decays faster because γ_2 is more negative than γ_1. Because the reverse response dies out more quickly, the total rotor response (bottom) shows an initial elliptical orbit evolving to a circular, forward, decaying spiral.

In the middle, the set of responses are for a system operating at the Threshold of Instability, where $\gamma_1 = 0$. In this case, $\gamma_2 < 0$, and the reverse orbit decays quickly, leaving only the forward orbit. The amplitude of the forward orbit is constant and stays that way forever.

At right, an unstable system is shown, where $\gamma_1 > 0$ and $\gamma_2 < 0$. The reverse response decays quickly, while the forward response grows. Once the reverse response disappears, only the unstable, forward orbit remains. If nothing changed in the system, the orbit amplitude would increase forever. It is interesting to note that it takes time for the orbit to increase in size. The smaller the positive value of γ, the more slowly the orbit grows.

In Appendix 6, we show that if we set $\gamma = 0$ and solve for the rotor speed, Ω, we obtain the same expression for the Threshold of Instability, Ω_{th}, as Equation 14-5. Thus, when $\gamma = 0$ the rotor is operating at the Threshold of Instability; any disturbance will leave the rotor vibrating in a circular orbit.

Each pair of roots will always have the same damped natural frequency, ω_d. However, for nonzero rotative speeds, each pair of roots will have different values of γ, where, typically, $\gamma_1 > \gamma_2$. For *subcritically damped* (*underdamped*) systems, when rotative speed is zero, $\gamma_1 = \gamma_2$, and the roots, s_1 and s_2, are complex conjugates. In this case, r_1 and r_2 will always have equal amplitudes and decay

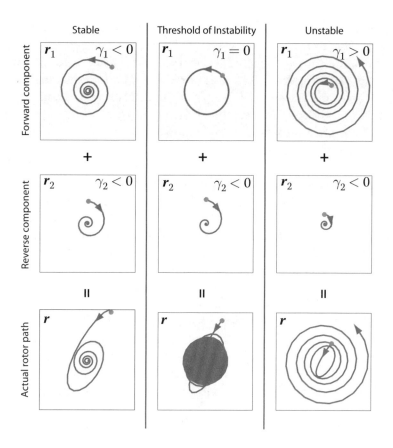

Figure 14-4. Effect of the growth/decay rate, γ, on the free vibration behavior of the rotor. Typical behavior for a stable system is shown in the left column. The forward (top) and reverse (middle) orbits start from an initial displacement (green dot) and decay in a circular spiral, but the reverse orbit decays faster than the forward orbit because γ_2 is more negative than γ_1. The total rotor response (bottom) is an elliptical orbit that evolves to a circular, forward decaying spiral. In the middle column, at the Threshold of Instability, $\gamma_1 = 0$ and $\gamma_2 < 0$. Again, the reverse orbit decays quickly, leaving only the forward orbit. The amplitude of the forward orbit is constant and the orbit continues forever with constant amplitude. In the right column is an unstable system, where $\gamma_1 > 0$ and $\gamma_2 < 0$. The reverse response decays quickly, while the forward response grows. The system proceeds into an unstable, growing, forward spiral orbit. If nothing changed in the system, the orbit amplitude would increase forever.

or grow at the same rate, producing a decaying (or growing) line orbit. Thus, when a subcritically damped rotor system is stopped, the system will theoretically behave like a simple linear oscillator. (Imagine displacing the stopped rotor by hand and releasing it. Without rotation-driven fluid circulation, there is no tangential force, and the spring force will try to return the rotor directly toward the equilibrium position. The result is that the rotor will vibrate like a string, in a line orbit. For machines with hydrodynamic bearings, this is an oversimplification, because at zero speed, there is no hydrodynamic bearing stiffness.)

State-Space Formulation of the Eigenvalue Problem

The characteristic equation we have developed for the simple model is quadratic and solvable using algebraic techniques (although the complex stiffness term creates considerable difficulty). More complicated systems will produce higher-order characteristic equations that must be solved numerically. For example, a 2-DOF model will generate a characteristic equation that is a 4th-order polynomial, which will produce four eigenvalues. In general, the order of the characteristic equation and the number of eigenvalues will be two times the number of degrees of freedom used in the model.

When numerical methods must be used, a *state-space matrix* approach to the problem is faster and easier to formulate. The state-space method starts with the homogeneous equation(s) of motion of the system. To illustrate the formulation method, we will use Equation 14-7 as our starting point:

$$M\ddot{r} + D\dot{r} + (K - jD\lambda\Omega)r = 0 \qquad (14\text{-}7)$$

The first step is to perform a *reduction of order* from a second order differential equation to an equivalent system of first order equations. To do this, we will make a variable substitution using a dummy vector variable, u. Let

$$\begin{aligned} u_1 &= r \\ u_2 &= \dot{r} \end{aligned} \qquad (14\text{-}15)$$

The variable substitution changes our single, second order differential equation into a system of two, first order equations,

$$\begin{aligned} \dot{u}_1 &= u_2 \\ M\dot{u}_2 + Du_2 + (K - jD\lambda\Omega)u_1 &= 0 \end{aligned} \qquad (14\text{-}16)$$

We solve the second equation for $\dot{\boldsymbol{u}}_2$, obtaining

$$\dot{\boldsymbol{u}}_1 = \boldsymbol{u}_2$$
$$\dot{\boldsymbol{u}}_2 = -\frac{D}{M}\boldsymbol{u}_2 - \frac{(K - jD\lambda\Omega)}{M}\boldsymbol{u}_1 \qquad (14\text{-}17)$$

This system can be expressed in matrix form as

$$\begin{pmatrix} \dot{\boldsymbol{u}}_1 \\ \dot{\boldsymbol{u}}_2 \end{pmatrix} = \begin{bmatrix} 0 & 1 \\ \dfrac{-(K - jD\lambda\Omega)}{M} & \dfrac{-D}{M} \end{bmatrix} \begin{pmatrix} \boldsymbol{u}_1 \\ \boldsymbol{u}_2 \end{pmatrix} \qquad (14\text{-}18)$$

where the square matrix is the *state-space matrix*. Once specific numerical values are loaded, modern computation software (such as MATLAB®) can operate directly on the state-space matrix and numerically obtain both eigenvalues and eigenvectors (which are beyond the scope of this discussion). In this case, the the numerical values of the two eigenvalues of Equation 14-12 would be obtained.

This method is easily extended to more complex systems. The homogeneous form of the anisotropic system of Equation 10-45 is

$$M\ddot{x} + D\dot{x} + K_x x + D\lambda\Omega y = 0$$
$$M\ddot{y} + D\dot{y} + K_y y - D\lambda\Omega x = 0 \qquad (14\text{-}19)$$

We reduce the order of this system using a dummy scalar variable, u,

$$u_1 = x$$
$$u_2 = \dot{x}$$
$$u_3 = y \qquad (14\text{-}20)$$
$$u_4 = \dot{y}$$

which leads to the system,

$$\dot{u}_1 = u_2$$
$$M\ddot{u}_2 + Du_2 + K_x u_1 + D\lambda\Omega u_3 = 0$$
$$\dot{u}_3 = u_4 \qquad (14\text{-}21)$$
$$M\ddot{u}_4 + Du_4 + K_y u_3 - D\lambda\Omega u_1 = 0$$

or, in matrix form,

$$
\begin{pmatrix} \dot{u}_1 \\ \dot{u}_2 \\ \dot{u}_3 \\ \dot{u}_4 \end{pmatrix} = \begin{bmatrix} 0 & 1 & 0 & 0 \\ \dfrac{-K_x}{M} & \dfrac{-D}{M} & \dfrac{-D\lambda\Omega}{M} & 0 \\ 0 & 0 & 0 & 1 \\ \dfrac{D\lambda\Omega}{M} & 0 & \dfrac{-K_y}{M} & \dfrac{-D}{M} \end{bmatrix} \begin{pmatrix} u_1 \\ u_2 \\ u_3 \\ u_4 \end{pmatrix}
\tag{14-22}
$$

Again, the square matrix is the state-space matrix, which in this case will produce four, complex eigenvalues.

The 2-CDOF model of Equation 10-53 can be converted to state-space form in the same way. First, we start with the homogeneous form of the equation of motion,

$$
\begin{aligned}
M_1 \ddot{r}_1 + D_1 \dot{r}_1 + (K_1 + K_2)r_1 - K_2 r_2 = 0 \\
M_2 \ddot{r}_2 + D_B \dot{r}_2 + (K_2 + K_B - jD_B\lambda\Omega)r_2 - K_2 r_1 = 0
\end{aligned}
\tag{14-23}
$$

Then we reduce the order, using the set of dummy vectors,

$$
\begin{aligned}
\boldsymbol{u}_1 &= \boldsymbol{r}_1 \\
\boldsymbol{u}_2 &= \dot{\boldsymbol{r}}_1 \\
\boldsymbol{u}_3 &= \boldsymbol{r}_2 \\
\boldsymbol{u}_4 &= \dot{\boldsymbol{r}}_2
\end{aligned}
\tag{14-24}
$$

This leads to the state-space formulation,

$$
\begin{pmatrix} \dot{\boldsymbol{u}}_1 \\ \dot{\boldsymbol{u}}_2 \\ \dot{\boldsymbol{u}}_3 \\ \dot{\boldsymbol{u}}_4 \end{pmatrix} = \begin{bmatrix} 0 & 1 & 0 & 0 \\ \dfrac{-(K_1 + K_2)}{M_1} & \dfrac{-D_1}{M_1} & \dfrac{K_2}{M_1} & 0 \\ 0 & 0 & 0 & 1 \\ \dfrac{K_2}{M_2} & 0 & \dfrac{-(K_2 + K_B - jD_B\lambda\Omega)}{M_2} & \dfrac{-D_B}{M_2} \end{bmatrix} \begin{pmatrix} \boldsymbol{u}_1 \\ \boldsymbol{u}_2 \\ \boldsymbol{u}_3 \\ \boldsymbol{u}_4 \end{pmatrix}
\tag{14-25}
$$

This matrix will also produce a set of four, complex eigenvalues.

The Root Locus Plot

Simple spring/mass systems have roots, or eigenvalues, that do not change with speed. However, in rotor systems, the two components of the eigenvalues, γ and ω_d, are both functions of the rotor speed, Ω. This means that the vibration behavior of the rotor system changes with speed; the rotor system is a complicated oscillator with speed-dependent properties. Because of this complexity, we need a way to present the roots in a way that is clear and concise.

The best way is the root locus plot. This plot was originally developed by Walter Evans [1] for use in automatic control stability analysis, where the roots are also called the *poles* of the system. (The terms roots, characteristic values, eigenvalues, and poles are different names for the same thing.) Several excellent modern texts [2,3,4] discuss the root locus from a control theory perspective, but this approach is oriented primarily to the needs of control system designers. We wish to examine stability and the control of stability problems from a rotor dynamics point of view, such as was pioneered by Lund [5].

The root locus plot is an *XY* plot; the coordinates of the plot represent the components, γ and ω_d, of the roots, s, of the characteristic equation. Because of this, the *XY* plane is typically called the *s-plane*. In the root locus plot (Figure 14-5), the horizontal axis is the growth/decay rate, γ (1/s), and the vertical axis is the damped natural frequency, ω_d (rad/s), with forward precession ($+\omega_d$) above and reverse precession ($-\omega_d$) below. The roots (yellow dots) correspond to r_1 at coordinates γ_1 and ω_d, and r_2 at coordinates γ_2 and $-\omega_d$.

The root locus plot is divided into two half planes. Response in the left half plane (yellow), where $\gamma < 0$, corresponds to stable behavior; disturbances produce vibration that decays over time. The farther to the left the root is in the left half plane (γ more negative), the faster free vibration will decay.

Response in the right half plane (red), where $\gamma > 0$, corresponds to unstable behavior; disturbances cause vibration that increases over time. *No real machine can operate for more than a short time in the right half plane.* Either the machine will self-destruct or a nonlinear effect will act to stabilize the system, return the root to the stable half plane, and limit vibration. The right half plane is a forbidden region of operation.

Moving farther away from the horizontal axis will increase the natural frequency, ω_d, of the free vibration. Positive values correspond to forward precession; negative values correspond to reverse precession. A point on the horizontal axis has zero frequency of vibration and corresponds to a case of either critical or supercritical damping (see Appendix 6).

The forward and reverse precession frequencies have the same meaning as the forward and reverse precession frequencies associated with the full spectrum (Chapter 8). The full spectrum displays the actual frequencies (within the

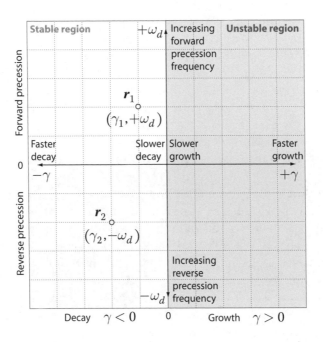

Figure 14-5. The root locus plot. The horizontal axis is γ (1/s), with stable operation to the left of center and unstable to the right. The vertical axis is the damped natural frequency, ω_d (rad/s), with forward precession above and reverse precession below. The root (eigenvalue) corresponding to r_1 is plotted at coordinates γ_1 and ω_d, and r_2 at coordinates γ_2 and $-\omega_d$. In the left half plane (yellow), disturbances produce vibration that decays. In the right half plane (red), disturbances cause vibration that grows. *No real machine can operate for more than a short time in the right half plane.* Moving farther away from the horizontal axis will increase the magnitude of the free vibration natural frequency, ω_d. Positive values correspond to forward precession; negative values to reverse precession. A point on the horizontal axis has zero frequency of vibration and corresponds to a case of either critical or supercritical damping.

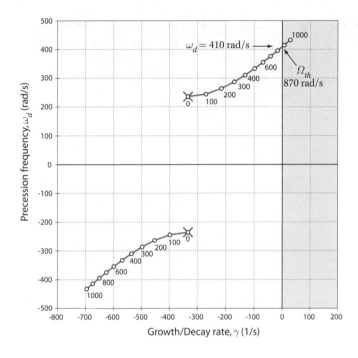

Figure 14-6. Root locus plot of the simple rotor model. The rotor speed is varied from 0 rad/s to 1000 rad/s. At zero rotor speed (the points marked with an "X") the two roots are complex conjugates (the system is subcritically damped), where $\gamma_1 = \gamma_2 = -325$ /s, and they plot directly above and below each other. As speed increases, the roots move in opposite directions, and both γ and ω_d change with rotor speed. The root with forward precession moves toward the unstable half plane, while the reverse precession root moves away. Eventually, at about 870 rad/s (8300 rpm), the rotor speed reaches the Threshold of Instability, when the forward root reaches the vertical axis of the plot. Above this speed, the root moves to the right half plane, where γ_1 is positive, and the system is unstable. At the Threshold of Instability, the frequency of vibration is at the natural frequency of the rotor system, $\omega_d = 410$ rad/s, 0.47X.

instrumentation bandwidth) that comprise the rotor *steady state* vibration behavior. Each pair of full spectrum frequency lines represents a description of the steady state orbit shape that corresponds to that frequency.

In contrast, the root locus plot displays the theoretical forward and reverse natural frequencies, $\pm\omega_d$, that, together with the associated growth/decay rates, γ_1 and γ_2, describe the predicted *transient* behavior of the system. Each pair of roots represents a description of the transient orbit that corresponds to that natural frequency. The transient orbit is the sum of the forward and reverse rotating vectors at that frequency. The shape and decay time of the free vibration orbit is determined by the relative magnitude of the two values of γ associated with the roots.

In control system applications, a mathematical model of the electromechanical system is created. A set of roots is calculated for the existing system parameters. Then, the gain of a feedback control component is changed slightly, and a new set of roots is calculated. This process is repeated until all the desired sets of roots are created and plotted on the *s*-plane, creating a *locus of roots*: the root locus plot. One objective is to determine how much feedback control the system can tolerate without going unstable.

In a typical rotor stability analysis, a rotor model is generated, and the roots are calculated for a group of rotor parameters (M, D, K, λ, Ω). Because the behavior and stability of a rotor system are related to speed, the most interesting parameter to change, at least at the beginning, is the rotor speed, Ω. Later in the analysis, a parameter such as the spring stiffness, K, or the Fluid Circumferential Average Velocity Ratio, λ, may be changed.

Fluid interaction in our rotor model causes both the growth/decay factors, γ_1 and γ_2, and the damped natural frequency, ω_d, to change with rotor speed. For systems with significant fluid interaction or gyroscopic effects, *changes in rotor speed modify the mechanical behavior of the rotor system*. At any particular speed, the system will have a free vibration behavior determined by the eigenvalues, which will be different than at another rotor speed. Because of this, a natural frequency responsible for a balance resonance at a lower speed may shift to a significantly different frequency at running speed.

In rotor systems with *no* fluid interaction ($\lambda = 0$), such as machines with rolling element bearings, no working fluid, no gas or liquid seals, and no gyroscopic effects, the speed-related changes in eigenvalues may be very small or even zero. An electric motor with rolling element bearings is unlikely to have eigenvalues that change with rotor speed.

In the root locus plot of our simple rotor model (Figure 14-6), the rotor speed has been varied from 0 rad/s to 1000 rad/s. (We could use rpm, but rad/s makes comparison with the natural frequency axis easier, and it is a natural input to the model.)

Our rotor model has one complex degree-of-freedom (1-CDOF), so it produces one pair of roots. For the set of parameters used in the figure, the model is subcritically damped. Thus, at zero speed, the two roots are complex conjugates, where $\gamma_1 = \gamma_2 = -325$ /s, and they plot directly above and below each other. With this value of γ, the amplitude of free vibration will decline, in one millisecond, to

$$e^{\gamma t} = e^{[(-325 \ /\text{s})(10^{-3}\text{s})]} = 0.72$$

or 72% of the amplitude at time $t = 0$.

As speed increases, the roots move in opposite directions. The root with forward precession (upper root) moves to the right toward the unstable half plane, while the reverse precession root moves to the left.

Eventually, at about 870 rad/s (8300 rpm), the rotor speed reaches the Threshold of Instability, and the forward root reaches the vertical axis of the plot, where $\gamma_1 = 0$. Above this speed, the root moves to the right half plane, where γ_1 is positive and the system is unstable.

At the Threshold of Instability, the natural frequency of the rotor system, ω_d, is 410 rad/s, considerably less than running speed. From Equation 14-4, $\omega = \omega_d = \lambda \Omega$. In the figure, $\Omega = \Omega_{th} = 870$ rad/s and $\omega_d = 410$ rad/s, yielding $\lambda = 0.47$. (In fact, this was the value of λ used in the model.) Thus, at the Threshold of Instability, the frequency of vibration is subsynchronous at 0.47X.

At rotor speeds higher than Ω_{th}, the root locus moves into the unstable region of the plot. This is purely an artifact of the linear model and cannot reflect actual machine behavior in practice.

In reality, nonlinear effects come into play at this point (Figure 14-7). As rotor speed increases past the Threshold of Instability, the root crosses into the right half plane. The system is now unstable, but because the root is still close to the vertical axis, γ_1 is a small positive number, and the vibration increases relatively slowly. The orbit diameter increases, and, if the source of instability is a fluid-film bearing, the increasing rotor dynamic eccentricity ratio causes an increase in the bearing spring stiffness, which is part of the overall system spring stiffness, K. If the source of instability is an internal seal, then the vibration amplitude might increase until a rub takes place, which will also increase the K of the system. Either way, the spring stiffness of the system will increase; Equation 14-5 predicts that an increase in K will produce an increase in Ω_{th}.

At this point, an amazing thing happens. If the increase in K raises Ω_{th} above running speed, then the system eigenvalue will shift to the left half plane (with a corresponding higher value of ω_d), and the vibration amplitude of the now sta-

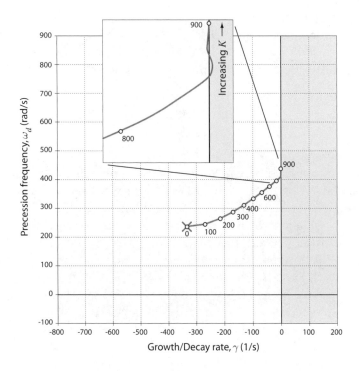

Figure 14-7. Nonlinear effects at the Threshold of Instability for a plain, cylindrical fluid-film bearing. As rotor speed passes the Threshold of Instability, the root crosses into the right half plane. Because the root is still close to the vertical axis, γ_1 is a small positive number, and the vibration increases relatively slowly. The orbit diameter increases and the increasing rotor dynamic eccentricity ratio causes an increase in the bearing spring stiffness, part of the overall system spring stiffness, K. If the increase in K raises Ω_{th} above running speed, then the system eigenvalue will shift to the left half plane, and the vibration amplitude will begin to decrease, producing a smaller eccentricity ratio, decreasing K and lowering Ω_{th}. If Ω_{th} falls below operating speed, then the eigenvalue shifts to the right half plane again, and vibration starts to increase. The system eventually self-stabilizes through changes in K in a condition of higher-amplitude subsynchronous vibration.

ble system will decrease. This produces a smaller eccentricity ratio, decreasing K, and lowering Ω_{th}. If Ω_{th} falls below operating speed, then the eigenvalue shifts to the right half plane again, and vibration increases. The result of all this activity is that the system self-stabilizes through changes in K in a condition of large amplitude, subsynchronous vibration. The eigenvalue will be located on the vertical axis, and the system will be operating in fluid-induced instability *whirl* or *whip*.

Further increases in rotor speed will push the eigenvalue into the right half plane again, and this nonlinear stabilizing process will repeat, resulting in a larger diameter orbit than before.

The Root Locus and Amplification Factors

Even though the eigenvalues, or roots, tell us much about the free vibration behavior of the system, they also have something to say about the forced response of the system. Whenever the frequency of a perturbation is equal to a natural frequency of a system, then a resonance will occur. The root locus can provide us with information about the nonsynchronous and synchronous amplification factors at resonance. To understand this, we will first examine the behavior of a simple, spring/mass system (a simple harmonic oscillator). In our rotor model, when $\Omega = 0$, the rotor system behaves like a simple oscillator, so this provides a good starting point.

For a simple oscillator, the damped natural frequency, ω_d, for a subcritically damped system is lower than the undamped natural frequency, ω_n, because the presence of the damping force acts to slow down the velocity of the system slightly. The damped natural frequency is

$$\omega_d = \omega_n \sqrt{1 - \zeta^2} \qquad (14\text{-}26)$$

where

$$\omega_n = \sqrt{\frac{K}{M}} \qquad (14\text{-}27)$$

and ζ (Greek lower case zeta) is the *damping factor*, given by

$$\zeta = \frac{D}{2\sqrt{KM}} \qquad (14\text{-}28)$$

The damping factor (derived in Appendix 6) is a nondimensional number that defines the decay behavior of an vibrating mechanical system. If $\zeta < 1$, the system is *underdamped (subcritically damped)*, and a freely vibrating system will vibrate with decreasing amplitude. The larger (closer to 1) the damping factor, the faster the vibration will die away. As the damping factor approaches zero, ω_d becomes ω_n (Equation 14-26).

When $\zeta = 1$, the system is *critically damped,* and the system will not vibrate but will return to the equilibrium position in the shortest possible time without overshooting.

Systems with $\zeta > 1$ are called *overdamped (supercritically damped)* and will return relatively slowly to the equilibrium position without any overshoot or oscillation.

Also, because there is no fluid interaction in a simple oscillator, the two growth/decay rates are always equal. They are related to the damping factor:

$$\gamma_1 = \gamma_2 = -\zeta\omega_n \qquad (14\text{-}29)$$

Equations 14-26 and 14-29 describe the components of the eigenvalues of a simple oscillator. The positive eigenvalue and its coordinates are shown in Figure 14-8. Trigonometry shows that the distance from the origin to the eigenvalue is ω_n. Then,

$$\sin\theta = \frac{\zeta\omega_n}{\omega_n} = \zeta \qquad (14\text{-}30)$$

Thus, for the simple oscillator, *radial lines from the origin of the root locus plot describe lines of constant damping factor.*

For the simple oscillator, it can be shown that the amplification factor at resonance, which we will call Q, is related to both the damping factor and the angle on the root locus plot:

$$Q \approx \frac{1}{2\zeta} = \frac{1}{2\sin\theta} \qquad (14\text{-}31)$$

Thus the angle, θ, on the root locus plot defines both the damping factor and the amplification factor, Q. For example, if $\gamma = -100$ /s, and $\omega_d = 800$ rad/s, then

$$\theta = \arctan\left(\frac{-\gamma}{\omega_d}\right) = \arctan\left(\frac{100\ /\mathrm{s}}{800\ \mathrm{rad/s}}\right) = 7.1^{\circ}$$

$$\zeta = \sin\theta = \sin(7.1^{\circ}) = 0.12$$

$$Q \approx \frac{1}{2\zeta} = \frac{1}{2(0.12)} = 4$$

As we have said, when either $\lambda = 0$ or $\Omega = 0$, the rotor system model behaves exactly like a simple oscillator. (Here we ignore the problem of fluid-film bearing stiffness at zero speed, but this is certainly applicable to rolling element bearing machines.) However, when both λ and Ω are nonzero, the relationship involving the damping factor and natural frequency is much more complicated and involves both fluid circulation effects and the rotor speed (see Appendix 6).

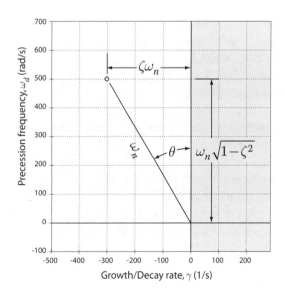

Figure 14-8. Coordinates of the positive eigenvalue in terms of the damping factor, ζ, and the undamped natural frequency, ω_n. The radial line from the origin represents a line of constant damping factor. See the text for details.

While the roots of a simple oscillator do not change with forcing frequency, rotor system eigenvalues are a function of rotor speed and move in the root locus plot. When they move, both components of the eigenvalues, γ and ω_d, change, changing the angle θ. Even if M, D, K, and λ *are not changed* (meaning that ζ, as defined by Equation 14-28, is not changed), a change in rotor speed produces a change in θ. We can see that the *effective* damping factor of the rotor system has changed. The fluid circulation around the rotor, $\lambda\Omega$, is solely responsible for the change in root position.

Equation 14-30 provides a good estimation of the effective damping factor of the rotor system, and we can use Equation 14-31 to estimate the steady state amplification factor, Q, of the rotor system when the rotor system is subjected to a periodic force. When the rotor system is operating at a constant speed, the eigenvalues will plot at a particular position on the root locus plot. The Q in Equation 14-31 represents the response of the rotor to a *nonsynchronous* perturbation while the rotor operates at a constant speed.

As a rotor system root approaches the vertical axis and the Threshold of Instability, the angle of the root, θ, approaches zero, and the amplification factor, Q, of the system increases. At the Threshold of Instability, the Quadrature Dynamic Stiffness is zero, the effective damping factor of the system is zero, and Q is infinite.

Figure 14-9 shows three positive eigenvalues and their associated amplification factors for nonsynchronous perturbation. Lines of constant Q are drawn for $Q = 2.5$, 5, and 10. API 684 [6] defines a *critical* as any balance resonance with a $Q > 2.5$, so the left line on the plot marks a boundary that satisfies this criterion. Any eigenvalue left of this boundary would not be considered to be a critical by the API's definition. API also defines any resonance with a $Q < 5$ as a low amplification factor and any resonance with a $Q > 10$ as a high amplification factor. The Bode plots show the nonsynchronous response to a rotating unbalance for each case.

Synchronous amplification factors are important during startup and shutdown. Nonsynchronous amplification factors are important because disturbances other than unbalance are capable of exciting rotor system natural frequencies. If the amplification factor of a particular natural frequency is high (θ on the root locus plot is small) then that frequency may show up as a significant vibration component of overall rotor response.

An example is aerodynamic noise in compressors. This kind of noise is often broad band, similar to white noise, and it will excite any natural frequency in the noise band. If the amplification factor of a natural frequency is high, then the noise will be amplified at that frequency, producing a noticeable line in a spectrum plot.

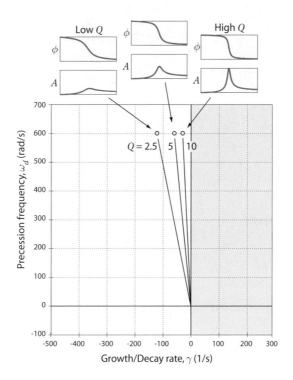

Figure 14-9. Forced response for three positive eigenvalues. The amplification factors for *nonsynchronous* perturbation are shown with lines of constant Q for $Q = 2.5, 5$, and 10. Bode plots show the amplitude (A) and phase (ϕ) of the response to a nonsynchronous rotating unbalance for each case. As the eigenvalue nears the vertical axis, the amplification factor rises sharply.

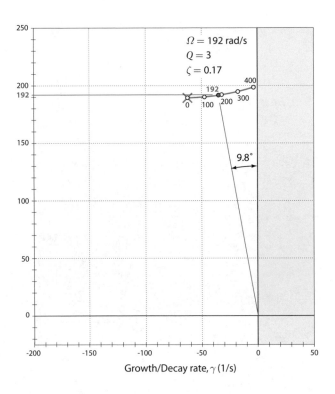

Figure 14-10. Estimated synchronous amplification factor, Q, at the balance resonance. When rotor speed is equal to a rotor system natural frequency, then a resonance is likely to occur. When $\Omega = \omega_d$, then the system must be close to the resonance peak, and the approximate Synchronous Amplification Factor is given by Equation 14-31. In this example, at the resonance speed of about 192 rad/s (1830 rpm), θ is 9.8°, the damping factor, ζ, is 0.17, and the estimated Q of the synchronous resonance is 3.

So far we have been discussing nonsynchronous behavior at a particular natural frequency unrelated to running speed. However, the root locus plot can be used to identify a synchronous balance resonance speed and estimate the Synchronous Amplification Factor.

A root locus plot can be generated by varying rotor speed. When rotor speed is equal to a rotor system natural frequency, then a resonance is likely to occur. Figure 14-10 displays the positive root of the rotor model. When $\Omega = \omega_d$, then the system must be close to the resonance peak, and the approximate Synchronous Amplification Factor is given by Equation 14-31. In this example, at the resonance speed of about 192 rad/s (1830 rpm), θ is 9.8°, the damping factor, ζ, is 0.17, and the estimated synchronous Q is 3.

Parameter Variation and the Root Locus

The root locus plot of Figure 14-6 was created by calculating pairs of roots for a series of rotor speeds. It is also possible to create a family of root locus plots which demonstrate how the basic plot of Figure 14-6 changes when a parameter is varied.

The plot family (Figure 14-11) was generated by selecting values for the rotor parameters (shown below the figure), calculating the roots for a range of speeds, then changing the value of K and repeating the process.

The plot has several interesting features. For $K = 31\ 250$ N/m, the combination of stiffness, mass, and damping results in an overdamped (supercritically damped) system. This produced the pair of root loci (orange) with their zero speed points on the horizontal axis of the plot and separated horizontally. This is typical for a supercritically damped system. At zero rotor speed, the system has a damped natural frequency of zero; thus, the system will not oscillate. However, once the rotor speed becomes nonzero, the roots leave the horizontal axis, and the natural frequency has a nonzero value.

For $K = 62\ 500$ N/m, the system is critically damped. Both root loci (blue) start at the same zero speed point on the horizontal axis and move away from each other on a straight line.

For the remaining two values of K, the system is underdamped. The zero speed points are located vertically above and below the critically damped zero speed point. For these cases, higher stiffness results in a higher natural frequency, as expected.

The red arrow shows that, at an operating speed of 400 rad/s, the system moves from the unstable region up and to the left into the stable region as the stiffness increases.

Figure 14-12 shows a similar set of root loci that was created by holding K constant and varying the damping, D, from 354 N · s/m to 1060 N · s/m. M and λ are the same as for the previous figure, and K is held at 125 000 N/m (714 lb/in). The zero speed points for the root loci have the same characteristics as in the previous example.

Note that the positive roots pivot around the same Threshold of Instability speed because, for the simple model, this speed does not depend on damping. This speed is the same as shown in Equation 14-5. Also, the pivot point occurs at the same precession frequency given by Equation 14-6.

Note that for the underdamped cases (green and violet) the natural frequency decreases as the damping increases. Increasing damping tends to slow down the system and lower the natural frequency.

Figure 14-11. A family of root locus plots produced from the 1-CDOF rotor model by varying spring stiffness. This plot was generated by selecting a value for the spring stiffness, K, calculating the root loci for a range of speeds, then changing the value of K and repeating the process. In this figure, four values of K were selected (displayed at upper right), and, for each value of K, the rotor speed was varied from 0 rad/s to 1000 rad/s. The rotor parameters are shown below the plot. See the text for details.

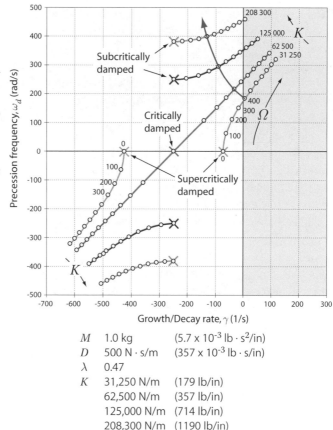

M	1.0 kg	(5.7×10^{-3} lb · s²/in)
D	500 N · s/m	(357×10^{-3} lb · s/in)
λ	0.47	
K	31,250 N/m	(179 lb/in)
	62,500 N/m	(357 lb/in)
	125,000 N/m	(714 lb/in)
	208,300 N/m	(1190 lb/in)

Figure 14-12. A family of root locus plots produced by varying the system damping. M and λ are the same as used in Figure 14-11, with $K = 125\,000$ N/m (714 lb/in), and four values of damping, D :

354 N · s/m   (2.02 lb · s/in)
495 N · s/m   (2.83 lb · s/in)
707 N · s/m   (4.04 lb · s/in)
1060 N · s/m (6.06 lb · s/in)

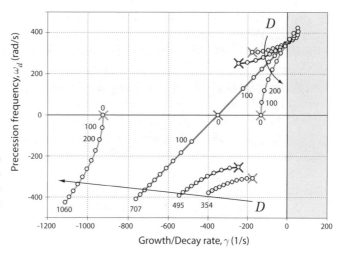

The Root Locus of Anisotropic and Multimode Systems

A mechanical system will have one pair of eigenvalues for each degree of freedom in the system. Our rotor model is isotropic, has only one mass, and was modeled as a 1-CDOF system that produces one pair of roots.

More complicated rotor models will produce more information in the root locus plot. These can range from multi-degree-of-freedom models that can handle many modes, to finite element models with very large numbers of degrees-of-freedom, which can produce a bewildering array of eigenvalues.

Because rotor systems are most likely to go unstable in the lowest mode of vibration, a large set of eigenvalues which describe large numbers of modes is not really necessary for stability analysis. However, a set of damped natural frequencies for the first several modes can be useful for detecting situations where a natural frequency may exist at some integer multiple of running speed. Excitation of such higher frequencies is possible if a machine has nonlinearities or vane and blade pass frequencies that coincide with these frequencies at running speed. The Campbell diagram was developed for analyzing this situation and will be discussed later.

In this section we will present an example of a root locus plot for a multiple mode system and for a system with anisotropic stiffness. Figure 14-13 shows root loci of a typical 2-CDOF (2 axial planes) rotor model that was generated using the state-space matrix of Equation 14-25. All roots were created by changing the rotor speed from 0 rad/s to 1000 rad/s. The first mode (blue) starts on the horizontal axis with damped natural frequency, ω_d, of zero. The zero speed root pairs are separated horizontally rather than vertically because the first mode is supercritically damped. If the system was critically damped, the zero speed root pairs would start at the same point on the horizontal axis. (As the damping factor increases above one, the zero speed roots separate farther on the horizontal axis.) Inspection of the root locus plot will show that, for the supercritically damped first mode, the rotor speed can *never* equal the damped natural frequency; thus, *no synchronous resonance is possible*. This mode is equivalent to a rigid body mode with high modal damping. The forward branch crosses into instability at a rotor speed a little over 300 rad/s. This linear model predicts that the forward branch will cross back into the stable half plane at a much higher speed. This does not reflect actual rotor behavior because, once unstable, system nonlinearities will come into play and change the system behavior.

The second mode (green) zero speed points form a conjugate pair; this mode is subcritically damped. There is a synchronous resonance near 240 rad/s, where the rotor speed equals the damped natural frequency. This is best seen on the forward branch. Both branches of the second mode move toward the unstable half plane, but the reverse branch will not cross the threshold. The forward

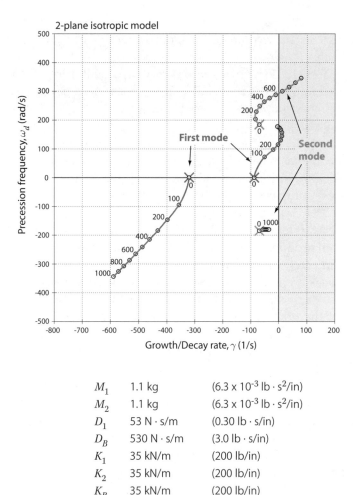

Figure 14-13. Typical root loci of a two-plane, isotropic, 2-CDOF rotor model using the state-space matrix of Equation 14-25 and the parameters above. Rotor speed is varied from 0 rad/s to 1000 rad/s. The first mode (blue) starts on the horizontal axis with a damped natural frequency of zero. The zero speed root pairs are separated horizontally, indicating that the first mode is supercritically damped. Because of this, the rotor speed will never equal the damped natural frequency, and no synchronous resonance for this mode is possible. The first mode forward branch crosses into instability at a rotor speed a little over 300 rad/s. The second mode (green) is subcritically damped with a synchronous resonance near 240 rad/s, best seen on the forward branch. The forward branch crosses into instability at a rotor speed of about 650 rad/s. However, the rotor system would go unstable in the first mode at 300 rad/s, so the second mode instability would not be seen.

branch crosses at a rotor speed of about 650 rad/s. However, the rotor system would go unstable in the first mode at 300 rad/s, so the second mode instability would not be seen.

The eigenvalue behavior versus speed is very easy to interpret when complex numbers are used in the rotor model. Forward precession roots move differently than reverse precession roots, and they are easily identified. That is not true for our next example.

Figure 14-14 shows the roots of an anisotropic, single plane rotor system. This two-real-degree-of-freedom model treats the rotor system as a single plane mass (isotropic), but with anisotropic horizontal (weak) and vertical (strong) spring stiffnesses. Compare this plot to Figure 14-6, which shows both roots of an isotropic, 1-CDOF system.

There are several important differences in the appearance of this plot. Each degree of freedom produces a pair of roots above and below the horizontal axis.

Concentrating on the forward set of roots, we can see that at zero speed, the natural frequencies are well separated. As speed increases, the two roots move vertically toward each other. The first of the synchronous split resonances is encountered on the green branch at approximately 160 rad/s; *this branch is associated with the weak, horizontal direction.* The second split is encountered on the blue branch near 220 rad/s; *this branch is associated with the strong, vertical direction.* At a rotor speed of about 260 rad/s, the two branches meet at an ω_d of about 190 rad/s. Then, the horizontal branch moves in the direction of instability, and the vertical branch moves toward higher stability.

The reverse set of roots are mirror images of the forward roots. The stability crossing of the reverse horizontal root occurs at exactly the same speed as for the forward root, a little over 500 rad/s. It appears that the weak, horizontal stiffness is responsible for triggering the fluid-induced instability.

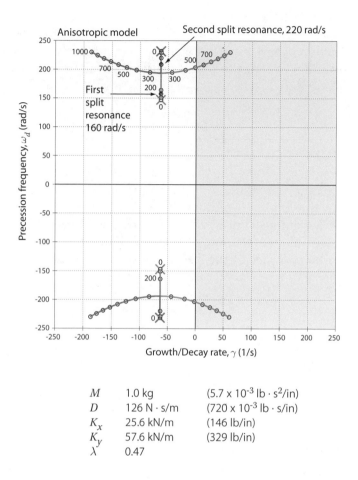

M	1.0 kg	(5.7×10^{-3} lb · s²/in)
D	126 N · s/m	(720×10^{-3} lb · s/in)
K_x	25.6 kN/m	(146 lb/in)
K_y	57.6 kN/m	(329 lb/in)
λ	0.47	

Figure 14-14. Roots of a single plane rotor system with anisotropic spring stiffness using the state-space matrix of Equation 14-22 and the parameters above. The rotor speed is varied from 0 rad/s to 1000 rad/s. (Compare this to Figure 14-6, which shows both roots of an isotropic system with different parameters.) Each pair of roots is symmetric above and below the horizontal axis. At zero speed, the natural frequencies on related branches are well separated. As speed increases, the two roots approach each other. The first of the synchronous, split resonances is encountered on the green branch at approximately 160 rad/s; the higher split is encountered on the blue branch near 220 rad/s. The two branches meet at a rotor speed of about 260 rad/s, where ω_d is about 190 rad/s. Then, as the green branch moves in the direction of instability, the blue branch moves toward higher stability. The stability crossing of the reverse root occurs at exactly the same speed as for the forward root, a little over 500 rad/s.

The Root Locus and the Logarithmic Decrement

The logarithmic decrement (log dec, δ) is a stability indicator that is based on the free vibration behavior of a system. In its simplest form, it is defined as the natural logarithm of the ratio of the transient vibration amplitude of two, successive peaks (Figure 14-15):

$$\delta = \ln\left(\frac{A_n}{A_{n+1}}\right) \qquad (14\text{-}32)$$

where ln is the natural logarithm, A_n is the amplitude at time t_n, and A_{n+1} is the amplitude at the time one cycle of vibration later, t_{n+1}.

Because the log dec is defined by the decay rate per cycle of vibration, it is related to the eigenvalues of the system. The free vibration amplitude is a function of time and is controlled by the real part of the eigenvalue, γ:

$$A_n = A_0 e^{\gamma t_n} \qquad (14\text{-}33)$$

where A_0 is the amplitude at time $t = 0$, and t_n is the time at which the vibration amplitude is A_n. One cycle of vibration later, the amplitude is

$$A_{n+1} = A_0 e^{\gamma t_{n+1}} \qquad (14\text{-}34)$$

Taking the natural logarithm of both expressions, subtracting the equations, and collecting terms, we obtain

$$\delta = \ln\left(\frac{A_n}{A_{n+1}}\right) = -\gamma\left(t_{n+1} - t_n\right) \qquad (14\text{-}35)$$

On the right side, the difference in time is the period, T, of one cycle of vibration,

$$t_{n+1} - t_n = T = \frac{2\pi}{\omega_d} \qquad (14\text{-}36)$$

Substituting this expression into Equation 14-35, we obtain

$$\delta = -2\pi \frac{\gamma}{\omega_d} = -2\pi \tan\theta \qquad (14\text{-}37)$$

where θ is the angle from the origin of the root locus plot to the eigenvalue (see Figure 14-8). This expression shows that it is possible to calculate the log dec from the components of an eigenvalue.

The log dec is often calculated from experimental data. Thus, if ω_d, the damped natural frequency of vibration, is measured (in rad/s), then γ can be obtained from the log dec by Equation 14-37.

Because of the negative sign in Equation 14-37, the stability criterion for the log dec is opposite that for the root locus. In the root locus plot, if $\gamma > 0$, then the system is unstable. The opposite is true for the log dec; instability occurs when $\delta < 0$.

Equation 14-37 reveals the major drawback of the log dec. Because the log dec presents the *ratio* of the two eigenvalue components, it *loses information*. The root locus plot is superior to the log dec because it displays both components of the eigenvalue. It allows us to see how rapidly a particular eigenvalue approaches the instability threshold with changes in either rotor speed or other parameters. At the same time, it allows us to see how the natural frequencies of the system are changing.

Figure 14-15. Calculating the logarithmic decrement. For a stable system, a free vibration waveform decays exponentially. The period of vibration can be used to find the relationship to the root locus eigenvalue. See the text for details.

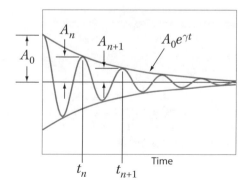

The Root Locus and the Campbell Diagram

The Campbell diagram is a plot of rotor system natural frequencies versus excitation frequencies (Figure 14-16). The plot allows a designer to detect when either running speed or its harmonics are close to a natural frequency of the system. The diagonal lines represent the running speed and potential harmonic frequencies that could be produced by the rotor system, and the vertical line is the actual running speed. The horizontal lines represent natural frequencies as they exist in the machine *when the machine is at operating speed.*

This plot, while useful, represents an oversimplification of rotor response. As we have seen, many damped natural frequencies in a rotor system *do* change with rotor speed, especially for modes where fluid interaction and bearing spring stiffness control rotor system response. The Campbell diagram presents only *frequency* information, and static frequency information at that; it would be desirable to be able to see stability information on the same plot.

The root locus plot presents eigenvalue data that represents both stability and frequency information, and it shows how natural frequencies change with rotor speed. Additionally, there is information about amplification factors at resonance; radial lines of constant Q make API boundaries easy to identify.

Figure 14-16. A typical Campbell diagram. The plot allows a designer to detect when harmonics of running speed coincide with a natural frequency of the system. The diagonal lines represent the frequencies produced by the rotor system as the speed varies between zero and running speed. The horizontal lines on the plot represent natural frequencies as they exist in the machine *when the machine is at operating speed.* While useful, the plot presents a very limited view of rotor system behavior.

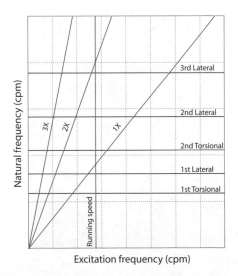

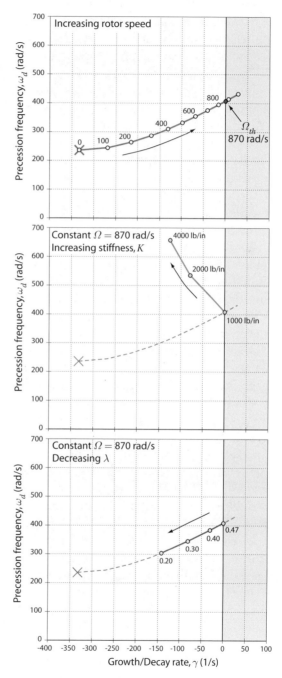

Figure 14-17. A root locus sensitivity analysis. At top, the speed is varied from 0 rad/s to 1000 rad/s, with all other rotor parameters held constant. The Threshold of Instability is about 870 rad/s. In the middle plot, the rotor speed is held constant at 870 rad/s, and the spring stiffness is increased from 1000 lb/in (the default value) to 4000 lb/in (175 kN/m to 700 kN/m). The increase in stiffness moves the rotor system root well into the stable half plane. In the bottom plot, rotor speed is held constant at 870 rad/s, and λ is reduced from 0.47 (the default value) to 0.20, also moving the system root well into the stable half plane. This is an example of what would be accomplished by using antiswirl injection in a bearing or seal.

Root Locus Analysis of Machine Stability Problems

In order to obtain eigenvalues over a wide speed range, a model must be constructed of the machine under study. This can range from a simple, lumped mass model to a more sophisticated finite element model.

The accuracy of the results will depend on the accuracy of the model. Given the current state of the modeling art, there are many uncertainties when modeling rotor system behavior. Bearing or seal stiffness, damping, and lambda are all functions of eccentricity ratio. Thus, rotor dynamic response may be strongly dependent on static radial loading, which indirectly affects these parameters. In many machines, static radial loading may change with operating conditions; for example, with nozzle settings in steam turbines. Thermal growth during startup can also affect alignment and bearing eccentricity ratio. Because of these uncertainties, it is unlikely that any model-based stability analysis will predict the Threshold of Instability speed with high accuracy.

Root locus analysis is best suited for sensitivity studies to solve a stability problem. Given a machine with a stability problem, how can the problem be eliminated in the most cost effective manner? Many possible engineering solutions may have to be evaluated, but most, directly or indirectly, involve changes in stiffness or lambda. The root locus can help sort through the possibilities and find the best solution.

Figure 14-17 shows an example of a root locus analysis. At top, the speed is changed from 0 rad/s to 1000 rad/s with all other rotor parameters held constant. The Threshold of Instability is about 870 rad/s. In the middle plot, the rotor speed is held constant at 870 rad/s, and the spring stiffness is increased from 1000 lb/in (the default value) to 4000 lb/in (175 kN/m to 700 kN/m). The increase in stiffness moves the rotor system well into the stable half plane. An increase in stiffness like this could be accomplished by alignment, which would increase the load on a previously lightly loaded bearing, or by increasing the pressure in a hydrostatic bearing. From this new position in the root locus plot, it would require a considerable increase in rotor speed to destabilize the rotor system.

In the bottom plot, rotor speed is held constant at 870 rad/s, and λ is reduced from 0.47 (the default value) to 0.20. This is an example of what would be accomplished by using antiswirl injection in a bearing or seal.

Both methods stabilize the rotor system (see Equation 14-5), but antiswirl injection moves the rotor root farther away from the Threshold of Instability.

Summary

A good, general definition of stability is that *a mechanical system is stable if, when it is disturbed from its equilibrium condition, it eventually returns to that equilibrium condition.* A system is *unstable* if, when it is disturbed, it moves away from the original equilibrium position.

Rotor systems that have significant fluid interaction have the potential to become unstable (a condition called *fluid-induced instability*) because of the tangential force caused by fluid circulating in bearings, seals, or around impellers. The rotor model predicts the Threshold of Instability given by Equation 14-5:

$$\Omega_{th} = \frac{1}{\lambda}\sqrt{\frac{K}{M}}$$

This expression is a very powerful diagnostic tool, and it is the key to understanding how to prevent and cure fluid-induced instability problems in rotor systems.

The simple rotor model was shown to have two roots, or eigenvalues. These complex numbers are of the general form $\gamma_{1,2} \pm j\omega_d$, where γ controls the rate of vibration growth or decay over time, and ω_d is the damped natural frequency of precession. The growth/decay rate, γ, is a useful stability criterion: $\gamma > 0$ implies growth of free vibration amplitude and an unstable system.

Rotor systems with significant fluid interaction have eigenvalues that change with rotor speed. A set of eigenvalues can be calculated from a mathematical model over a speed range and can be plotted on a root locus plot.

Radial lines from the origin of the root locus plot describe lines of constant damping factor, ζ, and constant amplification factor, Q. The Q at resonance is related to the damping factor and the angle on the root locus plot. The resonance is located approximately at the point on a forward root branch where the rotor speed equals the damped natural frequency.

The logarithmic decrement can be calculated from the two components of an eigenvalue, but it loses information because the components are in a ratio. The log dec concentrates on stability characteristics at the expense of frequency information.

The Campbell diagram does the opposite. It displays the natural frequencies of a system at the expense of stability information. The Campbell diagram frequencies are based on running speed only; the plot does not show how natural frequencies change with rotor speed.

The root locus plot is superior to both the log dec and the Campbell diagrams because of its ability to display both stability and frequency information.

References

1. Evans, Walter R., *Control-System Dynamics* (New York: McGraw-Hill, 1954).
2. Nise, Norman S., *Control Systems Engineering*, Third Ed., (New York: Addison-Wesley Publishing Company, 2000).
3. Ogata, Katsuhiko, *Modern Control Engineering*, (Upper Saddle River: Prentice Hall, Inc., 1990).
4. Kuo, Benjamin C., *Automatic Control Systems*, Fifth Ed., (Englewood Cliffs: Prentice-Hall, Inc., 1987).
5. Lund, J. W., "Stability and Damped Critical Speeds of a Flexible Rotor in Fluid-Film Bearings," *ASME Journal of Engineering for Industry* (May 1974): pp. 509-517.
6. American Petroleum Institute, *Tutorial on the API Standard Paragraphs Covering Rotor Dynamics and Balancing: An Introduction to Lateral Critical and Train Torsional Analysis and Rotor Balancing*, API Publication 684, First Ed., (Washington, D.C.: American Petroleum Institute, 1996), p. 3.
7. Bently, D. E., Hatch, C. T., "Root Locus and the Analysis of Rotor Stability Problems," *Orbit*, v. 14, No. 4, (Minden, NV: Bently Nevada Corporation, December 1993).

Chapter 15

Torsional and Axial Vibration

Radial, also called lateral, vibration is the most commonly measured type of vibration in machinery. It involves the lateral, oscillatory movement of machine components in planes perpendicular to the long axis of the machine in a combination of rigid body and bending motion. Measurement and control of radial vibration is important because of the potential for unwanted rotor to stator contact during machine operation and because the cyclic bending stresses associated with vibration can lead to fatigue failure of machine components. While we cannot measure radial vibration in all places in a machine, it can be relatively easily measured with currently available transducers.

However, lateral motion in the *XY* plane does not completely describe all the possible directions of motion of machine components. The rotor can also move relative to the machine casing in the *Z* direction (*axial* vibration), and it can statically and dynamically twist about its rotational axis (*torsional* vibration).

Torsional and axial vibration do not get the attention that they should. Since torsional vibration is more difficult to measure than radial vibration, it is often ignored, due to an "out of sight, out of mind" attitude. In fact, torsional vibration can be quite severe and is capable of producing damaging cyclic stresses that can cause a fatigue failure.

Axial vibration is relatively easy to measure using thrust position probes. Unfortunately, the usual application of thrust probe measurements is for static position measurements, and the dynamic information from these probes is often ignored.

Both radial and axial vibration can act through the spring-like elements in bearings to directly produce vibration in the casing and other attached machinery components. Torsional vibration cannot act *directly* through the bearings, because they have no spring-like element in the rotational direction, and they are designed to minimize power losses due to friction. Thus, few direct mechanisms exist for coupling torsional vibration to other parts of the machine.

However, both torsional and axial vibration can *indirectly* cross couple into radial vibration and vice versa. Thus, it is possible to see some of the effects of torsional or axial vibration in a radial vibration signal and not recognize them.

Axial vibration problems in machinery are relatively rare; torsional vibration problems, while more likely to occur, are harder to detect. Because of the relative importance of torsional vibration, it will be the primary emphasis of this chapter. We will describe what torsional vibration is and how it behaves. Then we will show how the dynamic parameters of torsional vibration are similar in concept to the mass, damping, and stiffness parameters of radial vibration, which leads to similarities in Dynamic Stiffness and vibration behavior.

We will discuss the sources of static and dynamic torsional loading in rotor systems and how the rotor responds to these loads. Then, we will discuss how radial vibration can produce torsional excitation and the reverse. Finally, we will present a summary of torsional vibration measurement techniques.

We will conclude the chapter with a brief discussion of axial vibration, starting with static and dynamic axial forces. We will follow with a discussion of axial/radial vibration cross coupling and axial vibration measurement.

The Torsional View of the Rotor

All rotating machines are involved in the delivery or transformation of power, and power delivery requires transmission of torque. The applied torque causes the shaft to twist about its rotational axis. Thus, instead of measuring displacement relative to an equilibrium position, torsion requires measuring the angle of twist of the shaft at different axial positions. Figure 15-1 shows the twist angles at several locations along a shaft. At each location, the angle θ represents the angular deflection of the shaft relative to the untwisted, equilibrium position represented by the black line.

Unfortunately, because the shaft must rotate to deliver power, we cannot directly observe particular spots on the shaft and calculate the angle of twist; the angle of twist of the shaft is added to (or subtracted from) the continuously increasing angle caused by the spinning shaft. Torsional deflection and vibration involve only the amount of twist of the shaft, but the spinning shaft is what makes the twist so difficult to measure.

Torsional deflection is measured as an angle, in degrees, which is analogous to the displacement measured in lateral deflection; analysis of torsional vibration also requires angular velocity and acceleration. Torsional vibration amplitude is usually measured in deg pp, angular velocity in deg/s pk, and angular acceleration in deg/s² pk. These values are usually converted to radians when used in equations, so be careful to keep track of the units.

We have modeled radial rotor system vibration using rotor parameters of force, mass, damping, stiffness, and lambda. Torsional vibration analysis uses the angular equivalents of the first four parameters: torque, moment of inertia, torsional damping, and torsional stiffness. In the torsional world, there is no equivalent to tangential stiffness, so lambda is not used.

A *torque* (also called a *moment of force*), *T*, is produced when a force is applied at some distance, called the *moment arm*, from the rotation axis. When you use a wrench to tighten a bolt, you apply a force to the end of the wrench. The length of the wrench is the moment arm, and the force produces a torque that causes the bolt to rotate. Torque has the unit of force times distance, N · m (lb · ft). In U.S. customary units, inches are sometimes substituted for feet. Technically, torque and angular displacement, velocity, and acceleration are three-dimensional vector quantities. Because we are limiting our discussion to one dimension (the axis of the machine) with no gyroscopic effects, we will treat all of these as scalar quantities.

The torsional equivalent of mass is the (*mass*) *moment of inertia, I*. The moment of inertia has the unit of mass times radius squared, or kg · m²

Figure 15-1. Measurement of torsional twist. Three disks are rigidly attached to a shaft. Because of dynamic forces, the shaft is twisted relative to the equilibrium position (black line). At each location, θ represents the angular deflection of the shaft relative to the equilibrium position.

(lb · ft · s²). As the units suggest, the moment of inertia depends on the amount of mass and the square of its distance from the spin axis. Rotor disks with a large amount of mass located relatively far from the spin axis (for example, large diameter pump impellers) will have a large moment of inertia. Gyroscopic forces in rotor systems are related to the moment of inertia and can modify the radial vibration characteristics of a machine.

Torsional damping, D_T, corresponds to the radial damping, D, the force per unit of velocity. The torsional analog is torque per unit of angular twist velocity (in deg/s), so D_T has units of N · m · s/deg (lb · ft · s/deg).

The damping associated with radial vibration is caused by the movement through a viscous fluid and produces a force that is proportional to the lateral velocity of the rotor centerline. However, the primary source of torsional damping is the internal frictional damping of the material. It produces a torque that is proportional to the angular velocity of twisting of the shaft (the rate of strain of the material). This weak damping torque can be supplemented by magnetic field effects in motors and generators, or by impeller vane and blade interactions with the working fluid in fluid-handling machines. It is usually assumed that these additional torsional damping effects are small; thus, for most machines, torsional damping is assumed to be very low.

Because there is no tangential force equivalent in torsional vibration (no lambda), the torsional Quadrature Dynamic Stiffness consists of only the torsional damping stiffness. The low quadrature stiffness results in very high amplification factors at torsional resonances. For this reason, special torsional dampers are sometimes installed in machinery. These dampers can take the form of fluid dampers or special couplings that contain rubber blocks. The rubber material provides some energy absorption that increases the system torsional damping. The rubber blocks also act like soft, torsional springs, reducing the torsional stiffness of the system. Elastomers can deteriorate and harden over time and lose their ability to absorb energy.

Torsional stiffness is defined by the angular deflection of the rotor in response to an applied torque. The unit of radial vibration stiffness is force per unit displacement; the unit of torsional stiffness is torque per unit of angular displacement: N · m (lb · ft) when radians are used and N · m/deg (lb · ft/deg) when degrees are used.

For a uniform, circular shaft, the torsional stiffness, K_T, is given by

$$\frac{T}{\theta} = K_T = \frac{JG}{L} \tag{15-1}$$

where θ is the angle of twist along a shaft section of length L, G is the shear modulus, or modulus of rigidity, and J is the polar moment of inertia, a cross-section property. For a hollow shaft with inside diameter d_i and outside diameter d_o,

$$J = \frac{\pi}{32}(d_o^4 - d_i^4)$$ (15-2)

This expression can be used for solid shafts by setting $d_i = 0$.

Equation 15-1 shows that the longer the shaft, the lower the torsional stiffness. Stiffer materials will have a higher shear modulus and produce a torsionally stiffer shaft. For example, the shear modulus of steel is about three times that of aluminum; thus, a steel shaft will have three times the torsional stiffness of an identical shaft made out of aluminum. Also, because J is related to the 4th power of the diameter, large diameter shafts are torsionally much stiffer than small diameter shafts.

Since most rotors are not uniform in diameter over their entire length, the torsional stiffness of a typical rotor shaft will vary with axial position. The total shaft stiffness will be equivalent to a number of short shaft segments in series, each with its own torsional stiffness. These segments behave like springs in series, so that the total torsional stiffness will be less than the stiffness of the weakest segment. For a shaft consisting of n segments,

$$\frac{1}{K_T} = \frac{1}{K_{T1}} + \frac{1}{K_{T2}} + \cdots + \frac{1}{K_{Tn}}$$ (15-3)

The power delivered by a shaft is the product of the torque and the angular velocity of the shaft,

$$P = T\Omega$$ (15-4)

where P is the power in watts, Ω is the rotor speed in rad/s, and T is the torque in N · m. If the power and speed are known, the torque can be found by inverting Equation 15-4. If the torque and torsional stiffness are known, the angle of twist, θ, of the shaft can be found from Equation 15-1. The angle of twist (windup or wrap-up) of most rotating machinery is quite small; a large steam turbine generator set may have a wrap-up of only one to two degrees from one end of the machine to the other.

The twist produces a material strain which is largest at the outer surface of the shaft. This strain produces a torsional shear stress, τ (Greek lower case tau), at the outer surface that is given by

$$\tau = \frac{Tr}{J} \tag{15-5}$$

where r is the radius of the outer surface of the shaft.

A comparison of the variables and typical units of measurement for radial and torsional parameters is presented in Table 15-1.

Table 15-1. Radial and torsional vibration parameters. For torsional vibration, radians are usually substituted for degrees in analytic calculations. See Appendix 7 for conversion factors.

Parameter	Radial vibration			Torsional vibration		
Displacement	r	µm pp	(mil pp)	θ	deg pp	
Velocity	$\dot{r}$	mm/s	(in/s)	$\dot{\theta}$	deg/s	
Acceleration	$\ddot{r}$	g		$\ddot{\theta}$	deg/s^2	
Force/Torque	F	N	(lb)	T	N·m	(lb·ft)
Mass/Moment of Inertia	M	kg	(lb·s^2/in)	I	kg·m^2	(lb·ft·s^2)
Damping	D	N·s/m	(lb·s/in)	D_T	N·m·s/deg	(lb·ft·s/deg)
Stiffness	K	N/m	(lb/in)	K_T	N·m/deg	(lb·ft/deg)

Static and Dynamic Torsional Response

A machine that is operating at a steady state speed is subjected to several torques that are in static balance. The driving torque originates either in a separate prime mover and is delivered through a coupling, or, if the machine is a prime mover, internally from multiple steam or gas turbine stages or magnetic fields. In a prime mover, this torque appears as an axially distributed set of torques, where some fraction of the total driving torque is input to the rotor at different axial positions. The driving torque is balanced by the load torque on the system. These loads originate in aerodynamic forces in compressors and fans, fluid loads in pumps, or in magnetic field interactions in generators.

As long as the driving torque is equal and opposite to the load torque, the rotor speed will remain constant, and the rotor shaft will be twisted slightly at a constant angular deflection. The amount of twist at each section will be determined by the local torque at each shaft section and by the requirements of Equation 15-1.

Any variation in driver torque or load torque will produce a change in the angular deflection of the shaft. Torque variations can be periodic in nature or impulsive. Steady state, periodically changing torque will produce a steady state, torsional vibration of the rotor system. Impulsive events will disturb the system and cause a decaying, free torsional vibration.

Sources of periodic torsional excitation include flow oscillation in fluid-handling machines, misaligned couplings (1X and 2X), rubs (subharmonics, 1X, and harmonics), gearbox tooth profile errors (harmonics or nonharmonics of running speed), reciprocating machine crank forces (1X and harmonics) and cross coupling of radial and axial vibration.

Impulsive torques can cause torsional ringing of the system. Impulsive torques can be caused by bad synchronization or sudden electrical distribution load changes in generators, or by rub impacts, faulty rolling element bearings, slipping poles in synchronous motors and generators, and older variable frequency drives.

Variable frequency drives use a synthesized electrical waveform, which is made up of a series of closely spaced voltage steps. Older drives have fewer and larger voltage steps and produce large torque steps that excite torsional ringing of the rotor system. Newer variable frequency drives have improved the smoothness of the voltage waveform and reduced the torsional ringing.

As in radial vibration, periodic torque variations produce a dynamic torsional response of the rotor. The torsional modeling of a rotor system is performed in a way similar to the modeling of radial vibration (Chapter 10). We will summarize the most important aspects of the torsional model to show the similarity between torsional and radial vibration dynamic equations and behavior.

Figure 15-2 shows the simplest torsional model of a rotating system. There are two rotor moments of inertia, I_1 and I_2, which represent a motor connected to a driven machine. The machines are connected by a shaft with torsional stiffness, K_T, and torsional damping, D_T. Each moment of inertia is capable of moving independently (subject to stiffness and damping constraints), so there are two angular displacement variables, θ_1 and θ_2. Two independent torques, T_1 and T_2, are applied at each end of the shaft.

Torsional vibration involves periodic, relative angular displacement of the two inertias and twisting of the shaft, not steady state rotation of the entire system. Remember, though, that any vibration angular displacement is added to whatever constant angle of static twist already exists due to the average load being transmitted through the shaft.

Figure 15-2. Simple torsional model of a rotor system. Two rotor moments of inertia, I_1 and I_2, represent a motor connected by a shaft and coupling to a driven machine. The shaft has torsional stiffness K_T and torsional damping D_T. Each moment of inertia is capable of moving independently (subject to stiffness and damping constraints), with angular displacement θ_1 and θ_2. Independent torques, T_1 and T_2, are applied at each end of the shaft.

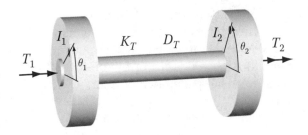

We will define the dynamic relative angular displacement (angle of twist) as ϕ (Greek lower case phi),

$$\phi = \theta_2 - \theta_1 \tag{15-6}$$

If $I_1 = I_2 = I$, we can develop a relatively simple equation of torsional motion of the system:

$$I\ddot{\phi} + 2D_T\dot{\phi} + 2K_T\phi = T_2 - T_1 = Te^{j(\omega t + \delta)} \tag{15-7}$$

Here, the difference in torques is expressed as T, which is assumed to change periodically at a nonsynchronous frequency, ω, and have an initial phase angle of δ. Solution of this equation leads to

$$\Phi e^{j\alpha} = \frac{Te^{j\delta}}{(2K_T - I\omega^2 + j2D_T\omega)} \tag{15-8}$$

where Φ (Greek upper case Phi) is the amplitude of torsional vibration, and α is the phase of the response. Here, we use the mathematically convenient exponential form even though we are not modeling the system in the complex plane. The physical result is the real part of the solution, equivalent to a cosine function.

The ω in Equation 15-8 represents any nonsynchronous vibration frequency. A synchronous expression can be created by substituting Ω for ω in the equation. The result will be identical in form to Equation 15-8, so it does not matter which form is used; the behavior will be the same.

The term in the denominator is the torsional Dynamic Stiffness, which, like the radial vibration Dynamic Stiffness, has a direct and quadrature part. The direct part has a torsional spring stiffness, related to the twisting of the shaft, and an inertial stiffness. Unlike radial vibration with fluid interaction, the quadrature part consists of only the torsional damping stiffness, which is typically small; there is no torsional equivalent for tangential stiffness.

The behavior of torsional vibration for this simple system is very much like the radial vibration behavior presented in Chapter 11, with one important difference. In torsional vibration, there is no analog for rotating unbalance, so the periodic forcing torque is assumed to have constant amplitude. This changes the low- and high-speed behaviors of the torsional system when compared to a rotating-unbalance-driven, radial vibration.

Figure 15-3 shows the response of the simple torsional model. At low frequencies, well below resonance, the torsional vibration will be approximately in phase with the forcing torque, and, at zero frequency, the amplitude becomes a steady state twist equal $T/2K_T$.

The definition of phase in torsional vibration needs some explanation. For torsional vibration, the "high spot" is the maximum of the torsional vibration timebase waveform, which, for angular displacement data, represents a maximum angle of twist. Like radial vibration, the absolute phase is defined as the number of degrees of the vibration cycle from the Keyphasor event to the first positive peak of the torsional vibration waveform.

At resonance, the amplitude of the vibration will peak sharply because of the low quadrature stiffness, and the phase of the response will lag the phase of the forcing torque by about 90°. Torsional resonance peaks are usually very narrow, with amplification factors five to ten times those for radial vibration. These very high amplification factors can produce high alternating shear stress levels when the rotor system experiences a resonance. These shear stresses are superimposed on the static torsional load stresses and any radial vibration bending stresses. The combination can produce damaging levels of stress and can lead to fatigue crack initiation. Running a machine at a speed equal to a torsional resonance or at a speed equal to a submultiple of a torsional resonance is a very bad idea. Fortunately, the narrowness of torsional resonances makes it less likely that this will happen by accident.

Figure 15-3. Torsional response of a simple rotor model. At frequencies well below resonance, the torsional vibration will be approximately in phase with the forcing torque, T, and the amplitude will be equal to $T/2K_T$ at zero frequency. Amplitude and phase relationships versus speed are similar to those for radial vibration. Because of low torsional damping, amplification factors at a torsional resonance can be quite high.

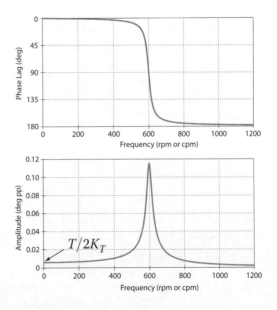

The resonance, and natural, frequency for this simple system will be near

$$\omega = \sqrt{\frac{2K_T}{I}}$$ (15-9)

Note the similarity to the resonance frequency for radial vibration (Equation 10-40). The frequency still involves the ratio of stiffness to mass, represented here by the moment of inertia.

For this single mode system, at frequencies well above resonance, *the amplitude of vibration will approach zero*, and the response phase will lag the forcing phase by about 180°. Thus, with slight differences, basic torsional vibration behavior is very similar to that of radial vibration.

As with radial vibration, more complex machines are capable of several modes of torsional vibration, with different mode shapes. Figure 15-4 shows two typical torsional mode shapes for a machine with three moments of inertia (another mode shape, not shown, is a degenerate, in-phase mode that is equivalent to rotation of the shaft). Each mode shape represents different twisting combinations in the machine. The first mode shape has two adjacent moments of inertia moving in phase, with the third out of phase. The second mode shape involves the middle moment of inertia moving out of phase with the two end moments of inertia. Actual mode shapes will depend on the magnitude and distribution of different inertias and on the torsional stiffness distribution in the shaft.

Figure 15-4. Torsional mode shapes. Two torsional modes are shown for a machine with three moments of inertia. (Another mode shape, not shown, is a degenerate, in-phase mode that is equivalent to rotation of the shaft.) In the first mode shape (top), two adjacent moments of inertia move in phase, with the third out of phase. In the second mode shape (bottom), the middle moment of inertia moves out of phase with the ends. Actual mode shapes depend on the magnitude and distribution of the moments of inertia and on the distribution of torsional stiffness in the shaft.

First mode

Second mode

Torsional/Radial Cross Coupling

In a simple, mathematical rotor model, radial and torsional vibration are completely independent. This situation is only true when the rotor shaft is vibrating in a circular, 1X orbit centered on the axis of the system. In reality, several things take place in a physical rotor system that cause radial vibration to produce a periodic torque and vice versa, a phenomenon called *cross coupling*.

Elliptical orbits produce changes in the bending of the rotor and cause a periodic torque to appear, which can cause torsional vibration. Figure 15-5 shows a rotor shaft suspended between two bearings. At left, the rotor shaft is straight and spins at angular velocity Ω. The driver of the machine sees a shaft moment of inertia, I, equal to the moments of inertia of the shaft and disk. At right, 1X radial vibration has deflected the shaft so that the shaft centerline is some distance from the axis (red) of the rotor system. Now the disk center also precesses around the spin axis with angular velocity Ω. Because I is proportional to mass times radius squared, the total moment of inertia is now $I_t = I + Mr^2$, where M is the mass of the disk.

In the absence of changing torques, the angular momentum of the rotor system, $I_t\Omega$, must remain the same. As the shaft deflection increases, the increase in I_t requires a reduction in shaft centerline angular velocity, Ω, and the driver sees a torque that tries to slow down the system. On the other hand, when shaft deflection decreases, the driver sees a torque that tries to speed up the system.

Because of these effects, any orbit that produces a change in position relative to the centerline of the rotor system will produce a variable torque. The excitation can be 1X or more complex, and it will appear as torsional vibration of the rotor system.

Through the same mechanism, any torsional vibration will cross couple into radial vibration, because torque variations will attempt to transfer rotational energy into radial vibration energy.

A different cross-coupling mechanism occurs when a rotating shaft has an asymmetric cross section, such as might result from a shaft crack, and is subjected to a static radial load. The asymmetry means that the bending stiffness of the shaft is not the same in all radial directions. Thus, when subjected to a static radial load, the shaft will deflect more when the weak shaft stiffness axis is oriented with the applied load and less when the strong stiffness axis is oriented with the load (Figure 15-6). The most interesting case is when the shaft is between these two conditions. Then, a static radial load will produce a deflection with a component at right angles to the load. Because the shaft is deflected away from the rotor system centerline, this perpendicular component acts as a crank, directly producing a torque in the rotor. The action occurs rapidly, producing a snapping action as the strong stiffness axis moves across the load.

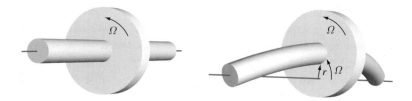

Figure 15-5. Effect of shaft deflection on the moment of inertia. At left, the rotor shaft is straight and spins at angular velocity Ω. The driver of the machine sees a shaft mass moment of inertia, I, equal to the sum of the moments of inertia of the shaft and disk. At right, 1X radial vibration has deflected the shaft, so the shaft centerline is some distance, r, from the spin axis (red) of the rotor system. Now the disk center precesses around the rotor shaft with angular velocity Ω. The system moment of inertia is much larger ($I + Mr^2$, where M is the mass of the disk) because mass has been moved farther away from the spin axis of the system.

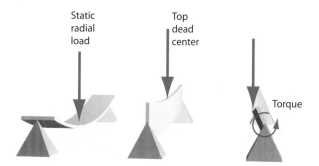

Figure 15-6. Torque caused by a rotating asymmetry and a static radial load such as gravity. A rectangular beam with an asymmetric cross section acts as a crank when subjected to a static radial load. At left, the beam is weakest, and the deflection is highest. In the middle, the strong axis is in line with the load, and the deflection is smallest. When the beam is between these two conditions, the radial load deflects the beam down and to the left, producing a torque about the rotor system centerline. Because the asymmetry repeats twice per revolution, there will be a 2X torsional excitation and a snapping action as the strong stiffness axis moves rapidly through the line of action of the load.

Because the shaft asymmetry repeats twice per revolution, this snapping action will produce a 2X torsional excitation in the rotor. The nonlinear nature of this mechanism can also generate higher harmonics, such as 3X, 4X, etc.

Gearbox reaction loads are another strong source of cross coupling. Gearboxes transfer torque through the action of the force at the gear mesh. This force also acts as an (ideally) static, radial load on the rotor. Any variation in torque will appear as a variation in this radial load and will also appear as a variation of the radial load on the shaft. Gear *profile errors*, therefore, will show up as both radial and torsional vibration. In fact, profile errors (either pitch radius or tooth spacing errors) are usually detected through frequency analysis of signals from gearbox-mounted accelerometers, which are sensitive to radial, but not torsional, vibration.

Torsional/radial cross coupling in gearboxes can produce large, radial vibration forces. Figure 15-7 shows a half spectrum cascade plot of startup data from a motor-driven compressor. A 6-pole synchronous motor (1200 rpm) is connected through a diaphragm coupling to a speed-increasing gearbox, which drives a 5614 rpm, 5500 hp (4100 kW) compressor. The plot shows shaft relative vibration data from the high-speed pinion.

The 6-pole synchronous motor has a startup torque oscillation that occurs at 6X *slip frequency*. This torsional excitation frequency (diagonal red line) varies from 7200 cpm, when the motor is stopped, to 0 cpm, when it is at full speed. This torque oscillation excites torsional vibration, which strongly cross couples into the observed radial vibration at critical frequencies. The torsional resonances, calculated at 1275 cpm and 3260 cpm, are excited in reverse order during the startup.

Torsional Vibration Measurement

Earlier, we defined torsional vibration as the dynamic twisting of the shaft. The angle of twist is the *difference* between the angular displacement, or angular position, at two, axially separated points (Equation 15-6). Ideally, to measure this twist, we would measure the angular displacement at two points; however, measurement of angular displacement is complicated by the rotation of the shaft. The shaft angular velocity, Ω, causes a continuous increase in angular displacement, $\theta = \Omega t$, on top of whatever torsional vibration may be present. Thus, θ is not a useful measurement for torsional vibration.

The change in angular velocity is a better measurement choice. At any axial position, torsional vibration will appear as a periodic variation in the angular velocity around the mean value, Ω. Virtually all torsional vibration measurement systems measure variations in angular velocity; because of this, this method is also called an *FM (Frequency Modulation) Incremental* technique. The resulting

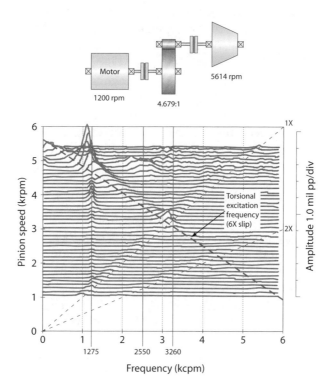

Figure 15-7. Torsional/radial cross coupling during startup of a synchronous motor driven compressor. A 6-pole (1200 rpm) synchronous motor drives a 5614 rpm compressor through a diaphragm-type coupling and a speed increasing gearbox. The half spectrum cascade plot of the startup shows shaft relative displacement vibration data from the high-speed pinion. The motor has a startup torque oscillation that occurs at 6X slip frequency. This torsional excitation frequency (diagonal red line) varies from 7200 cpm (twice line frequency) when the motor is stopped, to 0 cpm when the motor is at full speed. The torque oscillation excites torsional vibration, which strongly cross couples into the observed radial vibration near the calculated torsional resonances of 1275 cpm and 3260 cpm. The frequency peaks near 2550 cpm are the second harmonic of the 1275 cpm resonance. Note that the resonances are excited in reverse order during the startup. *Data courtesy of Charles Jackson [1].*

torsional vibration signal can be integrated to angular displacement and expressed in degrees.

Various types of noncontacting, torsional vibration transducers have been developed that measure changes in angular velocity. One type uses an eddy current probe to observe the teeth of a gear or toothed wheel (Figure 15-8) that is installed on the shaft. The timing of the pulses produced as the teeth pass next to the probe provides a measurement of the angular velocity.

The wheel rotates at an average speed, Ω, but torsional vibration causes this speed to vary periodically. A transducer observing the teeth provides timing pulses. The time between pulses, t, is constant when no torsional (or radial) vibration is present (top series of pulses). When torsional vibration is present, the time between pulses changes, and this information can be used to calculate the torsional vibration frequency and amplitude.

The signals from two probes are used to cancel out the effects of radial vibration. When using a single probe, radial vibration in a direction perpendicular to the probe axis produces a timing variation that looks like torsional vibration. The signal from the second probe on the opposite side of the shaft is compared to the first signal to cancel out the radial vibration component.

This measurement method has the advantage of robustness in an industrial environment; the system is relatively immune to dirt or oil contamination of the observed surface. The disadvantage is the need to install the toothed wheel on the shaft.

A variation on this principle substitutes an optical probe and a special tape that is attached to the surface of the shaft. The tape is printed with alternating light and dark bars, which generate the timing pulses in the probe output. The tape is easier to install, but is vulnerable to contamination, tape adhesion, and temperature problems.

With either the toothed wheel or tape, the torsional frequency response is limited by the number of timing pulses per second. The Nyquist criterion applies: the highest torsional frequency that can be measured is less than ½ the pulse rate. Thus, high frequency response requires many, closely spaced teeth or marks on the tape.

Lasers are now being developed for torsional vibration measurement. Typically, the laser beam is split and directed at the shaft in two, coplanar locations. The surface velocity of the shaft causes any reflected light to be shifted in frequency (Doppler effect). The laser light reflected back toward the sensor is recombined, and analysis determines the changes in velocity due to torsional vibration while negating the effects of radial vibration. Laser methods, though, can be sensitive to contamination problems in an industrial environment.

Another torsional measurement uses strain gages to measure the deformation strain of the shaft as it twists in response to an applied torque. The strain changes the resistance of the strain gages, which can be measured using a resistance bridge. The major technical problem involves getting the strain gage signal back to the outside world from the rotating shaft.

Once the signal is transferred, the strain, shaft geometry, and shaft material properties are used to calculate the torque that is being delivered through the shaft at that point. Because strain gages are dynamic transducers, they can be used to measure dynamic strain and torque.

Various methods have been used to transfer the strain gage signal across the rotating gap. Low-speed applications have used slip ring and brush assemblies, which can be noisy. Other methods use induction or an FM transmitter.

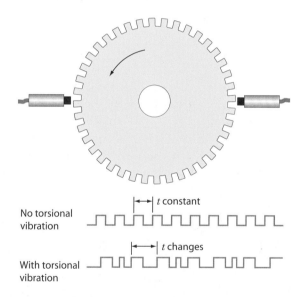

Figure 15-8. Measurement of torsional vibration with a toothed wheel. The wheel rotates at an average speed, Ω, but torsional vibration causes the speed to change periodically. A transducer observing the teeth provides timing pulses. The time between pulses, t, is constant (top) when no torsional or radial vibration is present. When torsional vibration is present, the time between pulses changes, and this information can be used to calculate the torsional vibration frequency and amplitude. The signals from both probes are used to cancel out the effects of radial vibration. When using a single probe, radial vibration in a direction perpendicular to the probe axis produces a timing variation that looks like torsional vibration. The signal from the second probe on the opposite side of the shaft can be compared to the first signal to cancel out the radial vibration component.

Strain gages provide a measurement of dynamic torsional strain, stress, and torque at a single axial position. This measurement is most useful for calculating dynamic power by multiplying torque by rotor speed using Equation 15-4. When power is measured at the coupling between two machines, it provides information for efficiency calculations.

Torsional vibration signals can be processed and displayed much the same as radial vibration signals. Timebase plots can display the filtered or unfiltered torsional vibration signal. Filtering can provide nX amplitude and phase (using a standard Keyphasor transducer as a reference), Bode and polar plots can display this data, and spectrum plots can provide frequency analysis.

Note that any torsional vibration measurement should be made at a location well away from a torsional vibration node of the system. Couplings are often a poor location because torsional nodes tend to be located nearby. It is a good idea to perform a preliminary lumped-model torsional analysis of the system to estimate the locations of both nodes and antinodes before deciding where to install torsional vibration transducers.

Axial Vibration

Axial vibration is another commonly overlooked behavior in rotating machinery. Most axial (thrust) measurement applications are concerned with the static position of the rotor, because of clearance issues during startup and operation, and the importance of monitoring thrust bearing health. Usually, little attention is paid to axial vibration; in fact, thrust probe installations often ignore the potential for vibration measurement and filter out dynamic information in the monitor. This is unfortunate, because malfunctions such as misalignment and surge generate axial vibration, and both radial and torsional vibration can cross couple into axial vibration.

Axial deflections of the rotor, like radial and torsional deflections, can be either static or dynamic. Static axial forces are caused by gravity in vertical machines, axial components of gear loads, and differential pressure effects in fluid handling machines, such as steam turbines, gas turbines, compressors, and pumps. Electric motors and generators do not normally produce significant static thrust loads, because magnetic forces maintain the position of the rotor. Static axial forces are balanced by thrust bearings, balance pistons, dual (opposed) flow configurations of stages, or by combinations of these.

Dynamic axial loads can appear because of flow irregularities in compressors and pumps, cocked wheels, coupling problems, or from cross-coupled torsional or radial vibration. The most dramatic example of dynamic axial vibration is surge in a compressor, where vibration amplitude can be large enough to cause violent rubs and machine destruction.

Because of the many sources of axial forcing, axial vibration measurements can be an important source of information for correlation when trying to solve a machinery problem.

Dynamically, axial vibration is most like the vibration of a simple, spring/mass system. The rotor represents a concentrated mass (which is actually equal to the weight of the rotor in this case). The active side of the thrust bearing provides the primary support stiffness in the axial direction.

When performing an analysis of axial vibration, it is important to include the effects of coupling stiffness. Couplings affect both the mass and stiffness behavior of the system. Rigid couplings provide very high axial stiffness, producing what is effectively one large rotor. On a long, rigidly coupled machine train, the rotor mass will equal the total mass of the rigidly coupled rotors, and the stiffness in the system will be supplied by the thrust bearings.

Gear couplings, because of their axial freedom of motion, provide zero axial stiffness under normal conditions and act to isolate rotors from each other. This effectively decouples axial vibration between machines.

Diaphragm and disk couplings act like axial springs and transmit vibration forces from one rotor to another. Thus, a machine with these types of couplings acts like a multiple-degree-of-freedom oscillator which is capable of multiple modes of axial vibration.

A simple model for axial vibration is shown in Figure 15-9. The rotor mass is modeled as a single, lumped mass, M, and the stiffness, K, and damping, D, are provided by the thrust bearing. A single variable, z, measures the displacement in the axial direction relative to the thrust bearing support. There is no tangential stiffness equivalent for axial vibration.

Figure 15-9. A simple model for axial vibration. The rotor mass is modeled as a single, lumped mass, M, and the thrust bearing provides the stiffness, K, and damping, D. The displacement is measured in the axial direction, z, relative to the thrust bearing support. There is no tangential stiffness equivalent for axial vibration.

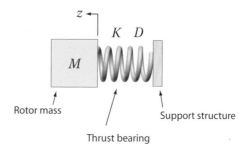

The model leads to the equation of motion,

$$M\ddot{z} + D\dot{z} + Kz = Fe^{j(\omega t + \delta)} \tag{15-10}$$

where z is the axial position of the rotor mass, M, D is the axial damping (provided by the thrust bearing or working fluid around an impeller), and K is the axial stiffness. The dynamic axial force is assumed to have constant magnitude, F (no rotating unbalance here), frequency, ω, and phase, δ, when the Keyphasor event occurs. As in the torsional model presented above, the exponential form is used for convenience, and only the real (cosine) part of the solution represents the measured vibration.

Solution of this equation leads to a form very much like that for radial vibration:

$$Ze^{j\alpha} = \frac{Fe^{j\delta}}{(K - M\omega^2 + jD\omega)} \tag{15-11}$$

where Z is the amplitude of axial vibration and α is the phase. The denominator is the *axial Dynamic Stiffness*, which has a direct and quadrature part. The behavior of the system is similar to that for torsional vibration, with a natural frequency and resonance near

$$\omega = \sqrt{\frac{K}{M}} \tag{15-12}$$

In Equation 15-11, the nonsynchronous frequency, ω, is used, but Ω can be substituted to obtain the synchronous response. In large, rigidly coupled machines, the natural frequency of axial vibration is likely to be low, because of the large effective mass of the rotor.

When multiple machines are coupled with diaphragm or disk couplings, the machine train can possess multiple modes of axial vibration, one mode for each major mass of the system. As for radial vibration (see Chapter 12), each mode will have its own characteristic natural frequency and associated mode shape. Axial mode shapes consist of longitudinal patterns of axial motion, with different phase relationships. As with other types of vibration, the most likely first mode shape is an in-phase motion of all coupled rotors (see Figure 12-1).

Radial vibration can cross couple into axial vibration. One such coupling mechanism is the bending of the rotor shaft during radial vibration. Bending shortens the length of the shaft slightly; as a shaft undergoes periodic changes in shaft centerline position during radial vibration, parts of that shaft will undergo a periodic change in axial position. This position change, together with the mass of the rotor, and coupling and bearing stiffnesses, generates periodic axial forces that can excite axial vibration.

Variable thrust loading from single helical gears is a source of radial and torsional cross coupling to axial vibration. Any periodic change in radial load or torque at the gear mesh will appear as a changing thrust load. This works both ways: axial vibration can couple into radial and torsional vibration through the same mechanism.

Turbine blades convert the energy of axially moving fluid to torque, while compressor blades convert the torque to energy in the fluid. As fluid flows around a blade, the force produced at each blade has both tangential (which produces the torque) and axial components. Any flow irregularities in these systems will show up as simultaneous changes in torque and axial force. Any flow variations can excite free or forced torsional and axial vibration.

Mechanical and electrical runout can look like axial vibration. Axial position is usually measured by thrust position probes that observe a thrust collar or the end of the shaft. A cocked or wavy thrust collar can produce periodic changes in transducer output. Runout can be as much as 25 to 50 µm pp (1 to 2 mil pp), but this is rare, and it is not usually a serious problem. Runout can be a more serious problem when the transducers are observing the end of an unprepared shaft. Runout compensation of axial vibration data can be performed if necessary.

Summary

Torsional vibration is the dynamic twisting of the rotor shaft about its rotational axis. This twisting is related to the difference in angular deflection between axially separated measurement planes.

The dynamic equations and rotor parameters are similar to those for radial vibration. Torsional stiffness is related to the material properties and cross-sectional geometry of the shaft. Torsional damping is provided primarily by material internal friction in the shaft and is usually very low. The torsional equivalent of mass is the (mass) moment of inertia, which is a measure of the radial mass distribution of the rotor.

Both static and dynamic sources of torsional loading exist in rotating machinery. As with radial vibration, torsional vibration is the ratio of dynamic torque to torsional dynamic stiffness. The behavior of torsional vibration over speed is similar to that of radial vibration, and the resonance frequency is related to the square root of the ratio of torsional stiffness to inertia (Equation 15-9).

Because of usually low torsional damping, torsional resonances tend to be narrow, with very high amplification factors.

Torsional vibration can cross couple to radial vibration and vice versa. Causes include deflected-rotor crank effects and gearbox reaction loads. Cross coupling of radial vibration can produce 1X torsional vibration. 2X torsional vibration can also be excited by rotor shaft asymmetries acting with a static radial load.

Measurement of torsional vibration usually involves the detection of variations in the angular velocity of the rotor shaft. Strain can be measured by strain gages; the strain, shaft geometry, and shaft material properties are used to calculate the dynamic torque in the shaft.

Axial vibration is the periodic axial movement of the rotor shaft. The primary sources of axial stiffness are thrust bearings and diaphragm or disk couplings. Axial vibration can be measured using thrust position transducers.

References
1.   Jackson, Charles, and Leader, Malcolm E., "Design, Testing, and Commissioning of a Synchronous Motor-Gear-Axial Compressor," *Proceedings of the 12th Turbomachinery Symposium*, Texas A&M University, Texas (November 1983): pp. 97-111.

Chapter 16

Basic Balancing of Rotor Systems

Uɴʙᴀʟᴀɴᴄᴇ ᴇxɪsᴛs ɪɴ ᴀʟʟ ʀᴏᴛᴀᴛɪɴɢ ᴍᴀᴄʜɪɴᴇʀʏ; when the vibration due to unbalance exceeds allowable limits, balancing is required.

Balancing is the act of adding or removing mass from a rotor so that the unbalance-induced vibration falls below a maximum acceptable level. Balancing can be performed one axial plane at a time, or it may simultaneously involve several planes. Balancing many planes simultaneously requires sophisticated balancing software and considerable knowledge of the machine.

In this chapter, we will examine the physical mechanism that causes unbalance, discuss how an unbalance force is generated, and show how unbalance affects rotor system behavior. After a brief discussion of the necessary transducers, we will discuss the techniques used for determining the location and magnitude of the unbalance and how to apply that information to single- and two-plane balance problems. Finally, we will develop a powerful tool for balancing, the *influence vector*, show how the influence vector is closely related to the Dynamic Stiffness of the rotor system, and show how one can be calculated from the other.

Unbalance and Rotor Response

An ideal rotor has a symmetric geometric shape and a uniform radial mass distribution. At each axial plane, the average of the centers of all of the geometric shapes defines the geometric center (centroid of area) of the rotor system; the average of the centers of all of the masses in the system defines the center of mass of the system. For an ideal system, the geometric center is at the same location as the mass center. Such a perfect, rotating system, assuming no other influences, would rotate absolutely smoothly with no vibration at any speed.

In practice, the radial mass distribution of a real rotor is not uniform for several reasons: nonhomogeneous rotor material, due to voids in castings or forgings; manufacturing tolerances, including machining and stacking errors; and nonsymmetric construction, due to keyways, keys, pins, etc.

For example, the blades in a gas turbine, no matter how carefully matched, will have slightly different masses. The mounting slots in the disk will not be located at exactly the same radius from the disk center. When a disk is machined to fit onto the rotor, the hole will not be perfectly centered in the disk. The result is that the location of the mass center will not coincide with the geometric center of the disk; it will be located some radial distance away from the geometric center of the rotor system, and it will be located at some particular angular location.

When you add to this the effects of disk stacking errors, shrink fit errors, keys and keyway effects, and rotor bow, it is easy to see that unbalance is built into a rotor from the beginning. Additional dynamic effects due to operating conditions, distortion, thermal bowing and warping, and long-term effects due to wear, corrosion, and erosion further complicate the picture.

Since each disk in a rotor can have a different amount and angular orientation of unbalance, an axial distribution of unbalance will exist in a machine. This unbalance distribution has a particular three-dimensional shape, similar to a mode shape. If this shape is a good fit to a rotor mode shape, then that mode can be strongly excited by the unbalance. If, however, it is a poor fit to a rotor mode shape, then the mode will be only weakly excited (see Chapter 12).

At any particular axial location, the mass center of a rotor system will be located some radial distance and in a particular direction from the geometric center of the system. In the enlarged view of a rotor cross section (Figure 16-1, middle), the mass center is located some distance, r_e, from the geometric center. The *unbalance* of the rotor system is the product of the rotor mass, M, and the distance, r_e. *When this product exceeds a recommended amount, the rotor is said to be unbalanced.*

The distance, r_e, is quite small. For example, a 2000 kg (4400 lb) rotor, operating at a maximum speed of 3600 rpm, and balanced to one industry standard [1] has a value of r_e less than 1.8 μm (69 μin)!

It is awkward to deal with masses this large and distances this small. It is more convenient to express the magnitude of the unbalance, U, as the equivalent product of a much larger distance, r_u, typically the radius of the balance circle (or ring), and a much smaller unbalance mass, m, (the *heavy spot*):

$$Mr_e = U = mr_u \qquad (16\text{-}1)$$

The units of unbalance are usually expressed in gram millimeters, ounce inches, or similar convenient dimensions.

When the shaft rotates, the unbalance produces a force on the rotor similar to that produced by a rock swinging at the end of a string. The force is a rotating vector, F, and it is produced by the reaction to the centripetal acceleration of the unbalance mass, which is located at an angle δ when the Keyphasor event occurs. The force is proportional to the mass and radius of the unbalance and to the square of the rotor speed, Ω, in rad/s:

$$F = U\Omega^2 \, \angle\delta$$
$$F = mr_u\Omega^2 \, \angle\delta \qquad (16\text{-}2)$$
$$F = Mr_e\Omega^2 \, \angle\delta$$

For diagnostic purposes, the phase is measured relative to a vibration transducer (Figure 16-1 right). As the rotor turns, the Keyphasor event acts like a strobe, illuminating the instantaneous location of the heavy spot. Equation 16-2 describes the force generated by an unbalance, but it can also be used to calculate the effect of a balancing weight addition to the rotor.

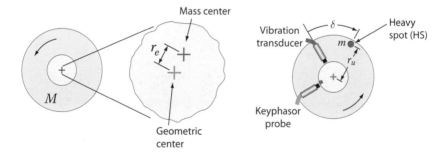

Figure 16-1. Mass and geometric centers of a rotor. The enlarged view of the center of the shaft shows the mass center (red cross) located some distance, r_e (the radius of eccentricity), from the geometric center (green cross). The unbalance of the rotor system is expressed as the product of the rotor mass, M, and the radius of eccentricity, r_e. The unbalance can also be expressed as an equivalent small mass, m (red dot), located at a radius, r_u (usually the radius of the balance ring), from the geometric center, and at a lag angle, δ (right). The lag angle is measured relative to the vibration measurement transducer (blue) when the Keyphasor event occurs.

When calculating the magnitude of the force, *care must be taken to ensure that consistent units of measurement are used.* It is common to describe balancing in terms of adding *weight* to a rotor. However, the balance weight is a *mass*, with units of grams (less often, kilograms), or in U.S. customary units, lb · s²/in. When using SI units (kilogram meter second), Equation 16-2 is quite simple. In the United States, it is common practice to use weight, which has units of force (ounces or pounds), rather than mass. Use of U.S. customary units can involve some tricky conversions:

Example 1
A balancing weight of 7 oz (200 g) is installed at a radius of 12 in (300 mm) on a machine running at 3600 rpm. What force is generated by this weight at operating speed?

Solution
The unbalance is commonly expressed as

$$U = (7 \text{ oz})(12 \text{ in}) = 84 \text{ in} \cdot \text{oz}$$

The units of U are convenient, but they cannot be used in the first of Equations 16-2 without conversion. To find the magnitude of the force, we use the second of Equations 16-2, ignoring the angle:

$$F = m r_u \Omega^2$$

$$F = \left[(7 \text{ oz}) \left(\frac{1 \text{ lb}}{16 \text{ oz}} \right) \left(\frac{1}{386 \text{ in/s}^2} \right) \right] [12 \text{ in}] \left[\left(3600 \ \frac{\text{rev}}{\text{min}} \right) \left(2\pi \ \frac{\text{rad}}{\text{rev}} \right) \left(\frac{1 \text{ min}}{60 \text{ s}} \right) \right]^2$$

$$F = 1900 \text{ lb} \ (8.6 \text{ kN})$$

Note that, if we had used U directly in the first of Equations 16-2, we would have obtained an incorrect result with incorrect units. *Proper bookkeeping is very important when working out these problems. Units should always be written out and carefully checked.* In this chapter, the terms weight and mass will be used interchangeably, with the understanding that calculations involve mass. (See Appendix 7 for another discussion of this problem.)

Balance mass and mounting radius combinations are related to the speed of the machine. At the small end of the scale, one high-speed, overhung compressor turning at 60 000 rpm had a balance weight of 0.1 g (0.004 oz) installed at a radius of 19 mm (0.75 in). At the other extreme, a hydro machine turning at 257 rpm had balancing weights ranging from 23 to 90 kg (50 to 200 lb) mounted at a radius of 5 m (16 ft). A typical power generator might have balance weights of 100 to 300 g (4 to 10 oz) mounted at a radius of 300 to 600 mm (12 to 24 in).

Because the unbalance mass is actually part of the rotor, the unbalance force rotates with the rotor at 1X rotor speed. The 1X unbalance force acts through the Dynamic Stiffness of the system to cause vibration:

$$\text{Vibration} = \frac{\text{Force}}{\text{Dynamic Stiffness}} \qquad (16\text{-}3)$$

The vibration caused by unbalance is primarily *synchronous* (1X), but may include harmonics caused by nonlinearities.

When a rotor operates at a speed near a natural frequency, the 1X unbalance force will excite the natural frequency, and the 1X vibration will be amplified. A balance resonance occurs when rotor speed approximately equals a natural frequency (see Chapter 11).

Vibration Transducers And Balancing

Balancing requires that we measure shaft vibration. We developed the rotor model in Chapter 10 using a rotor position vector that was measured relative to the center of a fixed, motionless bearing. The dynamic description of rotor motion uses *shaft absolute* position, that is, position relative to a fixed reference frame, to describe rotor vibration, and our conclusions regarding high spot and heavy spot relationships (Chapter 11) depend on this implicit assumption.

Unfortunately, in practice, we do not directly measure shaft absolute vibration. In fluid-film bearing machines we measure *shaft relative* vibration, where eddy current proximity probes are mounted on the casing or bearing structure to observe the vibration of the shaft relative to the transducer. As long as the bearing or machine casing does not move significantly, then shaft relative vibration will be a good approximation to shaft absolute vibration. In rolling element bearing machines, we usually assume that casing (actually bearing) vibration is a good approximation to shaft vibration.

1X rotor vibration appears as a dynamic load in the bearings. The bearing stiffness and damping transmit this load into the bearing support structure and machine casing, which are part of the extended rotor system. This system will have vibration modes that include the rotor and the machine casing. These modes may be in phase, where rotor and casing move approximately together, or out of phase, where rotor and casing move approximately opposite to each other.

For any given force, the amount of casing vibration will depend on several factors, including the relative masses of the rotor and casing, and the stiffnesses of the bearings, casing, casing mounting, and foundation (see Chapter 12).

When shaft relative transducers are mounted at a location that has significant vibration, then the transducers will also vibrate, and the measured shaft relative vibration will not be the same as shaft absolute. As a general rule, when the casing vibration (the vibration of the proximity transducer) exceeds ⅓ of the shaft relative vibration, then shaft relative measurements should be supplemented with *bearing absolute* (*casing*) vibration measurements, which, in this application, are intended to measure proximity probe vibration. For rotor-related frequencies, bearing absolute vibration is usually measured with a velocity transducer, and the velocity signal is integrated to displacement.

Assuming that the casing vibration is a good measurement of the proximity probe vibration, it can be added to the shaft relative vibration to calculate shaft absolute vibration:

$$r_s = r_c + r_{sr} \qquad (16\text{-}4)$$

where r_s is the shaft absolute displacement vibration vector, r_c is the casing displacement vibration vector, and r_{sr} is the shaft relative displacement vibration vector.

We do not recommend mounting the casing transducer on a bearing cover unless it is rigidly connected to the proximity probe mounting. If the cover can move independently of the proximity probe mounting, then measured casing vibration will not be the same as proximity probe vibration, and there will be errors in the calculation. Both shaft relative and casing transducers should be mounted as closely as possible to each other on the bearing itself.

A Keyphasor transducer is essential for efficient balancing. This is usually an eddy current transducer (sometimes an optical transducer) that is mounted so it can observe a once-per-turn mark on the shaft. The Keyphasor transducer provides the phase reference that makes it possible to locate the heavy and high spots on the rotor. Although machines can be balanced without phase information [2], it is a much less efficient process, requiring more startups to gather the necessary data.

Balancing Methodology

Before balancing, *make sure that unbalance is really the problem* (Chapter 18). There are many malfunctions that can produce unbalance-like symptoms; correcting the symptom and not the root cause can lead to more problems later on. Rotor bow (Chapter 19) can be easily mistaken for unbalance; if you balance a bow and the bow works itself out, you will have *unbalanced* the machine instead of balanced it.

When balancing, it is very helpful to know the rotor dynamic and physical characteristics of your machine. What is the mode shape of the rotor at operating speed? Because machines can influence each other across couplings, it is important to remember that system modes include all rigidly coupled elements of a machine train. Also, placement of weights at or near a nodal point for a mode will have little influence on that mode.

Know the location and number of *balance planes*, or *weight planes* (locations specifically designed for balancing weight addition), the balancing history of the machine, and what weights are currently installed. Know how your machine responds to weight placement (influence vectors, see below).

There are two basic kinds of balancing. *Shop balancing* is usually performed by the OEM or a balancing company, using a special test stand, before the assembled rotor is installed in the machine. *Trim balancing* is performed on-site after the rotor is installed in the machine, when the assembled rotor system includes the effects of the support and bearing stiffnesses, the coupling, and the rest of the machine train. Subsequent minor changes in unbalance will also be corrected on-site with a trim balance. In this chapter we will primarily discuss trim balancing, but the principles apply to both types of balancing.

Balancing usually involves the installation of one or more *trim weights*, which are relatively small balancing weights, on the rotor at a convenient radius. The mass and angular location of the weights are selected to move the mass center of the rotor to the geometric center. This is most often done by adding mass to the *opposite* side of the rotor from the heavy spot so that it exactly balances the heavy spot. Balancing can also be performed by removing an equivalent amount of mass from the same side of the rotor as the heavy spot.

The balancing procedure is repeated until the residual unbalance, U, falls below an appropriate specification. It is not possible to balance machines perfectly, and it can be expensive to try.

All balancing techniques depend on the assumption of *linearity*. The basic rotor model we developed in Chapter 10 is a linear model. This means that, if the magnitude of the force is multiplied by some factor, the magnitude of the vibration vector changes by the same factor. Also, if the phase of the force is rotated by some angle, then the phase of the vibration vector changes by the same angle. This linear behavior allows us to predict how the rotor will respond to the trim balance weights.

However, under some circumstances, rotor behavior can be nonlinear, where the Dynamic Stiffness of the machine changes as a function of rotor position or vibration amplitude. Most often, this occurs because of nonlinear spring stiffness. For example, fluid-film bearings have nonlinear spring stiffness at high eccentricity ratios. When unbalance produces high vibration, the dynamic eccentricity ratio may be high, producing high average spring stiffness. When the unbalance is reduced, the decrease in vibration and dynamic eccentricity ratio may cause the average spring stiffness to decrease. The decreased stiffness can shift the resonance and cause an unexpected change in amplitude and phase. Also, balancing on or near a resonance can make the machine very sensitive to slight changes in speed, because of the amplification factor and the rapid rate of change of phase due to the resonance. Partial rub also produces nonlinear stiffness effects. If a system is producing significant vibration harmonics (2X, 3X, etc.) then nonlinearity is usually present.

Balancing also requires *repeatability*. Unless you are very lucky, balancing a machine with no balancing history requires a minimum of two startups or shutdowns to collect data. An implicit assumption in this process is that nothing changes in the machine (the Dynamic Stiffness remains constant) except the variable you are changing, the balance weight. Changes in speed, temperature, load, or alignment can alter the Dynamic Stiffness of the machine, producing changes in response that are not related to the change in balance state. Advanced shaft cracks can produce changes in shaft stiffness from run to run, changing the rotor response. One of the symptoms of a shaft crack is difficulty in balancing (Chapter 23).

Balancing requires that we discover two pieces of information:

1. *Where do we place the balance weight?*

2. *How much weight do we add?*

To answer these questions, we must discover the direction and magnitude of the unbalance. Attempting to balance by guessing at these values would be time consuming, expensive, and unlikely to succeed. Instead, there are systematic procedures that can help us determine the balance weight (*balance shot*) accurately, with a minimum of wasted effort, and provide balancing information that can be used the next time.

Answering the first question requires that we determine the direction of the existing unbalance, or heavy spot. When little is known about the balancing characteristics of a machine, two basic methods for identifying the direction of the heavy spot are available: the *polar plot* method and the *calibration weight* method. When startup or shutdown data is available, a polar plot can be used, together with principles of rotor dynamic behavior, to identify the probable direction of the heavy spot. This information gives us a good chance to achieve an acceptable balance state with the first weight addition. Then, the calibration weight method can be used to determine the amount of additional weight to add, if necessary. When only steady state data is available, the calibration weight method must be used to answer both questions.

If the balance characteristics of a machine are well known, *influence vectors* can be used to calculate the required balancing weight addition. Influence vectors describe how a machine responds to weight addition. With them, it is usually possible to balance a machine on the first try. We will define and show how to use influence vectors later in this chapter.

Calibration weight balancing is the simple process of adding a weight and measuring its effect. We add a *calibration weight* (also called a *trial weight*), a known amount of weight at a known angular location, to the machine. When we restart the machine, the new vibration vector will be a combination of the original unbalance response and a new response due to the calibration weight. If the system is linear in behavior, these two responses combine by simple vector addition. Therefore, if we subtract the original response vector from the new response vector, we will obtain the response due to the calibration weight. Once we know this response, we adjust the size and angular location of the calibration weight until the predicted response exactly cancels the original unbalance response. The result of that exercise gives us the balancing solution.

Balancing an unknown machine usually involves a combination of polar plot and calibration weight techniques and follows this general procedure:

1. Identify the rotor speed at which the balancing operation will take place. This is usually the normal operating speed of the machine.

2. Determine where the machine operating speed is relative to the nearest resonance. This data is used to estimate the angular location of the heavy spot and is most easily acquired from startup or shutdown polar plots.

3. Install a calibration weight at a location opposite the estimated heavy spot location. This will, hopefully, improve the unbalance situation and provide important information on how the machine responds to weight addition.

4.   Start the machine and measure the vibration at operating speed. This will let you calculate how the addition of mass changed, or influenced, the rotor vibration.

5.   Use this information to calculate a balance solution.

6.   When the product of the next calculated trim weight and its radius of attachment ($U = mr_u$) is less than your balancing specification, then the rotor is "balanced."

In the next few sections, we will show how to apply this procedure to single-plane balancing. Later, we will extend it to two-plane balancing. We will discuss balancing from the point of view of *adding* weight to the opposite side of the rotor from the indicated heavy spot. Keep in mind that balancing can also be accomplished by *removing* weight from the same side as the heavy spot, which is equivalent to adding a *negative* balance weight to the rotor.

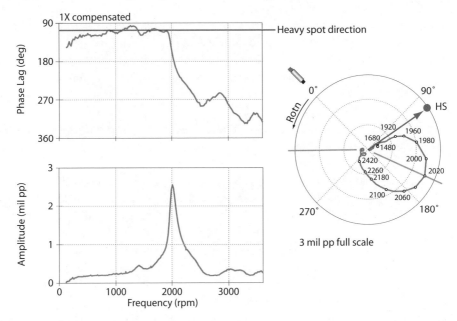

Figure 16-2. Bode and polar plots and the heavy spot. This 1X, compensated data from a small steam turbine shows the direction of the low-speed vector (heavy spot) indicated in red. On the Bode plot, the direction of the low-speed vibration vector is taken from a speed range just before the phase begins to change due to resonance. On the polar plot, the low-speed range is used. The resonance and high-speed relationships (ideally 90° and 180° from low speed) can be used to cross-check the low-speed vector direction.

Locating the Heavy Spot Using a Polar Plot

The polar plot is the most powerful plot format for use in balancing. While Bode plots provide the same information, the polar plot allows us to more quickly and easily determine the location of the heavy spot, a process known as *polar plot balancing*.

Transient data should be collected during the shutdown, if possible. Startup data can be used, but temperature changes can alter machine behavior, and axial thermal growth can change the slow roll vectors if the probes observe a different axial position on the shaft. For best results, the machine should be run long enough to reach thermal equilibrium, and transient data should be collected during shutdown.

To balance accurately and efficiently, we must eliminate the part of the vibration signal that is not due to unbalance; thus, we use *1X vibration data that is slow roll compensated*. Polar plots can be compensated by inspection, which makes them easier to use for balancing, but compensation of Bode plots must usually be done by calculation (Chapter 7).

These basic rules of rotor behavior are the fundamental to polar plot balancing:

1. At speeds well below a resonance, the heavy spot and high spot will be approximately in phase, and the displacement vibration vector will point in the direction of the heavy spot.

2. At resonance, the high spot lags the heavy spot by about 90°. The vibration vector at resonance will point about 90° away from the heavy spot in a direction opposite to rotation.

3. At speeds well above resonance, the high spot and heavy spot are about 180° out of phase. The vibration vector will point in a direction opposite to the heavy spot.

Figure 16-2 shows 1X, compensated Bode and polar plots from a small steam turbine, with the direction of the low-speed vector (heavy spot) indicated in red. The Bode plot provides a valuable cross-check on the polar plot interpretation.

The 0°, 90°, and 180° relationships can be used to cross-check the low-speed vector direction. In the figure, the green lines show the phase lag at resonance (2020 rpm) and at well above resonance. Ideally, these lines should be 90° and 180° from the heavy spot; however, anisotropic stiffness, structural resonances, and multiple modes distort these simple relationships. Even so, if you use the heavy spot location associated with either the low-, resonance, or high-speed response vector, it would be accurate enough for an initial balancing try.

In rotor systems with isotropic stiffness, polar plots from *XY* transducers will look like identical circles and yield identical estimates of the heavy spot location. However, anisotropic stiffness may cause the polar plots to look significantly different (Figure 16-3) and may produce different implied locations for the heavy spot. When balancing, whenever possible, *compare both polar plots*. The heavy spot locations can be averaged, or more sophisticated signal processing techniques can be applied, such as Virtual Probe Rotation or forward response vectors (see Chapter 13 and Appendix 5).

In rare instances, when there is a high ratio of tangential to spring stiffness for a flexible rotor supported in a fluid-film bearing, the indicated heavy spot on both polar plots may be tens of degrees ahead of the actual heavy spot [3]. However, in normally loaded, fluid-film bearings, the tangential stiffness is relatively low and does not cause this problem.

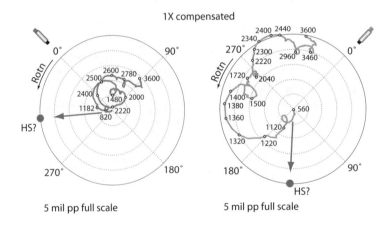

Figure 16-3. Heavy spot location in anisotropic systems. In rotor systems with *anisotropic stiffness*, the *XY* polar plots will typically identify different locations for the heavy spot. When balancing, whenever possible, *compare both polar plots;* you can average the directions or use the processing techniques described in Chapter 13 and Appendix 5.

Using Polar Plots Of Velocity and Acceleration Data

We have been discussing balancing using shaft relative, displacement vibration data. However, on many small machines, the only available transducer is a casing-mounted velocity or acceleration transducer. Often these small machines have rolling element bearings with good transmissibility to the casing, and the machine bearing caps move more or less in phase with the rotor at that location.

The rotor model we developed was based on displacement, and the high spot/heavy spot relationships are *displacement* relationships. The behavior of the model is different for velocity and acceleration.

The rotating, synchronous rotor response vector is

$$\mathbf{r} = Ae^{j(\Omega t + \alpha)} \tag{16-5}$$

where A is the amplitude, Ω is the rotor speed, t is time, and α is the phase of the response. We find the velocity, $\dot{\mathbf{r}}$, and acceleration, $\ddot{\mathbf{r}}$, by differentiating the displacement with respect to time,

$$\dot{\mathbf{r}} = j\Omega Ae^{j(\Omega t + \alpha)}$$
$$\ddot{\mathbf{r}} = -\Omega^2 Ae^{j(\Omega t + \alpha)} \tag{16-6}$$

Figure 16-4. Comparison of displacement (green), velocity (orange), and acceleration (violet) data on a polar plot. Data shown is based on the rotor model of Chapter 10. The actual heavy spot orientation is shown as a red dot. Arrows show the low-speed phase direction for each measurement. The displacement data converges to a point (constant amplitude) at high speed, while velocity and acceleration plots increase in amplitude. Note that the direction of the acceleration vector at high speed is the same as the heavy spot and the opposite of the displacement vector.

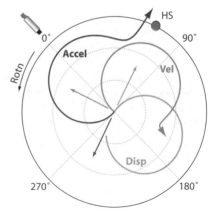

The *j* at the beginning of the velocity term tells us that the phase of the velocity is 90° ahead of (leads) the displacement. The minus sign in the acceleration, the result of *j* times *j*, tells us that the phase of acceleration is 90° ahead of the velocity, or 180° ahead of the displacement. Thus, *the phase relationships we have used to locate the heavy spot on a displacement vibration polar plot do not apply for velocity and acceleration.* All of the relationships are shifted by 90° and 180° for velocity and acceleration, respectively. Note that integrating velocity data to displacement shifts the phase 90° in a *lag* direction, making integrated velocity equivalent to displacement.

Figure 16-4 shows polar plots of displacement, velocity, and acceleration, based on the rotor model of Chapter 10, and the direction of their low-speed vibration vectors. The actual heavy spot orientation is shown as a red dot. *When using velocity or acceleration data to locate the heavy spot, you must allow for the phase shifts shown in these plots.* These changes are summarized in Table 16-1.

Selecting the Calibration Weight

If we have polar plots, we will place a balance weight *opposite* the heavy spot indicated on the plot. If we have only steady state data, and no previous information about the machine, then we will have to guess where to put it. If we have the balance history of the machine, including the influence vectors (see below), then we can directly calculate the balance solution in one step.

The calibration weight, also called a trial weight, will show us how the rotor responds to unbalance at this speed, allowing us to "calibrate" the machine's

Table 16-1. Phase relationships for displacement, velocity, and acceleration. The table lists the phase of the vibration vector relative to the heavy spot for three operating conditions. "Low Speed" means a speed well below the balance resonance; "High Speed" means a speed well above the resonance.

	Low Speed	Resonance	High Speed
Displacement	0°	90° Lag	180° Lag
Velocity	90° Lead	0°	90° Lag
Acceleration	180° Lead	90° Lead	0°

response. We will use that information to calculate exactly how much weight to add and where to put it to balance the machine.

But, when little is known about a machine's response, how do you know how much weight to add? If you add too much weight, it could damage the machine; if too little, then the change in vibration might be too small to detect. A good, conservative rule is to install an amount of weight that will produce a force equal to no more than 10% of the rotor weight, *at the highest anticipated operating speed*:

$$F = m r_u \Omega^2 = 0.10 W \qquad (16\text{-}7)$$

where W is the total rotor *weight* (N or lb) produced by the rotor mass: $W = Mg$, where M is the rotor mass (kg or lb $\cdot$ s^2/in), and g is the acceleration of gravity. We can solve Equation 16-7 for the mass of the balance weight,

$$m = \frac{0.10 W}{r_u \Omega^2} = \frac{0.10 Mg}{r_u \Omega^2} \qquad (16\text{-}8)$$

Example 2

Given a rotor mass of 1000 kg (2200 lb) that turns at 3000 rpm, find the calibration weight mass, in grams and ounces, that satisfies the 10% rule. The weight will be installed at a radius of 250 mm (9.8 in).

Solution

Because the rotor weight is given as a mass, we use the right side of Equation 16-8,

$$m = \frac{0.10\left[(1000 \text{ kg})(9.81 \text{ m/s}^2)\right]}{(250 \times 10^{-3} \text{ m})\left[(3000 \text{ rev/min})(1 \text{ min/60 s})(2\pi \text{ rad/rev})\right]^2}$$

$$m = 40 \times 10^{-3} \text{ kg} = 40 \text{ g}$$

Converting to ounces,

$$m = 40 \times 10^{-3} \text{ kg} (2.2 \text{ lb/kg})(16 \text{ oz/lb})$$
$$m = 1.4 \text{ oz}$$

Example 3
Given a rotor weight of 1250 lb (550 kg) that turns at 7800 rpm, find the trial weight, in ounces, that satisfies the 10% rule. The trial weight will be installed at a radius of 6.5 in (170 mm).

Solution
The rotor weight is given in units of force, so we use the left side of Equation 16-8,

$$m = \frac{0.10(1250 \text{ lb})}{(6.5 \text{ in})\left[(7800 \text{ rev/min})(1 \text{ min/60 s})(2\pi \text{ rad/rev})\right]^2}$$

$$m = 28.9 \times 10^{-6} \, \frac{\text{lb} \cdot \text{s}^2}{\text{in}}$$

The units of the balance weight are U.S. customary *mass* units. We convert to force by multiplying by the acceleration of gravity ($F = mg$),

$$m = \left(28.9 \times 10^{-6} \, \frac{\text{lb} \cdot \text{s}^2}{\text{in}}\right)\left(386 \, \frac{\text{in}}{\text{s}^2}\right)\left(16 \, \frac{\text{oz}}{\text{lb}}\right)$$

$$m = 0.18 \text{ oz}$$

Converting to metric mass,

$$m = (0.18 \text{ oz})\left(\frac{1 \text{ lb}}{16 \text{ oz}}\right)\left(\frac{1000 \text{ g}}{2.2 \text{ lb}}\right)$$

$$m = 5.1 \text{ g}$$

Relating Balance Ring Location To Polar Plot Location

The next step is to locate the physical position on the balance ring that corresponds to the angular location on the polar plot where we wish to add weight. We must be able to tell the people who will actually install the weight exactly where on the rotor that weight must go.

This can be a challenging problem in the field because of the many different phase and angular measurement conventions that exist. Be sure you understand the correspondence (mapping) between the phase indications on a vector plot and any markings on the machine. Verify that the direction of rotation indicated on the plot matches the actual machine rotation, and that you are looking down the machine train in the correct direction.

On horizontal machines, the external reference direction is usually toward the top of the machine, "Up." But on vertical machines, the external reference direction can be any convenient direction, such as "North" or "East," or a significant feature of the machine or building. Be sure you have identified the correct external reference for the machine in question. Verify that the probe mounting orientations relative to this reference are as shown on the data plot.

On Bently Nevada polar plots, the phase lag angles start at 0° at the transducer location and increase in a direction opposite to rotation. Also, the plots are oriented so that the 0° mark is oriented at the same orientation on the paper as the actual physical transducer is on the machine. For example, if the transducer is located at 45° R from the physical reference, usually "Up," then the polar plot will show the 0° mark at 45° R from the top of the page. This provides the same perspective on the heavy spot location as an observer would have looking down the machine train.

On the rotor, however, things are different. Some rotors can have continuous circumferential slots where weights can be installed, moved to any desired angular position, and locked into place. Other rotors have only discrete holes available for weight addition. In either case, reference marks on machines will usually conform to a different measurement system unrelated to the vibration transducers. Degree marks may increase either with or against rotation, and the 0° mark on the shaft is unlikely to have any relationship to the installed transducers.

Often, rotors have discrete weight mounting holes. These holes (typically 30 or so) are equally spaced around the circumference of the rotor and are sequentially numbered; the numbers may increase in a direction with or opposite to rotation. The person balancing the machine must clearly communicate to the plant technicians how much weight to add and which balancing hole to install it in. To identify the correct hole, a *weight map* should be created that illustrates the relationship between the instrumentation phase measurements and the physical hole numbers on the machine.

The Keyphasor notch and Keyphasor probe provide the link between the physical shaft and the polar plot. To establish this link, we must identify which balancing hole is aligned with the Keyphasor notch. Usually, there will be a machine drawing at the plant that shows balance hole orientations relative to some physical reference on the machine. The Keyphasor notch angular location must be established relative to that physical reference. Once this is done, the weight map can be completed.

Figure 16-5 shows an example of a typical weight map. In this example, rotation is X to Y when viewed from the driver looking toward the driven machine, and the vibration transducer is mounted at 45° L from the physical reference, in this case, "Up." The transducer phase lag angles are indicated on the outer perimeter. This balance plane, or *weight plane,* has 40 available holes, typical of the turbine and compressor balance planes of a Westinghouse 501 gas turbine. *The hole numbers on the map correspond to the hole number markings on the machine, and the holes are shown at the orientation when the Keyphasor notch triggers the Keyphasor probe* (bottom). The access port for installing weights is also shown where it exists on the machine. The balance weight radius is clearly indicated, and all installed weights are shown, with existing weights in brown and new (for the current balancing attempt) weights in red. (Any convenient symbols can be used for this purpose.) The table, right, shows the amount of weight that is installed in each hole.

Once the weight map is completed, the weight location that is indicated by the polar plot can be easily converted to a hole number that can be used by plant personnel. If at all possible, you should observe the weight installation process to confirm that things are happening the way you think they are.

Single Plane Balancing With Calibration Weights

In the following discussion, we will discuss balancing in a single plane using data from a single vibration transducer. If XY transducers are available, a good cross-check is to perform the calculations using data from both transducers. We will also assume that the balancing speed is the normal operating speed of the machine.

The calibration weight technique can be performed graphically or numerically. *We highly recommend that both methods be used.* At every step in the process, calculations should be checked for reasonableness. When using a calculator, data entry blunders or procedural errors can produce numbers that are incorrect and could even result in damage to the machine. Sometimes, it can be difficult to tell if a number is reasonable, and when the graphical solution is

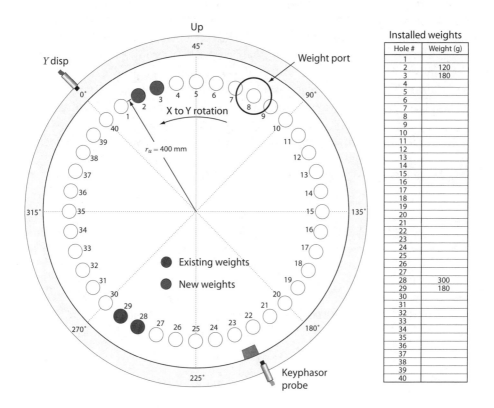

\multicolumn{2}{c|}{Installed weights}	
Hole #	Weight (g)
1	
2	120
3	180
4	
5	
6	
7	
8	
9	
10	
11	
12	
13	
14	
15	
16	
17	
18	
19	
20	
21	
22	
23	
24	
25	
26	
27	
28	300
29	180
30	
31	
32	
33	
34	
35	
36	
37	
38	
39	
40	

Figure 16-5. A typical weight map. This example shows 40 available balance hole locations and existing (brown) and new (red) balance weights. The holes are numbered to match the markings on the rotor when the Keyphasor probe and notch leading edge are aligned. The table, right, shows the amount of weight that is installed in each hole. Additional information includes the balance hole radius; direction of shaft rotation, viewed from the driver end of the machine; the vibration transducer location, 45° L; the physical reference, "Up;" the phase lag angles for this transducer; the Keyphasor probe location; and the location of the weight access port.

done in parallel, it is often much easier to interpret and set a level of confidence in the results.

Balancing calculations involve manipulation of vibration vectors, which are complex numbers. For this reason, numerical techniques are most easily done on a calculator that has complex number capability. Vector calculations can also be done algebraically by using the methods described in Chapter 3.

The graphical method requires polar coordinate graph paper, a pencil, an eraser (unless you are perfect), and a ruler. Two triangles allow easy drawing of parallel lines. The graph will represent the complex transducer response plane discussed in Chapter 3. Prepare the polar graph paper as follows (Figure 16-6):

1. Label the machine external reference direction at top.

2. Draw a curved arrow that indicates the direction of rotation, viewed from the driver toward the driven machine.

3. Locate the transducer at the appropriate angle from the reference direction. For example, if the transducer is located at 45° R, mark the perimeter of the plot at 45° R with the transducer identification.

4. Draw the phase lag scale around the perimeter of the plot, starting with 0° at the transducer location, and increasing in a direction *opposite* to rotation.

5. Label the plot with the rotor speed and other important machine variables, such as temperature, load, etc., that might affect the repeatability of the data.

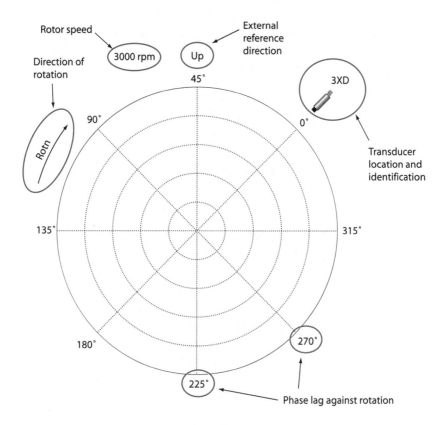

Figure 16-6. Polar graph prepared for balancing calculations. Information documented includes the transducer location and identification, phase lag angles referenced to the transducer and increasing opposite to rotation, the physical reference, direction of rotation viewed from the driver end, and machine speed.

We will show how to perform the graphical and then the mathematical techniques of calibration weight balancing. For the graphical calibration weight balancing technique (refer to Figure 16-7):

1. Measure the *Original*, 1X, compensated vibration vector, *O*. This is the vibration at running speed due to the unknown unbalance, before the calibration weight is installed. Decide on a full scale for the plot, draw this vector on the plot, starting at the origin (Figure 16-7a), and label it. The length of the vector corresponds to the amplitude (pp or pk, it does not matter, as long as you are consistent). In this example, $O = 80$ µm pp $\angle 125°$ (3.2 mil pp $\angle 125°$). Note that it is not absolutely necessary to draw the entire vector from the origin. Some prefer to draw and label just a point at the tip of the vector or a short vector that ends at the point to reduce clutter on the diagram.

2. Shut down the machine and install the calibration weight. Document the weight location on the graph with a box, and label it with the amount (Figure 16-7b). This weight behaves like a vector; it has magnitude (its weight) and direction (its angular position), so we will call it m_{cal}. In this example, the rotor weight is 1000 kg, and the 10% rule dictates a trial weight no larger than 40 g (see *Example 2*). We suspect that the machine is running above the first resonance, which means that the high spot is opposite the heavy spot. Install the trial weight opposite the heavy spot in the closest available hole, 135°.

3. Run the machine up to operating speed and measure the new vibration vector. This vector represents the machine's *Total* response, *T*, to the original, still unknown unbalance plus the response, *C*, due to m_{cal}. Draw *T* on the graph paper, starting at the origin, and label it (Figure 16-7c). In our example, $T = 50$ µm pp $\angle 155°$ (2.0 mil pp $\angle 155°$).

4. Find *C*, the response due to the calibration weight, m_{cal}. The total response is

$$T = O + C \qquad (16\text{-}9)$$

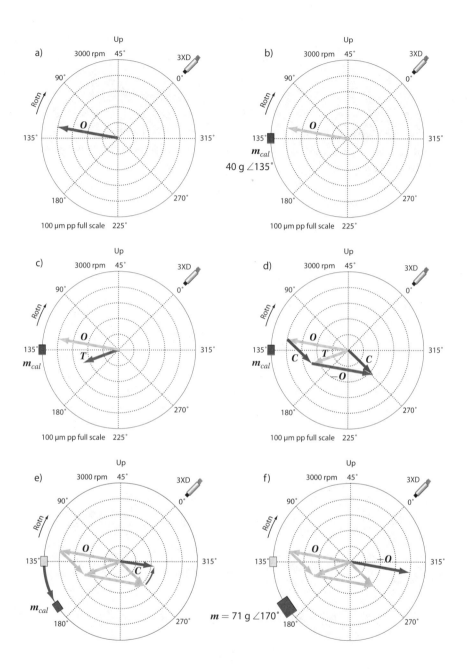

Figure 16-7. Single plane, graphical, calibration weight balancing. The sequence illustrates how the response to a calibration weight can be identified and used to graphically determine a balancing solution. See the text for details.

Thus,

$$C = T - O = T + (-O) \qquad (16\text{-}10)$$

As the equation shows, vector subtraction is equivalent to adding the *negative* of the vector being subtracted. This is a vector of the same length that points in the opposite direction. To subtract O from T, measure the length of O, and draw $-O$ on the plot, starting at the tip of T (Figure 16-7d). C is found by drawing a vector from the origin to the tip of $-O$. Alternatively, draw C from the tip of O to the tip of T. C is the rotor response to m_{cal} at this operating speed. In our example, we measure it graphically as 45 μm pp $\angle 270°$ (1.8 mil pp $\angle 270°$).

5. Rotate C so that it is in the opposite direction from O. m_{cal} and C are locked together by our assumption of linearity; if we rotate C to a different angular location, m_{cal} will rotate in the same direction by the same amount. Rotate m_{cal} by the same angle and mark the new location on the plot (Figure 16-7e). A weight placed here will produce a response that is opposite in direction from O. In our example, C is moved to 305°, opposite to O, which rotates m_{cal} to 170°.

6. Calculate the size of the final balancing weight. If we double the size of m_{cal}, the length of C will also double. Thus, all we need to do is scale m_{cal} so that C will be equal in length to $-O$. The size (magnitude) of the balance weight we need, $|m|$, is given by

$$|m| = \frac{|-O|}{|C|} |m_{cal}| \qquad (16\text{-}11)$$

This calculation assumes that the original calibration weight has been removed. The calculation will be different if m_{cal} is left in place (see below). In our example, we increase m_{cal} by 80/45 to produce $m = 71$ g $\angle 170°$ (Figure 16-7f).

Mathematically, this graphical procedure can be represented, using vectors, as

$$m = \frac{-O}{T-O} m_{cal} = \frac{-O}{C} m_{cal} \tag{16-12}$$

where phase is measured using instrumentation phase lag angles (Appendix 1). The angular location of m is the location of the balance weight on the polar plot and is

$$\angle m = (\angle O + 180°) - \angle C + \angle m_{cal} \tag{16-13}$$

and the magnitude of m is given by Equation 16-11).

Weight Splitting

The balance solution may point between balance holes, point to a hole that is full, or call for more weight than will fit in one hole. Or you may wish to (or have to) leave the calibration weight in place and install a final trim balance. When any of these happen, you can split the balance solution between available holes so that the result is equivalent. This process is called *weight splitting*.

Weight splitting combines the effects of two weights, mounted in available holes, so that they will have the same effect as the balance solution. In the example shown in Figure 16-8, the calculated balance solution, $m = m \angle\theta$, falls between balance holes. Two weights, m_1, and m_2 are to be mounted at angular locations θ_1 and θ_2, producing the mass vectors m_1, and m_2. These vectors must add to produce an equivalent weight, $m \angle\theta$. Our calculated balance solution is known, as are θ_1 and θ_2, the angular locations of the available balance holes. The problem is to define the values of m_1 and m_2 that satisfy the balancing requirement.

It is important to remember that the force produced by a balance weight depends on both the mass of the weight *and the radius*. If weights are to be split at different mounting radii, the radii must be included in the analysis. The following derivations assume that the radii are the same, which is most often the case.

The masses and angles can be treated as vectors (complex numbers), where the requirement becomes

$$\boldsymbol{m}_1 + \boldsymbol{m}_2 = \boldsymbol{m}$$
$$m_1 e^{j\theta_1} + m_2 e^{j\theta_2} = m e^{j\theta} \tag{16-14}$$

where the phase angles in this case are instrumentation convention phase lag angles. Equating real and imaginary parts, we obtain a system of equations,

$$\begin{bmatrix} \cos\theta_1 & \cos\theta_2 \\ \sin\theta_1 & \sin\theta_2 \end{bmatrix} \begin{pmatrix} m_1 \\ m_2 \end{pmatrix} = \begin{pmatrix} m\cos\theta \\ m\sin\theta \end{pmatrix} \tag{16-15}$$

which can be solved numerically. Or, we can use explicit functions:

$$m_1 = m \left[\frac{\sin(\theta_2 - \theta)}{\sin(\theta_2 - \theta_1)} \right]$$

$$m_2 = m \left[\frac{\sin(\theta - \theta_1)}{\sin(\theta_2 - \theta_1)} \right] \tag{16-16}$$

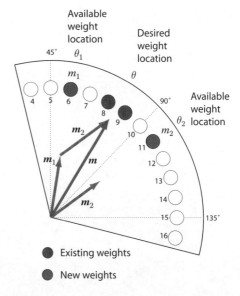

Figure 16-8. Weight splitting. Since the location where we want to install **m** is already occupied, two weights, m_1 and m_2, are mounted at angular locations θ_1 and θ_2 to produce the equivalent weight, $\boldsymbol{m} = m \angle \theta$.

Example 4
Calculations indicate that a balance weight of 5.0 g must be installed at 42°. Balance holes are available at 20° and 90°. The balance ring radius for all holes is 100 mm. Find the amount of weight to add in the two available holes.

Solution
Because the balance hole radius is the same for all holes, we can use Equation 16-16. $m = 5.0$ g $\angle 42°$. Thus, $m = 5$ g and $\theta = 42°$. Let $\theta_1 = 20°$ and $\theta_2 = 90°$. Applying Equations 16-16,

$$m_1 = 5 \text{ g} \left[\frac{\sin(90° - 42°)}{\sin(90° - 20°)} \right]$$

$$m_1 = 4 \text{ g}$$

$$m_2 = 5 \text{ g} \left[\frac{\sin(42° - 20°)}{\sin(90° - 20°)} \right]$$

$$m_2 = 2 \text{ g}$$

Thus, $m_1 = 4$ g $\angle 20°$ and $m_2 = 2$ g $\angle 90°$.

A different case exists when the calibration weight, m_{cal}, has already been installed, and we wish to leave it in place. A final trim weight needs to be added. m_{cal} effectively takes the place of m_1 above. Now the problem is to find an m_2 that, together with m_{cal}, satisfies the balancing requirement, m. Thus, we require that

$$m_{cal} + m_2 = m \tag{16-17}$$

or, in exponential form,

$$m_{cal}e^{j\theta_{cal}} + m_2 e^{j\theta_2} = me^{j\theta} \tag{16-18}$$

Thus,

$$m_2 = m_2 e^{j\theta_2} = m e^{j\theta} - m_{cal} e^{j\theta_{cal}} \tag{16-19}$$

or, in amplitude and phase notation,

$$m_2 = m_2 \angle\theta_2 = (m \angle\theta) - (m_{cal} \angle\theta_{cal}) \tag{16-20}$$

If you have a calculator that has complex number capability, this equation can be used directly. Otherwise, we can find algebraic expressions for m_2 and θ_2 by breaking Equation 16-19 into real and imaginary parts, which leads to

$$\theta_2 = \arctan 2\left[\frac{m\sin\theta - m_{cal}\sin\theta_{cal}}{m\cos\theta - m_{cal}\cos\theta_{cal}} \right]$$

$$m_2 = \sqrt{m^2 + m_{cal}^2 - 2mm_{cal}\cos(\theta - \theta_{cal})} \tag{16-21}$$

where the arctangent2 function is used to return a result between $\pm 180°$. If the result is negative, add 360°. Note that this solution can also be split using Equations 16-16 if necessary.

Example 5
Given the situation of the previous example, assume that a calibration weight, 10 g $\angle120°$, has already been installed. Find m_2 such that, together with m_{cal}, will produce $m = 5$ g $\angle42°$.

Solution
$m_{cal} = 10$ g $\angle120°$, and $m = 5$ g $\angle42°$. Applying Equations 16-21,

$$\theta_2 = \arctan 2\left[\frac{5\text{ g }\sin 42° - 10\text{ g }\sin 120°}{5\text{ g }\cos 42° - 10\text{ g }\cos 120°} \right]$$

$$\theta_2 = -31° = 329°$$

$$m_2 = \sqrt{(5 \text{ g})^2 + (10 \text{ g})^2 - 2(5 \text{ g})(10 \text{ g})\cos(42° - 120°)}$$

$$m_2 = 10 \text{ g}$$

The final trim weight is $m_2 = 10 \text{ g} \angle 330°$.

The final trim weight, m_2, can also be obtained graphically by adding a new weight, m_{cal}, with a new associated vector, C, and positioning and adjusting the size of this weight until it produces a response equal to $-T$.

The Influence Vector

An *influence vector* is a complex number that describes how the 1X vibration of a machine will change when a balance weight is added to the machine; in other words, how a balance weight will *influence* both the amplitude and phase of the vibration of the machine. An influence vector is sometimes called an influence *coefficient*; we prefer the term *vector* because it contains both amplitude and phase information.

The influence vector describes the effect of a weight in a single balance plane (weight plane) on the vibration in a measurement plane. The measurement plane can be nearby, or it can be far away from the weight plane; in this case, the influence vector is sometimes called a *longitudinal influence vector*. Each influence vector is specific to a particular combination of balance plane and measurement point (a particular transducer in a particular measurement plane) and to a particular set of operating conditions, including speed, load, temperature, and alignment state.

These characteristics follow from the fact that the influence vector is very closely related to the Dynamic Stiffness that exists between the weight plane and the measurement plane. Dynamic Stiffness and the influence vector are actually different expressions of the same thing, and, as we will show, it is easy to calculate one from the other. When balancing, it is important to remember that a change in the machine since the last balancing operation may have changed the Dynamic Stiffness and the influence vector. For example, a machine that has been overhauled may have a change in alignment that affects the Dynamic Stiffness and the influence vectors.

The influence vector is easily calculated using the results of calibration weight balancing (see above). Given a calibration weight, m_{cal}, the influence vector, H, produces an associated response vector, C, such that

$$C = Hm_{cal} \tag{16-22}$$

Thus, the influence vector, *H*, is

$$H = \frac{C}{m_{cal}} = \frac{(T-O)}{m_{cal}} \tag{16-23}$$

where *O* is the original unbalance response vector, and *T* is the total response, including the original unbalance response and the calibration weight response. The magnitude of *H* is found by taking the ratio of the magnitudes of *C* and m_{cal}:

$$|H| = \frac{|C|}{|m_{cal}|} \tag{16-24}$$

The angle of *H*, a lag angle measured against rotation, is found by subtracting the lag angle of the calibration weight from the lag angle of the response due to that weight:

$$\theta_H = \angle H = \angle C - \angle m_{cal} \tag{16-25}$$

What is the meaning of the influence vector? Going back to Equation 16-23, note that the difference, $T - O = C$, tells us that *H* measures the *change* in vibration that occurs when a weight is added to the machine. Because *H* is a vector, it tells us how both the *amplitude* and the *phase* of 1X vibration will change with the weight addition.

The equation also tells us that the influence vector is the ratio of the change in vibration, *C*, to the mass vector that produced that change, m_{cal}. Thus, the units of *H* are vibration amplitude per unit mass (or weight): for example, μm pp/g or mil pp/oz.

Suppose that we measure an influence vector on a machine running at 3600 rpm as *H* = 5.7 μm pp/g ∠135°. If we assume that the machine is *perfectly balanced* and the 1X vibration is zero, *H* tells us that, at 3600 rpm, each gram of weight we add in the balance plane will, at the measurement plane, produce a 1X vibration of 5.7 μm pp at 135° lag relative to the weight location (Figure 16-9).

If the original vibration was *not* zero, then the vibration vector produced by the weight addition will add to the existing vibration vector. For our example, the *change* in vibration will be 5.7 μm pp ∠135° per gram of weight added.

The phase angle of the influence vector is the same as the heavy spot/high spot relationship that exists in the machine at that speed. If a single mode machine is running well below a resonance, the influence vector phase should be close to 0°, indicating that the high spot and heavy spot are in phase. At the resonance, the phase should be about 90°, and well above the resonance, the phase should be closer to 180°. The presence of higher modes can complicate these simple relationships.

The influence vector allows us to balance easily and quickly. If we have a valid influence vector, we can calculate the required trim balance shot in one step. If O is the original unbalance response, then we want to add an amount of weight in a location that will produce a response exactly *opposite* to the original response. We require a balance shot, m, such that

$$Hm = -O \qquad\qquad (16\text{-}26)$$

Solving for m,

$$m = \frac{-O}{H} \qquad\qquad (16\text{-}27)$$

Figure 16-9. Example of an influence vector, $H = 5.7$ μm pp/g $\angle135°$. For this machine at 3600 rpm, *each gram* of weight will produce a change in 1X vibration of 5.7 μm pp at 135° phase lag relative to the weight. No matter where the mass is located, the influence vector and change in vibration will have the same magnitude and relative orientation. Doubling the weight will double the magnitude of the change in vibration to 11.4 μm pp $\angle135°$. The figure shows three positions of the weight; for each position, the influence maintains the same relative angular orientation, in this case, 135°.

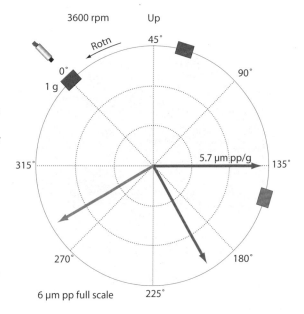

where the magnitude of m is

$$|m| = \frac{|-O|}{|H|} \tag{16-28}$$

and the angle of m is

$$\angle m = \angle(-O) - \angle H \tag{16-29}$$

If an influence vector is known for a particular machine, it is possible to calculate a balance shot using steady state data at running speed, before shutting down the machine. Then, the machine can be shut down, and the balance weight installed. After startup, the response can be compared to what was predicted, and a new influence vector can be calculated if the machine response has changed significantly. For most machines, the influence vector will provide an excellent initial estimate of the balance solution, even if the machine has changed and an additional trim balance is required. A change in the influence vector can draw attention to changes in the machine that could be important.

Example 6
A steam turbine is running at 3600 rpm. A shaft relative probe at 45° L measures a compensated, 1X vibration of 35 μm pp ∠240°. Experience has shown that this machine can be balanced by installing weight in a nearby balance plane. The influence vector for this speed and this location have been previously determined to be 5.7 μm pp/g ∠135°. What weight should be installed?

Solution
The O vector is 35 μm pp ∠240°, and H is 5.7 μm pp/g ∠135° (Figure 16-10). Applying Equations 16-28 and 16-29,

$$|m| = \frac{35 \ \mu m \ pp}{5.7 \ \mu m \ pp/g} = 6.1 \ g$$

$$\angle m = (240° + 180°) - 135° = 285°$$

180° is added because we want to create a vector equivalent to $-O$. Where do we install the weight? On the polar plot, the 6 gram weight would be installed

285° from the measurement transducer in a lag (opposite to rotation) direction. This location must then be translated through the weight map for the balance plane.

The influence vector we have been using is also called the *direct* influence vector. Its use requires that we perform a division, which can be awkward to do mentally. Instead, you can use the *inverse* influence vector to calculate a balance solution using multiplication. For this calculation, we use only the magnitude; the angle is calculated as before. The magnitude of the inverse influence vector is the reciprocal of the magnitude of the direct influence vector,

$$\left|\boldsymbol{H}^{-1}\right| = \frac{1}{\left|\boldsymbol{H}\right|} \tag{16-30}$$

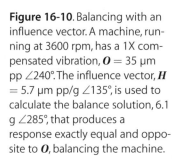

Figure 16-10. Balancing with an influence vector. A machine, running at 3600 rpm, has a 1X compensated vibration, $\boldsymbol{O}$ = 35 μm pp ∠240°. The influence vector, $\boldsymbol{H}$ = 5.7 μm pp/g ∠135°, is used to calculate the balance solution, 6.1 g ∠285°, that produces a response exactly equal and opposite to $\boldsymbol{O}$, balancing the machine.

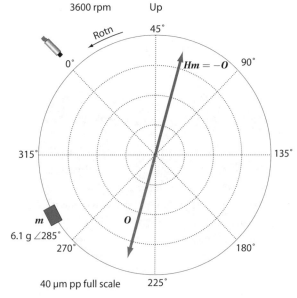

The inverse influence vector has units of weight (or mass) per unit vibration, g/μm pp or oz/mil pp. The magnitude of the balance solution is now,

$$m| = |O\|H^{-1}|$$ (16-31)

The Influence Vector And Dynamic Stiffness

The influence vector is the ratio of the change in vibration to the rotating unbalance *mass* that produced that change. Dynamic Stiffness is the ratio of the rotating unbalance *force* to the vibration produced by that force. Both involve rotor response to a rotating unbalance; thus, the Dynamic Stiffness and influence vector must be related.

The synchronous Dynamic Stiffness, K_S, is

$$K_S = K_S \angle\theta_K = \frac{mr_u\Omega^2 \angle\delta}{A \angle\alpha}$$ (16-32)

where m and r_u are the mass and radius of unbalance, Ω is the rotor speed in rad/s, δ is the phase of the unbalance, and A and α are the amplitude and phase of the vibration response due to the unbalance mass, m. Because this expression is based on the rotor model of Chapter 10, the phase angles in this expression are measured using the mathematical convention (positive phase lead).

The influence vector is H, where

$$H = H \angle\theta_H = \frac{A \angle\alpha}{m \angle\delta}$$ (16-33)

Here, we have substituted $A \angle\alpha$ for C in Equation 16-23; m and δ represent the magnitude and the angle of the calibration weight.

The phase angles used in influence vector calculations in this chapter are measured using the instrumentation convention (positive phase lag), while the mathematical convention is used in Equation 16-32. Note that the angle of the Dynamic Stiffness represents the difference between the angle of the force and the angle of the vibration response. The influence vector angle represents the same thing. Thus, except for the different measurement conventions, the two angles are equal to each other. All that is required to convert between the measurement conventions is to take the negative of the angle.

Solving both equations for $A \angle \alpha$, and setting the two equations equal to each other leads to

$$\boldsymbol{K}_S = \frac{r_u \Omega^2}{H} \angle \theta_H$$

(16-34)

$$\boldsymbol{H} = \frac{r_u \Omega^2}{K} \angle \theta_K$$

where the angles have been adjusted for the measurement conventions.

Example 7
A machine that rotates at 4850 rpm has an influence vector, $\boldsymbol{H} = 325$ mil pp/oz $\angle 41°$ (290 μm pp/g $\angle 41°$), where the angle is measured in degrees lag. The balance hole radius is 7.5 in (190 mm). Find the Synchronous Dynamic Stiffness.

Solution
Apply Equation 16-34,

$$\boldsymbol{K}_S = \frac{(7.5 \text{ in})\left[(4850 \text{ rev/min})(1 \text{ min/60 s})(2\pi \text{ rad/rev})\right]^2}{(1/2)(325 \text{ mil pp/oz})(1 \text{ in/1000 mil})(16 \text{ oz/lb})(386 \text{ in/s}^2)} \angle 41°$$

$$\boldsymbol{K}_S = 1900 \text{ lb/in} \angle 41° \; (337 \text{ kN/m} \angle 41°)$$

The factor of ½ in the denominator converts mil pp to mil pk. Stiffness is usually measured as lb/in or N/m, where the length units are peak, not peak-to-peak. Note that the acceleration of gravity (386 in/s²) is there to convert the balance weight unit (oz) to a mass unit. The angle of the Dynamic Stiffness vector is the same number (with the same sign) as for the influence vector.

The Dynamic Stiffness vector can be broken into direct (magnitude times the cosine of the angle) and quadrature (magnitude times the sine of the angle) parts if desired. For this machine, $K_D = 1430$ lb/in (250 kN/m) and $K_Q = 1250$ lb/in (219 kN/m).

Multiple Modes And Multiplane Balancing

Up to this point we have been discussing single-plane balancing. Most modern turbomachinery rotors operate above the first balance resonance, and many operate above the second, or even higher, mode. Machines with multiple modes often require more complex balancing, where two or more planes are balanced simultaneously. In this section, we will confine ourselves to a discussion of two-plane balancing. Although software exists that can handle many simultaneous planes of balancing, single- and two-plane balancing techniques are adequate to handle most of the trim balance problems you are likely to encounter in the field.

The amount of vibration at a resonance will depend on the unbalance distribution at various axial locations along the rotor, how well the shape of that distribution matches the mode shape of the rotor system, and the modal damping (more precisely, modal quadrature stiffness) for the mode. *If the shape of the unbalance distribution is a poor match for a mode shape, then that mode will be poorly excited or not excited at all.* On the other hand, *an unbalance distribution that matches a mode shape will excite that mode relatively strongly.* We can exploit this behavior to separately balance two different modes, one at a time.

In general, at any speed, the deflection shape of a flexible rotor is the result of a mixture of several modes of vibration. At a resonance, one mode will usually dominate the response. A rotor operating between resonances will usually have residual effects of the lower modes and, at the same time, the early effects of the higher modes, depending on how the shape of the unbalance distribution corresponds to the modes. Thus, the rotor deflection shape will vary with speed and modal contribution; between resonances, the relative phase of two axially separated planes can vary considerably due to the mixing of the modes.

As shown in Figure 16-11 (left), the first mode of a flexible rotor between bearings is usually a simple, predominantly *in-phase*, bending mode (overhung rotors have a different shape; see Chapter 12). In this mode, most of the length of the rotor will be deflected more or less in the same radial direction; thus, vibration measurements taken at different axial positions along the rotor will have approximately the same phase. For this mode, two nodal points (points of zero or minimum vibration) will exist, one near each bearing. The nodal points can be inboard or outboard of the bearings, depending on the stiffness and mass distribution of the system. (Note that, if a probe is located outboard of a nodal point, the phase at that location will be opposite to the predominant phase of this first mode. In such cases, mode identification probes can be installed to help identify the mode shape.) This in-phase mode will respond to an unbalance mass distribution that is predominantly in the same radial direction along the length of the rotor.

The second mode of a flexible rotor is usually an *out-of-phase* bending mode (Figure 16-11, middle). The deflection shape of this mode is approximately S-shaped, with an additional nodal point near the midspan of the rotor. Approximately one-half of the rotor will be deflected in one radial direction, with the other half in the opposite direction. The details of nodal point locations and deflection amplitudes will depend on the stiffness and mass distribution of the rotor. This out-of-phase mode responds well to an out-of-phase unbalance distribution, where the unbalance is predominantly in one radial direction for half of the rotor, and in the opposite direction for the other half of the rotor.

Higher modes have more complicated bending patterns, with one additional nodal point per mode. These modes cannot be described using the simple in-phase and out-of-phase terms we have been using. Trim balancing rotors which exhibit higher mode shapes can be challenging; fortunately, most machines operate below the first resonance or between the first and second resonances, and the influence of higher modes is limited. We will confine our discussion to the techniques involved in balancing the first two modes.

In Figure 16-11, the unbalance is assumed to be concentrated in the two masses shown. These masses are also assumed to be both the weight and measurement planes in the rotor. In general, this will not be the case; mass and unbalance will be axially distributed along the rotor.

The first mode will not respond to an out-of-phase unbalance distribution because, from the point of view of the first mode, the two unbalance forces can-

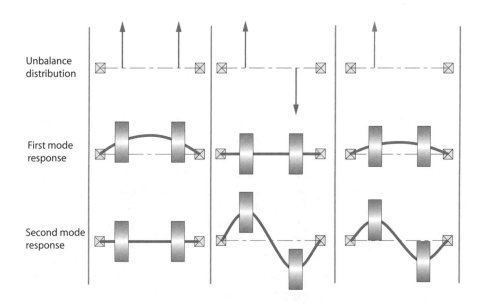

Figure 16-11. Unbalance distribution and mode excitation. The rotor shown has two modes: in phase and out of phase. The in-phase unbalance distribution (left) excites the first mode, but, since it does not fit the second mode shape, it does not excite the second mode. The out-of-phase unbalance distribution (middle) fits the second mode shape, but not the first. The asymmetric unbalance distribution (right) has characteristics of and excites both modes.

cel each other out. Similarly, the second mode will not respond to an in-phase unbalance distribution. Thus, if two identical weights are installed at the same angular location in both weight planes, the in-phase balancing force created will affect the first mode, *but will not excite the second mode*. Similarly, if two identical weights are installed 180° opposite each other in both weight planes, the out-of-phase balancing force created will excite the second mode, *but will not excite the first mode*.

If only one of the forces in the figure is active (right), the unbalance distribution will be able to excite *both* modes. It will be seen by the first mode as an unbalance acting in one direction and by the second mode as an axially asymmetric unbalance. A rotor with most of the unbalance concentrated at one end like this is said to have a *dominant end*.

Note that it is possible to apply these same principles to *rigid body* modes, where the rotor vibrates with little or no bending. Sometimes, two observable rigid body modes exist in a machine, an in-phase (*cylindrical*) mode and an out-of-phase (*pivotal*) mode. Often, these modes tend to be overdamped and are not observed.

In common usage, the in-phase unbalance condition is often called the *static* unbalance; if you support a rotor horizontally on two level knife edges, it will roll until the heavy side is at the bottom. This is a static condition that indicates where the heavy spot is located. A pair of equal balance weights that are mounted at the same phase angle (in phase) in two planes is also called a *static balance shot*.

The out-of-phase unbalance condition is also called the *couple* unbalance. A rotor can be statically balanced and still have a mass distribution that produces a moment (a couple) that creates vibration. This is why automobile wheels are dynamically balanced on a machine. A static balance will not reveal the unbalance caused by a couple in the wheel. A pair of equal balance weights that are installed 180° apart in two planes is also called a *couple balance shot*.

The ideal objective in multiplane balancing is to add weight in both planes so that both modes are balanced in one shot. In practice, simultaneously balancing both modes can be difficult; besides, usually one mode or the other dominates the problem. So, typically only the static or couple mode is addressed.

Balancing of both modes requires identification of the heavy spot location for each mode. Figure 16-12 shows polar plots of a startup of a small, experimental machine that experiences two modes. The polar plots show the response for the Inboard and Outboard measurement planes. Note that the polar loops for the first mode response (blue) are oriented in the same direction, indicating that vibration in both measurement planes is in phase, which identifies an in-phase

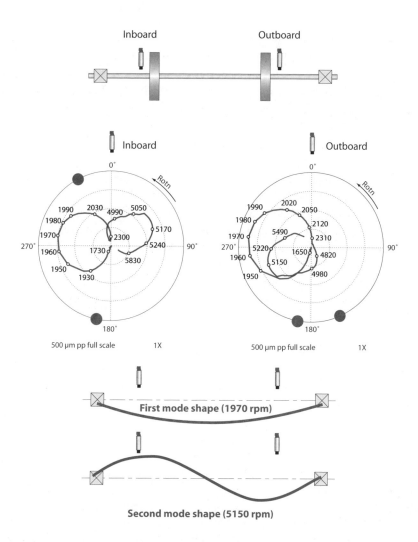

Figure 16-12. Two-plane unbalance response of a small, experimental machine that has two modes. The polar plots from the Inboard and Outboard measurement planes show the first mode (blue) and second mode (red) response. Note that the polar loops for the first mode response are oriented in the same direction, indicating that both measurement planes are deflected in the same direction, an in-phase mode. The indicated heavy spots (blue dots) for each plane are found by looking at the response phase at speeds well below the first resonance. The polar loops in the second mode are on *opposite* sides of the plots, indicating an out-of-phase mode. The heavy spots (red dots) for this mode can be found by looking at the response phase at the low end of the *second* mode resonance. Note that, like the polar loops, the indicated heavy spot locations are on opposite sides in the two measurement planes. At the Outboard end, the heavy spots for both modes are approximately in the same direction, indicating that this is the dominant end of the machine.

mode. The indicated heavy spots (blue dots) for each plane are found by looking at the response phase at speeds well below the resonance.

The polar loops for the second mode response (red) are on *opposite* sides of the plots, indicating that this is an out-of-phase mode. The heavy spots (red dots) for this mode are found using the same principle as for the first mode: look at the response of the rotor at the low-speed end of the *second* mode resonance (but above the first mode). The direction of that response identifies the heavy spot location for that mode. Note that, like the polar loops, the indicated heavy spot locations are on opposite sides in the two measurement planes. This is consistent with the behavior we have been discussing.

At the Outboard end, the heavy spots for the two modes are approximately in the same direction, indicating that this is the dominant end of this machine. If we were restricted to placing weight in only one plane to improve both modes, we would place weight in the Outboard end. However, in the following discussion, we will show how to affect the two modes independently.

We will start by balancing the first mode. Because the first mode response is an in-phase mode, we will install *two identical weights at the same angular location in each plane*, opposite the indicated heavy spots. In this experiment, 0.2 g was installed at 22.5° (the closest available weight hole) in both weight planes. The holes were all at the same radius, so we will ignore the radii in our discussion. If the balance hole radii were different in the two planes, then we would have to modify the amounts of weight added to produce an equal unbalance, $U = mr_u$, in each plane.

The machine response to these weights is shown in Figure 16-13. The first mode response has been significantly reduced, *but the second mode response is unchanged*. Since the second mode is an out-of-phase mode, it does not match the in-phase weight distribution that was added, so there was no change in response.

Next, we can modify the second mode response without affecting the first mode by adding a weight *couple*: two equal weights installed in opposite sides of the two planes. In this experiment, 0.4 g was installed at 135° in the Inboard plane, and 0.4 g was installed at 315° in the Outboard plane. These locations are approximately opposite to the indicated heavy spot for the second mode in each plane.

The machine response is shown in Figure 16-14. Now the second mode has been drastically reduced in size, but *the first mode is unchanged from the last run*. Since the first mode is an in-phase mode, it is insensitive to the out-of-phase weight distribution that was added.

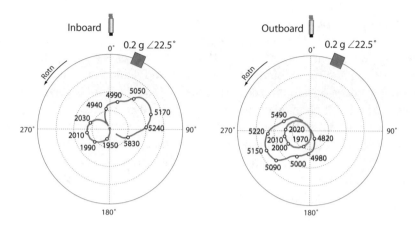

Figure 16-13. Response to in-phase weight addition. 0.2 g was installed at 22.5° in both weight planes of the machine in Figure 16-12. The polar plots show that the first mode response has been significantly reduced, but the second mode response is unchanged.

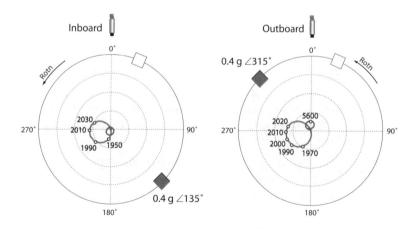

Figure 16-14. Response to out-of-phase weight addition. Without removing the previous weight correction, 0.4 g was installed at 135° in the Inboard plane, and 0.4 g was installed at 315° in the Outboard plane, approximately opposite to the indicated heavy spots for the second mode. The polar plots show that the second mode has been drastically reduced in size, but the first mode is unchanged from the last run. The first (in-phase) mode is insensitive to the out-of-phase weight correction.

Multiplane Balancing With Influence Vectors

In the previous section, we looked at two-plane balancing from a "global" perspective, looking at the response of the machine over the entire speed range. However, the balancing problem can also be solved using vibration vectors at a single operating speed, similar to what was done for single-plane balancing.

Two-plane balancing involves two weight planes and two measurement planes. Each weight that is added influences both measurement planes. For example, a weight added in Plane 1 will produce a response in Plane 1 and another response in Plane 2. Similarly, a weight added in Plane 2 affects both Plane 2 and Plane 1. Using a complete set of influence vectors, the desired balance solution can be described using a system of two equations,

$$-\boldsymbol{O}_1 = \boldsymbol{H}_{11}\boldsymbol{m}_{p1} + \boldsymbol{H}_{12}\boldsymbol{m}_{p2}$$
$$-\boldsymbol{O}_2 = \boldsymbol{H}_{21}\boldsymbol{m}_{p1} + \boldsymbol{H}_{22}\boldsymbol{m}_{p2} \tag{16-35}$$

or, in matrix form,

$$\begin{pmatrix} -\boldsymbol{O}_1 \\ -\boldsymbol{O}_2 \end{pmatrix} = \begin{bmatrix} \boldsymbol{H}_{11} & \boldsymbol{H}_{12} \\ \boldsymbol{H}_{21} & \boldsymbol{H}_{22} \end{bmatrix} \begin{pmatrix} \boldsymbol{m}_{p1} \\ \boldsymbol{m}_{p2} \end{pmatrix} \tag{16-36}$$

where all of the elements are vectors (complex numbers); $\boldsymbol{m}_{p1}$ and $\boldsymbol{m}_{p2}$ represent the desired final balance solutions in Plane 1 and Plane 2, and the influence vector subscripts, ij, describe the effect in plane i due to a mass in plane j. This set of equations can be easily extended to include more planes.

To calculate a solution to a two-plane balancing problem using this method, two independent calibration runs have to be made to generate a complete set of four influence vectors. For each run, a calibration weight is installed in one weight plane, and the change in vibration in each measurement plane is used to calculate two influence vectors; the process is repeated for the other weight plane. Once the set of influence vectors is obtained, Equations 16-35 or 16-36 can be used to compute the required balance solutions, $\boldsymbol{m}_{p1}$ and $\boldsymbol{m}_{p2}$. The balance solution can be expressed in matrix form as

$$\begin{pmatrix} \boldsymbol{m}_{p1} \\ \boldsymbol{m}_{p2} \end{pmatrix} = \begin{bmatrix} \boldsymbol{H}_{11} & \boldsymbol{H}_{12} \\ \boldsymbol{H}_{21} & \boldsymbol{H}_{22} \end{bmatrix}^{-1} \begin{pmatrix} -\boldsymbol{O}_1 \\ -\boldsymbol{O}_2 \end{pmatrix} \tag{16-37}$$

or algebraically as

$$m_{p1} = \frac{H_{12}O_2 - H_{22}O_1}{H_{11}H_{22} - H_{21}H_{12}}$$

$$m_{p2} = \frac{H_{21}O_1 - H_{11}O_2}{H_{11}H_{22} - H_{21}H_{12}}$$

(16-38)

In practice, it can be difficult to obtain the full set of influence vectors. Instead, we sometimes use a different type of influence vector that represents the effect due to the addition of a static or couple balance shot. In this technique, we decide which mode is most important to the balancing problem. If it is the first mode, then a best guess set of static (in-phase) calibration weights is installed in the two planes; if the second mode is deemed most important, then a best guess couple is installed. Once up to speed, the change in vibration in both planes is compared to the original. One plane is selected as a reference plane, and an influence vector is calculated using Equation 16-23.

This influence vector represents the effect of the pair of calibration weights that were installed, and the balancing operation can proceed as if it were a single-plane problem. The only difference (and an important one) is that the balance solution, m, actually represents both weights. Both weights must be scaled in size by the same amount, and both weights must maintain the same relative angle to each other as did the original calibration weights.

For example, given a two-plane machine, after inspection of the polar plots for both planes, you determine that the second mode dominates the unbalance response. You decide to attack only this second mode and install the following pair of calibration weights (a couple): 5 g $\angle 45°$ in Plane 1, and 5 g $\angle 225°$ in Plane 2. Using Plane 1 as a reference, you follow the single-plane calibration weight procedure and calculate a balance solution, $m = 7.2$ g $\angle 135°$. This solution tells you to increase the size of the calibration weight to 7.2 g and rotate it until it is located at 135° in Plane 1. In Plane 2, you remove the calibration weight and install a 7.2 g weight at 315°, 180° opposite the new Plane 1 weight.

If you must, you can leave in the calibration weights, and calculate the required trim weight in Plane 1 using Equations 16-19 and 16-20. For this example, m_{p2} will be the same size as m_{p1}, and m_{p2} will be located 180° relative to m_{p1}. Note that the weights can be split independently in each plane as necessary.

The success of this technique depends on the machine having clearly defined, in- and out-of-phase behavior. It works best on axially symmetric rotors and is frequently used to balance dual flow LP rotors. Long rotors with a high length-to-diameter ratio, such as power industry generators, often have balance planes located at the ends of the rotor and low sensitivity to static (in-phase) balance corrections. Some rotors may have a third, midspan balancing plane. This balancing plane can be used to balance the first, in-phase mode; the two outer planes can be used, with a couple correction, to balance the second mode.

When rotors are axially asymmetric (for example, have more mass near one end of the rotor), then the second mode nodal point will most likely be located nearer to one end of the rotor. This can produce higher vibration amplitude at the end of the rotor farthest from the nodal point; such a rotor may be more difficult to balance using a pure static or pure couple correction.

When balancing using this technique, there is no particular requirement that the two-plane calibration weights be exactly the same or exactly in or out of phase. The only requirement is that the *relative* masses and the *relative* angles remain the same. In practice, however, it is likely that a pair of weights at an arbitrary relative angle will affect both modes simultaneously, and the result of an unequal or arbitrary relative angle shot can be very difficult to predict. We recommend keeping the weights the same and either in phase or out of phase.

How Balancing Can Go Wrong

Balancing involves a complicated series of steps, from evaluation to weight installation to calculation and installation of a final shot. There are many ways a balancing job can go wrong. Here are a few things to think about.

You should always try to keep a global perspective on the problem when balancing. If at all possible, look at the data over the entire speed range, and plot data from both *XY* probes. Compare and cross-check the results of vector analysis with polar plots of the data and graphical solutions.

Make sure the polar plot and graphical plots have the correct rotation direction. When standing next to the machine, make sure you are looking down the machine train in the same direction indicated on your data. If you accidentally turn around without realizing it, you will install the weight at the wrong angular orientation.

In plants with multiple, identical machine trains, make sure you are working on the correct machine and your data comes from that machine.

Use hot shutdown data when possible. Axial growth can cause the target area of eddy current probes to change. This can change cold slow roll runout and adversely affect slow roll compensation. Shutdown data is generally preferred because the machine is hot, all the way down to slow roll speed. Polar plots are a superior tool for balancing partly because they will immediately reveal slow roll compensation errors, and they can be visually compensated.

Make sure the machine is not sensitive to changes in process conditions. Repeatability from run to run is essential for good results. Make sure the machine stabilizes at full load before judging its behavior.

Watch out for unbalance problems that are caused by other effects. Dirt or debris can shift inside a machine and cause the heavy spot to change from run to run. Balancing such a machine is futile until the situation is corrected. See the case history in Chapter 25.

Make sure the weight goes into the machine where you think it should. If at all possible, personally observe the weight installation.

Watch out for other personnel who might change something in your instrumentation setup while you are waiting. In one case, a jealous competitor deliberately switched probe leads in the middle of a balancing job. Fortunately, the change in data was noticed and allowed for.

Remember that, when trying to identify the heavy spot location, velocity and acceleration phase behavior is different from displacement behavior. Integrate velocity to displacement, or mentally adjust the heavy spot location. Calibration weight balancing will work fine with velocity or acceleration data.

Summary

Balancing is the act of adding or removing mass from a rotor in a way that reduces the unbalance-induced vibration below a minimum acceptable level. Balancing can be performed in a single axial plane, two planes, or it may involve simultaneously balancing several axial planes, which requires considerable knowledge of the machine and sophisticated balancing software. Most often, field balancing will involve only one or two planes.

Shop balancing is performed with the rotor removed from the machine and installed on a test stand; trim balancing is performed with the rotor in place in the machine. Trim balancing of shop balanced rotors may be required because of changes in Dynamic Stiffness of the assembled rotor system.

The unbalance force is proportional to the radius of unbalance and the square of the rotor speed. It acts through the Dynamic Stiffness to produce predominantly 1X vibration. The unbalance can be thought of as a small *heavy spot* that rotates with the rotor.

The polar plot is the best plot format for balancing. The vibration vectors at speeds well below the resonance point in the general direction of the heavy spot.

Calibration weight balancing is a multistep process that involves installing a known, *calibration weight* at a known angular location. The calibration weight and the change in vibration are used to calculate a final balance solution.

Weight splitting is a technique that is useful when the calculated location for the balance weight is not available. Two weights are installed in available locations so that the effect is equivalent.

An *influence vector* describes how the addition of a balance weight changes, or influences, the amplitude and phase of machine vibration. It is calculated by taking the ratio of the vibration change to the balance weight that produced that change. Influence vectors are valid only for a particular speed, weight plane, measurement plane, and significant machine operating conditions.

The first mode of a flexible rotor is usually a simple, predominantly *in-phase*, bending mode (also called a *static* mode); the second mode of a flexible rotor is usually an *out-of-phase*, or S-shaped, bending mode (also called a *couple* mode). These modes respond to unbalance mass distributions that approximately match the mode shape of the rotor. Multiplane balancing techniques exploit this behavior to allow independent balancing of separate modes. Polar plots can be used to identify the heavy spot location for each mode.

Sets of influence vectors can be found that allow calculation of a complete, two-plane balance solution, but they require one calibration run for each weight plane. More often, identical pairs of weights are used to develop special static or couple influence vectors. These influence vectors are used to calculate a final balance solution for the particular mode being balanced.

References

1. American Petroleum Institute, *Tutorial on the API Standard Paragraphs Covering Rotor Dynamics and Balancing: An Introduction to Lateral Critical and Train Torsional Analysis and Rotor Balancing*, API Publication 684 (Washington, D.C.: American Petroleum Institute, 1996), p. 117.

2. Jackson, Charles, *The Practical Vibration Primer*, (Houston: Gulf Publishing Company, 1979), p. 19

3. Bently, D. E., Hatch, C. T., and Franklin, W. D., *Cautions for Polar-Plot Balancing Using Measurements Taken Near Fluid-Lubricated Bearings*, ASME 94-GT-113, (New York: American Society of Mechanical Engineers, 1994).

Malfunctions

Chapter 17

Introduction to Malfunctions

WITH OUR STUDY OF VIBRATION FUNDAMENTALS, data plots, and rotor dynamics theory completed, we are now ready to examine a complex topic, machine malfunctions and their detection. Each chapter of this section will deal with a specific type or family of malfunctions that are common to most rotating machinery.

This chapter will present some basic facts about malfunctions and their detection. We will begin with a definition of a machine malfunction and what it means in terms of machine behavior and performance. We will then discuss how malfunctions can be detected and identified using changes in many different vibration characteristics, and how Dynamic Stiffness is the important primary link between a malfunction and observed vibration.

What is a Malfunction?

We generally think of a malfunctioning machine as one that is broken or does not perform its intended task. But a breakdown is usually the result of a long period of accumulating damage. Most machines will continue to run and perform useful work even with an active or developing problem. However, machines and lost product are too expensive for us to wait until a machine breaks down before thinking about malfunctions. We do not want to restrict our malfunction definition too tightly, because we want to detect and *prevent* unplanned machine downtime.

Proactive machinery management requires us to detect problems as early as possible in order to schedule maintenance, make repairs, or adjust the process. It is an economic imperative to prevent unplanned downtime and reduced output. This requires a definition of a malfunction that is compatible with this goal.

A malfunction is an operating condition or mechanical problem that, if not treated, may cause a degradation in performance, an unplanned shutdown, or a catastrophic failure.

Continued operation of a machine with a malfunction may result in higher than normal stresses, fatigue, or even direct mechanical damage. A loss of efficiency, an indirect effect due to damage in the machine, is also possible. A good example is an unbalanced compressor that passes through a poorly damped (high SAF) resonance and wipes internal seals. The increased seal clearance allows excessive interstage flow, causing reduced interstage pressure and efficiency. In this case, the unbalance is the malfunction, which leads to degradation of performance. Additionally, the higher stresses associated with the higher vibration may lead to long term fatigue failure of some part of the machine.

Some malfunctions, called *secondary malfunctions*, appear as a result of other malfunctions. A *root cause* is the primary malfunction that triggers a secondary malfunction. In the example above, the high vibration at the balance resonance produces a seal rub, a secondary malfunction. The actual root cause is the unbalance. It is vital to identify the root cause of any machine problem, otherwise, a malfunction may seem to be corrected, only to reappear again at some later time. In our example, replacing the damaged seal does not address the root cause malfunction.

Assuming a good initial design, malfunctions almost always result from unplanned deviations from expected behavior. The beautiful, perfect machine on the drawing board has perfectly straight and round shafts with no gravity sag; is perfectly balanced; has perfect internal and external alignment; operates within design loads; operates within designed radial and axial clearances; has correctly sized bearings and seals; has low stress levels; and has no radial, torsional, or axial vibration.

Unfortunately, real machines can have bowed, out-of-round rotors that sag from gravity and are unbalanced; internal and external misalignment that cause excessive radial loads; clearance problems due to differential thermal expansion during startup; over- or undersized bearings and seals (or improperly installed bearings); high stresses; and radial, torsional, and axial vibration. Usually some combination of these things will be present in any machine at any given time.

The design must allow for these conditions in the manufacture, installation, and operation of the machine. If these imperfections are within the allowed tolerances, then the machine will operate without a problem. A malfunction will occur when one or more of these imperfections exceed these limits.

Detection of Malfunctions

Our machinery management objective is to detect and identify machine malfunctions at the earliest feasible time, given a balance of economic and technical considerations. Timely malfunction detection relies on using all the data that is available for the machine. There are two basic types of measurements that are used to detect and identify machine malfunctions: direct measurements and indirect measurements.

Direct measurements give us information about the physical state of machine components. Direct measurements include vibration and position measurements, rotor speed, and bearing temperature.

Indirect measurements tell us how the machine is behaving as part of a larger system. Indirect measurements include process data, such as power; working fluid temperature, pressure, and flow; and performance data, such as efficiency. These measurements are very important for correlation with direct measurements, but we must have direct measurements to diagnose malfunctions.

Malfunctions are most often detected through changes in vibration. In Chapter 11 we learned that vibration is the ratio of the force to the Dynamic Stiffness of the rotor system (Figure 17-1). Thus, a change in vibration indicates that either the force has changed, the Dynamic Stiffness has changed, or both. The force in rotor systems is most often rotating unbalance, which can change due to the erosion or loss of material or accumulation of foreign material on rotating parts. However, most often, a change in vibration is caused by a change in Dynamic Stiffness.

Dynamic Stiffness consists of Direct and Quadrature Dynamic Stiffnesses, which can be broken down into rotor parameter-related stiffnesses. Thus, changes in any of these parameters can produce a change in Dynamic Stiffness and a change in vibration. While a significant change in mass is unlikely, and

Figure 17-1. Vibration is a ratio. Changes in vibration can occur due to a change in force or Dynamic Stiffness. A malfunction can cause a change in any of the rotor parameters (most often spring stiffness) and cause a change (not always an increase) in vibration. Dynamic Stiffness consists of Direct Dynamic Stiffness and Quadrature Dynamic Stiffness. Dynamic Stiffness is a function of the rotor parameters of mass, M, spring stiffness, K, damping, D, lambda, λ, and rotor speed, Ω; changes in any of these parameters change vibration response.

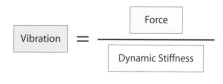

changes in damping produce subtle effects, changes in lambda and spring stiffness are more likely and will produce significant vibration changes.

Malfunction diagnosis depends on the detection of changes in key signal characteristics (Table 17-1): direct vibration amplitude, nX amplitude and phase, frequency content, direct and nX orbit and timebase shapes, and rotor position, including eccentricity ratio and attitude angle. These vibration and position changes must be correlated with our knowledge of the physical mechanisms of malfunctions, how the malfunctions affect rotor parameters, and the resulting response characteristics.

Most malfunctions have overlapping symptoms. Because of this, a single piece of data is rarely adequate to make a clear diagnosis, and many types of data must be cross correlated. Thus, vibration analysis should be performed using data from all operating modes of the machine (Table 17-2): *steady state*, *transient*, *slow roll*, and *stopped*.

Steady state data (data taken during operation at constant speed) gives us information about changes in overall vibration levels, frequency content, nX amplitude and phase, position, and orbit and timebase shape during slowly changing, or static, rotor dynamic and process conditions. This is an extensive amount of information, but the single operating speed provides only a narrow window on machine behavior.

Transient data (data taken during startup or shutdown) gives us a much wider picture of the rotor dynamic behavior of the machine. It gives us information about heavy spot locations, balance resonance speeds, and how vibration,

Table 17-1. Vibration signal characteristics.

Vibration signal characteristics	Data plots
Direct vibration amplitude	Orbit, timebase
nX amplitude and phase	Bode, polar, APHT
Frequency	Full spectrum, half spectrum
Position	Average shaft centerline
Orbit and timebase shape	Orbit, timebase

Table 17-2. Machine operating conditions.

Machine operating conditions	Description
Steady state	Constant speed, load can vary
Transient	Startup, shutdown (changing speed)
Slow roll	Low speed, negligible unbalance response
Stopped	Stopped

frequency content, position, and orbit and timebase shape change versus rotor speed.

Transient data is especially important because it reveals changes in the balance resonance speed, Ω_{res},

$$\Omega_{res} = \sqrt{\frac{K}{M}} \qquad\qquad (17\text{-}1)$$

where K is the rotor system spring stiffness, and M is the rotor mass. Many rotor system malfunctions produce changes in K and, therefore, the resonance speed. Also, changes in the shape of the resonance peak on a Bode plot can give us clues about the nature of the malfunction.

Slow roll data allows us to identify slow roll vectors, slow roll waveforms, slow roll shaft position, and mechanical and electrical runout under cold and hot conditions. Slow roll vectors and waveforms can be used to compensate transient vector plots, orbit plots, and timebase plots. Slow roll data can also reveal a bowed shaft.

When a machine is stopped, the shaft centerline position can be measured. This is most useful in horizontal machines, where the shaft should rest on the bottom of the bearing in a properly aligned machine. Shutdown or startup shaft centerline data can be plotted relative to the stopped readings to display the relative position of the shaft versus speed.

A stopped machine should not vibrate. This is the time to check vibration signals for the presence of adjacent or auxiliary machinery vibration, or for electrical noise in the transducer signal path. Adjacent machines can transmit vibration through the foundation or piping system and cause casing and shaft vibration in the stopped machine. When the stopped machine is restarted, the adjacent machinery vibration or noise signals will be present in the vibration signal. By knowing that another machine is the source of a particular vibration signal, a more effective diagnosis can be made.

To properly diagnose a machinery problem, you must understand the physical basis for a malfunction, the rotor dynamic response to it, and the vibration signal characteristics of it. In the following chapters, we will discuss the physical cause of each type of malfunction, note how the malfunction affects Dynamic Stiffness, and present typical symptoms and signal characteristics. Because there is so much overlap in malfunction symptoms, we will also list other malfunctions that have similar symptoms.

Chapter 18

Unbalance

UNBALANCE IS THE MOST COMMON ROTOR SYSTEM MALFUNCTION. Its primary symptom is 1X vibration, which, when excessive, can lead to fatigue of machine components. In extreme cases, it can cause wear in bearings or internal rubs that can damage seals and degrade machine performance. Usually, whenever increased 1X vibration is detected, the immediate suspect is unbalance. However, because there are many other malfunctions that produce 1X vibration, many machines have been balanced only to have the real root cause problem reemerge. Thus, to properly diagnose unbalance, it is important to understand both the mechanism that produces unbalance and the other malfunctions that produce 1X vibration.

The cause of unbalance and the techniques used to correct it have been discussed in Chapter 16. In this chapter, we will concentrate on the diagnosis of unbalance as a malfunction. We will discuss the effects of unbalance on rotor system behavior; how it is manifested in rotor and casing vibration, stresses, and secondary malfunctions, such as rub. We will list the other malfunctions that produce 1X vibration and mimic unbalance. Finally, we will discuss a special case of unbalance, the loose rotating part.

Rotor System Vibration Due To Unbalance

The 1X unbalance force acts through the Dynamic Stiffness of the system to cause 1X vibration:

$$\text{Vibration} = \frac{\text{Force}}{\text{Dynamic Stiffness}} \qquad (18\text{-}1)$$

Because the unbalance is part of the rotor, it rotates at the same speed as the rotor. Thus, the force caused by unbalance is *synchronous* (1X). A linear system will produce only 1X vibration for a 1X force. However, rotor systems possess nonlinearities, such as strongly increasing fluid-film bearing stiffness at high eccentricity ratios. Another source of nonlinearity would be any sudden change in rotor system stiffness, such as due to a rotor-to-stator rub or looseness in the support system. These nonlinearities can generate harmonics of 1X vibration, which can sometimes be seen on a spectrum cascade plot when the rotor is at a resonance. During resonance, the higher 1X vibration amplitude can cause the rotor to pass through a higher eccentricity ratio region in a fluid-film bearing, and the sharp increase in stiffness can produce harmonics.

1X rotor vibration appears as a dynamic load in the bearings. The bearing stiffness and damping transmit this load into the bearing support structure and machine casing, which are part of the extended rotor system. This system will have vibration modes that include the rotor and the machine casing. These modes may be in phase, where rotor and casing move approximately together, or out of phase, where rotor and casing move approximately opposite to each other. The amount of casing vibration will depend on several factors, including the relative masses of the rotor and casing, the stiffness of the bearings, the stiffness of the casing, and the stiffness of the casing mounting and foundation (see Chapter 12).

The masses, damping, and stiffnesses of the bearing, casing, and mounting combine into the Dynamic Stiffness of the overall rotor support, and it is this Dynamic Stiffness that will determine the relative amounts of shaft and casing vibration excited by the unbalance.

A high ratio of casing mass to rotor mass will usually result in low casing vibration. High pressure compressors and the HP unit of steam turbines fall into this category. Because of the high casing mass, vibration in these machines is best measured using shaft relative transducers.

A lower ratio of casing mass to rotor mass, or a soft support, is likely to produce significant amounts of both shaft relative and casing vibration, which requires casing transducers in addition to shaft relative transducers for a complete vibration picture. Shaft relative transducers move with the casing or bearing housing; if the rotor and casing are vibrating in phase, shaft relative vibration may be low, even though shaft absolute vibration may be high. If the rotor and casing are vibrating out of phase, then measured shaft relative vibration may be high, even though shaft absolute vibration may be low. For this reason, casing measurements should be used with shaft relative measurements to provide a complete picture of system vibration.

Aeroderivative gas turbines have low casing mass to rotor mass ratios and relatively flexible casings and supports. They also have rolling element bearings that provide high transmissibility of rotor vibration to the casing. The casings on such machines, due to their flexibility, may possess several modes of casing vibration, and casing transducers must be carefully positioned to avoid nodal points.

When an unbalanced rotor is highly loaded in a fluid-film bearing (perhaps due to misalignment), it operates at a very high eccentricity ratio. The bearing stiffness can become quite high and transmit rotor vibration very easily to the machine casing. At the same time, the high bearing stiffness can suppress the vibration of the rotor. When this occurs, shaft relative rotor orbits will be small and 1X casing vibration will be large.

Similarly, rolling element bearings, because of their extremely high stiffness, strongly suppress shaft relative rotor vibration near the bearings (although *midspan* shaft relative vibration can be quite large) and transmit vibration directly to the casing. A rolling element bearing machine with a rigid rotor behaves as though the casing and rotor are combined into a large, lumped mass with an unbalance. The resulting casing vibration depends to a great deal on the stiffness of the casing structure and the stiffness of the machine mounting. Very stiffly mounted machines have low levels of measurable 1X casing vibration even though internal dynamic forces and stresses may be high.

Stress and Damage

If a rotor centerline moves in a 1X, circular orbit centered on the rotor system axis, the rotor will maintain a constant deflection shape as it rotates. To an observer rotating with the shaft, the rotor will appear to be statically deflected. Under this condition, all areas of the rotor surface will see no change in stress (Figure 18-1, top).

A static radial load (either from a process load or the gravity load on a horizontal rotor) will deflect the rotor and produce 1X stress cycling. The constant stress due to the 1X, circular orbit is added to the alternating stress due to the static radial load deflection. If the orbit is elliptical, an additional 2X component of stress may appear (Figure 18-1, bottom). As the size of the orbit increases, the alternating component of the stress also increases. Add any nonsynchronous vibration, and it is easy to see that a typical rotor operates in a very complicated stress environment.

The nominal stresses due to bending of the rotor are increased by various stress concentration factors, such as diameter changes, keyways, (drilled) holes, shrink fits, surface finish defects, slag inclusions, and corrosion. Thus, rotors that experience large radial loads and high 1X vibration due to unbalance are at increased risk for crack initiation and fatigue failure.

Unbalance-induced vibration can damage couplings. The bending of the rotor due to unbalance increases stress on rigid, diaphragm, and disk-pack couplings, and increases wear in gear couplings.

1X vibration can also excite casing and piping resonances if their natural frequencies coincide with running speed. The high stresses caused by the resonance response can cause fatigue failure of either the casing or the piping. In one example, a poorly supported steam injection pipe attached to a gas turbine experienced large, 1X excitation of the resonance vibration during startups and, to a lesser degree, broadband rumble excitation of the resonance at running speed. The combination caused catastrophic fatigue failure of the pipe.

High 1X vibration can cause the rotor to contact stationary parts in the machine, a condition called rub. The rub is most likely to occur during a resonance and can damage seals, which can reduce efficiency.

Figure 18-2 shows a 1X Bode plot from a cold startup of a compressor with excessive unbalance. As the rotor approached the first resonance, a simple bending mode shape, it contacted a midspan seal, producing a rub. The effect of the rub is visible in the truncated resonance of the amplitude plot and the high rate of change of phase. The measurement probe was located near one of the bearings in this two bearing machine, so the midspan amplitude, where the rub occurred, was much larger than that shown on the plot.

Other Things That Can Look Like Unbalance

There is a temptation to view any high 1X vibration problem as an unbalance problem. Unfortunately, there are many conditions that can generate 1X vibration or indirectly cause an unbalance in the rotor. If the true root cause of the problem is not found, then balancing the machine may seem to be the only solution. But the symptoms will probably return, and the potentially damaging operating condition will continue. For example, a cracked rotor, because of crack-induced rotor bow, can look like an unbalance problem. But, balancing a cracked rotor will only temporarily address the symptoms of the problem, and the real root cause will remain.

If a machine does not balance or stay in balance after three (presumably correct) attempts at balancing, then the root problem is probably not simple unbalance. The problem lies elsewhere, and further investigation is warranted.

Many of the following malfunctions have one thing in common, a significant response at slow roll speed. *Any 1X response at slow roll speed must be due to something other than unbalance:* runout, a permanent bow in the rotor, severe misalignment, a coupling problem, etc.

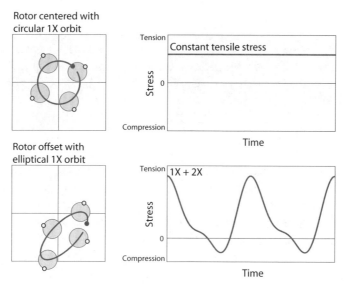

Figure 18-1. 1X vibration and stress cycling. A circular, 1X orbit, centered on the rotor system axis, produces a constant stress level (top). When the rotor is subjected to a static radial load, the constant stress due to the circular orbit is added to any alternating stress due to the static radial load deflection. If the orbit is elliptical, an additional 2X component of stress may appear (bottom).

Figure 18-2. 1X startup data from a compressor with excessive unbalance. When the rotor passed through its first-bending-mode resonance, it contacted a midspan seal, producing a rub. The rub is visible in the resonance amplitude and phase response, which has been modified from its usual classical appearance. The vibration was measured near one of the bearings in this two bearing machine, and the midspan vibration amplitude, where the rub occurred, was much larger.

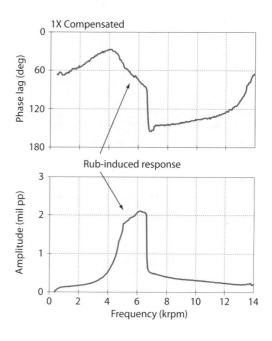

Runout

When mechanical runout is present, then the distance from the rotor surface to the probe will change as the rotor rotates about its geometric center; even though the rotor centerline does not move, the transducer signal is interpreted as vibration. *Mechanical runout* includes the effects of surface machining errors, irregularities due to damage, and rotor bow. It can consist of 1X (if the surface is circular and offset from the rotor axis), 2X (if the rotor is elliptical in cross section), higher orders, or a combination of frequencies.

Scratches in the rotor surface viewed by the probe are another form of mechanical runout. Scratches will produce negative-going voltage spikes (and sometimes positive-going spikes if there is material displacement, not just removal) on the transducer signals. The spikes produce recognizable orbit characteristics: *a scratch will produce spikes on an unfiltered orbit that usually point away from the probes.* A single scratch on the rotor will produce a 1X component and its harmonics in the vibration signal, and they will be visible in the spectrum over all speeds (Figure 18-3). If a shaft has multiple scratches, it is possible for two scratches to affect two probes simultaneously. When this happens, one spike will appear on the orbit that moves away from both probes (but not directly away from either), and two more will appear that move directly away from each probe. The three spikes will be spaced at 90° of rotation from each other.

Electrical runout occurs with eddy current transducers when the electrical conductivity or magnetic permeability varies around the circumference of the rotor. These variations are caused by differences in the microstructure of the alloy, due to alloy type, heat treatment, or cold working. Any of these effects can produce a 1X or higher order variation in the probe signal.

Runout always includes a combination of mechanical and electrical runout. Its primary characteristic is that it is constant in amplitude, even down to slow roll speed (see the figure), as long as the probe looks at the same circumferential path. Unbalance force, though, is proportional to the square of rotor speed, and it will not produce any detectable dynamic 1X rotor response at slow roll speed.

Rotor Bow

A rotor that is bent, or bowed, will produce 1X vibration, but unlike unbalance, *it will produce a 1X response at slow roll speed.*

A thermal rotor bow can develop while a machine is running. If a hot spot develops on one side of a rotor, that part of the rotor will expand. Because of the one-sided thermal growth, the rotor will develop a bow, which will change the 1X vibration response. If the source of the local heating is removed, then the thermally induced bow will disappear, unless the area has exceeded the yield limit of the material (see Chapter 19).

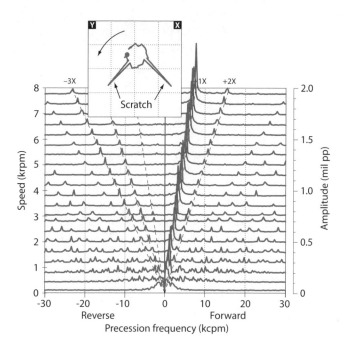

Figure 18-3. Direct orbit and full spectrum showing the effect of a scratch on the shaft in the probe viewing area. As the shaft rotates, the scratch first passes under the X transducer, producing a sharp, negative-going voltage spike in the orbit that points away from the X transducer. The scratch then passes under the Y transducer, producing another spike in the orbit that points away from the Y transducer. In the full spectrum, the 1X frequency consists of both the 1X rotor dynamic response and the once-per-turn scratch response. The scratch response persists to slow roll speed, and the sharpness of the scratch produces a rich, harmonic spectrum.

Electrical Noise in the Transducer System

Turbogenerator sets operate either at line frequency or at some submultiple of line frequency, depending on the number of poles in the generator. A 2-pole generator will operate at 3600 rpm (60 Hz) or 3000 rpm (50 Hz). If power line noise couples into the transducer signal line, then a line frequency component will appear in the vibration signal. This kind of noise has been mistaken for 1X rotor vibration. This can be checked by looking at a spectrum cascade plot during a startup or shutdown (Figure 18-5, bottom). As rotor speed changes, the spectrum line of the electrical noise remains constant in frequency while the 1X rotor frequency changes with speed.

Coupling Problems

Certain types of coupling problems can produce 1X vibration. If the rotor axes of two rigidly coupled machines are offset from each other (parallel misalignment), then, when the machines rotate, a cranking effect will produce 1X vibration in one or both machines. An off-center coupling bore or off-center coupling bolt circle will also produce this kind of 1X cranking action. While unbalance-induced 1X vibration will disappear at low speed, cranking-induced 1X vibration will continue at slow roll speed.

Gear couplings depend on lubricated slippage of the coupling elements for their operation. If a gear coupling should lock up, a sudden change in 1X vibration can take place, along with a change in average shaft centerline position.

Shaft Crack

As a shaft crack propagates across the rotor, the rotor bending stiffness decreases in the vicinity of the crack. Thus, the rotor is less able to resist the dynamic forces that try to deform the rotor and will usually bow as the crack develops. Because the bow moves rotor mass away from the rotor axis, the effective heavy spot of the rotor changes. The crack-induced bow changes the 1X vibration response of the machine.

Shaft cracks usually cause changes in 1X amplitude or phase over time. In the first weeks to months of crack propagation, the 1X response will usually change slowly. The changes in 1X vibration may be mistaken for simple unbalance. While balancing may reduce the vibration due to the crack-induced bow, the root cause problem still remains, and the 1X response will change again.

If the crack is well developed, the large amplitudes of vibration associated with resonance can plastically deform the rotor in the vicinity of the crack, suddenly changing the bow, 1X slow roll vectors, and the effective heavy spot. Balancing calculations based on shutdown data may not be correct after the rotor experiences high amplitude resonances during startup. In this scenario, the rotor will have an erratic response to repeated balancing attempts.

Loose Part or Debris

If a part shifts position on the rotor, or debris shifts position in the rotor, the unbalance distribution and the resulting 1X vibration response of the rotor will change. Such a change can happen occasionally (for example, during a startup or shutdown), intermittently, or continuously.

A rotor disk or thrust collar that has become loose may rotate on the rotor. Under some circumstances, a machine component can also move axially. Most likely, the part will slip intermittently whenever the applied torque exceeds the friction at the rotor interface. Such a change in position will produce a step change in 1X vibration that could be detected on an APHT or acceptance region plot. If the part slips during a startup or shutdown, the observed vibration will be different when compared to previous data. Note that the movement of the part might actually *reduce* 1X vibration if the part moves to a position where its unbalance partially or completely cancels the rotor unbalance.

Catastrophic failure of a component, such as a broken turbine blade, will also produce a step change in 1X vibration, but that is likely to be of much larger magnitude than what would be produced by a shift in position of a rotor part.

If the friction between the part and the rotor is low enough, the part may slip on the rotor and rotate more slowly than the rotor. The unbalance of the loose part will continuously change the effective unbalance of the rest of the rotor. This case will be discussed in more detail below.

Fluid or debris can become trapped inside a rotor. When the rotor is shut down, the debris can shift position, changing the unbalance of the rotor. In one case, a 6 m (20 ft) diameter, 300 kW (400 hp), 880 rpm induced-draft fan exhibited a recurring unbalance problem. Over a period of two years, the fan was balanced 24 times! Finally, a new consultant was called in, and he discovered that dirt was trapped in the hub of the fan. Every time the fan was shut down for balancing, the dirt shifted position, rendering the balance shot useless. Once the fan was cleaned and sealed, the problem disappeared. See the case history in Chapter 25.

In another case, the LP shaft borehole plug of a 300 MW steam turbine generator came loose and settled inside the turning gear ring. Each time the turbine was stopped, it settled in a different position. It was only when the turning gear was removed to facilitate alignment that the troubling unbalance problem was solved.

Rub

If a rotor begins to rub lightly on the stator once per turn, the friction at the contact point will cause local heating and bow and transfer energy of rotation to lateral vibration. Thus, the 1X vibration amplitude and phase will change once the rub starts. Over time, the rub may wear away part of the contacting element, and the rub-induced 1X vibration changes may become smaller or disappear.

Under rare circumstances, it is possible to develop a light rub that produces a continuous change in amplitude and phase while the machine is operating in a steady state condition. This type of rub can produce circles on a polar trend plot, with a cycle time of minutes to hours. See Chapter 19 for an example of this behavior. Rub can also modify the spring stiffness of the rotor system and increase or decrease vibration.

Changes in Spring Stiffness

Changes in any of the rotor parameters (mass, damping, spring stiffness, lambda, and rotor speed) will change the Dynamic Stiffness and the 1X vibration response of the rotor. The term that is most likely to change, the spring stiffness term, K, can be affected by many different rotor malfunctions. Table 18-1 lists different operating conditions and malfunctions and their effects on spring stiffness.

When a rotor operates near a resonance, changing K can increase *or* decrease 1X vibration amplitude, depending on whether the rotor operates above or below resonance (Figure 18-4). However, a *decrease* in spring stiffness will always *increase the 1X phase lag* near a resonance, and vice versa.

Thus, an increase in 1X vibration amplitude can look like an unbalance problem when the real problem may be a reduction in rotor system spring stiffness due to a deteriorating foundation, a loose foundation bolt, a change in eccentricity ratio in a fluid-film bearing (possibly due to misalignment), or even a shaft crack. If a spring stiffness *increase* shifts a resonance closer to running speed, vibration may also increase (Ω_4 in Figure 18-4, left).

Electric Motor Related Problems

Electric motors, because of their construction, may become unbalanced in normal operation due to shifting windings and loosened wedges. However, various induction motor malfunctions can also produce 1X vibration and vibration at near 1X frequencies.

The rotor in an electric motor is built from a set of thin, insulated sheets of metal (laminations) that are stacked together along the rotor. If the insulation breaks down, or if the laminations become smeared due to rotor/stator contact, then adjacent laminations can come into electrical contact and larger eddy cur-

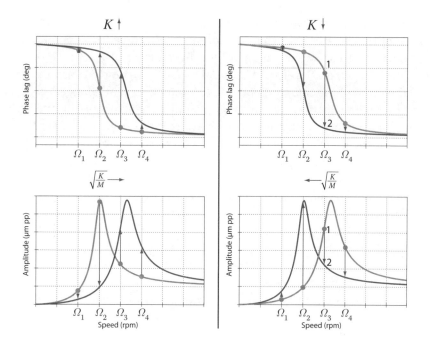

Figure 18-4. Changes in spring stiffness versus changes in vibration. In all plots, the original rotor response curves are green. On the left, the spring stiffness, K, has increased, causing the resonance to shift to a higher speed (red curves). On the right, K has decreased, shifting the resonance to a lower speed. The arrows show how the vibration amplitude and phase would change if the machine operated at speeds above and below the resonance.

Table 18-1. Causes of changes in spring stiffness, K.

Characteristic	Spring stiffness becomes
Shaft crack	Lower
Deteriorating foundation	Lower
Oversize bearing	Lower
Fluid-film bearing lower eccentricity	Lower
Fluid-film bearing higher eccentricity	Higher
Rub	Higher
Locked floating seal	Higher

rents will circulate in the sheets. This condition is called *shorted rotor iron*. Because of the resistivity of the lamination metal, the eddy currents dissipate energy, and, because the currents act locally, a local hot spot can form in the region of the contact. Because of thermal expansion, the rotor will tend to bow in the direction of the hot spot and create a temporary unbalance.

The currents in the rotor are highest during startup of the motor, when torque requirements are highest, causing maximum heating. Thus, the unbalance due to the thermal bow caused by smeared rotor laminations will usually be highest immediately after startup and decrease as the motor reaches equilibrium temperature.

This kind of unbalance can also be load related. If smeared rotor laminations are the problem, then reducing the load on the motor should cause a decrease in the 1X vibration response of the motor. Note that, if the location of the shorted rotor iron is opposite to the rotor residual unbalance, then the bow due to shorted rotor iron may *reduce* the unbalance. Under this circumstance, reducing load might *increase* the 1X vibration.

A broken rotor bar in an induction motor does not carry current. Because of this, the rotor will be cooler on that side and bow away from the broken bar. This bow creates an unbalance that will also tend to be load dependent.

In addition, the bow due to the broken rotor bar will create an uneven air gap between the rotor and the stator. The overall effect will be to modulate the amplitude of the 1X vibration of the rotor at a beat frequency equal to the number of poles of the motor times the slip frequency.

Two tests are helpful, but not conclusive, in diagnosing a broken rotor bar. Cutting power to the motor should cause the beat frequency to immediately disappear, and a load change should change the amplitude of the modulated 1X vibration.

Eccentric rotor iron will produce a 1X rotor vibration. But the interaction of the rotor with the rotating stator magnetic field will produce a modulation of 1X vibration similar to that produced by a broken rotor bar. Cutting power will cause the modulation to disappear, confirming that the problem is not a simple unbalance problem.

If line frequency electrical noise gets into a transducer system, then a 60 Hz (or 50 Hz) frequency will appear in the signal. If the machine train is driven by a 2-pole induction motor, then the line frequency will be only slightly above the 1X frequency. With poor spectral resolution, it may not be possible to separate the line frequency from the rotor frequency. Depending on the signal to noise ratio, the 1X vibration may appear to be modulated at a beat frequency equal to the slip frequency, which is the difference between the rotor speed and twice the line frequency divided by the number of poles.

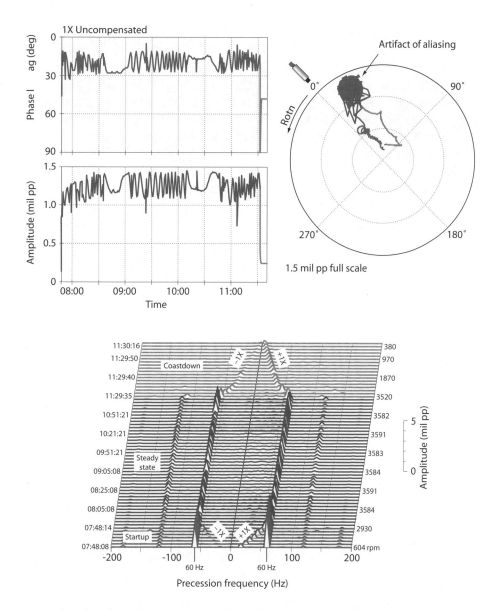

Figure 18-5. The effect of electrical noise in the transducer system of a 2-pole induction motor. In the full spectrum waterfall plot (bottom), the 1X rotor vibration and the large line frequency component can be seen during startup (blue). During steady state operation (red), the two components combine in one frequency bin, but the 1X APHT plots (top) show the modulation of the 1X vibration component by the line frequency component. (The red circular region is filled in because of aliasing. See the text.) Note that line frequency amplitude is highest during the high current demand during startup, drops during steady state, and disappears when the power is cut.

For example, a 2-pole induction motor operating at 3585 rpm (59.75 Hz) is only 0.25 Hz away from the line frequency of 60 Hz. This line frequency will modulate the 1X rotor vibration with a beat frequency of 0.25 Hz, or one cycle in 4 seconds. If the noise level is high enough, the 1X orbit will change size over a period of 4 seconds. Also, 1X data trend plots, such as APHT plots, will show variations in amplitude and phase over this period. If the sampling frequency is too low, aliasing will make the data appear to alternate between the extremes of the modulation. Look at a spectrum cascade plot of a shutdown to see if the 60 Hz line remains when the machine is shut down.

Figure 18-5 shows the effect of electrical noise in the transducer system of a 2-pole induction motor. In the full spectrum waterfall plot (bottom), the motor startup (blue) shows a large, line frequency component while the 1X rotor vibra-

Table 18-2. Other malfunctions that can produce 1X vibration.

Malfunction	Symptom or test
Mechanical or electrical runout	Significant 1X at slow roll
Rotor bow	Significant 1X at slow roll
Thermal bow	VAR test generators
Scratches in shaft	Orbit spikes point away from transducers
Electrical line noise in xdcr system	Always at line frequency, vary rotor speed
Coupling problems	Significant 1X at slow roll
Shaft crack	1X usually changes slowly over time, erratic balancing response
Loose part	Periodic or sudden change in 1X
Debris inside rotor	Erratic balancing response
Rub	Modified 1X response in resonances, periodic 1X changes
Spring stiffness changes	Resonance frequency changes
Induction motor problems	
Shorted rotor iron	Load change affects 1X
Broken rotor bar	1X modulated at poles times slip, power cut
Eccentric rotor iron	1X modulated, power cut

tion is increasing. During steady state operation (red), there is not enough spectral resolution to separate the 1X from the line frequency. But the 1X APHT plots (top) show disturbances in both amplitude and phase versus time. Note that a motor speed of 3584 rpm corresponds to a slip frequency of 0.27 Hz, with a period of 3.75 seconds per cycle. The sampling interval for this data was one sample per minute, so the amplitude and phase data show aliasing and are not representative of the real-time, instantaneous behavior. The solid red region in the polar APHT plot is filled with lines because of aliasing; consecutive samples of the modulated response have significantly different amplitude and phase. Without aliasing, the data would have formed an open circle in the polar plot.

Note that line frequency amplitude is highest during startup, drops during steady state, and disappears when the power is cut for shutdown (green).

Table 18-2 summarizes the different malfunctions that can look like unbalance. This is not a complete list of all possibilities. See specific malfunction chapters for more information.

Loose Rotating Parts

The various parts that are attached to a rotating shaft all contribute some part of the overall unbalance state of the rotor. As long as these parts remain fixed to the rotor, and no thermal bowing, deposition, or erosion processes are at work, the unbalance state should not change significantly.

However, when a disk that is normally attached to the rotor becomes loose, it can shift angular position relative to the shaft, producing a change in the mass distribution of the rotor.

Loose parts can occur for several reasons. Nonintegral thrust collars are often secured with a locknut that can loosen. When this happens, the thrust collar can intermittently or continuously move relative to the rotor. Balance pistons and impellers in compressors can also loosen. In stacked rotors, if an impeller has not been assembled properly onto the rotor, it can "ratchet," or move intermittently relative to the rotor shaft. This is most likely to occur during thermal transients, which affect the shrink fit. It is also possible for a loose part to chatter and excite natural frequencies of the rotor.

Note that debris or fluid that is trapped inside the rotor can change position, either during operation or, most likely, during startup and shutdown. The induced draft fan case history in Chapter 25 is an example of this kind of problem.

The continuous or intermittent change in angular position of the loose part will change the magnitude and direction of the overall unbalance vector, producing a change in 1X vibration, dependent on the amount of unbalance in the part.

Rarely, the part will move continuously, and the 1X vibration vector will change in a periodic way. When the unbalance vector of the part points in the same direction as the unbalance vector of the rest of the machine, the two vectors will add, increasing the 1X response. When the unbalance vector points in the opposite direction from the machine unbalance vector, then the two vectors will subtract.

The frequency of the vibration modulation (beat), f, in Hz is related to the difference between the rotor speed, Ω, and the speed of the loose part, ω (in rpm):

$$f\,(\text{Hz}) = (\Omega - \omega)\left(\frac{\text{rev}}{\text{min}}\right)\left(\frac{1\ \text{cycle}}{\text{rev}}\right)\left(\frac{1\ \text{min}}{60\ \text{s}}\right) \qquad (18\text{-}2)$$

The speed of the loose part is determined by the combination of the hydrodynamic or aerodynamic drag forces that act on the part and the friction force between the part and the rotor surface.

Figure 18-6. Behavior of 1X orbits with a loose rotating part. The top row of orbits shows orbit behavior when the ratio of part unbalance to rotor unbalance is low. The Keyphasor dot moves in a small circle, but remains in the same quadrant of the orbit. The middle row shows the behavior when the part unbalance to rotor unbalance ratio is comparable. In this case, the orbit size will change dramatically, shrinking to a point and reappearing, while the Keyphasor dot moves around the orbit. In both cases, the orbit appears to pulsate at a frequency defined by Equation 18-2. The bottom row shows the effect of a large, loose part unbalance combined with a rotor with little or no unbalance. The orbit remains open while the Keyphasor dot moves around the orbit in a direction opposite to rotation.

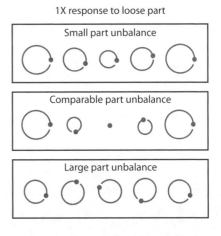

If the sample rate for the 1X vector plots is not at least twice the beat frequency, aliasing may produce strange results on the plots. For this reason, the modulation of 1X vibration is best seen in 1X timebase plots or on an oscilloscope. The series of 1X orbits (Figure 18-6 top) shows loose rotating part behavior when the ratio of part unbalance to rotor unbalance is low. The Keyphasor dot moves in a small circle, and remains in the same quadrant of the orbit, indicating a small variation in unbalance. The series of 1X orbits (middle) shows behavior when the ratio of loose part unbalance to rotor unbalance is comparable. In this case, the orbit size will change dramatically, collapsing to a point and reappearing, while the Keyphasor dot moves around the orbit in a direction opposite to rotation. In both cases, the orbit appears to pulsate at a frequency defined by Equation 18-2. When the rotor has very little unbalance, a loose, unbalanced part can produce an orbit that remains relatively constant in size, where the Keyphasor dot moves around the perimeter in a direction opposite to rotation (bottom).

Summary

The primary symptom of unbalance is 1X vibration. Unbalance can produce high rotor and casing vibration, and it can produce vibration in foundation and piping systems.

1X vibration can also contribute to stress cycling in rotors, which can lead to eventual fatigue failure. Unbalance-induced vibration can also cause internal rubs in machinery, especially when passing through balance resonances.

Diagnosis of unbalance can be complicated by the fact that many different malfunctions can produce 1X vibration. Mechanical and electrical runout, rotor bow, thermal bow, electrical noise, coupling problems, shaft cracks, loose rotating parts, trapped debris or fluids, rub, decreasing foundation spring stiffness, and various electric motor problems can all produce 1X or near 1X vibration. Because so many malfunctions can masquerade as unbalance, the machinery diagnostician should be careful to establish unbalance as the root cause before balancing a machine.

A loose rotating part can cause an intermittent or continuous change in 1X vibration.

Chapter 19

Rotor Bow

IN THE PREVIOUS CHAPTER, WE STUDIED UNBALANCE as a malfunction of rotor systems. Rotor bow is another malfunction that can produce 1X vibration. Rotor bow has been known to cause expensive delays in the startup of large steam and gas turbines and has led to significant internal damage of machines. In severe cases, a rotor bow can produce such high levels of vibration that it becomes impossible to pass through a balance resonance. Thus, prevention of rotor bow is an important part of machinery management. Machinery operation guidelines should be strictly followed, supplemented by a thorough understanding of the physical causes of rotor bow.

We will start with a definition of rotor bow and how it is measured. Then we will discuss the underlying physical cause of rotor bow so we can understand why it occurs and how it can be prevented. We will follow with a discussion of the rotor dynamic behavior of rotor bow, its symptoms, and a list of other malfunctions that may exhibit similar symptoms. Finally, we will talk about how to cure rotor bow when it does occur.

What is Rotor Bow?

Rotor bow is a condition that results in a bent shaft centerline. The shaft centerline is most often bent in a single plane, but it can have a three-dimensional corkscrew shape. There are three general categories of bow: elastic, temporary, and permanent.

Elastic bow occurs because of static radial loads on the rotor which do not exceed the yield strength. They can be caused, for example, by process fluid loads in pumps, internal misalignment, and partial arc steam admission in steam turbines, but the most common static load is due to the weight of the rotor in a horizontal machine. The stresses associated with the gravity load of a rotor (tensile on the bottom of the rotor and compressive on the top) are quite small. For example, a solid steel rotor that has a bearing span of 6 m (20 ft) and is 1 m (3 ft) in diameter will have a midspan elastic gravity sag of about 130 μm (5 mil). The maximum bending stress for this deflection is only 3 MPa (500 psi). Annealed 4140 steel has a yield strength of about 420 MPa (60 000 psi, or 60 ksi). Thus, the gravity load of the rotor produces stresses that are far below the lowest yield strength of a typical rotor steel. However, we will see later that these stresses can contribute indirectly to permanent rotor bow.

Temporary bow can occur due to uneven heating of the rotor surface or due to anisotropic thermal material properties. If a hot spot develops on one side of a rotor, it will thermally expand and become longer than the other. If the rotor is unconstrained, the resulting deflection of the rotor will not be permanent, and the rotor will return to its original shape when the temperature difference is eliminated.

Permanent bow results when the rotor has deformed to a condition that is not self-reversing without special intervention. For this to be true, the stresses in some part of the rotor must have exceeded the yield strength of the material.

Temporary and permanent rotor bows are almost always temperature-related problems; because of this, they are sometimes referred to as *thermal bow*.

All high temperature rotors are vulnerable to permanent bow. HP, IP, and LP steam turbine rotors, gas turbine rotors with shrunk on disks, and rotors built up with disks and tie bolts (typically gas turbine rotors) can experience bow problems.

Eccentricity describes the measurement (in μm pp or mil pp) of shaft bow at low rotor speeds. It is usually measured at the end of the exposed rotor shaft, well away from the bearing. For steam turbines, this is usually near the free end of the HP shaft. Eccentricity monitors are used to measure rotor bow during startup and to alarm when it exceeds an upper limit.

Causes of Rotor Bow

Rotor bow is a complex, often temperature-related problem. During startup and after shutdown, most rotors undergo significant temperature changes. If a hot rotor cools with a uniform surface temperature distribution, and if the material properties are uniform, then the rotor contracts uniformly and remains straight. Uneven cooling is more typical and, when combined with variations in geometry and material properties, causes the resulting rotor thermal behavior to be quite complex. There are several ways that an initially straight rotor can become thermally bowed.

An operating rotor can experience an uneven circumferential temperature distribution. This can be caused by uneven heating in generator and motor windings, shorted turns in generators, and broken rotor bars or shorted rotor iron in induction motors. It can also be caused by the local frictional heating from a rub or uneven heating in fluid-film bearings. The uneven heating causes the rotor to thermally expand on, and bow toward, the hot side. This is usually a temporary bow, which goes away when the uneven heating disappears. However, if the rub is intense and concentrated, the heat generated in the rub region can cause the material to yield in compression. When the rotor cools, the local, permanent plastic deformation will cause the rotor to be slightly shorter in that area, and a permanent bow will develop in the opposite direction from the rub.

Temporary bow forms as a result of differential thermal expansion of the rotor (Figure 19-1). At the top, a stopped, unconstrained rotor is at a uniform temperature in free space (no gravity load). When the top of the rotor is heated and the bottom is cooled, compressive stresses form inside the upper half of the rotor, and tensile stresses in the bottom half (middle). These stresses produce a bending moment that warps the rotor in the warm direction until the differential stresses disappear. After warping, the top surface is longer and the bottom surface is shorter, and no internal stresses exist in the rotor. (If they did, they would have to relieve themselves by further warping of the rotor.) When the source of differential heating is removed from the rotor, the process will reverse and return the rotor to its original shape.

Figure 19-1. Thermal warping of a rotor. At top is a solid rotor in free space, at uniform temperature, with no gravity load. When the top of the rotor is heated and the bottom is cooled, compressive stresses (negative) form inside the upper half of the rotor, with tensile stresses (positive) in the bottom half. These stresses produce an internal bending moment that warps the rotor until the differential stresses disappear. After warping, the top surface is longer and the bottom surface is shorter, and no internal stresses exist in the rotor.

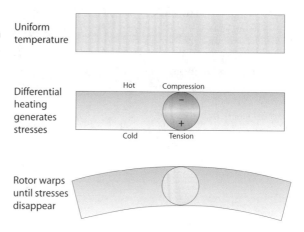

Uniform temperature

Differential heating generates stresses

Hot   Compression

Cold   Tension

Rotor warps until stresses disappear

A rotor, stopped or not, can develop a temporary thermal bow if the material properties are nonuniform across the section. During manufacturing, rotors made from a solid forging that experience different rates of cooling (leading to differences in heat treatment and microstructure), can have a slightly different value of thermal conductivity or coefficient of thermal expansion in different regions in the rotor. Differences in thermal conductivity will contribute to an unequal temperature distribution during thermal transients. Differences in the coefficient of thermal expansion in different areas will cause variation in the thermal expansion. The combination of these factors can cause bow during both transient and uniform temperature conditions.

This mechanism is similar to the thermal changes in a bimetal strip, which consists of two, dissimilar metals bonded together. One of the metals has a thermal expansion coefficient higher than the other. When subjected to a uniform temperature increase, the metal with higher thermal expansion will expand more than the other, causing the bimetal strip to warp.

After shutdown, it is common for a *temperature stratification* to occur inside a steam or gas turbine machine casing (Figure 19-2), which produces a higher temperature at the top of a horizontal rotor. The cooler (bottom) side of the rotor will contract more than the warmer (top) side. Because the cool side becomes shorter than the warm side, the rotor will deflect in the warm direction, a thermal bow. As long as the rotor is unconstrained, the stresses that develop in the rotor will be small. However, if the upward-bowing rotor contacts

Temperature gradient
during operation

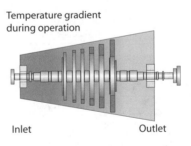

Inlet   Outlet

Figure 19-2. Thermal stratification in steam turbines. During operation (top), an axial temperature gradient exists in the steam turbine, with the hot end (red) on the inlet side. After shutdown (bottom), the warmest steam moves to the top of the machine casing, and the coolest moves to the bottom, forming a vertical (top-to-bottom) thermal gradient.

Temperature gradient
after shutdown

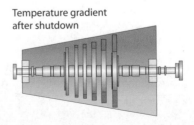

internal stator parts, it will become constrained, and the internal rotor stresses can build to high levels, with tension on the bottom and compression on the top. If the stresses exceed the yield limit, then, after reaching thermal equilibrium, the rotor will be shorter on top and longer on the bottom and will bow downward.

Immediately after shutdown, a stopped rotor will begin to cool at the outer surface. Because of the size and heat capacity of large turbine rotors, it can take hours for the rotor to reach thermal equilibrium. During this period, another thermal gradient exists between the outer surface and the center of the rotor (or the surface of the bore hole), and thermal stresses appear in the rotor that can reach a significant fraction of the yield strength. For a hot rotor that is cooling, the outer surface tries to shrink and forms tensile stresses, while compressive stresses develop at the bore hole surface. For a cold rotor that is

---

Thermal Shock

Thermal shock occurs whenever an object is subjected to a sudden temperature change on its surface. The stresses generated can be so high that they can cause fracture and catastrophic failure of the object.

For example, if you drop an ice cube (the colder the better) into warm water (sometimes even tap water will do), it is very likely to shatter *inside*, generating a network of cracks in the middle of the cube. This is thermal shock: the outer surface heats rapidly and tries to expand, but the surface material is constrained by its attachment to interior material. As a result, the interior material is put into tension. If the tensile stress exceeds the strength of the material, then the ice cube, a brittle material, fractures.

Thermal shock caused by rapid cooling of the surface of a hot object causes the outer surface to attempt to contract faster than the interior. As a result, the outer surface goes into tension, and the interior goes into compression. If the stresses are high enough, cracks can form on the surface of the object.

---

heating, the stresses change sign: tension appears at the bore hole surface, with compression at the outer surface.

The thermal stresses add to any other stresses that may be present in the rotor, such as elastic bow stresses due to gravity sag or stresses due to thermal stratification. It is the combination of these stresses that can produce permanent bow of the rotor. To understand how permanent bow takes place, we will work through a shutdown sequence and look at how these different stresses interact.

Assume that the rotor in the high pressure case of a large steam turbine has been operating long enough to be at thermal equilibrium. For an inlet steam temperature of 540 °C (1000 °F), the first stage rotor temperature is typically 480 °C (900 °F). When shutdown is initiated and the load is dumped, the rotor coasts down.

At this point, good operating practice dictates putting the rotor on turning gear when it reaches a low speed, to prevent the sequence we are going to describe. Let us assume that, for some reason, the rotor stops. The hot rotor is statically deflected downward by its own weight, producing low level, axial tensile stresses at the bottom and equal compressive stresses at the top.

As the rotor begins to cool, two things typically occur, temperature stratification in the machine casing and overall cooling of the rotor surface.

Temperature stratification inside the machine casing creates a *top-to-bottom temperature gradient* in the rotor, which causes the top of the rotor to expand relative to the bottom. The rotor deforms upward, producing, at this point, a temporary thermal bow. The thermal bow is easily able to overcome the gravity load of the rotor. If the rotor does not contact the stator, no new stress will appear due to this thermal gradient. However, because of the gravity load, the top of the rotor is still in compression, the bottom of the rotor is still in tension, and a low stress distribution exists across the entire rotor section (Figure 19-3a).

If the rotor contacts the stator and becomes constrained, the thermal expansion of the top surface will continue, but the rotor will be unable to move to relieve the situation. The axial compressive stress at the top of rotor, and the axial tensile stress at the bottom will both increase. Two sources of axial stress now exist, the gravity stress and the constrained thermal stress due to the top-to-bottom thermal gradient (Figure 19-3b). Both stresses have the same effect: compression on the top of the rotor, tension on the bottom.

In practice, when the temperature stratification occurs, the casing also tends to bow (*hog*), and the center of the casing rises, to some extent, along with the rotor. This actually helps delay contact between the rotor and the casing. There have been cases where, after the rotor failed to go on turning gear, operators tried to turn it manually, only to find that the rotor turned freely at first, but became tight after 180° of rotation, where the bow of the rotor was down and the bow of the case was up.

While temperature stratification creates a top-to-bottom thermal gradient, overall cooling of the rotor surface creates a *surface-to-core thermal gradient*, which produces another set of high stresses inside the rotor. These stresses are due to a situation similar to *thermal shock* (see Sidebar). This thermal gradient produces high tensile stresses near the outer surface of the rotor and compressive stresses in the center of the rotor or at the surface of the bore hole (Figure 19-3c). These stresses act in the circumferential and axial directions.

When all of the stresses are considered, the surface-to-core tensile stress at the rotor surface *subtracts* from the other compressive stresses at the top of the rotor, while it *adds* to the other tensile stresses at the bottom (Figure 19-3d). If the total tensile stress at the bottom is greater than the yield strength of the

Figure 19-3. Stresses in a hot, stopped, horizontal rotor. The rotor, with a bore hole, sags due to its own weight. This produces low level tensile stress (orange) at the bottom of the rotor and compressive stress (violet) at the top (a).

After shutdown, thermal stratification often develops in the machine casing, and the resultant vertical thermal gradient in the rotor causes it to bow upward. If the rotor contacts the stator when it bows upward, then large stresses will develop at the rotor surface (b).

Another stress distribution forms as a result of the surface-to-core thermal gradient created as the entire rotor cools (c).

This produces large stresses that are tensile at the surface and compressive at the bore hole surface. All of these stresses add to produce the total stress distribution on the rotor (d).

If no rotor to stator contact occurs, then only the gravity sag and surface-to-core stresses will exist. With either scenario, the potential exists to develop very large tensile stresses at the bottom of the rotor. If these stresses exceed the yield strength, plastic deformation will occur, usually around stress concentrators such as inclusions and geometric discontinuities, and the rotor will bow downward when cool.

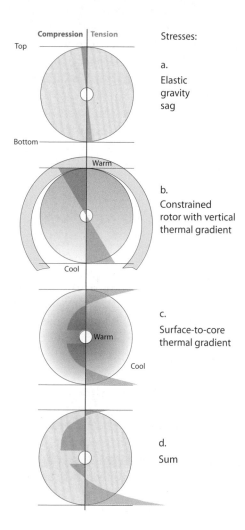

Stresses:

a.
Elastic
gravity
sag

b.
Constrained
rotor with vertical
thermal gradient

c.
Surface-to-core
thermal gradient

d.
Sum

material, then gross plastic deformation will occur along the bottom of the rotor over a large area.

Even if the stress at the bottom remains below the yield strength, there are still several factors that can increase the stress. Slag inclusions in the rotor forging or geometric discontinuities (such as diameter changes) are localized stress concentrators that multiply the nominal stress. Thus, the combination of elastic gravity stress, top-to-bottom thermal gradient stress (which will be significant only if stator contact occurs), surface-to-core thermal gradient stress, and stress concentrators can produce yielding in areas of the bottom of the rotor, even if the nominal stress remains below the yield strength.

Once they have yielded, these areas become longer than corresponding areas on the top of the rotor. When the rotor cools to thermal equilibrium, it will have a residual, permanent bow in the *downward* direction, in addition to the original elastic gravity bow. If the rotor bow was constrained by stator contact, the resulting bow can be quite severe. If the yielding occurred only locally near inclusions or at geometric discontinuities, though, then the result is likely to be a mild permanent bow that can be worked out later during startup.

To summarize, the primary causes of permanent thermal bow in a stopped rotor are

1. Stresses due to a top-to-bottom temperature gradient due to temperature stratification in the machine casing. If the rotor is constrained by contact with the stator, high tensile stress can develop near the bottom of the rotor, with compressive stress on top.

2. The high surface tensile stress due to the powerful surface-to-core thermal gradient that develops as the rotor begins to cool.

3. The relatively weak bending stresses due to the gravity sag of the rotor, which produce tensile stress at the bottom of the rotor and compressive stress at the top.

4. The presence of any inclusions or geometric discontinuities that produce stress concentration factors.

Rotors can bow during startup if heat is applied too suddenly or unevenly. During a startup, as the rotor surface is heated, surface-to-core thermal gradient stresses appear again, but with reverse sign. The surface of the rotor becomes hotter than the interior, producing tension in the interior. For a typical steam turbine startup, the outside surface temperature of the rotor can be 100 °C (180 °F) higher than the bore hole surface temperature, and this difference is maintained for hours. For our large, 1 m (3 ft) diameter rotor with a 130 mm (5 in) bore diameter, circumferential and axial stresses at the bore hole surface are about 240 MPa (35 ksi), a substantial fraction of the yield strength of rotor steel. Again, stress concentration factors can increase these nominal stresses significantly and can cause cracking of the bore hole surface or rotor interior, most likely near stress raisers, such as inclusions. Because of the potential for damage due to thermal stress, rotors must be heated very slowly.

Rotors that go through many startup and shutdown cycles experience cyclic thermal stresses that are capable of initiating and propagating fatigue cracks, a process called *thermal fatigue*. Thermal fatigue is most likely in HP and IP rotors that operate at 430 °C (800 °F) and higher.

Our discussion has focused primarily on forged and machined steam turbine rotors. However, both temporary and permanent bows can develop on "built-up" rotors, such as turbine rotors with shrunk on disks and those built up with disks and tie bolts (typically gas turbine rotors). Gravity loads, the temperature effects we have discussed, and *axial* thermal gradients all cause stresses that must be transmitted across mechanical joints between disks and the rotor. Any shifting of parts relative to each other creates differences in position that can lead to bow. This problem can develop during both heating and cooling of the rotor.

Another kind of permanent bow can develop in built-up rotors that are stationary for a long time. As we have seen, the stresses due to the gravity load are too low to cause a permanent bow by themselves, but a built-up rotor of any type may develop a "bow memory" if it is stationary for a long time. Rotors with shrunk-on disks are most vulnerable; because of this, spare rotors of this type are best stored in a vertical position.

Finally, shipping a rotor without adequate midspan support can lead to bow. In this case, dynamic shock loads while in transit can multiply the normal gravity bow many times. If the rotor ends are pushed up rapidly, the midspan sag will increase, producing large tensile stress at the bottom and compressive stress at the top. If these stresses exceed the yield strength, the rotor will develop a permanent, downward bow. Rotors should always be carefully supported during shipment.

Use of a torch on a local region of the rotor can alter the heat treatment properties of the area. Welding can change the properties of the metal and leave residual stresses that are different from those on the opposite side of the shaft, resulting in a permanent bow. For this reason, *the casual use of a torch is not recommended.*

Rotor Dynamic Effects of Rotor Bow

The elastic bow due to gravity or process-related, static radial loads *does not turn with the shaft*; it tends to remain at the same position angle while the rotor turns, producing a low level of 1X stress cycling that is usually not damaging. It is possible, however, for large cyclic stresses to develop as a result of radial side loads in vertical pumps, and, when combined with concentration factors, these stresses have led to fatigue failure of the shaft.

Elastic bow in built up rotors has also been known to cause *friction instability* in rotors, a condition that manifests itself as large amplitude, subsynchronous vibration. This was a serious problem in turbines built in the early 20th century, but newer designs rarely encounter it.

Temporary or permanent bows *turn with the shaft*, and the displaced mass of the rotor creates a new, rotating unbalance. If the bow changes during operation, as can happen with temporary bows, the result will be a change in the 1X amplitude or phase of the rotor response.

Permanent rotor bow creates an unbalance in the rotor that leads to 1X vibration, but there are fundamental differences between rotor response due to unbalance and rotor response due to bow. To illustrate this, we will use a variation of the simple rotor model that was developed in Chapter 10.

We start by assuming that a permanent rotor bow has displaced the rotor mass, M, a distance, r_e, from the rotor system centerline in a direction, δ. In reality, r_e will change in response to the dynamics, but we will assume that it is constant. This produces a measurable rotor bow response vector, $\boldsymbol{r}_1$, at low speed, where there is negligible dynamic response:

$$\boldsymbol{r}_1 = r_e e^{j\delta} \tag{19-1}$$

The bow also produces an effective unbalance of the rotor system. In the absence of any other source of unbalance, the bow-induced unbalance produces a synchronous rotor response, $\boldsymbol{r}_2$, similar to that of Equation 10-37:

$$\boldsymbol{r}_2 = A e^{j\alpha} = \frac{M r_e \Omega^2 e^{j\delta}}{\left[K - M\Omega^2 + jD(1-\lambda)\Omega \right]} \tag{19-2}$$

The only difference between this equation and Equation 10-37 is that the unbalance is due to the bow, not due to a conventional unbalance. The dynamic rotor response due to bow is the sum of the two responses,

$$\boldsymbol{r} = \boldsymbol{r}_1 + \boldsymbol{r}_2 = r_e e^{j\delta} + \frac{M r_e \Omega^2 e^{j\delta}}{\left[K - M\Omega^2 + jD(1-\lambda)\Omega \right]} \qquad (19\text{-}3)$$

At low speed, the unbalance force is very small, and the response is primarily due to the bow term, $\boldsymbol{r}_1$. At speeds well above resonance, where the spring stiffness term, K, and the quadrature stiffness term, $jD(1-\lambda)\Omega$, can be neglected (see Chapter 11), the rotor response becomes

$$\boldsymbol{r} = r_e e^{j\delta} + \frac{M r_e \Omega^2 e^{j\delta}}{-M\Omega^2} = r_e e^{j\delta} - r_e e^{j\delta} = 0 \qquad (19\text{-}4)$$

The model tells us that *rotor response due to the bow is zero above the resonance.* This is why it is said that, once you get a machine above resonance, the bow will often "balance itself out." This self-balancing feature of the bow is helpful, but if the bow is severe enough, vibration levels may exceed allowable levels *before* reaching the resonance peak. In this case, it is not possible to pass through the

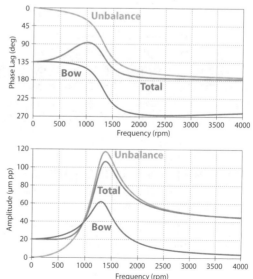

Figure 19-4. 1X Bode plots for a rotor system with bow and unbalance. The unbalance response (green) shows that, at zero speed, the amplitude is zero and the phase of the unbalance is 0°, while the bow response (red) has an eccentricity of 20 μm pp (0.8 mil pp) and a high spot phase of 135°. At low speed, the total response (blue) is dominated by the bow. Above the resonance, the bow begins to balance itself out and disappear, leaving only the residual unbalance response. Because of the phase relationship between the unbalance and the bow eccentricity in this example, the amplitude at resonance is lower than would be the case for unbalance alone.

resonance without risk of serious damage, and the bow must be removed before a startup is possible.

Equation 19-4 states that the vibration due to the bow is zero at speeds well above resonance. However, the total response of the rotor includes yet a third term, the ordinary response due to some *other* unbalance. The 1X Bode plots in Figure 19-4 show the response of a rotor system with a combination of bow and unbalance. The unbalance response (green) shows that, at zero speed, the amplitude is zero and the phase of the unbalance is 0°, while the bow response (red) has an eccentricity of 20 μm pp (0.8 mil pp) and a high spot phase of 135°. At low speed, the total response (blue) is dominated by the bow. Above the resonance, the bow begins to balance itself out and disappear, leaving only the residual unbalance response. Because of the phase relationship between the unbalance and the bow eccentricity in this example, the amplitude at resonance is lower than would be the case for unbalance alone.

Thermal Bow During Operation

Temporary thermal bow can increase or decrease the 1X vibration amplitude at operating speed depending on the phase relationship of the bow to the unbalance. Shorted turns in generators, and broken rotor bars or shorted rotor iron in induction motors, can produce local hot spots on the rotor that cause a temporary thermal bow.

Even generators in new condition can have small asymmetries in slots, windings, and cooling gas flow that produce uneven heating and thermal bow. Manufacturers will often set up *offset balancing* (the act of deliberately unbalancing slightly to compensate for later thermal changes) in a generator so that it will run smoothly at full load. However, even when this is done, changes in load or excitation can produce temperature changes that lead to a thermal bow that is different from what was anticipated, causing increased 1X vibration.

Generator rotors also deteriorate over time as repeated startups and shutdowns cause shifting of internal parts. As this happens, cooling passages may become partially or fully blocked, causing a change in the temperature distribution of the rotor. Thus, after some time in service, generator rotors may have to be rebalanced.

Rub can produce a hot spot and a bowed rotor. Imagine a rotor that is turning at constant speed. In this situation, a once-per-turn rub will occur at the same location each revolution of the shaft, and the friction at the contact area will cause local heating and a hot spot. The rotor will then bow toward the hot spot, creating a new unbalance in the rotor system. The new unbalance adds vectorially with the original unbalance, and, if the total unbalance increases, the rub will be maintained. When this happens, it is possible for the 1X vibration response vector to move cyclically in a direction opposite to rotation. This behavior typically occurs with the following sequence (Figure 19-5):

1. Before the rub, the rotor response (high spot) lags the heavy spot by some amount, α, that is constant for the operating speed. A gentle, wiping, once-per-turn seal rub occurs at the high spot, which is the part of the rotor that is farthest from the rotor system center.

2. A hot spot develops at the rub location, and the hot spot causes a rotor bow in the direction of the rub.

3. The mass of the bowed rotor produces a new heavy spot in the direction of the high spot. The new heavy spot adds vectorially with the original (unbalance) heavy spot to produce a single, effective heavy spot, which is located between the original heavy spot and the bow direction.

4. The rotor dynamics dictate that the high spot must lag the new effective heavy spot by the same amount, α. Thus, the rotor high spot shifts to a new location that lags the effective heavy spot by α.

5. The cycle repeats as the rotor rubs at this new high spot location, creating a bow in this direction.

As this cycle continues, the 1X response vector slowly rotates in a direction opposite to rotation. The time to complete one cycle can be anywhere from several minutes to hours. The polar APHT plot (Figure 19-5, bottom) shows data from a small, high-speed turbine that encountered this type of rub. The rotation direction is Y to X (CW), and the 1X vibration vector slowly moves opposite to rotation, completing one full revolution of the plot in about 5 minutes. This behavior can occur on any type of machine when the high spot lags the heavy spot by less than 90° or so.

Other cases lead to different behavior. If the high spot (contact point) is significantly out of phase with the heavy spot, then the thermal bow will reduce the total unbalance and the vibration response, and the rub contact may cease or reappear periodically. If the contact point happens to *lead* the heavy spot, the resulting thermal bow will tend to shift the vibration vector in the *forward* direction.

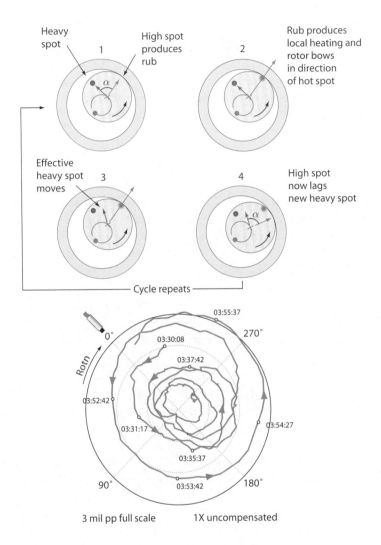

Figure 19-5. Evolution of thermal bow due to rub at constant speed. The four diagrams at the top illustrate the sequence that produces a slowly changing, 1X vector that moves opposite rotation. See the text for details. The 1X APHT plot (bottom) shows the effect on the vibration vector in a high-speed turbine of a thermal bow caused by a mild seal rub. In this machine, the vector completes one revolution of the polar plot in about 5 minutes.

Another source of thermal bow is the differential heating of the rotor due to the difference in fluid-film bearing film thickness that occurs as the journal vibrates. Journals in hydrodynamic bearings typically operate at average eccentricity ratios of 0.6 to 0.8, but dynamic motion produces an orbit around the average position. With large, 1X responses, the journal high spot passes closer to the bearing wall than does the opposite side of the journal (Figure 19-6). In overhung compressors, this type of bow has been observed to produce slow, *forward* motion of the 1X vector [1].

The thermal bow occurs because fluid-film friction is proportional to the velocity gradient in the oil film. As the journal high spot surface nears the bearing wall, the oil film becomes very thin, the velocity gradient between the journal surface and the bearing wall becomes high, and more heat is produced. One-half revolution later, the journal "low spot" passes near the wall, but the rotor centerline is now on the opposite side of the orbit, so the instantaneous eccentricity ratio is lower, and the heat input is smaller.

Thus, the high spot of the journal experiences more heat input from oil film friction than the opposite side. This process produces a temperature gradient between opposite sides of the journal. The differential thermal expansion can produce a temporary bow that has been known to produce high amplitude, cyclic, 1X vibration in machines with overhung rotors or large coupling moments.

Figure 19-6. Differential heating of rotor due to variable film thickness in a fluid-film bearing. When the 1X response is large and the orbit is offset from the bearing centerline, the high spot side of the journal will pass closer to the bearing surface than the other side. Frictional heating of the oil, which is proportional to the velocity gradient, will heat one side of the journal more than the other, causing a thermal bow of the rotor.

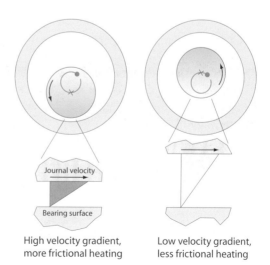

High velocity gradient, more frictional heating

Low velocity gradient, less frictional heating

It is possible for a steam turbine rotor to become suddenly and severely bowed during operation. This can happen to HP and IP rotors when a boiler control failure or loss of firing produces low quality (high liquid content) steam, which causes dramatic cooling of the surfaces of both the rotor and casing. Typically, this event will immediately cause a temporary rotor bow, since the quenching effect is uneven from side to side. Heavy rubbing then occurs, and the rotor bow becomes more severe because of the local heating of the rotor surface. It is also quite common for rotors which have been steam quenched to become temperature sensitive afterwards because the thermal properties of the rotor have become anisotropic. Such a severe thermal shock can very easily cause cracking of the rotor surface.

A similar mechanism can occur in LP rotors operating in cold climates. With very cold cooling water, the condensate temperature can become low. If a system upset occurs, very cold saturated steam can move back into the LP turbine casing and thermally shock the rotor. This scenario can produce a sudden rotor bow or shaft surface cracking.

Diagnosing Rotor Bow

Permanent rotor bow is a malfunction that produces 1X vibration behavior that is very similar to unbalance. Unlike unbalance, however, bow produces a significant, forward 1X response *at slow roll*. At high speed, above the resonance, the bow response becomes small, and most of the residual 1X vibration is due to unbalance.

The most obvious symptom of permanent rotor bow is a 1X vibration that occurs on startup. Bow is probable on a machine if

1. The machine was shut down hot and not put on turning gear.

2. The machine did not exhibit 1X vibration at slow roll during the shutdown, but does at startup.

3. 1X slow roll vectors have dramatically changed compared to historical values.

4. Eccentricity measurements exceed the maximum allowable when attempting to start up.

Be aware that a shaft crack can also exhibit symptoms 2, 3, and 4. See Chapter 23.

When trying to diagnose rotor bow, examine *uncompensated* direct and 1X slow roll orbits. The 1X slow roll data from several measurement planes can be correlated to infer the possible shape of the bow. A good way to do this is to plot a set of 1X orbits at the same scale and lay them on a table with spacing proportional to the axial measurement locations.

Several other malfunctions can look like rotor bow. Coupling problems can produce 1X vibration at slow roll speed; a locked gear coupling will produce an eccentric motion of the shaft that can look exactly like bow.

Mechanical and electrical runout (glitch) of the probe viewing surface results from an improperly treated or handled probe viewing surface. Beware if the rotor was lifted using chains, or even straps, that contacted the probe viewing area. The load of the rotor on the straps can modify the mechanical and electrical properties of the surface, producing a 1X runout. Also, a single scratch on the rotor can produce a 1X component and harmonics in the vibration signal. Examine a direct, uncompensated orbit or timebase plot.

A nonconcentric journal and shaft will produce a measurable eccentricity that is unrelated to bow. A shrunk-on part, which is vulnerable to concentricity or cocking problems, can produce an apparent bow in eccentricity or radial vibration measurements.

A shaft crack will almost always produce a bowed rotor. As a shaft crack propagates across the rotor, the rotor bending stiffness becomes lower in the vicinity of the crack. Thus, the rotor is less able to resist the dynamic forces that try to deform the rotor, and the rotor will usually bow as the crack develops. If the size of the crack changes in response to repeated startups, the 1X slow roll vector may change in amplitude and phase. See Chapter 23.

Removing Rotor Bow

For permanent rotor bow, prevention is the best cure. Once a machine is shut down, a hot rotor should be put on turning gear before it has a chance to stop. As the rotor is turning, the surface temperatures will even out, and the top-to-bottom thermal gradient in the rotor will disappear, even if the gradient remains in the casing.

However, the powerful surface-to-core thermal gradient will remain, and the rotor should be cooled as slowly as possible. Turning the rotor tends to even out any plastic deformation that may be taking place.

If a turbine stops while hot and cannot be turned, rotor-to-casing contact may occur at the top of the rotor. *A common mistake is to panic and turn the rotor by force*, which can result in severe internal damage to the machine. A better solution is to wait until the rotor cools enough to turn, then carefully rotate it 180° to even out the bow.

Because the symptoms of rotor bow are so similar to unbalance, there is a temptation to balance a bowed rotor in an attempt to cure the symptoms. *This is not a recommended practice*, because, if the bow goes away, which it often does, the balance weight will become an unbalance weight.

Completely removing a permanent rotor bow requires that the rotor be subjected to a series of steps that produce equal and opposite plastic deformation, a difficult thing to accomplish. In most cases, bow is relatively mild, and it can be reduced by operating the machine at a slow speed. This will *roll out* the rotor bow until the eccentricity readings drop to a low enough level to allow the machine to be started up. Once above the resonance, the bow will often balance itself out.

More difficult bows can be removed by starting the machine, running the speed up until the vibration reaches a predetermined limit, and heat soaking for a period of time. The machine is then slowed down and allowed to cool while on turning gear. This cycle may need to be repeated several times. The object is to get the rotor hot enough so that, when cooled, large surface-to-core thermal gradient stresses will appear and cause enough plastic deformation to even out the bow.

After a hard rub, the rotor may be not only bowed, but also have surface microcracking in the vicinity of the rub. If untreated, these cracks can lead to fatigue cracks in the rotor. Because of this, the affected area should be carefully treated to remove these cracks.

Rotors with permanent bows have been remachined over the outer surface and in the journal area. Because of changed clearances, it may also be necessary to replace seals. Bearing clearances will be affected, and the rotor may still retain a measureable eccentricity.

Extreme bows may require special heat treatment, removal of the entire rotor for heat treatment in a vertical furnace, or scrapping. *Do not casually use a torch to remove a bow!* The residual stress field that remains after local heat application may cause unpredictable thermal characteristics. However, carefully controlled local heat treatment, with attention to resulting material properties, has been used successfully to remove a bow. Heat is applied on the high side of the bow in order to generate local compressive stresses that exceed yield strength, causing the rotor to become shorter in that area.

Summary

There are three general types of rotor bow: elastic, temporary, and permanent. Elastic bows are caused by static radial loads such as gravity or process loads. Temporary bows can be caused by uneven heating of the rotor surface, which causes differential thermal expansion. Permanent bows are caused by plastic deformation of rotor material when stress exceeds the yield strength.

Permanent rotor bows are often caused by failing to put a hot rotor on turning gear before it stops. Thermal stratification in the machine casing causes a top-to-bottom thermal gradient that warps the rotor upward. If the rotor contacts the stator, high stresses can appear. High tensile stresses also appear on the surface due to the surface-to-core thermal gradient produced when the rotor surface cools below the core temperature. When these thermal stresses are added to the stress associated with elastic gravity bow, they can exceed the yield strength of the material.

During startup, thermal gradients generate stresses with the opposite sign, compressive on the outer surface and tension in the center or at the surface of the bore hole. Startups must be conducted very carefully to avoid thermal shock of the rotor, bowing, and cracking.

Temporary thermal bow can be produced during operation by localized heat sources or cool spots in the rotor, such as shorted turns in generators, or broken rotor bars and shorted rotor laminations in induction motors.

Temporary thermal bow can also be caused by light, once-per-turn rubs on seals and by differential heating effects in the thin film region in fluid-film bearings.

Rotor bow produces a 1X vibration that exists even at low speeds. At speeds well above resonance, the bow will often balance itself out, and the 1X vibration due to bow will be greatly reduced, leaving conventional unbalance vibration.

Modulated 1X vibration can be produced by rub-induced thermal bow. The contact point will tend to move around the rotor as the bow changes the effective heavy spot location and the 1X vibration vector.

Rotor bow is recognized primarily by the 1X vibration that exists at slow roll speed. However, many other malfunctions can also produce low-speed 1X vibration, such as coupling problems, surface problems, concentricity problems, and a shaft crack.

Mild permanent rotor bow can usually be rolled out by operating the machine at low speeds for a length of time.

References

1. de Jongh, Frits M., and van der Hoeven, Pieter, "Application of a Heat Barrier Sleeve to Prevent Synchronous Rotor Instability," *Proceedings of the Twenty-Seventh Turbomachinery Symposium*, Texas A&M University, College Station (September 1998): pp. 17-26.

Chapter 20

High Radial Loads and Misalignment

T<small>HE MOST COMMON COMPLAINT BY OPERATORS</small> of rotating machinery is high vibration. The *second* most common complaint is high bearing temperature. High bearing temperature is almost always associated with a high dynamic or static radial load; such a load can be caused by process conditions, various mechanical factors, coupling malfunctions, or misalignment. Radial loads and misalignment have similar symptoms; in fact, misalignment usually produces high radial loads in one or more bearings. Thus, the diagnosis of both of these malfunctions uses closely related techniques. For that reason, we will study both malfunctions in this chapter.

We will start with a discussion of the sources of static radial loads in rotating machinery, only one of which is misalignment. We will then concentrate on misalignment and discuss the definition, causes, and symptoms.

Static Radial Loads

A *static radial load* is a force that acts on the rotor in the radial direction and does not change magnitude or direction with time. This is in contrast with a dynamic radial load, such as unbalance, that changes in magnitude or direction (rotates). Static radial loads are sometimes called *radial sideloads* or *preloads*. The term preload is also used to describe bearing geometry (having nothing to do with a force), so, to avoid confusion, we will reserve the term preload for bearing applications.

Static radial loads can be classified into two general categories, *soft* and *hard*. *Soft* radial loads do not change dramatically with changes in rotor position. Examples include gravity, fluid loads, and partial arc steam admission. Soft radial loads are usually accounted for in the design of machinery and are not likely to cause damage. Gear mesh forces are also allowed for in machine designs but have the characteristics of hard radial loads. *Hard* radial loads involve rotor interaction with some mechanical boundary. Loads due to locked couplings, misalignment, and rub are examples of hard radial loads, and these loads appear directly or indirectly as a result of a machine malfunction.

The force of gravity is the simplest example of a soft static radial load, and it exists on all horizontal machines. (In vertical machines, this force appears as an axial load.) If the bearings have been properly designed, gravity is not likely to cause any problems in a machine.

Fluid radial loads appear in pumps because of asymmetries in the design of the volute. This type of load is also called a *hydraulic preload* or *hydraulic sideload*. Single volute pumps generate significant loads as a byproduct of the pressure distribution that exists in the pump, while double volute pumps minimize the sideload due to the symmetry of the volute design. The loads are also minimized when the pump operates at its best efficiency point (BEP). When operated off the BEP, these loads can become much larger.

Inlet guide vane (IGV or wicket) problems in a hydro turbine can cause an asymmetric pressure distribution and a static radial load.

Partial arc steam admission in turbines creates a relatively high pressure region on one side of the rotor. The resulting pressure distribution around the rotor produces a static radial load. If the steam admission occurs on the bottom side of the rotor, the load can be strong enough to overcome gravity and lift the rotor. If the rotor moves to a low eccentricity ratio operating point in a fluid-film bearing, this situation can trigger fluid-induced instability.

All of the types of loads presented so far are examples of soft radial loads. Hard radial loads, because of the physical constraint they impose, are much more likely to cause problems in machinery.

Gear mesh forces are more like hard radial loads than soft loads. At the gear tooth contact point, the orientation of the surface is not on a radius of the gear, but is inclined at an angle, the pressure angle. The gear mesh force can be resolved into a *tangential force* and a radial *separation force*. The tangential force is directly related to the torque delivery of the gears. The torque delivered is the product of the tangential force and the *pitch radius* of the gear. The separation force acts in a direction toward the shaft, attempting to separate the gears; for a typical 20° pressure angle, it is about 37% of the tangential force. In addition to these two forces, single helical gears also generate a large axial force.

Gear mesh forces can be quite large. For example, in a high-speed, single-stage, increasing gear drive, transmitting 27 500 hp with an 8640 rpm, 330 mm (13 in) diameter pinion, the tangential force is 140 kN (31 500 lb), and the separation force is 52 kN (11 700 lb). The vector sum of these two forces is a large static load that is many times the weight of the pinion and gear.

Hard radial loads can be caused by coupling problems. Properly operating gear couplings have very low axial stiffness and tolerate moderate misalignment. However, these couplings must be properly lubricated; if the lubricant either fails or is inadequate, the coupling can lock and transmit high radial loads in addition to dynamic loads.

Hard radial loads often appear as a result of misalignment. Table 20-1 lists many sources of misalignment loads, all of which can be quite damaging. Because of its importance, misalignment will be dealt with in more detail below.

Rub occurs when the rotor contacts a stationary part of the machine. The contact can be intermittent and generate a dynamic load and response, or, if it is severe enough, it can be continuous and produce a high static radial load.

Table 20-1. Sources of static radial loads.

Source	Classification
Gravity	Soft
Fluid loads	Soft
Pump off operating point	
Wicket problems in hydro machines	
Partial arc steam admission	Soft
Gear mesh forces	Soft/Hard
Tangential forces	
Separation forces	
Locked gear couplings	Hard
Misalignment	Hard
Cocked bearings	
Distorted diaphragms	
Locked floating seals	
Thermal warping of casing	
Piping strain	
Foundation problems	
External misalignment	
Rub	Hard

When any rub occurs, the spring stiffness of the rotor system greatly increases and the contact area acts as a hard constraint on the rotor motion. Rub is often caused by misalignment.

Soft radial loads and gear mesh forces are a normal part of machine operation, and, if the machine is properly designed and aligned, they should not produce a problem. However, hard radial loads are not normal and can easily exceed design limits, causing internal rubs, coupling wear, or wear and failure of bearings.

While coupling problems can produce excessive radial loads, the most common source is misalignment. For that reason, the primary emphasis for the rest of this chapter will be on the causes and diagnosis of high radial loads caused by misalignment.

What Is Misalignment?

Before discussing misalignment, we should define alignment. When a machine is operating at thermal equilibrium, and the rotor is subjected to normal operating loads, perfect *internal* alignment exists when, at each axial location, 1) the average shaft centerline position is in the center of each interstage diaphragm or seal, and 2) the average shaft centerline of the rotor operates at the design position in the bearing. Two machines are in perfect *external* alignment if, when operating at thermal equilibrium, the shaft centerlines are collinear at the coupling (Figure 20-1, top) and the shafts operate in their design axial positions within each machine.

In practice, some degree of internal and external misalignment always exists. *When the external misalignment between two machines exceeds the allowable tolerances of the coupling, seals, bearings, etc., the machines are misaligned.*

There are three basic types of external misalignment. *Parallel misalignment* occurs when the shaft centerlines of two machines are parallel, but offset (Figure 20-1, middle). *Angular misalignment* occurs when the shaft centerlines are not parallel (Figure 20-1, bottom). The most common situation is a combination of parallel and angular misalignment. *Axial misalignment* occurs when the axial position of the two, coupled shafts exceeds coupling tolerances. (Axial misalignment can also be a problem in motors and generators when the allowable magnetic centering is exceeded.)

The external misalignment tolerance for two machines will depend on the type of coupling that is used. Rigid couplings have a very low tolerance for misalignment, disk pack and diaphragm couplings, which are usually used in pairs, have more tolerance, and gear and elastomer couplings have the highest tolerance for misalignment.

Figure 20-1. Types of external misalignment. Two machines are in perfect external alignment (top) when their shaft centerlines are collinear at the coupling within an allowable tolerance zone (red). Parallel misalignment (middle) occurs when the shaft centerlines are offset, but parallel. Angular misalignment (bottom) occurs when the shafts are not parallel. Misalignment usually involves a combination of parallel and angular misalignment. In the figure, the shafts are shown centered in the bearings. In reality, shafts in properly aligned machines with fluid-film bearings would operate at the design eccentricity ratio.

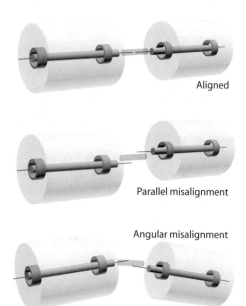

Aligned

Parallel misalignment

Angular misalignment

Temperature Changes and Alignment

While a machine is operating, the temperature can vary significantly from one part of the machine to another and can vary with load. The resulting thermal growth causes changes in the linear dimensions of the machine compared to the "cold" or off condition.

For the purposes of this discussion, "hot" will indicate a machine that is running and in thermal equilibrium, and "cold" will indicate a machine that is stopped and in thermal equilibrium. A machine that handles cold fluids will still be called hot when it is running and in thermal equilibrium. Note that a large machine, like some steam turbine generators, may take one to two days to reach thermal equilibrium after startup or shutdown.

As the temperature changes during a startup, the linear dimensions of a machine will change in complicated ways, with the hotter parts growing more than the cooler parts. Dimensional changes in the machine supports and casing will cause the machine to rise or fall, lengthen or shorten, and change angular orientation. Another, coupled machine will probably exhibit a different growth pattern. Thermal conduction into the foundation will also affect machine position and orientation. Thus, if a machine train is aligned in the cold condition, it is likely to be misaligned in the hot condition. For this reason, machines are deliberately and carefully misaligned in the cold condition so that they will become correctly aligned in the hot condition (Figure 20-2).

Because the temperature of a machine can vary with load, alignment can also change with load. It may be difficult to set a cold alignment that produces acceptable hot alignment for all anticipated load conditions.

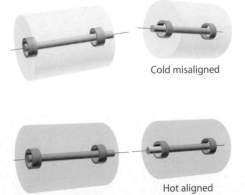

Figure 20-2. Cold alignment compensates for thermal growth. Machines are deliberately and carefully misaligned in the cold condition (top) so that thermal growth will produce correct alignment in the hot condition.

Cold misaligned

Hot aligned

Causes of Misalignment

Assuming that a machine train has been properly aligned to begin with, misalignment symptoms can be caused by anything that produces a change in position of internal parts relative to the shaft, or a change in the position of one machine relative to another. There are several general causes:

1. Internal parts may have been installed incorrectly or may have become damaged.

2. Thermal growth of machine components may not be as expected.

3. Piping strain or a soft foot condition can warp the machine casing.

4. Grouting or foundation deterioration may cause a shift in machine position.

When misalignment symptoms are present, it is important to first eliminate all other possible problems before performing an alignment. Often, when the problem is corrected, the alignment state of the machine will revert to an acceptable level. A true misalignment condition exists only when all of these other factors are accounted for or corrected and the problem still exists. Of all the items in the list, only thermal growth can be compensated for by a physical realignment of the machines.

Internal misalignment can be produced by cocked bearings, incorrectly positioned or distorted diaphragms, or floating seals that become locked off center.

Piping strain, soft foot, and grouting and foundation problems are not the same as misalignment; they are separate malfunctions that produce misalignment symptoms.

Piping strain can misalign a machine by warping the machine casing. The warped casing misaligns the bearing supports, effectively moving the bearings relative to the shaft. Pipe strain can result from loose or locked piping hangers; bent, broken, or missing piping supports; or poor piping fit. Always check the piping system of a machine with misalignment symptoms for signs of pipe hanger or pipe support problems. Poor piping fit can put tremendous loads on the machine casing; *piping should never be forced to mate with the machine.* Instead, the piping and pipe support system must be designed to mate perfectly at the attachment flanges. This mating must be correct in position (3 dimensions) and angle (3 more dimensions).

Soft foot occurs when one or more machine feet are not coplanar with the soleplate (baseplate) or foundation. When one foot (the soft foot) is not properly supported, tightening it down will warp the machine casing, changing the relative position of machine components. Soft foot can be caused by inadequate shimming or by an excessive number of shims; *more than 4 shims under a foot can produce a springy support.* Soft foot can also be caused by a warped, bowed, or improperly installed soleplate; improper machining of feet or the soleplate; a foot not parallel to the soleplate; or a warped or bowed machine casing.

Foundation problems, such as cracked grouting, a loose soleplate, and loose anchor bolts, can cause a shift in machine position over time. Oil-soaked concrete can lead to deterioration of the concrete foundation and loss of support strength. Grouting serves to provide a high stiffness interface designed to distribute loads between the soleplate and the surface of the underlying foundation. Grout is very strong under compressive loads and weak in tension. Because of this, grout should always be kept in compression. *Cracked grout indicates that it has been subjected to tension and that the foundation system of the machine has failed.*

Table 20-2. Symptoms of high radial load and misalignment.

Symptom	High Radial Load	Misalignment
High bearing temp in overloaded bearings	X	X
Low bearing temp in underloaded bearings		X
Bearing wear, premature bearing failure	X	X
Premature coupling failure		X
Low rotor vibration	X	X
High casing vibration	X	X
Axial vibration from disk/diaphragm couplings		X
High eccentricity ratio	X	X
Low eccentricity ratio		X
Abnormal average shaft centerline position	X	X
Fluid-induced instability		X
Flattened or banana-shaped orbits	X	X

Symptoms of High Radial Load and Misalignment

Above- or below-normal radial loads and misalignment produce characteristic symptoms (Table 20-2); *for misalignment, some symptoms occur in pairs.* For example, a bearing that is overloaded due to misalignment will typically have a neighbor that is underloaded. The overloaded bearing will have a high bearing temperature, while the adjacent bearing will have an abnormally low temperature. The average eccentricity ratio can be high in one bearing and low in an adjacent bearing, and the shaft centerline position may be in one quadrant in one bearing and in the opposite quadrant in an adjacent bearing. Often the paired characteristic will occur across a coupling. These symptoms will be discussed in the following sections.

Bearing Temperature

Misalignment will often unload one bearing at the expense of another (Figure 20-3), leading to abnormal bearing temperatures. *High fluid-film bearing temperature is often the first warning of a possible misalignment condition.* Normally loaded fluid-film bearings have a babbitt temperature of 70 °C to 80 °C (160 °F to 180 °F). Overloading a fluid-film bearing will reduce the minimum clearance, producing higher shear forces in the oil and higher oil temperature in

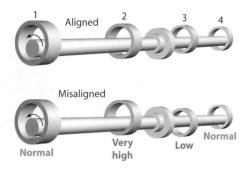

Figure 20-3. Average shaft position in an aligned machine versus a misaligned machine. The coupled shafts are vertically loaded by gravity. Misalignment shifts the load among the bearings. In this example, bearing 2 experiences a very high load and will run abnormally hot. Bearing 3 is essentially unloaded and will run cooler than normal. The two outboard bearings are approximately normally loaded. The shaft centerline position in bearing 3 is in the upper left quadrant; this is an abnormal position for a gravity-loaded shaft that is rotating X to Y (CCW) in a fluid-film bearing.

the load zone of the bearing. This heat will transfer into the babbitt. Babbitt will be significantly weakened and start to creep at 125 °C (260 °F) and melt at 240 °C (460 °F), leading to bearing failure. Extreme misalignment can result in metal-to-metal contact (wiping), and melting of the babbitt (Figure 20-4).

Note that *oil drain temperature is not a very useful indicator of the temperature in the load zone of the bearing*. It is limited because the oil exiting the bearing is a mixture of oil that has passed through the load zone of the bearing and oil that has bypassed it. Oil drain temperature is best used for plant heat load calculations or oil temperature regulation; it only provides a vague picture of the machine condition.

Resistance temperature detectors (RTDs) or thermocouples can be imbedded in the bearing to provide better warning. Ideally, the RTDs should be installed at several circumferential positions in the bearing backing (not in the babbitt) for two reasons. First, in some machines, the direction of the radial load on a bearing can vary with operating conditions, and it can be difficult to predict where the maximum load occurs in a bearing. Second, if a machine becomes misaligned, load shifting can produce radial loads that act in unpredictable and unexpected directions.

While a high bearing temperature indicates overloading, an abnormally low bearing temperature indicates a below-normal load. Given the load shifting that takes place with misalignment, bearings with above- and below-normal loads will typically be adjacent. For this reason, bearing temperatures along the machine train should be monitored and compared.

Extreme misalignment can lead to polishing or wiping of babbitt material. When a machine is disassembled, bearings should be carefully examined for evidence of any damage (Figure 20-4).

Figure 20-4. Misalignment damage on a tilting pad bearing. The wiping and discoloration at the edge of the pad was caused by misalignment, while the center of the pads were damaged by electrostatic discharge (ESD).

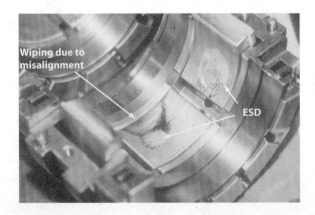

Rolling element bearing life is inversely proportional to the cube of the applied radial load. High radial loads will cause premature failure of rolling element bearings. Chronic premature failure of one or more rolling element bearings in a machine could be evidence of a misalignment problem.

Vibration Changes

Rotor vibration amplitude is related to the spring stiffness in a fluid-film bearing, which is a function of the eccentricity ratio. A rotor operating in a lightly loaded bearing will operate at a lower than normal eccentricity ratio. The reduced rotor support stiffness can lower the resonance frequency and cause a change in vibration.

Assuming that the vibration forcing function originates in the rotor (for example, unbalance), the amount of casing vibration will depend partly on how much rotor vibration is transmitted through the bearings. (Casing vibration will also depend upon how well the machine is mounted to the foundation.) When a rotor is at a high eccentricity ratio, the very high fluid-film stiffness of the bearing more effectively couples the rotor to the casing. Thus, in a misaligned machine, the machine may experience higher than normal casing vibration. Shaft relative vibration, because of the increased constraint on the rotor, may decrease as more of the vibration energy is transmitted to the casing.

If a particular bearing is unloaded, the rotor-to-case coupling will decrease (transmissibility will decrease) at that location, and the casing vibration there may decrease. Under this circumstance, shaft relative vibration may increase as the stiffness of the rotor support decreases.

The foregoing discussion applies when a rotor is operating at a speed where spring stiffness dominates the response of the system. If a rotor operates above a nearby resonance, a reduction in spring stiffness can shift the resonance to a lower speed and cause a *decrease* in shaft relative vibration (see Figure 11-6 in Chapter 11).

Thus, either an increase or decrease in casing vibration, especially when the opposite change occurs in the shaft relative vibration, could be an indication of misalignment.

Casing vibration can change if the machine support structure weakens or loosens, or if the machine develops a soft foot. Sometimes, tightening loose foundation bolts will return casing vibration to normal levels. Figure 9-4 shows an example of increasing shaft relative *and* casing vibration caused by a deteriorating foundation.

Parallel misalignment at the coupling offsets the shafts and makes them act like a crank. This will usually produce 1X and 2X shaft relative vibration components that exist over the entire speed range of the machine. The vibration may transmit to the casing, but only shaft relative measurements will reveal the cranking action at slow roll speeds. The 2X component occurs because adjacent bearings alternately experience increased loading during each revolution of the shaft.

A skewed coupling bore or a bent shaft (an angular misalignment) can produce 1X or 2X vibration. An out-of-round coupling can produce a runout indication that looks like shaft displacement, but is not.

Disk and diaphragm couplings can produce an axial "pumping" action (axial vibration) when shafts are misaligned. This axial forcing can excite axial resonance frequencies of the rotor system. It is also possible for the axial vibration to couple into lateral (radial) vibration. Properly functioning gear couplings are much more axially compliant and less likely to produce axial vibration from misalignment.

Stresses and Wear

The increased load and changes in position that are associated with misalignment can affect critical components of the machine. Excessive loads can produce high stresses, leading to low- or high-cycle fatigue of shafts, couplings, and bearings. A misaligned rotor may come into contact with seals, causing wear or damage to the seals or shaft and a loss of efficiency.

Misalignment can cause wear, damage, or coupling lockup of flexible couplings. It can also cause fatigue failure of both flexible and rigid couplings.

The high bearing loads associated with misalignment can cause overheating, wear, and fatigue of babbitt in fluid-film bearings. Misalignment can also drastically reduce a rolling element bearing's useful life, which is a strong function of radial load. The L_{10} life (the time during which 10% of similar bearings will fail) for a point contact ball bearing is inversely proportional to the cube of the applied load.

Abnormal Average Shaft Centerline Position

In machines without gearing loads, and where the primary radial load is gravity, normally loaded, plain cylindrical, hydrodynamic bearings will usually have a rotor position angle of between 30° and 45° and an eccentricity ratio of 0.6 to 0.8. During a startup or shutdown, the shaft centerline will move in a typical way due to the effect of the fluid support wedge (Figure 20-5, green).

Remember that the *attitude angle* is determined by the shaft position relative to the applied radial load (Chapter 6). In a horizontal machine with a dominant gravity load, we expect the attitude angle to be equal to the position angle. If a significant radial load appears that acts in another direction, the position angle will be different. Gear mesh forces can easily overcome gravity and move gears to positions that are very different from what would be expected for a horizontal machine.

Load shifting among bearings will cause shaft centerline behavior to depart from normal. The radial load due to misalignment is likely to be in an unexpected direction, and the direction and amount of the misalignment load can change as the machines heat up. Heavily loaded bearings will have operating eccentricity ratios that are higher than normal, and lightly loaded bearings lower than normal. If the misalignment becomes severe enough, shaft operating positions may move to unusual locations, such as near the top of a bearing (Figure 20-5, red). In a horizontal machine, this is a sign that the radial load is no longer dominated by gravity.

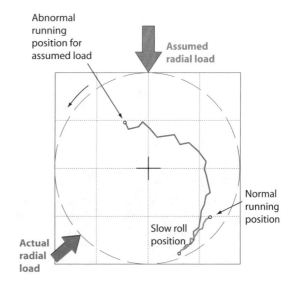

Figure 20-5. Shaft centerline behavior for a plain, cylindrical, fluid-film bearing. A typical startup or shutdown centerline plot (green) is shown for a horizontal machine with gravity as the dominant load. When the load changes (red), the startup and shutdown centerline response, for this case, changes significantly.

While a high radial load can be detected with shaft position data from a single bearing, misalignment is often revealed by comparing position data from adjacent bearings. Differences in operating position can be most apparent across a coupling, where the rotor may operate in different or opposite quadrants of the bearings (Figure 20-6). Note that the misalignment effectively moves the bearings relative to the shaft; the combination of bearing position shift and changing load in the bearings causes the measured shaft position to change.

Average shaft centerline plots should be examined at every axial position and compared for signs of abnormality. They are most useful when clearance circles are included on the plot; operation in an abnormal quadrant can be more easily detected. The plots should also be compared to archived data.

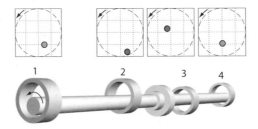

Figure 20-6. Misalignment and operating position. Misalignment of the machines moves the locations of the bearings relative to the shaft. This causes the measured position of the shaft to deviate from normal. In this example, bearing 2 is heavily loaded, and the shaft operates at a high eccentricity ratio. Across the coupling, bearing 3 is lightly loaded, and the shaft operates at a low eccentricity ratio in the opposite quadrant.

Most couplings are designed to accommodate the residual misalignment that exists in all machine trains. A properly operating coupling isolates the shafts from the loads that would occur due to this residual misalignment.

If, for any reason, a gear coupling becomes locked in position, unable to freely move, then large loads can appear in the bearings of the coupled machines. Often, this will cause sudden changes in the average shaft centerline position in these bearings (Figure 20-7). This situation can also produce large changes in 1X vibration behavior.

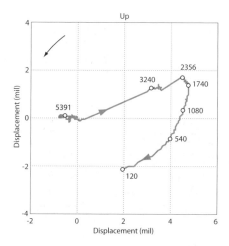

Figure 20-7. Coupling lockup and shaft centerline behavior. During this shutdown, the gear coupling between the pipeline compressor and its gas turbine driver was locked up from operating speed down to about 2300 rpm. The average shaft centerline plot at the inboard, low-pressure, gas turbine bearing shows abnormal response until the coupling unlocks. The shaft behaves normally for the remainder of the shutdown.

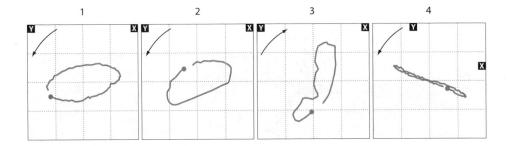

Figure 20-8. Unfiltered orbits showing progressive degrees of misalignment symptoms. Case 1 is a normal orbit from a generator bearing on a small steam turbine generator set. The orbit is mildly elliptical and predominantly 1X. Case 2 is from a Frame 6 gas turbine bearing. The orbit shows evidence of constraint along the lower edge. Case 3 is from the exciter bearing on a 500 MW steam turbine generator set. Note the highly elliptical banana shape, which produces a 2X vibration component. The curvature of the right side of the orbit suggests that the shaft may be following the geometry of the bearing. Case 4 is from an HP steam turbine bearing. The orbit is highly flattened, suggesting a high, misalignment-induced, radial load. (Note that line orbits can occur for other reasons.)

Orbit Shape

Orbits are very helpful for diagnosis of high loads and misalignment. The orbits in Figure 20-8 illustrate increasing degrees of misalignment-induced bearing loading in four different machines. Normally loaded rotors operating in fluid-film bearings tend to produce unfiltered (direct) orbits that are elliptical in shape and predominantly 1X (Figure 20-8, case 1). The ellipticity of such orbits can fall into a wide range and still be considered normal.

The shape of a direct orbit is sensitive to the amount of radial load that acts on the rotor. As the radial load increases, the orbit becomes more flattened, and part of the orbit path may follow the curvature of the bearing (Figure 20-8, case 2). (Note that orbits in elliptical and lemon bore bearings tend to be aligned with the bearing geometry and more elliptical than orbits in plain, cylindrical bearings.)

With increasing radial load, the orbit may become banana shaped, partially follow the curvature of the bearing, and contain a 2X vibration component (Figure 20-8, case 3). 2X components can be amplified if the rotor operates near half of a resonance speed.

In cases of high radial load or extreme misalignment, the rotor may become so constrained that it may become completely flattened (Figure 20-8, case 4) or, if unbalance is small, shrink to nearly a point. This is why gear shaft orbits tend to be very small. Assuming that unbalance is the primary source of rotor vibration, the orbit behavior will depend on the degree of radial load, the amount of unbalance, and the shaft attitude angle and eccentricity ratio.

A rotor that is unloaded in a bearing will operate at a low eccentricity ratio and have an orbit that is nearly circular. When elliptical orbits are the norm, a circular orbit suggests an unusually low radial load.

Orbits should be compared for every axial position in the machine train during steady state and transient operation. If startup or shutdown data is available, these orbits should be examined over the entire speed range of the machine for evidence of high radial loads. The orbits (dynamic position information) should be correlated with average shaft centerline plots (average position information).

Rub

Rub may occur on seals if the rotor is misaligned. The rub can occur during startup, shutdown, or steady state operation. Symptoms may include changes in 1X vibration behavior through resonances and changes in steady state vibration behavior. See Chapter 21.

A rub on interstage seals may open up clearances, resulting in higher leakage flows and a loss of efficiency. Any machine that shows a loss of efficiency over time should be carefully evaluated for the root cause, and misalignment should be considered as a possibility.

Fluid-Induced Instability

If a plain, cylindrical, fluid-film bearing becomes underloaded because of misalignment, the journal may operate near the center of the bearing at an abnormally low eccentricity ratio. This can cause the bearing to become fully (360°) lubricated, making the rotor system vulnerable to fluid-induced instability.

Fluid-induced instability manifests itself as a predominantly forward, subsynchronous vibration, usually in the frequency range from 0.3X to a little below 0.5X, although it can occur outside this range (Figure 20-9). See Chapter 22.

There have been several cases of machines that have run for years without any problems, were overhauled, and encountered fluid-induced instability when started up. Misalignment during reassembly was the culprit. After the machines were realigned, the fluid-induced instability disappeared. Correct alignment properly loaded the bearings, resulting in normal, partially lubricated operation.

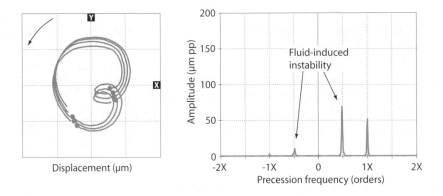

Figure 20-9. Fluid-induced instability orbit and full spectrum. The orbit contains a mixture of 1X and 0.48X instability frequencies. The full spectrum is plotted to the same scale.

Summary

A *static radial load* is a force that acts on the rotor in the radial direction and does not change magnitude or direction with time.

Static radial loads can be classified into two general categories, *soft* and *hard*. *Soft* radial loads do not dramatically change in magnitude with changes in rotor position. *Hard* radial loads involve rotor interaction with some mechanical boundary. Excluding gear mesh forces, hard radial loads usually appear as a result of a machine malfunction. Misalignment is only one potential source of high radial loads.

Internal misalignment occurs when the centerlines of internal parts of a machine are not collinear within an acceptable tolerance. External misalignment occurs when the centerlines of the shafts of two coupled machines are not collinear within an acceptable tolerance at the coupling.

Parallel misalignment exists when centerlines are parallel but offset from each other, while angular misalignment exists when the centerlines are not parallel. Usually, misalignment involves a combination of both types. Axial misalignment occurs when the axial position of two, coupled machines exceeds coupling tolerances.

There are several general causes of misalignment: internal parts may have been installed incorrectly or may have become damaged, a machine train may not have been properly aligned to begin with, thermal growth of machine components may not be as expected, piping strain or a soft foot condition may have warped the machine casing, or grouting or foundation deterioration may have caused a shift in machine position.

There are many symptoms of high radial loads and misalignment: high bearing temperatures in overloaded bearings, low bearing temperatures in underloaded bearings, bearing wear, premature bearing failure, fluid-induced instability, changes in rotor vibration or casing vibration, axial vibration, unusual orbit shapes, premature coupling failure, and abnormal shaft centerline position. Misalignment symptoms often occur in pairs.

Chapter 21

Rub and Looseness

Rᴜʙ ᴀɴᴅ ʟᴏᴏsᴇɴᴇss ᴀʀᴇ ᴛᴡᴏ ᴅɪғғᴇʀᴇɴᴛ ᴘʜᴇɴᴏᴍᴇɴᴀ that, because of their similar rotor dynamic behavior, produce remarkably similar symptoms. Both malfunctions are capable of producing changes in 1X vibration, as well as generating super- and subsynchronous vibration. The two phenomena are, in some respects, mirror images of each other. For that reason, we will discuss both types of malfunctions in this chapter.

We will start by defining rub and looseness; we will then discuss the physical sequence of a partial rub, the most common manifestation of rub and looseness, and briefly discuss the more unusual full annular rub, an extension of partial radial rub.

Rub and looseness affect the forces applied to and the Dynamic Stiffness of the rotor system; thus, the effects can be complex. We will discuss the forces that act on the rotor, how rub and looseness change the Dynamic Stiffness of the system, how the rotor system dynamically responds to these changes, and the symptoms. We will also discuss other malfunctions that can produce similar symptoms.

Rub and Looseness

Rub is an undesired contact between a rotating and stationary part. Normally, bearings keep the rotating part of a machine from contacting the stationary part. When machine parts move to a position where clearances are reduced, or vibrate so that clearances are taken up, contact can occur at places other than the bearings; the moving and stationary parts will "rub." During the contact, rub produces an additional constraint on rotor motion.

On the other hand, looseness is a condition where a normally present constraint on the rotor motion does not act during part of the vibration cycle. Worn or oversize fluid-film bearings or a loose bearing support are examples of looseness. While the root cause is different, the dynamic response due to looseness often leads to rub; for that reason, looseness will be discussed as a type of rub.

Rub causes direct damage to the contacting parts (Figure 21-1). The damage can range from mild, for light rub, to complete destruction of the machine.

Rub is always a secondary effect that is caused by some other malfunction that produces a combination of average and dynamic shaft centerline position that uses up the available clearance between the rotor and the stator. Extreme average shaft centerline position can be caused by excessive radial loads, looseness, and external or internal misalignment caused by a warped casing, piping strain, foundation problems, uneven thermal growth, a locked gear coupling, or an out-of-position internal part. Extreme dynamic shaft position can be caused by high vibration, due to excessive unbalance, rotor bow, or instability. Even when vibration is not extreme, it produces dynamic motion about the average shaft centerline position. Rub will occur whenever the instantaneous position of the rotor uses up the available clearance (Figure 21-2).

Rub contact can occur in the radial direction or in the axial direction, or in combination (Figure 21-3). Axial rub can result from a mismatch in the thermal growth rates between the rotor and casing. During a cold startup, a steam turbine rotor expands faster than the more massive casing. For this reason, large steam turbines are usually heat soaked several times during the startup process to allow the casing time to catch up to the thermal growth of the rotor. A related problem can occur when a slideway on the machine casing hangs up and prevents free movement of the casing during startup or shutdown. The constrained machine casing can deform, displace internal parts, and cause an internal rub. Surge in compressors or in the compressor stage of gas turbines can cause highly damaging axial rubs on blades and impellers; thrust bearing failure can produce catastrophic axial rub.

Partial Radial Rub

When the actual rub/stator contact occurs over a small fraction of the vibration cycle, it is called *partial rub*. When it occurs over the entire vibration cycle, maintaining continuous contact, it is called *full annular rub*. Partial rub is the most common manifestation of rub. Partial radial rub is the most common form of rub; it can be divided into two general categories, normal-tight and normal-loose.

In *normal-tight* rub, the machine rotor normally operates in an *unconstrained* condition. When the rotor contacts a bearing wall, seal, or some other part, it becomes constrained, or *tight* (Figure 21-4). By restricting free motion of

Figure 21-1. Seal damage due to a rub. A rub destroyed the labyrinth seal on the discharge end of this compressor.

Figure 21-2. Limit of shaft motion in a clearance. The dynamic motion of the shaft centerline (orbit) adds to the average shaft centerline position. When the total displacement equals the allowable clearance, a rub will occur.

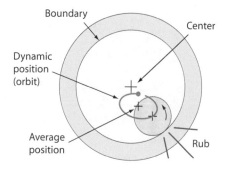

Figure 21-3. Directions of rub contact. Rub can occur in the radial direction, in the axial direction, or in a combination of both.

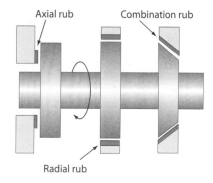

the rotor shaft, the rotor system spring stiffness increases. Normal-tight is the most common form of partial radial rub.

Normal-loose rub is the manifestation of looseness in a machine. In this situation, the rotor operates normally in a *constrained* condition. At some point, usually because of high vibration, the rotor moves clear of the constraint and becomes *loose*. A worn bearing or loose support structure can allow normal-loose behavior. If a rotor normally operates close to a bearing wall (is constrained by the bearing, perhaps operating near the bottom), and the rotor vibration reaches a level such that it dynamically moves the rotor well away from the bearing constraint, the spring stiffness of the rotor system will decrease, producing a change in vibration response. Alternatively, a loose bearing support structure can allow the rotor and bearing to lift or move away from contact with the support, producing a sudden reduction in support spring stiffness. Normal-loose rub occurs when the rotor recontacts the bearing or support structure at some point in the vibration cycle. This produces behavior which is very similar to normal-tight rub, but with some important differences in behavior that we will discuss below.

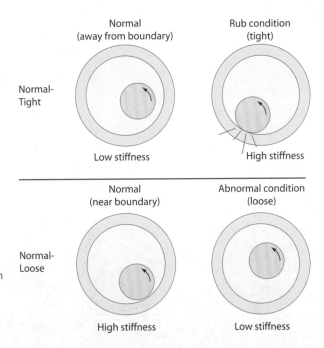

Figure 21-4. Types of rub. In *normal-tight* rub, the machine rotor normally operates in an *unconstrained* condition (left). When the rotor contacts a bearing wall, seal, or some other part, it becomes constrained, or *tight* (right). *Normal-loose* (bottom) implies a condition where the rotor operates normally in a *constrained* condition (left). At some point, the rotor moves clear of the constraint and becomes *loose* (right). Normal-tight is the most common form of partial radial rub.

The mechanism of partial rub usually involves a temporary, sliding rotor contact with the stationary part. During some part of its vibration cycle, the rotating shaft approaches the stationary part. While the stationary part has zero velocity, the shaft surface velocity is nonzero. The shaft contacts the stationary part and maintains contact for some period of time determined by the dynamics of the situation (Figure 21-5).

During the period of contact, a force acts perpendicular to the surface (called a *normal* force), pressing the two objects together. At the same time, the shaft spins relative to the stationary part, so a tangential friction force develops that is proportional to the normal force and the coefficient of friction at the interface. This force acts in the direction opposite to the shaft surface velocity. Usually, this is also opposite to the direction of precession of the shaft centerline. Thus, the friction force acts to accelerate the rotor in the reverse direction, producing reverse components in the full spectrum.

At some point, the rotor breaks contact with the stationary part and moves away to complete the vibration cycle. During the next vibration cycle, the rotor repeats the process. The period of time during which the rotor maintains con-

Figure 21-5. The mechanism of partial rub.

1. The rotor moves in its orbit, free of contact, for a period of time determined by the dynamics of the situation.

2 - 4. The rotor contacts and slides, generating radial and tangential forces (shown for position 3). The tangential force acts in a direction opposite to rotation.

4. The rotor eventually breaks contact and continues in its orbit until contact recurs.

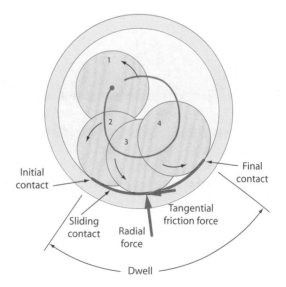

tact with the stationary part is called the *dwell time* (Figure 21-6). Partial rub, by definition, has a dwell time that is less than the period of vibration.

Most of the time, partial rub contact occurs once per revolution of the rotor (1X rub). Less often, rub contact will occur once per several revolutions of the rotor, producing subsynchronous vibration.

Rub can occur with lubricated or unlubricated contact, but most often occurs with unlubricated contact. Because of this, local friction forces can be quite high and generate sufficient local heating to cause rotor bowing, severe wear, local melting or welding of the contacting surfaces, or plastic deformation of the shaft.

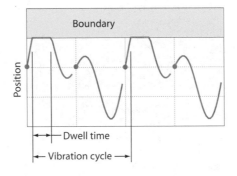

Figure 21-6. Partial rub and dwell time. The timebase waveform contains a mixture of unbalance (1X) and rub-generated (1/2X) vibration. The period of time the rotor contacts the boundary is called the *dwell time*. For partial rub, the dwell time is less than the period of one vibration cycle.

Full Annular Rub

When the dwell time is 100% of the vibration cycle, the result is a *full annular rub*. Imagine a rotor that is precessing in a 1X, circular orbit that is almost perfectly concentric with a seal (Figure 21-7). If the rotor orbit is large enough, it will come into contact with the clearance. Full annular rub occurs when that contact is maintained for a complete vibration cycle.

Full annular rub can be either forward or reverse. If the rotor is precessing in the forward direction (most common), the relative surface velocity of the shaft at the contact point can be quite high. If the contact surface is lubricated and the contact force is small, so that the friction force is small, a forward, full annular rub will occur. If the surface is poorly lubricated or the contact force high, the friction force will try to drive the rotor in the reverse direction. In both cases, the rotor will lock into a rotor system natural frequency that has been modified by the contact stiffness.

In both cases, there will almost always be sliding between the rotor and the stator. For a reverse rub, if there is no sliding contact (that is, the rotor and stator have zero relative surface velocity), the rotor system will behave like a planetary gear system. This situation is unlikely to occur outside the laboratory. Reverse full annular rub, while rare, can generate high vibration and rapidly destroy the machine.

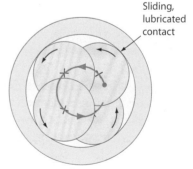

Figure 21-7. Full annular rub. The rotor maintains continuous contact with the boundary. For forward, full annular rub (shown), which involves sliding, lubricated contact, the rotor precession direction is forward.

Sliding, lubricated contact

Forward, full annular rub

Rub-Induced Forces and Spring Stiffness Changes

Remember that vibration is the ratio of the input force to the Dynamic Stiffness of the rotor system (Chapter 11):

$$\text{Vibration} = \frac{\text{Force}}{\text{Dynamic Stiffness}} \qquad (21\text{-}1)$$

Rub produces simultaneous, nonlinear changes in both the force and the Dynamic Stiffness, so the rotor dynamics of rub can become quite complicated. In this section, we will look at how the forces and stiffness are changed; in the next section, we will discuss how these changes affect vibration.

When a rub occurs, contact forces suddenly appear and disappear. As the rotor contacts the stationary part, the stator pushes on the rotor while the rotor pushes in an equal and opposite manner on the stator. This contact force can be separated into *radial* and *tangential* (frictional) components.

When contact occurs, the radial force acts in the direction of the rotor center to strongly accelerate the rotor away from the contact point. The radial force changes during the dwell time of the contact period and is proportional to the instantaneous radial acceleration, $\boldsymbol{a}$, of the rotor ($\boldsymbol{F} = M\boldsymbol{a}$). For a short time, the rotor shaft may deflect in response to the inertia of the rotor while the average radial velocity of the rotor centerline decreases. After the radial velocity reaches zero, the rotor shaft rebounds and the rub contact is broken.

During the period of contact, the tangential friction force appears, which is proportional to the instantaneous magnitude of the radial force and the coefficient of friction at the sliding interface. The tangential friction force acts opposite to the surface velocity of the shaft. It produces a torque on the rotor and, at the same time, tries to accelerate the rotor centerline in the reverse precession direction. For this reason, partial radial rub usually produces reverse components in the full spectrum.

This situation is similar to a wheel spinning on ice that suddenly encounters dry pavement. The sudden contact between the tire and the road produces a friction force that pushes the car in a direction opposite to the surface velocity of the tire at the contact point. The amount of force depends on the weight of the car and the coefficient of friction between the road and tire.

A side effect of the tangential friction force is that it acts as an agent to transfer the energy of rotation to radial vibration. Thus, the magnitude of unfiltered vibration is likely to change with rub onset, as is the amplitude and phase of filtered vibration. Direct (unfiltered) orbits can reveal changes in rotor trajectory due to rub.

For partial radial rubs, a shallow (low angle of incidence) approach to the contact zone will produce a gentle, wiping contact, which does not greatly change the forces in the system. This kind of rub usually produces only a modified 1X response.

However, if the approach to the contact zone is steep, the rub contact can also be sudden and relatively violent. In this case, the radial and tangential frictional forces due to rub are *impulsive* by nature. They appear suddenly, build to high levels, and disappear suddenly. The effect is similar to hitting the rotor shaft with a hammer; an impulse force produces a *impulse response* that includes many of the free radial vibration modes in the rotor. When the rotor rebounds from the contact, it will ring in free vibration at one or more natural frequencies.

The tangential force impulse, combined with the radius of the shaft, also produces a torque impulse that can excite the torsional natural frequencies of the system.

Rotor system spring stiffness consists of the series and parallel combination of all of the stiffness elements that exist between the effective rotor mass and solid ground. This includes the stiffness of the rotor shaft, the bearing stiffness, bearing support stiffness, and foundation stiffness. The shaft spring acts in series with the springs in the bearings, supports, and the foundation. For any series combination of springs, the stiffness of the combination is always weaker than the weakest spring in the series.

Flexible rotor shafts are often one of the weakest springs in the system. They behave like beams; the stiffness of the shaft is related to the cross-section geometry and the length of the shaft between supports. For a simply supported shaft with a constant cross section, a concentrated midspan load, and no coupling effects at the ends, the spring stiffness is

$$K_{shaft} = 48\frac{EI}{l^3} \tag{21-2}$$

where E is the modulus of elasticity (Young's Modulus) of the shaft material, I is the section moment of inertia, and l is the unsupported length of the shaft. As the equation shows, the spring stiffness of the shaft is very sensitive to its unsupported length.

When a rotor shaft contacts the stator surface (a normal-tight rub), the contact point is usually somewhere well away from the bearings. It provides an additional constraint that effectively decreases the length of the shaft and increases the stiffness of the rotor system. This sudden increase in stiffness lasts for the dwell time of the contact and disappears when the rotor breaks contact with the stationary part. If this cycle repeats periodically, then the step increase in stiffness also repeats. This cycle produces a time-averaged, effective stiffness that is a function of the two values of stiffness and the dwell time. The average stiffness due to normal-tight rub will be *higher* than for the no rub case (Figure 21-8); normal-loose behavior *lowers* the average stiffness.

The stiffening due to temporary contact can be illustrated with a simple pendulum where the mass is supported by a string (Figure 21-9). The pendulum is in free vibration at a natural frequency that is related to the length of the string. When the string is not contacting the boundary (left), the frequency of vibration is low. When the string contacts the boundary (right), the pendulum is shorter, and the natural frequency is higher while the contact is maintained (the dwell time). The pendulum actually switches between low and high natural frequencies (long and short string). When viewed over the entire vibration cycle, the pendulum has an average natural frequency between these two values.

Rub and Steady State 1X Vibration

The modification of the spring stiffness part of the Dynamic Stiffness causes changes in both steady state and transient vibration behavior. Any change in the spring stiffness, K, affects the natural frequency, ω_n, or balance resonance speed, Ω_{res}, of the rotor system:

$$\omega_n = \Omega_{res} = \sqrt{\frac{K}{M}} \tag{21-3}$$

where M is the rotor mass (Chapters 10 and 11). Increasing K increases the balance resonance speed, while decreasing K decreases it.

A change in resonance speed can have a direct affect on the steady state vibration of the system. Figure 21-10 shows how steady state, 1X vibration can change due to normal-tight (left) and normal-loose (right) conditions. If a machine is operating at a speed slightly below a balance resonance (Ω_1), a normal-tight rub will shift the natural frequency upward and move the resonance peak away from the operating speed. This will decrease the vibration amplitude and phase lag. Conversely, if the rotor was originally operating above a resonance (Ω_2), the normal-tight rub will shift the natural frequency upward and closer to the operating speed. This could cause an increase in vibration amplitude and a decrease in phase lag.

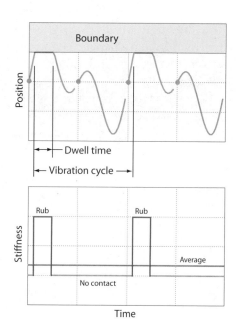

Figure 21-8. Stiffness change during normal-tight rub. Shaft spring stiffness plot (bottom) and timebase plot (top) show correlation of stiffness versus shaft position. When there is no contact (green), the stiffness is lowest. During contact (red), the stiffness is much higher. The average stiffness (blue) depends on the rub stiffness and the dwell time

Figure 21-9. The stiffening effect in a pendulum. A simple pendulum consists of a mass supported by a string. The pendulum is in free vibration at a natural frequency that is related to the length of the string. When the string is not contacting the boundary (left), the frequency of vibration is low. When the string contacts the boundary (right), the pendulum is shorter, and the natural frequency is higher while the contact is maintained (the dwell time). The pendulum actually switches between low and high natural frequencies (long and short string). When viewed over the entire vibration cycle, the pendulum has an average natural frequency between these two values.

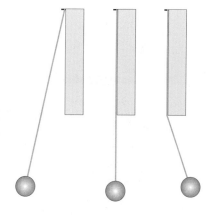

As shown by the four sample operating speeds, vibration amplitude can increase or decrease depending on the relationship of operating speed, the no-rub resonance speed, and the new, rub-modified resonance speed. Note that if the rotor operates well below a resonance, then the higher stiffness due to normal-tight rub is likely to cause a significant reduction in vibration response.

The reverse situation applies for normal-loose behavior. The average rotor system stiffness becomes lower, and the rotor response changes from the high stiffness case to the low stiffness case in the figure. The changes in rotor behavior will be the opposite of those for normal-tight rub.

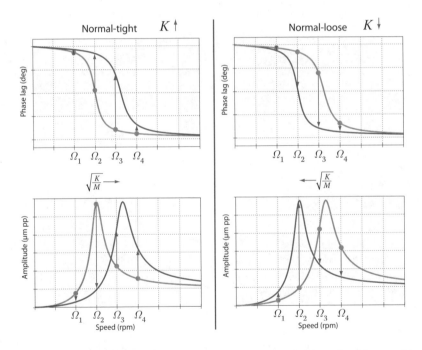

Figure 21-10. Steady state, 1X vibration changes due to normal-tight (left) and normal-loose (right) conditions. If a machine is operating at Ω_1 below a balance resonance, and a normal-tight rub develops, the natural frequency increases, moving the resonance peak away from the operating speed, and the vibration amplitude and phase lag decrease. Conversely, if the rotor is operating well above a resonance (Ω_4), and a normal-tight rub develops, the resonance will be shifted closer to the operating speed, the vibration amplitude will increase, but the phase lag will decrease. These results are reversed for normal-loose behavior.

Rub and 1X Vibration During Resonance

It is possible for a rotor to go into normal-tight rub due to the high vibration associated with a balance resonance. When contact occurs, the sudden increase in stiffness will shift the resonance speed upward and modify the rotor response.

The response is similar to a nonlinear mechanical system with stiffness that increases with displacement. The response also depends on whether the rotor is approaching the resonance during startup or during shutdown (Figure 21-11). During startup (red), the phase lag will be delayed since the resonance peak is shifted to a higher speed. If vibration amplitude increases further, the dwell time of the rub is likely to increase, increasing the average stiffness and moving the resonance even higher. The rotor, in effect, chases the resonance by increasing the average spring stiffness of the system as its speed increases. (See also Figure 18-2.)

Under some circumstances, this gradual stiffening, and resulting increase of the resonance speed, can continue until the rotor ends up operating, with a rub, on or very close to the highly modified resonance. In one compressor with a heavy rub on a locked floating seal, the resonance shifted from the nameplate value of 5200 rpm to somewhere near the operating speed of 10 480 rpm (see Chapter 24).

Figure 21-11. Experimental data showing modification of the balance resonance speed by normal-tight rub. During startup (red), the phase lag will be delayed because the resonance peak is shifted to a higher speed. If vibration amplitude increases further, the dwell time of the rub is likely to increase, increasing the average stiffness and moving the resonance even more to the right. During shutdown (blue), the system will behave normally until just above the resonance, when the rotor initiates rub contact. The sudden increase in stiffness increases the resonance frequency, possibly above the current rotor speed. The rotor encounters the resonance peak sooner than normal, or may even find itself operating slightly below the rub-modified resonance. When this occurs, the phase lag will decrease very suddenly, and the rotor will pass through the resonance more quickly than normal.

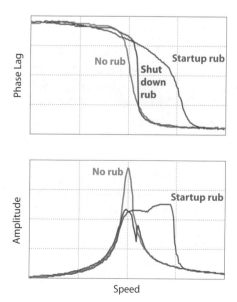

During shutdown (blue), the situation is different. The system will behave normally until vibration increases, at just above the resonance, and the rotor initiates rub contact. The sudden increase in stiffness immediately moves the resonance to a higher speed, which may even be slightly above the current rotor speed. The rotor encounters the resonance peak sooner than expected, or may find itself operating slightly below the rub-modified resonance. When this kind of jump occurs, the phase lag will decrease very suddenly, and the rotor will pass through the resonance more quickly than normal.

Subsynchronous Vibration

Partial radial rub usually occurs once per turn of the rotor, but under some circumstances, it can produce a self-excited, large amplitude, subsynchronous vibration at subharmonic (½X, ⅓X, ¼X, etc.) or, more rarely, simple integer ratio (⅔X, ¾X, etc.) frequencies. This self-excited vibration is always associated with a modified natural frequency of the rotor system.

Impulse forces produce a wide spectrum of energy, which is available to excite system natural frequencies. If the impulse *does not* recur, then the resulting free vibration will die away. However, if the rotor system has a natural frequency at a subharmonic of the rotor operating speed, then, after one cycle of this subsynchronous free vibration, the rub impulse *will* recur (Figure 21-8). 1X vibration can also play a role by increasing the lateral velocity of the rotor at the moment of contact, thereby increasing the contact force.

During the dwell time of the contact, the tangential friction force acts to transfer some kinetic energy of rotation to radial vibration energy. This process produces a self-excited vibration that is larger in amplitude than would be possible without the energy transfer.

The effect here is similar to pushing a child on a swing. When the push (the impulse) is applied, the child moves away, acting as a pendulum in free vibration. When the child returns, if the push is applied *with the correct timing*, then more energy is added to the child and the amplitude of free vibration will increase. If, however, the timing is incorrect, energy may be removed from the system, and the amplitude will decrease. The whole process depends on adding energy at just the right moment.

In the same way, if the timing of repeated rub contacts is correct, the subsynchronous rotor vibration can be excited, amplified, and sustained as long as nothing in the system changes. Wear of the contacting surface is a factor that can change the contact relationship, as can local heating and rotor bow, leading to modification or eventual cessation of the rub.

Because of the time required for a subsynchronous vibration cycle, this kind of rub is usually associated with a *light* radial rub with a short dwell time. A heavy rub (with a typically long dwell time) so strongly constrains shaft motion that there is insufficient time for a complete cycle of free vibration.

Even though we are discussing a subsynchronous, self-excited vibration, the 1X unbalance response also plays a role; the 1X response, when added to the free subsynchronous vibration, affects the timing of the contact between the rotor and the stator.

Subharmonic (½X,⅓X, ... ¹⁄ₙX) vibration produces a timing relationship where every rub contact occurs at the same location on the rotor surface and the contact occurs once every n revolutions. If the contact friction causes local heating and bowing of the rotor, then the effective heavy spot and unbalance response vector may change, causing modification or cessation of the rub.

However, vibration at simple integer ratios (⅔X, ¾X, ... ᵏ⁄ₙX) produces *k* rub contacts for every n revolutions; the contacts occur at *k different* locations on the rotor surface, with a contact recurring at the same place on the surface once every n revolutions. For this type of vibration to maintain itself, the 1X unbalance response of the rotor must be relatively small; a large 1X vibration component would cause the contact timing to be significantly different for the *k* successive vibration cycles. Thus, only shafts with a small unbalance response have the potential to exhibit nonsubharmonic integer ratio vibration, and this kind of subsynchronous rub is less common.

An important factor in the timing of subsynchronous rub is the modification of the rotor natural frequency caused by the rub itself. For normal-tight rub, the constraint active during the dwell time of the rub causes an increase in the average spring stiffness of the rotor and its natural frequency, which we will call the *modified natural frequency*. For subsynchronous vibration to take place, the modified natural frequency must be a subharmonic (½X, ⅓X, etc.) or simple integer ratio (⅔X, ¾X, etc.) of running speed.

For a normal-tight rub, the modified natural frequency will be *higher* than the no-rub natural frequency. For a normal-loose condition, the spring stiffness is modified downward, and the modified natural frequency will be *lower*.

Because of the critical impulse timing needed to sustain subsynchronous vibration, it can appear only if the machine obeys certain rules. There are different, but similar rules for normal-tight and normal-loose conditions. In both cases, for subharmonic vibration to be sustained, *the rotor must rotate at a speed that is an integer multiple of the modified natural frequency*. For example, for ½X rub (either normal-tight or normal-loose) to occur, the rotor must operate at 2 times the *modified* natural frequency of the rotor. This seems obvious when you think about it, but this statement is the key to understanding why the rules that are presented below work.

The first rule applies to *normal-tight* rub. It states that, for $\frac{1}{n}$X vibration to appear, the rotor speed, Ω, must be greater than n times the no-rub natural frequency:

Normal-tight subharmonic $\Omega > n\omega_n$ (21-4)

where n is an integer (2, 3, 4, ...), and ω_n is the no-rub (unmodified) natural frequency of the rotor given by Equation 21-3.

For example, for normal-tight rub, $\frac{1}{2}$X vibration can appear only if the running speed of the rotor is greater than two times the *unmodified* natural frequency of the rotor. Similarly, for $\frac{1}{3}$X vibration to appear, the rotor must operate at a speed greater than three times the unmodified natural frequency.

Why is this true? Figure 21-12, top shows the case for normal-tight rub. The green frequency line corresponds to the unmodified natural frequency, ω_n. Two possible rotor speeds are shown, Ω_1 (which is twice ω_n) and Ω_2. Any rub will stiffen the system and move ω_n to a higher frequency, the modified natural frequency (red). If this happens, then Ω_1 is now less than twice the modified natural frequency, and $\frac{1}{2}$X vibration cannot occur. The rotor speed, Ω_2, which is greater than twice ω_n, is now twice the modified natural frequency, and $\frac{1}{2}$X vibration is possible.

The second rule applies to a *normal-loose* condition. $\frac{1}{n}$X normal-loose subharmonic vibration requires that

Normal-loose subharmonic $\Omega < n\omega_n$ (21-5)

For example, for $\frac{1}{2}$X vibration to appear, the running speed of the rotor must be less than twice the *unmodified* natural frequency of the rotor. Similarly, for $\frac{1}{3}$X vibration to appear, the rotor must operate at a speed less than three times the unmodified natural frequency.

The normal-loose condition (Figure 21-12, bottom) modifies ω_n by moving it to a *lower* frequency (red). If the rotor operates at exactly twice the unmodified natural frequency (Ω_1), then any shift of ω_n to a lower frequency will leave the rotor operating at more than twice the modified natural frequency, and $\frac{1}{2}$X vibration will be impossible. For $\frac{1}{2}$X vibration to occur, the rotor speed must be *less* than twice the unmodified natural frequency (Ω_2). Then, when the natural frequency shifts down to exactly one half rotor speed, $\frac{1}{2}$X vibration can take place.

The examples in the figure are for $\frac{1}{2}$X vibration. The same relationships apply to rub vibration at $\frac{1}{3}$X, $\frac{1}{4}$X, etc.

These two rules can be helpful for diagnosing whether a subsynchronous vibration is due to a normal-tight or normal-loose condition. If startup or shutdown data is available, and if the balance resonance associated with the subharmonic vibration can be identified, then, for $\frac{1}{n}X$ vibration,

1. If the rotor speed is more than n times the balance resonance frequency, or if the subharmonic frequency is higher than the balance resonance frequency, then the rub is probably normal-tight.

2. If the rotor speed is less than n times the balance resonance frequency, or if the subharmonic frequency is less than the balance resonance frequency, then it is probably normal-loose.

In both cases, the self-excited, subharmonic vibration is occuring at the modified natural frequency of the balance resonance.

Figure 21-12. Rotor speed requirements for 1/2X vibration due to rub. For normal-tight rub, top, the green frequency line corresponds to the unmodified natural frequency, ω_n, which is exactly one half Ω_1. The rub will move ω_n to a higher frequency, the *modified* natural frequency (red). Ω_1 is now less than twice the modified natural frequency, and 1/2X vibration cannot occur. Ω_2 is greater than twice ω_n, and it is possible to increase the natural frequency up to a value that is exactly one-half Ω_2, making 1/2X vibration possible. For the normal-loose condition, bottom, ω_n will move to a *lower* frequency (red). Ω_1, which is twice the unmodified natural frequency, is more than twice the modified natural frequency, and 1/2X vibration will be impossible. When the natural frequency is shifted down so that it is exactly one-half Ω_2, 1/2X vibration can take place. The behavior for other subsynchronous frequencies is similar.

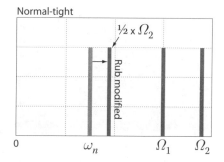

Normal-tight

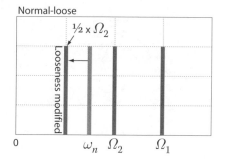

Normal-loose

Subsynchronous vibration, when it appears, will often track running speed for a while during a startup or shutdown. For the frequency to satisfy the rules when the rotor speed is changing, some mechanism must exist that modifies the natural frequency appropriately. The rotor system adjusts the dwell time of the rub to control the modified spring stiffness.

This adjustment can only be done over a limited speed range. When the rotor system is no longer able to adjust the stiffness to satisfy the rule, then the subsynchronous vibration will either stop, or it will shift to another frequency that does satisfy the rule. Rub during the startup of a gas turbine was observed to begin with ½X, track running speed for a while, then shift to and track at ⅓X, and continue shifting to and tracking at ¼X and ⅕X.

A full spectrum cascade plot (Figure 21-13) can show these subsynchronous components. As the rotative speed increases, the vibration may suddenly drop to the next lower ratio when the condition for that ratio is satisfied.

Occasionally, subsynchronous vibration has been observed at simple integer

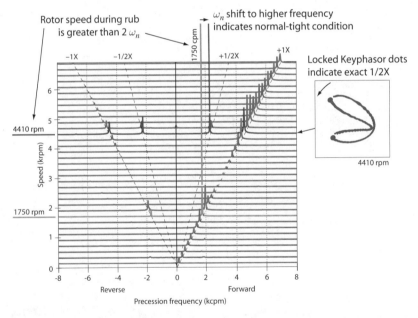

Figure 21-13. Full spectrum cascade of normal-tight rub. The 1/2X rub occurs during the second balance resonance. The rotor speed of 4410 rpm is more than twice the unmodified natural frequency of 1750 cpm, satisfying Equation 21-4. The shift of ω_n to a higher frequency indicates normal-tight rub is taking place. The locked Keyphasor dots in the orbit show that the frequency of vibration is exactly 1/2X.

ratios such as ⅔X, ¾X, etc. The basic rules above still apply to this situation. For example, for normal-tight rub to produce vibration at ⅔X, the rotor speed must be greater than 3⁄2 times the unmodified natural frequency of the system; a normal-loose response would require a rotor speed less than 3⁄2 times the unmodified natural frequency.

Symptoms of Rub

Rub produces changes in both the forces and the Dynamic Stiffness of the rotor system. Because rub involves rotor interaction with a hard constraint, rub also introduces nonlinearities in the rotor system. The result of these effects is a complex rotor dynamic response that produces a wide variety of symptoms.

Like most malfunctions, diagnosis of rub involves correlation of different types of data. It is important to look at steady state and transient data, including direct orbit and timebase plots; full spectrum, including full spectrum cascade plots; 1X Bode and polar plots; and average shaft centerline plots. The symptoms of rub are summarized in Table 21-1.

Table 21-1. Symptoms of rub. Not all symptoms will be present at the same time.

Changes in 1X vibration
Abnormal orbit shape
Subsynchronous or subharmonic vibration
Reverse precession components
Harmonics in spectrum
Thermal bow
Changes in average shaft centerline position
Wear, damage, loss of efficiency

Changes in 1X vibration. During steady state operation, rub will produce changes in 1X vibration because of rotational energy transfer to radial vibration energy and because of changes in stiffness. A light rub is more likely to increase 1X vibration amplitude, while heavy rub can severely constrain the rotor and reduce 1X vibration. Heavy rub can also result in more energy transfer to the machine casing, causing an increase in 1X casing vibration.

If the rotor system is operating near a balance resonance, the 1X vibration amplitude can increase or decrease, depending on whether the machine is operating above or below the resonance (Figure 21-10). For normal-tight rub, the resonance is moved to a higher speed because of the rub-induced stiffness increase.

During startup and shutdown, rub-induced changes of the balance resonance speed can produce changes in observed behavior through the resonance (Figure 21-11). For this reason, it is always good to have reference startup and shutdown Bode and polar plots available.

Abnormal orbit shape. Direct (unfiltered) orbits should be examined and correlated with any other unusual activity that may be taking place in the machine. Changes in direct orbit shape should be noted, although the farther away the measurement point is from the rub, the less distinct the changes will be. Very importantly, only direct orbits with Keyphasor dots can be used to verify that subsynchronous vibration is an integer ratio of running speed. On an orbit, the number of displayed Keyphasor dots yields the denominator of a frequency ratio. For example, two Keyphasor dots could indicate ½X, ³⁄₂X, ⁵⁄₂X and so on. If the frequency really is locked to an integer ratio, then the Keyphasor dots will remain locked in place through subsequent vibration cycles (Figure 21-13). If they move along the path of the orbit, then the frequency is not an integer ratio.

Vibration that consists of a mixture of 1X and rub-induced ½X can produce orbits with complicated shapes (see the orbit in Figure 21-14). This orbit shows the path of the shaft centerline for eight shaft revolutions. The two stationary sets of Keyphasor dots show the vibration to be exactly ½X.

Subsynchronous/subharmonic vibration. Subsynchronous rub will follow the rules in Equations 21-4 and 21-5. Because of stiffening, normal-tight rub will produce vibration at a frequency *above* the unmodified natural frequency, while normal-loose will produce vibration at a frequency *below* the unmodified natural frequency. Full spectrum cascade plots can be used to identify which way the frequency shift is occurring, aiding diagnosis (Figure 21-13).

Note that it is not possible to verify that a vibration frequency is an exact integer ratio by using spectrum data. There is always some uncertainty in the displayed frequency on a spectrum plot because of the limited resolution of the spectrum. A direct orbit with Keyphasor dot display should be used to verify the integer relationship.

Harmonics in the spectrum. As the rotor meets and rebounds from the contact surface, the changes in stiffness can produce sudden changes in the rotor trajectory and sharp corners on orbits and timebase plots. Because of this, harmonics of the fundamental vibration frequency can appear. If the fundamental frequency is 1X, then 2X, 3X, or higher harmonics may be visible in vibration data. If the predominant rub-induced vibration frequency is ½X, it is possible to see 1X (as a mixture of normal 1X rotor response and the harmonic of ½X), ³⁄₂X, ⁴⁄₂X, ⁵⁄₂X, etc. (Figure 21-14).

Reverse precession components. Because the rub usually involves tangential friction forces acting against the direction of rotation, full spectrum plots will often show significant reverse precession components at the subsynchronous frequency (Figures 21-13 and 21-14).

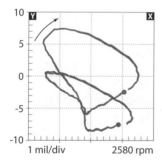
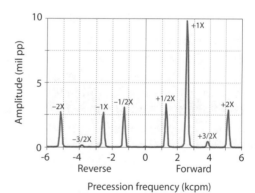

Figure 21-14. Orbit and full spectrum from a steam turbine with a 1/2X rub. The full spectrum shows forward and reverse 1/2X fundamental components and harmonics, including 3/2X and 2X. The nearly equal amplitudes of the 1/2X full spectrum lines indicate that the response at that frequency is nearly a line orbit.

Thermal bow. The frictional forces that act during radial rub produce local heating of the surface. If, at a steady operating speed, a rub occurs repeatedly in the same place on the rotor, the frictional heating of the surface and associated thermal expansion in that area will cause the rotor to bow in the direction of the rub contact. This bow effectively changes the unbalance magnitude and direction, which changes 1X rotor response. Under special circumstances, the local heating due to a light, 1X rub can produce a continuously changing 1X response vector (see Chapter 19).

Changes in average shaft centerline position. Rub will often change the trajectory (orbit) of the rotor, which can change the average shaft centerline position, too. Sudden changes in average shaft centerline position during startup, shutdown, or steady state operation can be symptomatic of a rub. Correlation of shaft centerline position changes with other data can help confirm a diagnosis.

Wear, damage, and loss of efficiency. Rub can cause extreme wear of contacting parts (Figure 21-1). Seals are especially vulnerable, and, because machine efficiency often depends on tight clearances, seal wear will usually result in degraded operating efficiency.

Machines suspected of rubbing should be carefully inspected for evidence of seal damage. Also look for discoloration of parts due to high temperature, scratched or smeared babbitt, and damaged seals, turbine blades, compressor blades, or pump impellers.

Other Malfunctions with Similar Symptoms

Fluid-induced instability produces subsynchronous vibration that is sometimes misdiagnosed as a rub. In general, there are two aspects of subsynchronous vibration that help discriminate between the malfunctions. First, subsynchronous vibration due to rub will usually lock to a simple integer ratio frequency, ½X, ⅓X, etc., while fluid-induced instability is most likely to produce vibration at a noninteger ratio (such as 0.47X). Second, the full spectrum of rub at the subsynchronous frequency will tend to have significant a reverse component; fluid-induced instability tends to be predominantly forward (see Chapter 22).

The diagnosis is further complicated because the large amplitude, subsynchronous vibration due to a fluid-induced instability can create a rub. This causes the rotor system to lock to an integer ratio frequency and the root cause fluid-induced instability to manifest itself as a rub. Both of these malfunctions may be active at the same time. They have a similar rotor dynamic property: the subsynchronous vibration is associated with a natural frequency of the rotor system.

Direct orbits (with Keyphasor dots) and the full spectrum are the best tools for discriminating between fluid-induced instability and rub. Vibration that occurs at an integer ratio will produce an orbit on which the Keyphasor dots are locked (do not change position with time). Fluid-induced instability is unlikely to occur at an exact integer ratio; thus, the Keyphasor dots will move around the orbit. A spectrum does not usually have the resolution to make this determination with certainty.

Full spectrum does give us powerful information about the direction of precession of frequency components (see Chapter 8). The subsynchronous vibration due to fluid-induced instability is predominantly forward, while rub may contain a significant reverse component. If the only diagnostic tool available is half spectrum, it is nearly impossible to tell the difference between these two malfunctions (Figure 21-15, top). On an oscilloscope, the fluid-induced instability orbit is not steady because the components are not harmonically related; the orbit shrinks and grows (breathes) as the components go in and out of phase, an internal loop rolls around the orbit, and the Keyphasor dots move along the orbit path. Some of this activity can be seen in the instability orbit (Figure 21-15, bottom right). Compare this to the rub orbits on the left, which are relatively steady.

To summarize (see Table 21-2), the subsynchronous vibration due to a partial radial rub will tend to have a frequency that is an integer ratio, and it may have significant reverse components at the subsynchronous frequency.

Table 21-2. Fluid-induced instability or rub?

Fluid-induced instability	Rub	Use this tool
Noninteger ratio (e.g. 0.47X)	Integer ratio (1/2X, 1/3X, 2/3X, ...)	Direct orbit with Keyphasor dots
Circular orbit, forward precession at instability frequency	Significant reverse components	Full spectrum, Direct orbit

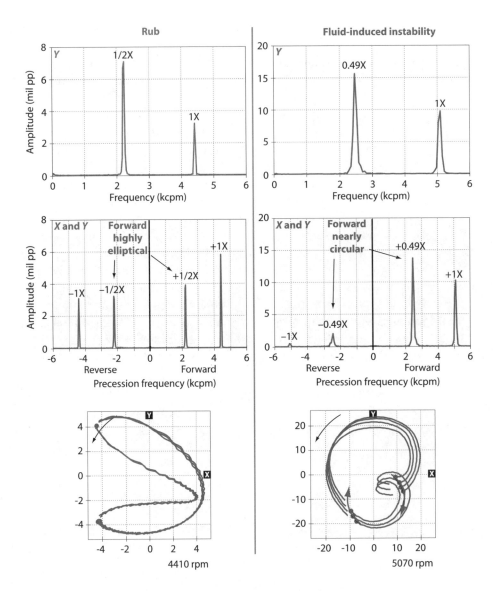

Figure 21-15. Comparison of rub (red) and a fluid-induced instability (blue) data. Note the similarity of the two half spectrum plots (top). The full spectrum plots clearly reveal the difference in the subsynchronous vibration: the subsynchronous component of the rub orbit is extremely elliptical; that of the fluid-induced instability orbit is forward and nearly circular. In the rub orbit, the Keyphasor dots are locked, indicating exact 1/2X vibration; in the fluid-induced instability orbit, the Keyphasor dots move around the orbit path indicated by the red arrows.

Scratches seen by eddy current probes will also produce harmonics in the spectrum. If the shaft has multiple scratches, a full spectrum display may show a complicated set of forward and reverse lines at harmonics of running speed. On a spectrum cascade plot, the amplitude of these spectrum lines will show little change with speed, from slow roll speed to operating speed. Harmonics due to rub, when they appear at all, will be visible only for the speed range that the rub is active.

A locked gear coupling can produce a sudden change in 1X vibration response together with a change in average shaft centerline position. A locked coupling may produce 2X vibration as well. Coupling problems will not produce subsynchronous vibration.

Summary

Rub is an undesired contact between a rotating and a stationary part, while looseness is a significant decrease in stiffness of the rotor constraint during part of the vibration cycle. *Rub is always a secondary malfunction*: it is caused by some other malfunction that reduces the available clearance in the rotor system. The reduced clearance can be caused by rotor deflection toward the stator, by out-of-position stationary parts, or by high vibration.

Rub contact can occur in the radial direction or in the axial direction, or in a combination of both.

The actual rub/stator contact can occur over a small fraction of the vibration cycle, a *partial rub*, or it can occur (rarely) over the entire vibration cycle, a *full annular rub*. Full annular rub can be *forward*, involving lubricated contact, or *reverse*, usually involving poorly lubricated or unlubricated contact.

Partial rub is the most common manifestation of rub. The period of time during which the rotor maintains contact with the stationary part is called the *dwell time*.

There are two general categories of partial rub, normal-tight and normal-loose. In *normal-tight* rub, the machine rotor normally operates in an *unconstrained* condition. When the rotor contacts a bearing wall, seal, or some other part, it becomes constrained, or *tight*. *Normal-loose* implies a condition during which the rotor operates normally in a *constrained* condition. At some point, the rotor moves clear of the constraint and becomes *loose*.

Rub contact produces both radial and tangential friction force components. The friction force acts opposite to the direction of rotation and tries to push the rotor in the reverse direction; it also produces a torque that can excite torsional vibration.

Normal-tight rub increases the stiffness of the rotor system, and a normal-loose condition decreases it. The stiffness change, and resulting natural frequency change, modifies the vibration response of the rotor system.

Heavy rub generally produces only modified 1X vibration. Light rub can produce subsynchronous vibration that is an integer ratio of running speed, usually ½X, ⅓X, etc., but occasionally ⅔X, ¾X, etc. For subsynchronous, $\frac{1}{n}$X vibration to appear with normal-tight rub, the rotor must operate at a speed more than n times the unmodified natural frequency; for a normal-loose condition, the rotor must operate at less than n times the unmodified natural frequency.

Rub can occur due to high vibration during a balance resonance. When this happens, the resonance frequency increases as the system becomes stiffer.

Rub symptoms can include changes in 1X vibration; abnormal orbit shape; subsynchronous and subharmonic vibration; reverse precession frequency components; harmonics in spectra; thermal bow; changes in average shaft centerline position; and wear, damage, and loss of efficiency.

Chapter 22

Fluid-Induced Instability

Fʟᴜɪᴅ-ɪɴᴅᴜᴄᴇᴅ ɪɴꜱᴛᴀʙɪʟɪᴛʏ ɪꜱ ᴀ ᴄᴏɴᴅɪᴛɪᴏɴ that is caused by rotor interaction with a surrounding fluid. It can produce large amplitude, usually subsynchronous, self-excited vibration of a rotor, leading to rotor-to-stator rubs on seals, bearings, impellers, or other rotor parts. The vibration can also produce significant alternating stresses in the rotor, leading to fatigue failure. Because it is so potentially damaging, fluid-induced instability should be eliminated and avoided.

The term "instability" is somewhat of a misnomer. As we discussed in Chapter 14, when a rotor operates in fluid-induced instability, it is actually operating in a stable limit cycle of high vibration. But the rotor is unstable in the sense that it is operating outside desired operational limits.

In Chapter 14, we presented two mathematical approaches to stability analysis based on Dynamic Stiffness and eigenvalues. In this chapter, we will be primarily concerned with the detection of fluid-induced instability as a rotor system malfunction. First, though, we will revisit the Dynamic Stiffness view of instability and combine it with a discussion of the physical origin of fluid-induced instability. We will follow that with a discussion of the two primary modes of instability, whirl and whip, and show how they are actually the same phenomenon, caused by different sources of dominant stiffness in the rotor system.

After discussing the symptoms of fluid-induced instability, we will list other malfunctions that have similar symptoms and the characteristics and techniques used to make a correct diagnosis. Finally, we will show various strategies for eliminating and preventing fluid-induced instability.

The Cause of Fluid-Induced Instability

Rotating machines exist to convert the energy of rotation into useful work. This often involves rotor interaction with a working fluid, either gas or liquid. Also, most bearings in large machines are hydrodynamic, fluid-film bearings. The rotational interaction with surrounding working or bearing fluid always ends up swirling the fluid to some extent. This swirling is the primary cause of fluid-induced instability.

When a fluid, either liquid or gas, is contained in the annular region (gap) between two, concentric cylinders that are rotating relative to each other, the fluid will be set into motion. This situation exists in fully (360°) lubricated fluid-film bearings, in seals, around impellers in pumps, or when any part of a rotor is completely surrounded by fluid trapped between the rotor and the stator. It also exists to a lesser extent in partially lubricated bearings. In this chapter, we will talk primarily about cylindrical, fluid-film bearings. However, everything written here about these bearings also applies to seals, pump impellers, and any other region in a machine where a liquid or gas is contained in a small clearance between two parts that rotate at different angular velocities.

The fluid next to the rotor will have the same velocity as the surface of the rotor, while the fluid next to the bearing will have its velocity, usually zero. The fluid in the gap will have some average angular velocity, $\lambda\Omega$, where λ is the Fluid Circumferential Average Velocity Ratio, and Ω is the rotor speed. For a plain, cylindrical, fully lubricated bearing, λ is typically a little under ½, around 0.48 or so. But the value of λ is influenced by the geometry of the bearing, the rate of end leakage out of the bearing, the eccentricity ratio of the rotor in the bearing, and the presence of any pre- or antiswirling that may exist in the fluid. (See Chapter 10 for a full discussion of the meaning of λ.)

As we saw in Chapter 10, when a rotor is displaced from the center of a bearing, the converging fluid forms a pressure wedge. The pressure profile creates a force that can be separated into two components, a radial spring force, $-K\mathbf{r}$, that points back toward the center of the bearing, and a tangential force, $jD\lambda\Omega\mathbf{r}$, that acts at 90°, in the direction of rotation.

The strength of the tangential force depends on the rotative speed, Ω, and on the fluid circulation around the rotor, λ. Since properly loaded hydrodynamic bearings are normally only partially lubricated, λ is usually relatively small. Thus, a *properly loaded* bearing is unlikely to be a source of very large tangential forces unless it becomes flooded. Note that, because of misalignment, a fluid-film bearing can become lightly loaded and transition to fully lubricated operation, increasing λ and generating high tangential forces.

To see how the tangential force affects rotor stability, imagine a rotor rotating in the center of a fluid-film bearing. If the rotor is displaced from the center and released, the spring force will push the rotor back toward the center. But, at the same time, the tangential force will push the rotor in the direction of rotation, 90° from the spring force. The rotor will begin to move at some angle determined by the ratio of the tangential force and the spring force. Once the rotor starts moving in response to these forces, the fluid damping will produce a force that is opposite to the direction of instantaneous rotor centerline motion. This force acts to slow down the motion, while the inertia of the rotor tries to keep the rotor moving in the same direction. All of these forces act together in a complicated way. The result is that the stable, rotating rotor cannot return directly to the center of the bearing; it follows a decaying spiral path (Figure 22-1a). The precession frequency of this spiral path is equal to the *damped natural frequency* of the rotor system.

As rotor speed increases, the tangential force becomes stronger, while the spring force and damping forces do not, because they are relatively independent of rotor speed. At some speed (the Threshold of Instability), the tangential force becomes so strong that the rotor will not return to its original position (Figure 22-1b). If the rotor speed remains constant, the rotor will continue in a constant amplitude orbit, or perhaps an increasing spiral orbit (Figure 22-1c). When this happens, the rotor is experiencing fluid-induced instability.

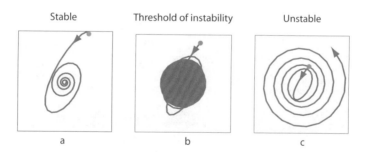

Figure 22-1. Path of the rotor centerline for three conditions of stability. In all three cases, the rotor is released after being displaced from its equilibrium position to the green point. In (a), the system is stable, but the displaced rotor cannot return directly because of the tangential force. The rotor returns to equilibrium by following the decaying spiral path. In (b), the rotor is operating at the Threshold of Instability, and, after an initial transient, the rotor moves in a circular orbit of constant diameter. In (c), the system is unstable; the orbit diameter increases.

These various forces can be viewed as stiffness elements and combined into the nonsynchronous Dynamic Stiffness, K_N,

$$K_N = K - M\omega^2 + jD(\omega - \lambda\Omega) \tag{22-1}$$

Dynamic Stiffness controls the response when the rotor is subjected to a static or dynamic force. The onset of fluid-induced instability occurs when the Dynamic Stiffness become zero.

Dynamic Stiffness is a complex quantity: it contains both direct and quadrature parts. For the Dynamic Stiffness to equal zero, both the direct and quadrature parts must be zero, *simultaneously*. Thus, the Direct Dynamic Stiffness is zero,

$$K - M\omega^2 = 0 \tag{22-2}$$

and the Quadrature Dynamic Stiffness is zero:

$$jD(\omega - \lambda\Omega) = 0 \tag{22-3}$$

For this last expression to be true, the term in parentheses must be to equal zero:

$$\omega - \lambda\Omega = 0 \tag{22-4}$$

Because Equations 22-2 and 22-4 are equal to zero, they are equal to each other. We can find the rotor speed that satisfies this system of equations. Combining expressions, eliminating ω, and solving for Ω, we define the *Threshold of Instability*, Ω_{th}, as

Threshold of Instability $\qquad \Omega_{th} = \dfrac{1}{\lambda}\sqrt{\dfrac{K}{M}} \tag{22-5}$

This is the rotor speed at or above which the rotor system will be unstable. *This expression is a very powerful diagnostic tool, and it is the key to understanding how to prevent and cure fluid-induced instability problems in rotor systems.*

As the system becomes unstable, it begins to vibrate at a frequency equal to the undamped natural frequency of the system. Equations 22-2 and 22-4 tell us that, at the Threshold of Instability, the vibration frequency is

$$\omega = \lambda \Omega = \sqrt{\frac{K}{M}} \qquad (22\text{-}6)$$

Because λ is usually less than 0.5, the vibration is subsynchronous. More complex rotor systems can experience the onset of subsynchronous instability vibration at frequencies different from $\lambda\Omega$.

How does the increase in tangential stiffness with rotor speed cause the complete loss of Dynamic Stiffness? Figure 22-2 shows the nonsynchronous Direct Dynamic Stiffness (top) and Quadrature Dynamic Stiffness (bottom) for our simple rotor model (see Chapter 11). The horizontal axis of these plots represents the frequency, ω, of some outside disturbing force that is independent of rotor speed (a nonsynchronous perturbation). The Direct Dynamic Stiffness is

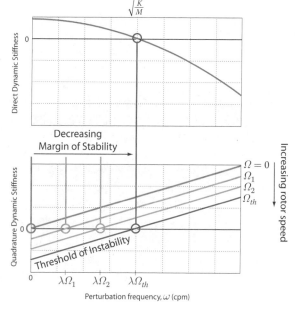

Figure 22-2. Nonsynchronous Direct (top) and Quadrature (bottom) Dynamic Stiffness plots and the Threshold of Instability. When rotor speed is zero (blue), the quadrature stiffness line starts at the origin of the plot. At this rotor speed, when the quadrature stiffness is zero, the direct stiffness is non zero, and some Dynamic Stiffness remains. As rotor speed increases, the quadrature stiffness line moves down, causing the zero crossing point of the quadrature plot to move to the right. As long as the quadrature stiffness and the direct stiffness are not simultaneously zero at any frequency, the rotor system will be stable. When the rotor reaches a speed at which the quadrature stiffness and the direct stiffness are both zero (red), the rotor is at the Threshold of Instability , Ω_{th}.

independent of rotor speed, and the zero crossing of the direct stiffness parabola occurs at the undamped natural frequency of the rotor system,

$$\omega = \omega_n = \sqrt{\frac{K}{M}} \tag{22-7}$$

The Quadrature Dynamic Stiffness changes with rotor speed because of the tangential stiffness term, which is the y intercept of the plot. When the rotor speed is zero, the quadrature stiffness line (blue) passes through the origin of the plot, and the quadrature stiffness is zero. The direct stiffness at this frequency is nonzero, though, and the system is stable. We define the *Margin of Stability* as the frequency difference between the direct and quadrature zero crossings.

As rotor speed increases, the quadrature stiffness line moves down (the tangential stiffness increases), causing the zero crossing point of the quadrature stiffness line to move to the right and the Margin of Stability to decrease. The system remains stable until the quadrature stiffness and the direct stiffness become zero at the same frequency (value of ω). This happens when the rotor speed reaches the Threshold of Instability, Ω_{th} (red). At this point, the Margin of Stability is zero.

Once the rotor system becomes unstable, subsynchronous vibration amplitude will increase until nonlinear effects near the bearing surface increase the spring stiffness. In extreme cases, K can also increase because of a rub due to the high vibration. The rotor will eventually establish itself in a "stable" limit cycle of high amplitude, subsynchronous vibration in either whirl or whip.

Modes of Instability: Whirl and Whip

To understand the different ways that fluid-induced instability manifests itself in rotor systems, we must first understand how the spring stiffness of a fluid-film bearing behaves and how it combines with the stiffness of a flexible rotor shaft.

The spring stiffness in fluid-film bearings is a strong function of rotor position in the bearing and can vary over a very wide range of values. The stiffness of a fully flooded bearing is at a minimum when the rotor is operating in the exact center of the bearing. As the rotor begins to move away from the bearing center, the spring stiffness does not change much at first. However, as the rotor nears the bearing surface, the spring stiffness starts to increase dramatically and becomes extremely high very close to the wall. It is this effect that produces the high load-carrying capacity of a fluid-film (hydrodynamic) bearing.

Up to now, we have treated the spring stiffness, K, as a single spring that acts in the radial direction. However, the situation is usually more complicated than that. A flexible rotor can be thought of as a mass that is supported by a shaft spring, K_S, which is in turn supported by a bearing spring, K_B (Figure 22-3, left). Thus, K actually consists of two springs in series, with the total stiffness given by:

$$K = \frac{1}{\left(\dfrac{1}{K_S} + \dfrac{1}{K_B}\right)} = \frac{K_B}{\left(1 + \dfrac{K_B}{K_S}\right)} = \frac{K_S}{\left(1 + \dfrac{K_S}{K_B}\right)} \qquad (22\text{-}8)$$

For any series combination of springs, the total stiffness is always less than the stiffness of the weakest spring, and the weak spring controls the system stiffness, K.

Typically, the bearing stiffness at the center of the bearing is much lower than the shaft stiffness. In this case, the ratio K_B/K_S is small, and K is a little less than K_B (Equation 22-8, center). Therefore, *at low eccentricity ratios, the bearing stiffness controls the system stiffness.*

On the other hand, the bearing stiffness close to the bearing surface is typically much higher than the rotor shaft stiffness. In this case, the ratio K_S/K_B is small, and K is a little less than K_S (Equation 22-8, right). Thus, *at high eccentricity ratios, the shaft stiffness controls the system stiffness.* The behavior of the system stiffness, K, versus eccentricity ratio is shown in Figure 22-3, right.

Fluid-induced instability causes the rotor to precess at the natural frequency of the system (Equation 22-7), which is a function of K and, by extension, the eccentricity ratio. This is the key to understanding the difference between whirl and whip.

The full spectrum cascade plot (Figure 22-4) shows the startup data of a rotor system where the rotor is initially centered in a fully lubricated, fluid-film bearing. When the rotor speed crosses the Threshold of Instability (2470 rpm), the rotor enters fluid-induced instability and develops a forward, subsynchronous vibration at a system natural frequency that tracks the rotor speed. At about 2900 rpm, the instability disappears due to the high vibration amplitude during the balance resonance, but reappears at 4670 rpm when the 1X amplitude decreases. The subsynchronous vibration frequency continues to track rotor speed for a while and then transitions to a constant frequency of about 3100 cpm. *The instability behavior is called whirl when it tracks rotor speed, and whip when it locks to a particular frequency.*

At the beginning of whirl, the rotor starts precessing at the natural frequency that corresponds to the stiffness near the center of the bearing: the *low-eccentricity natural frequency* of the rotor system. At this point, the bearing stiffness

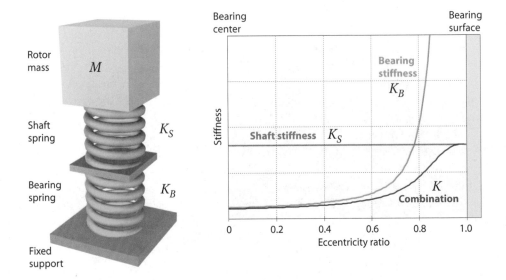

Figure 22-3. Rotor system stiffness versus eccentricity ratio. The system stiffness consists of the series combination of the shaft spring stiffness, K_S, (blue) and the bearing spring stiffness, K_B (green). The combination stiffness (red) is always less than the weakest spring in the system and is a function of eccentricity ratio. At low eccentricity ratios, the bearing stiffness, which is a strong function of eccentricity ratio, controls the combination stiffness; at high eccentricity ratios, the shaft spring, which is constant, controls the combination stiffness.

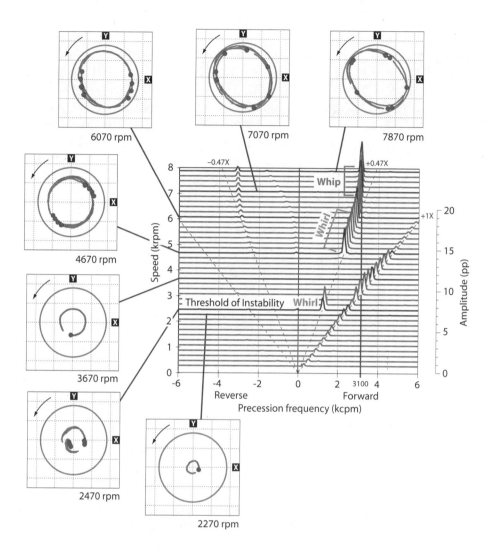

Figure 22-4. Full spectrum cascade plot showing whirl and whip during startup of an experimental machine. The measurement probes were mounted in the fully flooded, fluid-film bearing. The rotor system starts into whirl instability at about 2470 rpm, the Threshold of Instability. The orbits show the dynamic position of the rotor versus the approximate bearing clearance (gray). The Keyphasor dots (red) in the whirl orbits (2470 and 4670 rpm) are shifting slowly in a direction opposite to rotation, indicating that the frequency of vibration is a little less than 1/2X. See the text for details.

controls the rotor system stiffness and the natural frequency. Because the shaft spring stiffness is relatively high compared to the bearing stiffness, the instability vibration mode shape is likely to be a rigid body conical or cylindrical mode of the system.

For this case, when the rotor starts into fluid-induced instability, it spirals away from its stable operating point. The diameter of the orbit increases, and the orbit is approximately circular. While the *average* eccentricity ratio is close to zero, the *dynamic* eccentricity ratio increases as the orbit diameter increases. If the fluid-film bearing had a constant stiffness profile, this orbit would continue to increase until the rotor system destroyed itself.

However, this is not the case. The bearing stiffness increases as the dynamic eccentricity ratio increases, increasing K. This higher stiffness increases the natural frequency of the rotor system and the Threshold of Instability (Equation 22-5). When K moves the threshold speed to a value equal to the rotor speed, the rotor settles into a "stable" limit cycle of subsynchronous vibration at the new natural frequency of the rotor system. This is the situation at 2470 rpm.

At any constant speed above the Threshold of Instability, the subsynchronous vibration will maintain itself. If the orbit diameter increases, the dynamic eccentricity ratio and bearing and system spring stiffness also increase, pushing the Threshold of Instability above operating speed. This momentarily causes the rotor system to begin to return to *normal* stable operation. The orbit diameter decreases, decreasing the system stiffness, and decreasing the Threshold of Instability. When the Threshold of Instability falls below operating speed, subsynchronous vibration begins to increase again. Thus, the rotor system has a built-in, self-regulating mechanism that maintains the subsynchronous vibration at a certain level.

As the rotor speed continues to increase, it will exceed the current Threshold of Instability. The orbit diameter further increases until the bearing stiffness drives the Threshold of Instability high enough to "restabilize" the rotor. This cycle continues, and the subsynchronous vibration frequency (which is the natural frequency of the rotor system) *tracks running speed* as the rotor accelerates. The rotor operates on the continuously changing Threshold of Instability, with increasing orbit diameter, dynamic eccentricity ratio, bearing and system spring stiffness, and natural frequency.

For the simple rotor we have been discussing, the frequency of precession in fluid-induced instability can be found from Equation 22-6. The simple model is a good fit to the rotor in the experiment. The rotor is operating on the Threshold of Instability, and the precession frequency is close to $\lambda\Omega$. If λ is about 0.47, then the subsynchronous precession in whirl will take place at a frequency of about

0.47X. This relationship is not so simple for more complex rotor systems, but it does provide a useful estimate.

At about 2900 rpm, the rotor system encounters a balance resonance associated with a bending mode of the system. The temporarily higher 1X vibration amplitude moves the rotor to a higher dynamic eccentricity ratio, increasing K and moving the Threshold of Instability above running speed. The fluid-induced instability disappears until the 1X vibration amplitude decreases above the resonance. When the dynamic eccentricity ratio decreases again, K decreases, moving the Threshold of Instability back down through running speed, causing the instability to reappear at 4670 rpm.

As speed continues to increase, the dynamic eccentricity ratio approaches its limit as the rotor approaches the bearing surface, and the bearing stiffness becomes so high that it is no longer the weakest spring in the rotor system. The shaft spring stiffness, which is constant, becomes the weakest spring, and it controls the stiffness of the rotor system.

Because the shaft stiffness is now the upper limit of K, the vibration frequency (the natural frequency of the rotor system) asymptotically approaches a constant value, the *high-eccentricity natural frequency*. In this region, the whip region, the frequency of precession of the rotor system is constant. The high-eccentricity natural frequency often correlates well with the "nameplate critical" in rotating machinery, because normally loaded, fluid-film bearings operate at moderately high eccentricity ratios, where the bearing stiffness is significantly higher than the shaft stiffness.

Because $K_B \gg K_S$, whip vibration is usually associated with a bending mode of the rotor. Note that the whip frequency of 3100 cpm in Figure 22-4 is associated with the 1X balance resonance that occurred earlier. During whip, vibration at the bearing is limited by the bearing clearance, but the bending mode can produce very high vibration amplitudes at locations between bearings. The resulting rubs and severe stress cycling can be very destructive.

Rotors normally operate at high average eccentricity ratios in partially lubricated bearings. If such a bearing becomes flooded with lubricant, it is possible for fluid-induced instability to suddenly appear as whip, completely skipping whirl. For whirl and its characteristic speed tracking to occur, the rotor natural frequency must be less than its maximum value at high eccentricity. This condition is most easily met when the rotor operates at a low eccentricity ratio near the center of a fluid-film bearing (as can happen due to misalignment). If the rotor encounters fluid-induced instability while operating at a high eccentricity ratio, then the instability will appear as whip.

Symptoms of Fluid-Induced Instability

Subsynchronous vibration. The primary symptom of fluid-induced instability is forward, subsynchronous vibration, typically at less than ½X. The frequency of the subsynchronous vibration in whirl is related to the Fluid Circumferential Average Velocity Ratio, λ, at the location that is the source of the instability. This subsynchronous frequency can range from 0.3X to 0.8X or higher if fluid has been preswirled. However, in whip the frequency of vibration will lock to the frequency of a rotor system bending mode (typically the lowest).

Unlike rub, fluid-induced instability almost never produces a simple integer ratio vibration frequency such as ⅔X, ½X, ⅓X, ¼X, etc. Instead, fluid-induced instability is most likely to produce mostly irrational subsynchronous frequencies. *However, if the lubricant film breaks down between the rotor and the bearing, or if the large amplitude instability vibration causes a rub, then fluid-induced instability can transition to rub and lock to an integer ratio.*

The subsynchronous vibration caused by fluid-induced instability is almost purely forward (Figure 22-4). This is a very useful way to discriminate between rub and fluid-induced instability. Rub tends to produce significant reverse components at the subsynchronous frequency.

During a startup or shutdown, whirl due to fluid-induced instability will track a percentage of running speed, while whip tends to lock to a constant frequency (Figure 22-4). It is possible for whip to suddenly appear without any whirl.

Fluid-induced instability is always associated with a natural frequency of the rotor system (usually the lowest mode). The whip frequency in Figure 22-4 is associated with a visible 1X balance resonance frequency (seen almost directly below the whip frequency). The 1X balance resonance vibration of a mode will not be visible, though, if the mode is supercritically damped (overdamped), as can happen with rigid body modes. For example, the whirl onset in Figure 22-4 is associated with an overdamped rigid-body mode, which does not produce a visible 1X resonance.

Orbit. If the vibration at the measurement plane is dominated by fluid-induced instability, then the direct orbit will be predominantly forward and circular (Figure 22-4). If the orbit is filtered to the instability frequency, it will always be approximately circular and forward.

The behavior of the Keyphasor dots will depend on the relationship of the subsynchronous frequency to running speed. The number of visible Keyphasor dots is related to the denominator of the integer ratio that is closest to the actual vibration frequency. Their direction of motion tells whether the ratio is greater or less than the integer ratio. For example, given a subsynchronous vibration frequency near ½X, the denominator indicates that two Keyphasor dots will be visible. If the Keyphasor dots move in a direction *opposite* to rotation, then the ratio is slightly *below* ½X (this is the case in Figure 22-5). If the Keyphasor dots move in the *same direction* as rotation, then the ratio is slightly *above* ½X. Vibration near ⅓X will produce a set of three Keyphasor dots in the orbit that behave in a similar way. See Chapter 5.

When the subsynchronous vibration is not near an integer ratio, the Keyphasor dots will tend to form a jumbled pattern consisting of a great many dots. This is more typical for whip orbits. Whip orbits, because of the lower subsynchronous frequency ratios at which they usually occur, are more likely to show complicated Keyphasor dot behavior than whirl orbits (Figure 22-4, whip orbits).

If the vibration at the measurement plane contains a mixture of 1X and subsynchronous vibration, then the orbit will be more complex in shape. The subsynchronous vibration will cause the orbit to continuously change shape, but the motion of the Keyphasor dots (for frequencies close to an integer ratio) will still tend to migrate in a circle (Figure 22-5).

Average shaft centerline position. It can be useful to correlate the onset of subsynchronous vibration with movement of the shaft centerline toward the center of the bearing and the resulting modification of the natural frequency. When fluid-induced instability occurs and the orbit grows larger in whirl or whip, the average shaft centerline position may move closer to the bearing center. However, if the source of the instability is in a seal, which is normally concentric with the shaft, then the shaft centerline position may not change significantly.

Figure 22-5. Whirl orbit showing a mixture of 1X and 0.48X vibration. In this case, because the frequency of vibration is slightly less than 1/2X, the Keyphasor dots move slowly opposite to the direction of rotation, in a small, circular path. The orbit continuously changes shape as the frequency components change their relative phase.

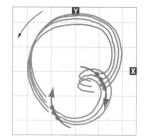

Other Malfunctions That Can Produce Similar Symptoms

Rotating stall and aerodynamic instabilities in compressors. Rotating stall is a phenomenon that can occur in both axial and centrifugal compressors when they are operated near the surge point. In rotating stall, partial flow separation creates one or more regions of impaired flow that rotate around the rotor disk or diffuser at a subsynchronous frequency. The vibration produced by rotating stall is, like fluid-induced instability, forward at the subsynchronous frequency, and it tends to track running speed. At times, rotating stall can look so much like fluid-induced instability that it can be very difficult to make an accurate diagnosis.

There are some clues that can be helpful. Rotating stall can occur at subsynchronous frequencies that are both lower and higher than the typical range for fluid-induced instability. Rotating stall in an impeller or axial blade section typically occurs at a frequency from 0.60X to 0.80X. Diffuser stall typically occurs in the range 0.10X to 0.30X.

Rotating stall, while *aerodynamically* self-excited, is not usually associated with a rotor system natural frequency. Thus, it is likely to occur at frequencies unrelated to observed balance resonance frequencies. However, the frequency of fluid-induced instability, which *is* associated with a system natural frequency, may also not correlate to a visible balance resonance if the rotor system is over-damped in that mode.

The subsynchronous spectral line from rotating stall can be sharp, or it can be broad and unsteady. Fluid-induced instability tends to produce a smooth, sharp, well-defined spectral line.

Rotating stall most often occurs when compressors are operated near the surge point. If rotating stall is suspected, keep the speed constant and change the machine operating condition to a point farther away from the surge point. If the problem is rotating stall, it may disappear. (An additional complication can result if something is obstructing the flow path in a compressor. Then it is possible to trigger rotating stall when the compressor is operating far from the surge point.)

Aerodynamic instability in compressors can produce a broad band of frequencies that are available to excite a rotor natural frequency. This type of excitation usually manifests itself with both forward and reverse subsynchronous frequency components in a full spectrum. The frequency lines are broad and noisy and, because they excite natural frequencies, the subsynchronous vibration frequency is often correlated with a rotor balance resonance. This type of excitation does not track running speed. It can sometimes look like fluid-induced whip, but the whip subsynchronous vibration is usually predominantly forward with a sharp spectral line.

Surge is an aerodynamic instability in compressors that involves large scale axial flow oscillations. Surge typically occurs at very low frequency, such as 0.10X. Even though surge is an axial flow phenomenon, it usually produces detectable lateral vibration as well as significant axial vibration of the rotor.

Rub. Rub can also produce subsynchronous vibration. However, there are significant differences between the subsynchronous vibration due to rub and that due to fluid-induced instability.

Fluid-induced instability tends to produce a predominantly forward, subsynchronous precession of the rotor. However, the subsynchronous vibration due to rub usually has significant reverse components, and it will lock to a frequency that is an integer ratio, such as ½X or ⅓X, or, more rarely, ⅔X, ¾X etc. Although fluid-induced instability occurs over a range that includes many of these frequencies, it is improbable that it will occur exactly at one of these integer ratios. It is very difficult to tell the difference between fluid instability and rub if the only tool available for diagnosis is a half spectrum, which has limited resolution and lacks rotor precession information.

A direct orbit with Keyphasor dots is the best tool for determining whether or not the frequency is an integer ratio (Figure 22-6). If the Keyphasor dots steadily change position in the orbit from one vibration cycle to the next, then the vibration is not an integer ratio, and the malfunction is not likely to be rub. In the figure, the Keyphasor dots steadily shift position in the fluid-induced instability orbit, and the orbit shape changes over time because of the changing phase of the frequency components. On an oscilloscope, the Keyphasor dots would steadily change position, following a nearly circular track. Part of that track can be seen in the figure.

Partial radial rub, when it manifests itself as steady subsynchronous vibration, tends to produce vibration at a subharmonic frequency. On a direct orbit, the Keyphasor dots will remain in approximately the same position for many cycles. Note that, in the figure, the Keyphasor dots on the rub orbit remain more tightly locked in position, and the orbit maintains the same shape and position over time.

Subsynchronous rub usually causes reverse precession components in the rotor response, whereas fluid-induced instability tends to produce a forward, nearly circular orbit when filtered to the instability frequency. The full spectrum can be very helpful for determining if the subsynchronous frequency is predominantly forward or has significant reverse components (Figure 22-6).

When a rotor is precessing in fluid-induced instability whip, the high amplitude vibration may cause occasional breakdown of the fluid film in the bearing. When this happens, metal to metal contact can occur, producing a rub, and the

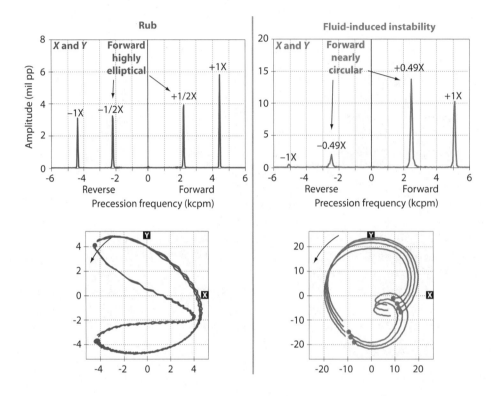

Figure 22-6. Comparison of rub and fluid-induced instability orbits and full spectra. Both orbits contain a mixture of 1X and subsynchronous vibration. This is frequently called "rabbit ears." The fluid-induced instability orbit (blue) is predominantly forward at the subsynchronous frequency. Also, the Keyphasor dots move, indicating that the orbit is not exactly 1/2X. The rub orbit (red) is locked to exactly 1/2X, and the subsynchronous frequency contains a significant reverse precession component in the full spectrum.

vibration frequency may lock to an integer ratio. During startup, Keyphasor dots may temporarily lock, then unlock, as the rotor passes through narrow speed ranges that are centered on integer ratios of the whip frequency to rotor speed. This phenomenon is essentially a type of lubricated rub, but the root cause is fluid-induced instability.

To summarize (Table 22-1), the subsynchronous vibration due to a partial radial rub will tend to have a frequency that is an integer ratio, and it will have significant reverse components at a, typically, subharmonic frequency.

Table 22-1. Partial radial rub or fluid-induced instability? This table compares the symptoms of fluid-induced instability and rub, and shows the best diagnostic plot to discriminate between the two conditions.

Fluid-induced instability	Rub	Use this tool
Noninteger ratio (e.g. 0.47X)	Integer ratio (1/2X, 1/3X, 2/3X, ...)	Direct orbit with Keyphasor dots
Circular orbit, forward precession at instability frequency	Significant reverse components	Full spectrum, Direct orbit

Locating the Source of Instability

When a machine is diagnosed as having a fluid-induced instability problem, the next step is to locate the source of the problem. Fluid-induced instability can originate in fluid-film bearings and seals, around pump impellers, or in any part of the machine where fluid is contained between two concentric cylinders that are rotating relative to each other. Machines that are equipped with stabilizing bearing designs (such as tilting pad bearings or externally pressurized, or hydrostatic bearings) can still experience fluid-induced instability in oil control rings, seals, or some other part of the machine.

The subsynchronous vibration due to fluid-induced instability originates at the source of the instability and propagates through the machine. A phase delay will occur that depends on the distance of the measurement plane from the source, the dynamic behavior of the rotor system, and, of course, the relative angular orientation of the measurement transducers.

While in fluid-induced instability, the rotor is operating on a rotor system natural frequency. Thus, the amount of the phase lag in the rotor will also depend on the mode shape of the natural frequency associated with the instability. Rigid body modes are likely to have small relative phase lags (perhaps only a few degrees), while bending modes can have substantial relative phase lags of many tens of degrees.

For any particular set of measurements taken at different distances from the source and adjusted for transducer orientation, the plane showing the largest relative phase *lead* is likely to be closest to the source of the instability.

Eliminating Fluid-Induced Instability

To ensure stability, all we need to do is ensure that Ω_{th} stays above the highest anticipated operating speed of the rotor, where

$$\Omega_{th} = \frac{1}{\lambda} \sqrt{\frac{K}{M}} \qquad (22\text{-}9)$$

We can increase Ω_{th} by adjusting the parameters in this equation; we can decrease the fluid circulation, λ, increase the spring stiffness, K, or decrease the rotor mass, M. In reality, system damping can also play a role, but it has a relatively small effect, and our simple model neglects it. (See Chapter 29 for a case history where this effect may have been important.) We cannot easily change the rotor mass, M, but we *can* increase the spring stiffness, K, or reduce the fluid circulation in the clearance, λ. The following discussion will address the practical aspects of changing λ and K in rotor systems.

Reduction of fluid circulation (λ). The fluid circulation around the rotor is fundamentally responsible for the instability. The Fluid Circumferential Average Velocity Ratio, λ, is a measure of the strength of this circulation. Note that, in Equation 22-9, λ is outside the radical. Therefore, *anything that acts to disrupt fluid flow around the clearance will reduce λ and be most effective in increasing the Threshold of Instability*.

Reduction of λ is commonly done by using bearing geometries that depart from simple cylindrical shapes or introduce discontinuities to the lubricant flow (Figure 22-7). Tilting pad bearings are an example of this; because the pads are not continuous, fluid flow is disrupted in the bearing and stability is enhanced.

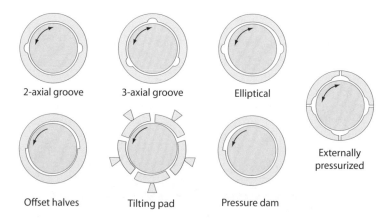

2-axial groove   3-axial groove   Elliptical

Offset halves   Tilting pad   Pressure dam

Externally
pressurized

Figure 22-7. Bearing geometries that impair fluid circulation. These are several different types of bearings that have been developed over the years to break up circumferential fluid flow (reduce λ) and stabilize the bearing. The externally pressurized bearing can also enhance bearing stiffness.

Antiswirl injection involves injecting working fluid tangentially into the bearing or seal in a direction opposite to rotation (Figure 22-8). The injected fluid acts to reduce the average fluid angular velocity and, consequently, reduce λ. This technique has been proven to be very effective in both bearings and seals.

Externally pressurized bearings with antiswirl. New, externally pressurized (hydrostatic) bearing designs are emerging that can also incorporate antiswirl injection into their design. These externally pressurized bearings are fully lubricated by design, and they can produce high inherent spring stiffness, K_B. Additionally, the antiswirl injection reduces λ, making these bearings highly stable. The principle can be extended to pressurized seal design, which, by acting

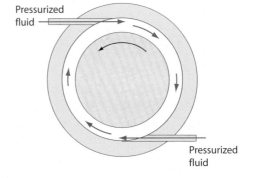

Figure 22-8. Antiswirl injection. The working fluid is injected tangentially, in a direction opposite to rotation, into the bearing or seal. The injected fluid disrupts the circumferential fluid flow, reduces λ, and increases the Threshold of Instability. For the last fifteen years, antiswirl injection has been regularly demonstrated in Bently Nevada lectures on rotating machinery behavior.

Pressurized fluid

Pressurized fluid

to stiffen the rotor system near midspan, can eliminate whip. Chapter 23 explains in detail externally pressurized bearings and machinery diagnostics.

Proper loading of hydrodynamic bearings. Fluid-induced instability often originates in hydrodynamic bearings that are operated below design load. Misalignment can shift the load from one bearing to one or more other bearings in the machine. The lightly loaded bearing will tend to position the rotor closer to the center of the bearing. This will weaken the bearing spring stiffness, K_B, and reduce the Threshold of Instability. At the same time, if the bearing becomes flooded and fully lubricated, then λ can increase dramatically and further reduce the Threshold of Instability. Either one of these changes may trigger fluid-induced instability.

Proper loading of the bearing will force the rotor to operate at a normal eccentricity ratio, which will keep K_B high and λ low. If a machine that once ran acceptably now exhibits fluid-induced instability, check the shaft centerline plot to see where the rotor is operating in the bearing clearance. If the rotor is found to be operating at a low eccentricity ratio in a particular bearing and high eccentricity ratios in adjacent bearings, then the external and internal alignment of the machine should be checked. See Chapter 20. It may be possible to cool or heat a bearing pedestal to temporarily affect the alignment and keep the machine running.

At the design level, fluid-film bearings in a machine should be designed with an appropriate load capacity. Hydrodynamic bearings with excessive load capacity can end up lightly loaded and be vulnerable to a fluid-induced instability problem.

Adjustment of supply pressure. Hydrostatic bearings normally operate in a fully lubricated condition. In these bearings, the spring stiffness of the bearing is strongly influenced by the lubricant supply pressure. Increasing the supply pressure will increase the bearing stiffness and may eliminate the instability.

Some seals act like hydrostatic bearings. The rotor in the seal area is normally completely surrounded by the working fluid of the seal, and the rotor is designed to operate in the center of the seal. Thus, increasing the seal fluid supply pressure may increase the stiffness of the seal and, if the seal is the source of the instability, eliminate the instability. Unfortunately, this will usually require a modification of the seal system.

Hydrodynamic bearings, on the other hand, normally operate in a partially lubricated condition at a relatively high eccentricity ratio. *Increasing the lubricant supply pressure may actually flood the bearing*, causing it to operate in a fully lubricated condition, potentially destabilizing the rotor system. If a hydrodynamic bearing is suspected of being the source of the fluid-induced instability, then reducing lubricant supply pressure may eliminate the flooded condition and stop the instability. Obviously, care must be taken to avoid reducing the supply pressure to such a low level that it causes damage to the bearing.

Adjustment of lube oil temperature. Fluid viscosity affects both K_B and the bearing damping, D. For the simple rotor model, the bearing damping has no effect on the Threshold of Instability (Equation 22-9). For more complex rotor systems, the bearing damping can have an effect. Thus, changing the fluid viscosity may have a significant effect on the fluid-induced instability.

The viscosity of lubricating oil is a strong function of temperature. Increasing the oil temperature reduces the viscosity, reducing both K_B and D. Decreasing the oil temperature increases the viscosity, increasing both K_B and D. In complex machines, a favorable change in K_B may be offset by an unfavorable change in D, or vice versa.

Thus, it is difficult to predict ahead of time how changes in oil temperature will affect the Threshold of Instability. In some cases, a change in oil supply temperature of only a few degrees has produced dramatic changes in the fluid-induced instability behavior of the machine. Try cooling down low viscosity fluids or heating up high viscosity fluids, a few degrees at a time.

Summary

Fluid-induced instability is a condition that can produce large amplitude, usually subsynchronous, self-excited vibration of a rotor, leading to rotor-to-stator rubs on seals, bearings, impellers, or other rotor parts.

Fluid-induced instability can occur wherever a fluid is contained between two concentric cylinders that are rotating relative to each other. It can occur in fluid-film bearings and seals and around impellers.

The onset of fluid-induced instability involves a loss of Dynamic Stiffness of the rotor system. Both the Direct and Quadrature Dynamic Stiffness become zero simultaneously.

The speed at which the instability onset occurs is called the *Threshold of Instability*, and is given by

$$\Omega_{th} = \frac{1}{\lambda}\sqrt{\frac{K}{M}}$$

Whirl occurs when the shaft operates near the center of a bearing and is usually associated with a rigid-body mode of the rotor. In whirl, the subsynchronous vibration tracks running speed.

Whip occurs when the shaft operates in the bearing at a high eccentricity ratio and is usually associated with a bending mode of the rotor. In whip, the subsynchronous vibration locks to a single frequency.

Curing fluid-induced instability involves increasing Ω_{th} above the highest anticipated operating speed of the machine. In the most practical sense, this can be done by reducing the fluid circulation, λ, or by increasing the system spring stiffness, K.

Reduce λ by using bearing geometries, such as tilting pad bearings or other bearings of noncontinuous geometry, that break up fluid circulation, or by anti-swirl injection.

Increase K by using externally pressurized (hydrostatic) bearings or by properly loading hydrodynamic bearings at normal eccentricity ratios (which also reduces λ).

Chapter 23

Externally Pressurized Bearings and Machinery Diagnostics

In previous sections of this book, we have discussed machinery diagnostics from the point of view of conventional bearing technology. The technology continues to evolve, and new bearing developments promise to change the behavior of machines and the way we look at machinery data. The externally pressurized bearing is undergoing rapid development, and, because of its external pressure source, it has the capability of producing variable spring stiffness under operator or automatic control. As the externally pressurized bearing enters general use, it promises to change rotor behavior in ways that will affect diagnostic methodology.

In this chapter, we will discuss the machinery diagnostic implications of variable stiffness. We will start by comparing the stiffness behavior of rolling element bearings, conventional hydrodynamic (internally pressurized) bearings, and externally pressurized bearings. Then, we will show how variable stiffness can affect rotor behavior. Finally, we will discuss the implications of variable stiffness for future machinery diagnostics.

Types of Bearings

The bearings used in large rotating machinery can be divided into two general types: rolling element bearings and fluid-film bearings. Fluid-film bearings can be further subdivided into internally and externally pressurized bearings.

Rolling element bearings most often find their application in small, balance-of-plant machinery, very low-speed machinery, or machines where the weight or complexity of a lubricant supply system for a fluid-film bearing cannot be justified. Rolling element bearings do not allow significant rotor motion near the bearing; they have very high spring stiffness and low damping, both of which are essentially independent of load. Because of their high stiffness, rotor nodal points tend to be located within or very close to the bearings.

To provide more damping to machines equipped with rolling element bearings, squeeze-film dampers are sometimes used. For the same bearing design, a squeeze-film damper will tend to reduce the overall bearing stiffness and allow more shaft motion in the bearing plane.

Fluid-film bearings are used in most large rotating machines, where a thin film of lubricant keeps the journal and bearing separated. The film thickness in these bearings is typically on the order of tens of micrometers (a few mils). The lubricant is most often oil, but it can also be the working fluid of the machine; for example, water or even a gas.

Fluid-film bearings can be *internally* or *externally* pressurized.

Internally Pressurized Fluid-Film Bearings

Internally pressurized bearings support the rotor with the dynamic pressure of the lubricating fluid created inside the bearing by the action of the rotating journal. In these bearings, a continuous flow of oil is supplied to the bearing at low pressure, typically around 1 to 2 bar (15 to 30 psi). The bearing normally supports the journal at a moderate to high average eccentricity ratio, and the journal acts like a pump that produces circumferential flow of the fluid. As the fluid is drawn into the reduced clearance by the journal, the local fluid dynamic pressure increases, some of the fluid escapes axially, and the remaining fluid provides the support for the rotor. When a rotor is normally loaded and operating at design eccentricity ratios, plain cylindrical journal bearings are partially lubricated; that is, the bearing cavity is often not completely flooded with lubricating fluid.

When plain cylindrical journal bearings are lightly loaded, perhaps due to misalignment or radial loads on the rotor that act against gravity, the journal can move to low eccentricity ratios, and the bearing can become fully flooded. When this happens, it can trigger fluid-induced instability. The root cause of this instability is the tangential force produced by the differential pressure associated with the converging and diverging circulating fluid (see Chapter 22).

In an attempt to counteract this effect by disrupting the fluid flow, various bearing geometries have evolved, such as axial groove, elliptical, offset half, and pressure dam bearings. Even with these designs, fluid-induced instability is occasionally a problem.

Tilting pad bearings were developed to provide an inherently more stable, internally pressurized, fluid-film bearing. They have several separate, pivoted pads that support the journal. Each pad rests on a single pivot or rocker that, ideally at least, cannot support a moment. The design ensures that the support force is directed through the pivot toward the center of the journal. When this condition is satisfied, no tangential forces can develop, and the bearing will be stable. However, fluid-induced instability has been known to occur in tilting pad bearing machines because of circumferential oil flow in the oil control (retainer) rings of these bearings or because of circumferential fluid flow elsewhere in the machine, such as in seals or around turbine or impeller disks. Tilting pad bearings are effectively fully flooded, with a hydrodynamic oil film existing at all times on all of the pads, and the journal normally operates at eccentricity ratios close to zero. Tilting pad bearings are in widespread use on many types of rotating machinery.

Externally Pressurized Fluid-Film Bearings

An externally pressurized fluid-film bearing operates in a fully flooded condition by design. Fluid at relatively high pressure is supplied to a set of inlet orifices that restrict the flow and create a pressure drop, and pockets distribute the fluid pressure over parts of the journal (Figure 23-1). The fluid escapes axially through the journal/bearing radial clearance.

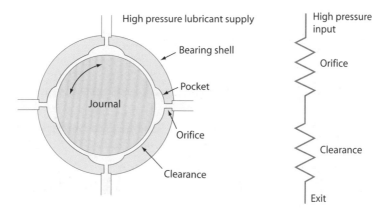

Figure 23-1. Externally pressurized bearing and equivalent resistance network. The high pressure supply feeds multiple inlet ports. The pressure drops across an orifice to an intermediate level. The clearance between the journal and the bearing creates another flow resistance that changes when the journal position changes in the bearing.

The pressures and fluid flow in an externally pressurized bearing are similar to the voltages and electric current in a series resistor circuit. The orifice is equivalent to one resistor; the flow resistance created by the journal/bearing clearance is the second. Thus, the fluid in the pocket is at a lower pressure than the supply pressure, but is higher than the pressure at the exit of the bearing.

When a nonrotating journal is centered in an externally pressurized bearing, the fluid flow is equally divided between the bearing pockets. In this condition, the pressure in each bearing pocket is equal, and no net force is produced on the rotor.

When a nonrotating journal is displaced from the center, the flow becomes more restricted in the narrow clearance and less restricted in the wider clearance. The lower restriction in the larger clearance lowers flow resistance, reducing the pressure in that pocket. Meanwhile, on the opposite side of the bearing, the narrower clearance increases flow resistance, increasing the pocket pressure on that side. The net result is a pressure differential and a restoring force that attempts to push the rotor back toward the center of the bearing. The differential pressure is approximately proportional to the displacement from the center and produces the equivalent of a spring stiffness.

If the journal is rotating, then displacement from the center also creates a hydrodynamic pressure wedge similar to that in an internally pressurized bearing. Thus, the stiffness of an externally pressurized bearing is a due to a combination of static and dynamic pressure effects (Figure 23-2). If the supply pres-

Figure 23-2. Stiffness versus eccentricity ratio for different bearing types. Hydrodynamic bearing stiffness (blue) is minimum when the journal operates at the center of the bearing (eccentricity ratio zero); stiffness rises rapidly near the bearing wall (eccentricity ratio one). Pure hydrostatic bearing stiffness (violet) is maximum when the journal is near the center of the bearing (low eccentricity ratio). Typical externally pressurized bearing stiffness (green) has characteristics of both types: high stiffness at low eccentricity ratios and high stiffness at high eccentricity ratios.

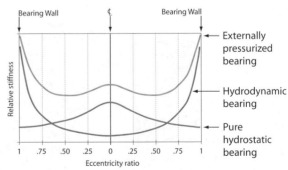

sure is sufficiently high, static pressure effects dominate, hence the name *hydrostatic* bearing.

For the same size bearing, externally pressurized bearings have higher stiffness than internally pressurized bearings. Also, an externally pressurized bearing can be pressurized before startup to lift the rotor, eliminating metal to metal contact and bearing wear, and allowing very low starting torque. The high stiffness of this bearing forces the journal to operate near the center of the bearing clearance most of the time. At such low eccentricity ratios, the attitude and position angles can become unimportant.

The hydrodynamic behavior of the externally pressurized bearing can cause fluid-induced instability problems. The hydrodynamic pressure wedge produces a tangential force component similar to that in an ordinary, plain cylindrical, internally pressurized bearing. In relatively low-speed turbomachinery applications, it is possible to defeat this circumferential flow problem by antiswirl injection. At the time of this writing, considerable research is taking place on how to eliminate circumferential flow and ensure stability in high speed turbomachinery applications.

Damping in externally pressurized bearings is more independent of stiffness than in hydrodynamic bearings. When oil is used as a lubricant, damping can be largely controlled by changing lubricant temperature (viscosity). Spring stiffness is largely independent of damping in these bearings.

Stiffness and Modal Damping in Fluid-Film Bearings

Compared to rolling element bearings, all fluid-film bearings have inherently high damping. The damping force produced by a fluid-film bearing is proportional to the amplitude and frequency of vibration in the bearing. However, even if a bearing has a high damping coefficient, if the amplitude of vibration in the bearing is low, little damping force will be generated. To generate a significant amount of damping force, the shaft must laterally move in the bearing; the amount of motion will depend on the mode shape.

Modal damping is the damping that is actually available for a particular mode, and it is inversely related to the observed Synchronous Amplification Factor *for that mode*: a low SAF produces high modal damping. High modal damping will occur when nodal points are located well away from bearings; conversely, when nodal points are located inside a bearing, little or no shaft motion can take place, resulting in low modal damping.

Rigid body modes (high shaft stiffness relative to bearing stiffness) tend to have nodal points located well away from the bearings, relatively large vibration amplitudes inside the bearings, and high modal damping. For this reason, rigid body modes are often overdamped (supercritically damped); machines will not exhibit a visible balance resonance associated with overdamped modes during startup or shutdown. Rigid body modes that are underdamped still tend to have relatively high modal damping with low Synchronous Amplification Factors.

Flexible rotor modes (low shaft stiffness relative to bearing stiffness) tend to have nodal points closer to or inside the bearings and lower vibration amplitudes inside the bearings. High bearing stiffness, by constraining rotor motion, tends to move nodal points closer to the bearing. (This is easy to understand if you imagine tightly squeezing the rotor at the bearing. The tighter you squeeze, the smaller the allowable motion at that point.) Nodal points near the bearing reduce shaft vibration in the bearing, decrease interaction with the lubricating fluid, and result in low modal damping. Thus, bearing stiffness, because of its effect on the location of nodal points relative to bearings, has a powerful effect on modal damping. Small changes in nodal point location can have a dramatic effect on modal damping. It is not sufficient to have bearings with high damping; the bearing stiffness must position nodal points in a way that allows enough movement in the bearing to provide adequate *modal* damping. Often the best compromise design occurs when bearing stiffness is approximately equal to the shaft stiffness.

Variable Stiffness in Internally Pressurized Bearings

While internally pressurized bearings are passive devices, they have spring stiffness that is a strong function of eccentricity ratio (Figure 23-2). Spring stiffness is minimum near the center of the bearing (eccentricity ratio of zero) and increases dramatically near the bearing wall (eccentricity ratio of one). In horizontal machines with plain cylindrical bearings, operation near the center of the bearing can only occur when a bearing is very lightly loaded, either as a result of misalignment or a radial load that cancels the gravity load of the rotor; for example, partial arc steam admission in a steam turbine.

Rotor speed and radial load both affect the average shaft centerline position of the journal within the bearing. The dependence of stiffness on eccentricity ratio means that it also depends on speed and load. As rotor speed increases, the dynamic pressure in the fluid film also increases, causing an increase in stiffness and a change in rotor position. This is easily visible on an average shaft centerline plot as a rotor moves off the bearing during startup. At any given rotor speed, changes in the magnitude of the radial load will also produce changes in the rotor eccentricity ratio and changes in stiffness.

Stiffness changes will change the rotor dynamic behavior. The undamped natural frequency, ω_n, of a rotor system can be expressed in its simplest form as

$$\omega_n = \sqrt{\frac{K}{M}} \tag{23-1}$$

where K is the modal stiffness of the rotor system, and M is the modal mass. In this equation, K includes the modal effects of the series and parallel combination of all the stiffnesses in the rotor system: the shaft stiffness, bearing stiffness, bearing support stiffness, and foundation stiffness. If we assume that the support and foundation stiffnesses are essentially infinite (rigid), K can be expressed as the series combination of the bearing stiffness, K_B, and the modal shaft stiffness, K_S:

$$K = \frac{1}{\left(\dfrac{1}{K_S} + \dfrac{1}{K_B}\right)} = \frac{K_B}{\left(1 + \dfrac{K_B}{K_S}\right)} = \frac{K_S}{\left(1 + \dfrac{K_S}{K_B}\right)} \tag{23-2}$$

When the bearing stiffness is relatively low, as is usually the case for the lowest rigid body modes, it will control the stiffness of the combination, and K can be expressed by the middle equation in Equations 23-2. In this case, because K is a function of eccentricity ratio in the bearing, ω_n will also be a function of eccentricity ratio.

This effect can often be observed in the lowest, rigid body modes on a critical speed map, a plot of rotor system natural frequencies versus bearing stiffness (Figure 23-3). On these plots, the natural frequencies of these modes often show a strong dependence on bearing stiffness, while the natural frequencies of the higher, bending modes, where stiffness is controlled by the shaft stiffness, are

Figure 23-3. Typical critical speed map. The map shows how rotor system balance resonance speeds (vertical axis) change with different values of bearing stiffness (horizontal axis). Several modes are shown. The lowest modes tend to be more sensitive to changes in bearing stiffness than higher modes.

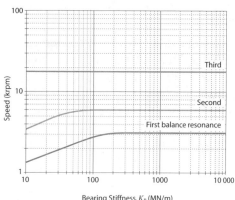

relatively insensitive to changes in bearing stiffness. This last situation can be represented by the rightmost equation in Equations 23-2.

These stiffness effects are responsible for the observed behavior of whirl and whip during fluid-induced instability (Figure 23-4). During whirl, the frequency of the instability vibration tracks rotor speed because, as the subsynchronous orbit diameter increases, the dynamic eccentricity ratio increases, which increases the bearing stiffness and the natural frequency. In the speed range where whirl is taking place, the bearing stiffness is significantly less than the shaft stiffness, the middle equation of Equations 23-2 applies, and changes in eccentricity ratio and bearing stiffness cause a change in rotor system natural frequency. When the eccentricity ratio becomes high enough, the bearing stiffness becomes significantly larger than the shaft stiffness, and the system transitions to whip. In whip, the natural frequency is constant because the shaft stiffness is significantly less than the bearing stiffness, and the shaft stiffness controls the combination stiffness, the right equation of Equations 23-2, and cannot be changed.

At very high eccentricity ratios, where the bearing stiffness is higher than the shaft stiffness, the natural frequency of that mode is relatively high compared to the natural frequency at lower eccentricity ratios; this natural frequency is called the *high-eccentricity natural frequency*. The high-eccentricity natural frequency is approximately the same as the balance resonance frequency documented by the manufacturer, the *nameplate critical*. Most often, in large horizontal machines, the high-eccentricity natural frequency is observed in conjunction with shaft bending modes.

If, for some reason, the lightly loaded rotor operates at an abnormally low eccentricity ratio, the bearing stiffness and natural frequency will also be relatively low, the *low eccentricity natural frequency*. It is only likely to be encountered during abnormal conditions, where the bearing operates below design load.

Thus, a particular balance resonance frequency may exist in a *frequency band* that depends on the operating conditions of the machine. When the machine is operating normally, the journals operate, by design, at moderate to high eccentricity ratios. (This discussion pertains primarily to plain cylindrical journal bearings. Journals supported by tilting pad bearings tend to operate at lower eccentricity ratios.) When the machine is significantly misaligned or subjected to unexpected radial loads, the journals operate at very low or very high eccentricity ratios. If the machine has primarily rigid body modes, where the bearing stiffness is the weakest spring in the system during normal operating conditions, then these rigid body natural frequencies may actually occur at speeds from significantly below to above their nameplate criticals. Systems with

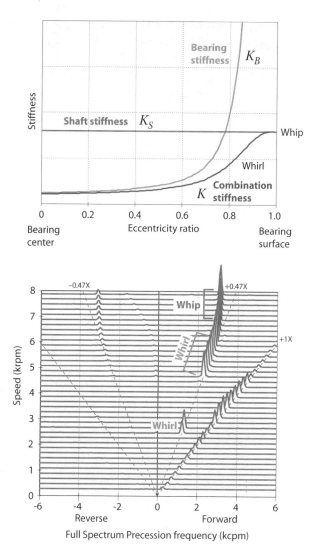

Figure 23-4. Bearing stiffness, shaft stiffness, and whirl and whip. The upper plot shows stiffness as a function of eccentricity ratio. The combination stiffness (red) is always less than its weakest component, bearing stiffness (green) or shaft stiffness (blue). As journal eccentricity ratio increases during whirl, the overall stiffness increases until it becomes approximately equal to the shaft stiffness. At this point, the whirl transitions to whip and locks to a single natural frequency controlled by shaft stiffness (lower plot).

flexible rotors, where shaft stiffnesses control resonance frequencies, will show a much smaller change.

Variable Stiffness in Externally Pressurized Bearings

The stiffness of externally pressurized bearings includes a combination of static and hydrodynamic effects. The static component of stiffness depends on the supply pressure; the diameter of the orifices; the number, area, and shape of pockets; the bearing radial clearance; and, to a lesser extent, the eccentricity ratio. The hydrodynamic component of stiffness depends on eccentricity ratio. At low eccentricity ratios, the combination of these effects produces an overall bearing stiffness that is higher than that of an internally pressurized bearing and is also a function of eccentricity ratio.

The externally pressurized bearing has an additional, important advantage. For any given physical bearing geometry, the static component of stiffness can be controlled by varying the supply pressure; higher pressure produces higher stiffness. The externally pressurized bearing also provides the opportunity to put bearing stiffness under either operator or automatic control. Control is accomplished by statically or dynamically adjusting pocket pressures in groups or individually.

In its most basic form, the externally pressurized bearing operates in a completely passive mode, with a preset operating pressure applied to all the inlet orifices. In this case, each pocket will produce a uniform, constant hydrostatic stiffness component around the bearing.

The bearing can also be operated in a semiactive mode to provide variable stiffness under either automatic or operator control. In this operating mode, a single valve can be used to change all the pocket pressures simultaneously when desired. When bearing stiffness is comparable to or less than shaft stiffness, variable stiffness control gives the operator the opportunity to shift the balance resonance frequencies to different speeds. The amount of the frequency shift will depend on how much influence the bearing stiffness has over the system natural frequency for that mode. Under some conditions, the resonance can be moved rapidly through running speed, and some or most of the vibration amplification associated with passage through a resonance can be avoided.

If pocket pressures are adjusted individually by separate control valves, it is possible to produce a change in average shaft centerline position. For example, given a radial load which moves the journal away from the center of the bearing, if the pressure is increased in pockets opposite the load and decreased in pockets on the same side of the load, the net force will push the average shaft centerline of the journal back to the bearing center. This can be done by sensing the position of the journal, comparing it to a predefined set point, and using an automatic control system to make the adjustments. Because the average of the individual pocket pressures does not change, the overall bearing stiffness remains approximately the same.

Finally, the bearing can be operated in a fully active mode, where rotor position information is provided to an automatic feedback control system that continuously adjusts the individual pocket pressures and the forces applied to the journal. The type of control used determines the effects of these pressure changes. The use of proportional control can provide the equivalent of a rotating stiffness, derivative control can provide synthetic damping, and integral control can be used to adjust the dc offset to move the rotor to the desired average set point.

The fully active bearing will suppress vibration (for example, in the event of sudden blade loss), and the control signal can be used to provide input to a diagnostic system.

Rotor Dynamic Implications of Variable Stiffness Bearings

Changing bearing stiffness changes how the rotor system responds to the static and dynamic forces that exist in the machine. The effects of variable bearing stiffness depend on the ratio of bearing stiffness to shaft bending stiffness. In the following discussion, we assume a shaft with stiffness K_S is supported by two variable stiffness bearings with total stiffness K_B. The modal stiffness depends on the combination of the shaft stiffness and the deflection mode shape of a particular mode. Modal damping depends on both the amount of damping in the bearings and the locations of nodal points relative to the bearings. These effects can be divided into three general cases. The following discussion is qualitative in nature; particular machines may behave differently.

$K_B << K_S$. The bearing stiffness is significantly less than the shaft stiffness. In this situation, the rotor is effectively rigid, and bearing stiffness controls the rotor system natural frequency (the middle equation of Equations 23-2). Changing bearing stiffness will have a relatively strong influence on the rotor system natural frequency. Nodal point locations will remain far from bearings, producing relatively small changes in modal damping.

$K_B \approx K_S$. Bearing stiffness is comparable to shaft stiffness. Changes in bearing stiffness will have some effect on the rotor system natural frequency. Stiffness changes will move nodal points and affect modal damping.

$K_B >> K_S$. The bearing stiffness is significantly greater than the shaft stiffness. In this situation, the rotor is flexible, and shaft stiffness controls the rotor system natural frequency, which will be relatively insensitive to changes in bearing stiffness. With stiff bearings, rotor nodal points will be close to the bearings, and stiffness changes will have a large influence on nodal point locations relative to the bearing. As the bearing stiffens, nodal points will approach and enter the bearings, shaft vibration in the bearings will decrease, modal damping will drop, and amplification factors at resonance will increase. Similarly, reducing bearing stiffness will increase shaft vibration in the bearings, increase modal damping, and reduce amplification factors at resonance. Thus, for this case, variable stiffness will have more of an effect on modal damping than on natural frequency. Note that the American Petroleum Institute recommends that $K_B \leq 4K_S$ to avoid high amplification factors at resonance [1].

Figure 23-5 shows, when $K_B \approx K_S$, how the balance resonance frequency can be changed by changing bearing stiffness. The left Bode plot displays the vibration response of the simple rotor model of Chapter 10 for three ratios of K_B/K_S. This model is not sophisticated enough to show the effects of changes in nodal point location. The value of K was calculated using Equations 23-2, and the values of mass and damping were unchanged. The resonance frequencies increase with increasing stiffness ratio. The Synchronous Amplification Factor is affected somewhat by the increase in stiffness, even though the modal damping was not changed.

The right Bode plot displays the vibration behavior for the same three stiffness ratios, using a finite element rotor model. This model is sophisticated enough to show nodal point location effects on modal damping. The change in amplification factor is much more dramatic because the stiffness changes produced changes in the nodal point location and, hence, in the modal damping. The change in modal damping is also revealed by the changes in the slope of the phase data.

For most machines, variable stiffness bearings will allow some adjustment of natural frequencies and mode shapes while the machine is running. The stiffness adjustment will also affect modal damping. Since spring stiffness and modal damping are a part of Dynamic Stiffness, changes in bearing stiffness will cause changes in vibration amplitude and phase (see Figure 23-5). Shifting the resonance away from running speed may cause dramatic changes in amplitude and phase.

At any particular speed, a change in bearing stiffness will change the influence vectors of the machine, which are closely related to the Dynamic Stiffness (Chapter 16). This has important implications, discussed below, for the repeatability needed for balancing.

Changes in bearing stiffness will also have an effect on the unbalance response of the rotor system. As we discussed in Chapters 16 and 18, 1X vibration depends on the amount, angular location, and axial distribution of unbalance along the rotor and *how well that distribution fits the rotor vibration mode shape.* If that mode shape is changed by adjustments in bearing stiffness, the unchanged unbalance distribution may fit the new mode shape better or worse than the original mode shape, increasing or decreasing the unbalance response of the rotor. Thus, when bearing stiffness is changed, 1X vibration will change for two reasons: the unbalance force distribution fit to new the mode shape and the new Dynamic Stiffness.

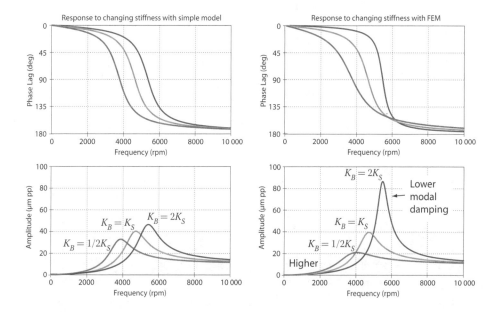

Figure 23-5. Variable stiffness effects on natural frequency and modal damping. The left Bode plot displays the vibration response of the simple rotor model of Chapter 10 for three ratios of K_B/K_S. The value of K is calculated using Equations 29-2, and the values of mass and damping are held constant. The resonance frequencies increase with increasing stiffness ratio. The Synchronous Amplification Factor is affected by the stiffness increase, even though the modal damping is not changed (the phase slope remains constant). The right Bode plot displays the vibration behavior of a more sophisticated finite element rotor model for the same three stiffness ratios. The model includes the effects of nodal point location changes. The change in amplification factor is much more dramatic because the stiffness changes produce changes in the nodal point location and hence in the modal damping.

Diagnostic Implications of Variable Stiffness Bearings

Changes in static spring stiffness are often the primary indicator of various malfunctions: rub increases stiffness, a shaft crack decreases stiffness, and misalignment can do either. Spring stiffness is a component of Dynamic Stiffness. We use the rotor behavior resulting from forces interacting with Dynamic Stiffness to interpret the state of a machine; for example, we deduce the heavy spot location for a particular mode by examining the Bode or polar plot data from a startup or shutdown. This vector data depends on the Dynamic Stiffness of the machine, which, in healthy machines with conventional bearings, remains approximately constant over speed and time.

However, variable stiffness bearings allow changes in spring stiffness that affect Dynamic Stiffness. Thus, changing bearing stiffness during a startup or after a machine reaches running speed alters the Dynamic Stiffness of the machine and the machine response. This has important implications for the diagnosis of machine malfunctions.

For example, the balance resonance is usually thought of as occurring at a fixed operating speed, where running speed coincides with a rotor system natural frequency. With an externally pressurized bearing, the natural frequency and balance resonance speed now become variables under the machine operator's control. By changing the bearing spring stiffness, the natural frequency can be quickly moved to another speed, enabling the operator or machine control system to jump the resonance rapidly through the machine during startup or shutdown. This will greatly alter, and possibly even eliminate, the usual balance resonance signature that is used to identify the heavy spot location in a polar or Bode plot (Figure 23-6). If a resonance is shifted to a different speed, then heavy spot/high spot relationships may have a different appearance. For example, what was above a resonance might now be below, or vice versa. Response that was out of phase might now be in phase. Influence vectors will depend on bearing settings, and bearing settings will have to be similar to provide repeatability of data.

Changes in bearing stiffness can also change the rotor mode shape. A mode associated with low bearing stiffness, for example, a rigid body mode, could be modified by higher bearing stiffness to a bending mode. This change in mode shape could change the match to the unbalance distribution, producing a change in unbalance response. It is possible that the existing unbalance distribution would become a better match to the new mode shape and that the rotor would have to be balanced specifically at particular bearing settings.

Some malfunctions manifest themselves as a self-excited vibration at a system natural frequency. Because of the new, variable nature of the balance resonance, this natural frequency will exist somewhere in a frequency band, which will depend on the range of bearing settings and their effect on rotor modal stiffness.

Some malfunctions produce vibration at a system natural frequency. Subsynchronous rub vibration and fluid-induced instability whip are examples. It is a common diagnostic practice to look at a cascade plot to see if a malfunction vibration frequency is near a balance resonance frequency. With rub, the vibration frequency is often shifted above the original balance resonance speed because of the stiffening of the rotor due to the rub contact. With variable stiffness bearings, these relationships may be shifted farther than expected, and in a different direction. For example, the frequency of a resonance encountered with a stiff bearing setting may be higher than the frequency of a subsynchronous rub vibration with a softer bearing setting.

Under some circumstances, the bearing will allow the operator to move the natural frequency to a place where the malfunction vibration cannot occur. The diagnostician will need to understand how this kind of variable-parameter bearing operation will affect his or her interpretation of the data and how it can be

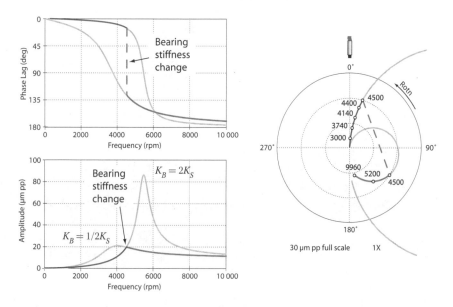

Figure 23-6. Effect of changing bearing stiffness during startup or shutdown. Finite element rotor model data shows the effect of suddenly changing bearing stiffness. The machine is started up with relatively high bearing stiffness (red). The bearing stiffness is suddenly lowered when the machine reaches 4500 rpm, changing the machine response (blue). A sudden phase change (dashed) is associated with the resonance moving through the machine, and the polar plot looks significantly different from the circular shape that would be expected with a normal bearing.

used to suppress unwanted vibration. For example, for ½X rub to occur, a machine must operate at a speed that is more than twice the natural frequency for the no rub condition; an externally pressurized bearing can be used to move the natural frequency associated with the ½X vibration to a higher frequency where this condition is no longer satisfied, eliminating the subsynchronous vibration.

Externally pressurized bearings, because of their high stiffness, will force the journal to operate near the center of the bearing clearance by default. Thus, average shaft centerline plots will show smaller changes during a normal start-up or shutdown. Variable stiffness, when used, will change the average shaft centerline position somewhat. Externally pressurized bearings can also be used to control the average shaft centerline position without significantly changing bearing stiffness. In either case, the appearance of average shaft centerline plots will be different from what would be expected with a conventional bearing.

All of the possible changes caused by variable stiffness will need to be kept in mind by the machinery diagnostician when examining data: Shifts in natural frequencies and resonances, including changes in amplification factors; misalignments between subsynchronous vibration frequencies and balance resonance frequencies; changes in mode shape with associated unbalance changes; and shaft centerline position changes.

Summary

The bearings used in large rotating machinery can be divided into two general types: rolling element bearings and fluid-film bearings. Fluid-film bearings can be further subdivided into internally and externally pressurized bearings.

Internally pressurized bearings support the rotor with the dynamic pressure of the lubricating fluid created inside the bearing by the action of the rotating journal. Internally pressurized bearings are normally partially lubricated. They are passive devices, and they have spring stiffness that is a strong function of eccentricity ratio.

An externally pressurized fluid-film bearing operates in a fully flooded condition by design. Fluid at relatively high pressure is supplied to a set of inlet orifices that restrict the flow and create a pressure drop, and pockets distribute the fluid pressure over parts of the journal. The stiffness of externally pressurized bearings includes a combination of static and hydrodynamic effects. The static component of stiffness can be controlled by varying the supply pressure; higher pressure produces higher stiffness.

The externally pressurized bearing also provides the opportunity to put bearing stiffness under either operator or automatic control. Control is accomplished by statically or dynamically adjusting pocket pressures in groups or individually. Changing bearing stiffness changes how the rotor system responds to the static and dynamic forces that exist in the machine. The effects of variable bearing stiffness depend on the ratio of bearing stiffness to shaft bending stiffness.

Variable stiffness can produce shifts in natural frequencies and resonances; changes in amplification factors; misalignments between subsynchronous vibration frequencies and balance resonance frequencies; changes in mode shape with associated unbalance changes; and minor shaft centerline position changes.

References

1.   American Petroleum Institute, *Tutorial on the API Standard Paragraphs Covering Rotor Dynamics and Balancing: An Introduction to Lateral Critical and Train Torsional Analysis and Rotor Balancing*, API Publication 684 (Washington, D.C.: American Petroleum Institute, 1996).

Chapter 24

Shaft Cracks

A SHAFT CRACK IS A SLOWLY GROWING FRACTURE of the rotor. If undetected in an operating machine, a crack (also called a fatigue crack) will grow until the remaining, reduced cross section of the rotor is unable to withstand the dynamic loads that are applied to it. When this happens, the rotor will fail in a fast brittle fracture mode. The sudden failure will release the large amount of energy that is stored in the rotating system, and the rotor will fly apart. Shaft fractures have caused machine parts to penetrate the machine casing and even penetrate building walls. Damage due to this kind of failure is catastrophic and can cause serious injury or death to anyone unfortunate enough to be standing near the machine at the moment of failure. Obviously, shaft crack detection is a very serious matter, and machines that are suspected of having a crack must be treated with the utmost respect.

In this chapter, we will start with a description of how shaft cracks start, propagate, and affect the shaft stiffness and rotor dynamic response of the machine. We will discuss these effects and develop two important rules for shaft crack detection. After discussing design and operation considerations for minimizing the risk of crack development, we will provide monitoring recommendations that can help in the early detection of cracks.

Crack Initiation, Growth, and Fracture

Rotors are subject to periodically changing, or cyclic, stresses as they rotate. If a rotor orbits about the center of the rotor system in pure 1X, circular precession, no location in the rotor will see a change in stress. However, if the rotor is deflected in bending from the center of the rotor system (the rotor sags, for example), then the rotor will see a 1X variation in stress, and the maximum stress will occur at the outer surface. If the 1X orbit is elliptical (as it typically is), then the rotor sees 2X stress cycling, whether or not the rotor is deflected (Figure 24-1). Thus, even under normal, 1X operation, real rotors live in a complicated stress environment that contains a mixture of 1X and 2X stress cycling. Any sub- or supersynchronous vibration that may be present will produce an additional complicated pattern of cyclic stresses in the rotor.

Cracks are initiated in the shaft in regions of high local stress. Shafts are subjected to large-scale stresses due to static and dynamic bending and torsional twisting, static radial loads, constrained thermal bows, thermal shock, and residual stresses from heat treatment, welding, or machining operations. These larger-scale stresses can be concentrated by geometric factors such as step changes in shaft diameter, shrink fits, keyways, drilled holes, threads, or other discontinuities. Further concentration can occur at the microstructure level, where surface machining imperfections, chemical surface damage and corrosion, and material discontinuities (such as produced by voids, slag inclusions, or chemical impurities) can produce high, local stress concentrations. All of these stresses combine to produce a local stress field that changes periodically. The end result can produce a small, local region where stresses exceed the maximum that the material can withstand, and a microcrack will form in the material.

Rotor bending tends to produce the highest stresses at the outer surface of the shaft; rotor cracks often start at or near the outer surface. Cracks can also be initiated on the surface of steam turbine rotors as a result of quenching and thermal shock due to boiler upsets. However, rapid heating of a rotor can produce high tensile stresses in the center or at the bore hole surface of a rotor (See Chapter 19). Sometimes, because of chemical or other processing problems in the rotor billet, a microcrack may already exist inside the rotor before it is put into service.

If the cyclic stresses are sufficiently high, the leading edge of the crack (the crack tip) will slowly propagate so that the plane of the crack is perpendicular to the orientation of the tensile stress field. The orientation of this stress field is affected by the type of stress (bending or torsional) and by geometric factors. If a rotor is subjected only to simple bending stresses, then the stress field will be oriented along the long axis of the rotor, and the crack will propagate directly into and across the rotor section, forming a *transverse crack* (Figure 24-2, top).

Pure torsional stress will produce a tensile stress field that is oriented at 45° relative to the shaft axis. A crack in this stress field will propagate into the rotor and tend to form a spiral on the shaft surface (Figure 24-2, bottom). In most rotor systems, the stress field contains a mixture of bending and torsional stress. Bending stress is usually the dominant component; thus, the crack will usually

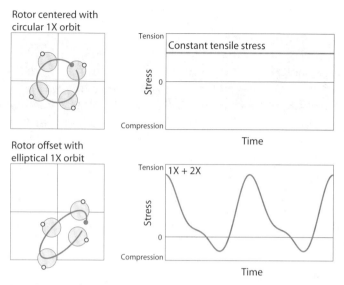

Figure 24-1. Stress cycling in a rotating rotor. A circular, 1X orbit, centered on the rotor system axis, produces a constant stress level (top). When the rotor is subjected to a static radial load, and is deflected in bending, the constant stress due to the circular orbit is added to any alternating stress due to the static radial load deflection. If the orbit is elliptical, an additional 2X component of stress may appear (bottom). Sub- and supersynchronous vibration frequencies further complicate the stress picture.

Figure 24-2. Transverse (top) and torsional (bottom) cracks. A transverse crack that results from bending stress in the shaft propagates directly into the shaft. A crack that results from torsional stress forms a spiral at 45° to the long axis of the shaft. Most shafts contain a mixture of bending and torsion stress. The local stress field at the crack tip, which can be influenced by local geometry, determines crack propagation direction. The crack tip propagates perpendicular to the direction of the tensile stress field (yellow).

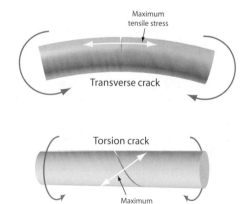

propagate into the rotor more or less as a transverse crack. However, other crack geometries are possible.

In a typical high-cycle fatigue situation, about 90% of the life of the part is spent initiating and growing the microcrack. During this period, the crack is either nonexistent or microscopic in size and propagating very slowly.

As the crack reaches measurable size, the crack enters its second phase of growth. During this last 10% of the part life, the rate of crack of growth increases rapidly, but enough shaft material remains to resist the static and dynamic loads. In an operating machine, the crack must be detected during this relatively short period of time.

The last phase of crack propagation is fast fracture. As the crack grows, less material is available to transmit loads along the shaft, and the local stress across the remaining shaft material becomes higher. At some point, the remaining cross section becomes so small that, during the next load application, the local stress intensity exceeds the strength of the remaining material, and the remaining section undergoes a fast, brittle fracture, breaking the rotor.

The *fracture toughness* is a measure of the material's resistance to fast fracture and is a function of the alloy, heat treatment, the material temperature, and the rate of loading. A material with high fracture toughness will be able to withstand a higher stress intensity without fracture than a material with low fracture toughness. Also, the fracture toughness of steel is higher when the rotor temperature is above the ductile/brittle transition (nil ductility) temperature, which, for most rotor steels, is near or above room temperature. Cold rotors may be below the ductile/brittle transition and have low fracture toughness. This is one reason why steam turbine rotors must be heated very carefully; a rotor that is below its ductile/brittle transition temperature will have low fracture toughness and be much more vulnerable to cracking due to thermal shock.

Rotor shafts are usually manufactured out of materials that possess high fracture toughness at their operating temperature. Rotor shaft cracks have exceeded 90% of the shaft cross sectional area before final fracture, but don't depend on this. It is not an easy matter to determine crack size in an operating machine, and any machine suspected of having a shaft crack should be shut down as soon as possible.

Reduction of Shaft Stiffness Due To a Crack

Shaft bending stiffness is related to the shaft cross-section area. As a crack propagates across the shaft, the remaining cross section becomes smaller, and the bending stiffness of the shaft decreases. For a given radial force on the rotor, if the stiffness decreases, the rotor deflection increases.

This reduction in shaft stiffness causes the rotor to bow more in response to a static or dynamic load, such as a rotating unbalance. Depending on the orientation of the crack, the original heavy spot location, and the relationship of running speed relative to resonance, the rotor could bow in virtually any direction. Thus, it is likely that crack propagation will produce a change in *both* 1X amplitude and phase.

The 1X vibration vector is likely to change slowly in the early stages of crack growth. But, as the crack continues to propagate across the shaft, further reducing the shaft stiffness, 1X amplitude is likely to increase more rapidly. 1X phase can also change dramatically in the later stages of crack growth.

Rotor bow will have a significant influence on 1X slow roll vectors. As the crack propagates across the shaft, the slow roll vector is likely to change dramatically from one shutdown to the next. High vibration during a resonance may cause the rotor to yield at the weak point and cause a dramatic change in 1X response.

Natural frequencies are affected by changes in rotor stiffness. As a crack propagates across the rotor, a balance resonance speed may shift downward (Figure 24-3). Depending on the rotor mode shape and the location of the crack, some resonances (modes) could be affected more than others. If a crack devel-

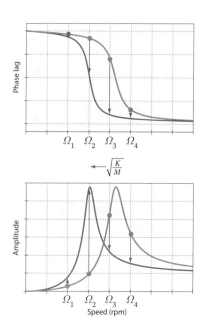

Figure 24-3. Effect of shaft crack on 1X vibration. A shaft crack reduces the spring stiffness of the system, K, shifting the resonance to a lower speed. The amplitude and phase of steady state, 1X vibration changes from the "no crack" condition (green) to the cracked condition (red). The amplitude of vibration increases or decreases, depending on the relationship of operating speed to the resonance frequency. Rotor bow due to a crack may also change the magnitude and location of the heavy spot, adding to the effect shown here.

ops in an area near an inflection point of the rotor (where no significant bending exists for that mode), then that mode may see little or no change in resonance frequency. A crack in an area of significant curvature (bending) for a particular mode is likely to have a larger effect on that mode's resonance frequency. Thus, rotor mode shapes may change, depending on the location of the crack and how it affects the stiffness distribution of the shaft.

Shaft Asymmetry and 2X Vibration

As a transverse crack propagates across the rotor, the remaining, uncracked material will become increasingly asymmetric (Figure 24-4). This shape produces a rotating, anisotropic stiffness in the rotor.

This can be demonstrated with a flexible ruler (Figure 24-5). The ruler is a beam with an asymmetric cross section, and the stiffness in one direction is very much larger than the stiffness in the perpendicular direction. If the ruler is supported horizontally at its ends, and a steady, unidirectional force is applied at midspan, the resulting deflection will be very different for different orientations of the ruler; the deflection will be maximum when the force is applied to the long side, and minimum when the force is applied to the short side. Furthermore, when the ruler is between these orientations, the force produces a response that has a quadrature component. As the ruler rotates, the weak/strong/weak transition will produce a "snapping" action two times per revolution: a 2X vibration component.

In a rotor shaft, the crack produces a similar anisotropic stiffness. *If the rotor is subjected to a static radial load that produces shaft bending near a crack, then the crack will tend to produce a 2X component in the rotor response.* The radial force acting on the rotor could be due to gravity in a horizontal machine, fluid reaction forces in a horizontal or vertical machine, partial arc steam admission in a steam turbine, misalignment, etc.

The 2X snapping action due to the crack also produces a strong 2X torque impulse, which is available to excite any torsional resonance at that frequency in the rotor system. Because torsional vibration can easily cross couple into lateral vibration, this is also likely to influence the 2X lateral vibration.

The 2X component of lateral vibration can be greatly amplified if a rotor operates at half the speed of a lateral or (because of cross coupling) torsional resonance. As we will see, this behavior can provide a piece of information that is useful for diagnosing a possible shaft crack. But remember, for a crack to produce 2X vibration, a radial, unidirectional load must be present in the rotor system, and this is not the case for all machines.

Figure 24-4. Crack growth and shaft asymmetry. As a crack grows, the remaining shaft cross section becomes asymmetric. This produces an anisotropic shaft stiffness (red arrows), which rotates with the rotor.

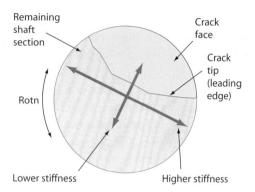

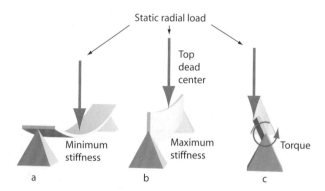

Figure 24-5. Shaft crack, anisotropic stiffness, and 2X vibration. Identical, vertical loads (red arrows) are applied to a simply supported, asymmetric beam (ruler) in three positions. In (a), the ruler has minimum stiffness and largest deflection. In (b), it has maximum stiffness and smallest deflection at top dead center. In (c), when the load is applied between the two stiffness axes, the ruler has a horizontal (quadrature) component of deflection. As the ruler rotates, a snapping motion will be seen two times per revolution (2X).

When it occurs, the 2X vibration due to a crack is likely to cause an increase in stress cycling, promoting more rapid crack growth and hastening the failure of the rotor.

The First Rule of Crack Detection (1X)

The first rule has to do with 1X vibration: *If a rotor is cracked, it is very likely to be bowed*, and that bow is likely to change over time. A change in rotor bow will change slow roll response as well as change the effective location and magnitude of the heavy spot, which will change the 1X rotor response.

Changes in 1X amplitude and phase are the best primary indicator of a shaft crack. As the crack grows and the associated bow develops, 1X amplitude and phase are likely to change continuously in a nonrepeating way (Figure 24-6). The time scale of this change can range from months to weeks in the early stages of crack growth, to weeks to days as the rotor begins to seriously weaken, and to hours as the rotor nears catastrophic failure.

As the crack propagates and the bow of the rotor changes, the amplitude and phase of the 1X slow roll vector will change.

As failure nears, 1X vibration amplitude will usually increase rapidly. At this point, 1X vibration is likely to be the dominant source of vibration in the system, so direct (unfiltered) vibration will also increase rapidly. Thus, steady increases in peak-to-peak vibration should be taken very seriously and investigated thoroughly.

Occasionally, a diagnostician may encounter a machine with a "balance problem" where there had been no problem before. Growth of a shaft crack will change the rotor bow and the location and magnitude of the effective heavy spot of the rotor. When this happens, a previous balance correction may be rendered ineffective, and, because of shaft stiffness changes, influence vectors may change. If the root problem is a shaft crack, repeated attempts to balance the machine will not solve the problem.

Changes in 1X rotor behavior in resonances are an indication that something has changed in the rotor system. A significant downward shift in a balance resonance speed is a clear indication that the stiffness of the rotor system has decreased. Always ask yourself why this has happened. A weakened shaft due to a crack is a possibility.

1X vibration is usually very sensitive to the presence of a shaft crack because of the relationship between crack growth and rotor bow, and it can provide significant early warning of a crack.

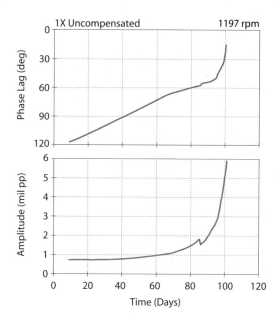

Figure 24-6. Development of a crack in a vertical pump. The 1X, uncompensated APHT plot shows the changes in amplitude and phase as the crack develops. Note that the phase was more sensitive to the change in the early period of crack growth. Vibration amplitude began to increase very rapidly in the last 20 days. The data ends when the pump was shut down for inspection; a 120° crack was found.

The Second Rule of Crack Detection (2X)

The second rule has to do with 2X vibration: *If a rotor with a crack has a steady, unidirectional radial load, then a strong 2X response may appear when the rotor is turning at half of any balance resonance speed.* The 2X snapping action of the rotor produces lateral and torsional impulses in the system. Because these impulses occur twice per revolution, the rotor will respond at the 2X frequency. If a resonance exists at twice running speed, then the 2X vibration will be amplified. This appears as a vertical relationship on a half or full spectrum cascade plot (Figure 24-7).

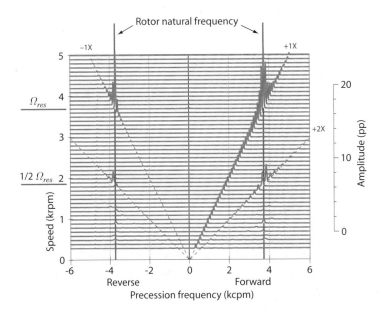

Figure 24-7. Amplification of 2X at half a resonance speed. The data is from an experimental machine with a simulated crack and a static radial load. When the rotor speed is one-half the balance resonance speed, Ω_{res}, the 2X response excites the natural frequency of the rotor, amplifying the 2X vibration. This forms a vertical relationship on the full spectrum cascade plot.

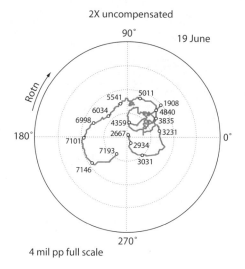

2X uncompensated

90°

19 June

180° ─────────── 0°

270°

4 mil pp full scale

Figure 24-8. 2X polar plots showing evidence of a shaft crack. The dual flow LP turbine had markedly different behavior on 28 June (bottom) compared to its behavior nine days earlier (top). While the earlier data looks normal, the later data shows large changes in amplitude and anomalous phase behavior; the phase lag decreases with increasing speed (red).

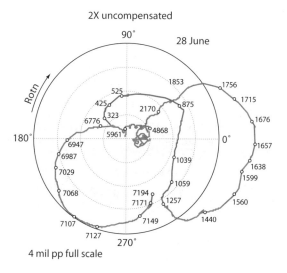

2X uncompensated

90°

28 June

180° ─────────── 0°

270°

4 mil pp full scale

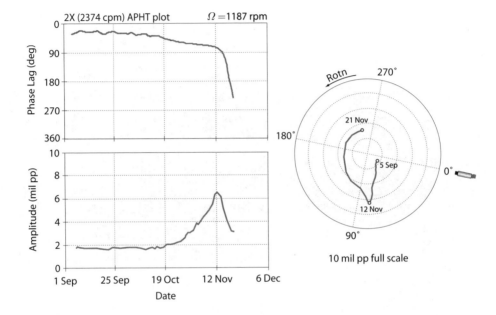

Figure 24-9. 2X APHT plots of a vertical reactor-coolant pump with a developing shaft crack. The pump is running at a constant speed during this entire period. The 2X vibration vector changes dramatically as a resonance moves down through twice running speed.

Many machines pass through such a 2X speed relationship during startup or shutdown. It is less likely that such a relationship will exist at normal operating speed (although this has happened). For this reason, and because a unidirectional radial load must be present, a crack may not produce significant 2X vibration at running speed.

In fact, in most cases, 2X vibration does not appear at operating speed. For this reason, *2X vibration should never be used as the only tool* for crack detection. 2X vibration data should be used together with 1X data to ensure the earliest and most reliable detection of a shaft crack.

Like 1X vibration, 2X vibration amplitude and/or phase is likely to change as the crack propagates through the rotor. Startup and shutdown 2X Bode and polar plots should be examined for any evidence of change (Figure 24-8).

2X amplitude and phase should be trended during steady state operation. In one case, a reactor coolant pump developed a crack while the pump was operating at a constant speed. As the crack propagated, the shaft stiffness decreased so much that a resonance that was above twice the operating speed moved down through the 2X frequency before the pump was finally shut down (Figure 24-9).

Other Malfunctions That Produce 1X Vibration Changes

A loose bearing support or soft foot can cause a change in 1X vibration. Usually, but not always, this manifests as an increase in 1X vibration amplitude. Because it mimics the behavior of a shaft crack, it can be very difficult to determine the root cause. An increase in casing vibration with little or no increase in shaft relative vibration might suggest a soft foot problem, while an increase in shaft relative with little increase in casing might suggest a crack. But, there are no firm rules here.

Thermal growth and subsequent changes in alignment can affect the bearing stiffness and produce changes in 1X vibration, as can a thermal bow of a rotor. These changes in vibration should stabilize once the machine reaches thermal equilibrium at steady speed and load.

Rub can cause changes in both 1X and 2X vibration. These changes can be sudden, occurring at operating speed or during startup or shutdown. Rub can disappear if the parts in contact wear away (this can happen in seals). If the rub is severe, contact may be maintained for a considerable time. However, rub is not as likely to produce a steadily increasing 1X vibration level over a long period of time.

A loose rotating part can also produce changes in 1X response. If a part moves to a different angular or axial position on the rotor, the resulting total unbalance of the rotor is likely to change, and the 1X amplitude and phase will change accordingly. Loose parts can shift occasionally, producing stepwise changes in 1X response, or they can shift continuously, producing a continuously changing response. Continuously moving parts will produce cyclic behavior on a polar or APHT plot. A loose part is not likely to produce a steady, long-term increase in 1X vibration amplitude.

Shifting debris or liquid inside a rotor can produce significant changes in the heavy spot location in a machine. This will produce corresponding changes in 1X vibration response and cause a machine to go out of balance frequently.

A locked gear coupling can also produce a sudden step change in 1X vibration.

The key to crack identification is to realize that a developing crack is likely to produce a steady and accelerating increase in 1X vibration amplitude over time as the shaft stiffness decreases. While some malfunctions will produce periodic changes in 1X vibration amplitude and/or phase, shaft cracks will tend to produce nonrepeating patterns on polar and APHT trend plots, and ever higher levels of 1X vibration amplitude.

Other Malfunctions That Produce 2X Vibration

Nonlinearities in rotor system stiffness can cause harmonics (2X, 3X, etc.) of running speed to appear in spectra. Nonlinear stiffness can be caused by high shaft eccentricity ratios in fluid-film bearings or by rub. Misalignment, high radial load, and coupling problems can produce 2X vibration.

If any source of 2X vibration exists in a machine, it will be available to excite a resonance at half of a balance resonance speed. Thus, the presence of 2X at half a resonance, while suspicious, is not, in and of itself, confirmation of a crack.

Design and Operating Recommendations

Shaft cracks usually result from a combination of design shortcomings, improper machine installation, or poor operating practice. At the design level, any stress concentration can lead to trouble if it is not properly accounted for in the fatigue life of the design. Keyways, notches, drilled holes, threads, and step changes in shaft diameter are all capable of producing large stress concentrations in the shaft. Shrink fits produce high tensile stresses at the surface of the rotor in the vicinity of the fit. Retaining-pin holes and grooves near or under shrink fits can lead to very high local stresses because of the combination of shrink fit stresses and geometric stress concentrations.

Estimated vibration mode shapes can be helpful in the prediction of deflections and stresses, but the dynamic behavior of individual machines can change when several machines are coupled together. For this reason, the dynamic characteristics of the entire coupled machine train should be taken into account when estimating mode shapes, deflections, and stresses.

Good machine train alignment will help minimize the chance of a shaft crack. Severe misalignment between adjacent machines in a train can cause bending of the rotor between machines. This can result in high, 1X cyclic stresses that may exceed the limits of the design.

Startup and shutdown of high and low temperature machines should be done carefully to minimize the possibility of thermal shock and microcracking of the rotor surface or interior. A boiler upset can cause low quality steam to contact the hot steam turbine shaft surface and produce a severe quench and thermal shock. The low temperature condensate of steam turbines operated in cold climates may cause thermal shock to the LP turbine rotor. These types of thermal shock produce tensile stresses that can cause a microcrack on the rotor surface. Hard rubs have also caused local microcracking, due to extreme frictional heating, local compressive yielding, and subsequent cooling.

Vibration trends are important to diagnosing a crack, but vibration amplitude is a poor indicator of stress levels important to crack generation; low vibration can be due to high radial loads and severe misalignment, both associated with high stress levels. High vibration can produce higher cyclic stresses than the designer may have anticipated in the design. High, dynamically induced stresses have combined with geometric factors to produce catastrophic cracks.

Operation of machines on or near a resonance should be avoided. It can produce high sensitivity to unbalance and high vibration, with the potential for high stresses. Operation of a machine at half of any lateral or torsional resonance should also be avoided. If 2X vibration is present, it is likely to be amplified by the resonance at twice running speed. The 2X vibration will produce cyclic stresses and increase the risk of a shaft crack. 2X Bode or polar plots should be examined for any evidence of a resonance at or near twice operating speed.

Monitoring Recommendations

During a startup, a steam turbine that encountered high 1X vibration was shut down. The problem was assumed to be an unbalance problem. Successive attempts to restart the unit encountered increasing 1X vibration levels and the appearance of some 2X vibration. A decision was made to disassemble the unit, and a partial shaft crack was found in the rotor. Subsequent examination of all of the vibration data showed that there had been, in addition to the high 1X vibration amplitude, a significant 1X phase shift of nearly 40° during the attempted startup. But the phase had not been monitored, even though the equipment had been available to do so. Remember: if you don't look for signs of a shaft crack, you may not detect one in time to prevent a catastrophe.

Unfortunately, it is rarely possible to look at a single piece of data and positively diagnose a shaft crack. Many times it is difficult to make a diagnosis with all the data at hand. However, if you apply the following monitoring recommendations, you will have a much better chance of detecting a shaft crack in a timely manner.

1. At operating speed, monitor and trend direct (unfiltered) vibration levels and 1X and 2X amplitude and phase. The trend can be as simple as a list of hand-logged data (1X and 2X amplitude and phase) or, better, as computer-generated APHT and polar plots. In addition, 1X and 2X acceptance regions should be defined so significant changes in vibration can be detected. Different acceptance regions may need to be established for different load conditions. Steady state monitoring of this kind has provided warning as early as a 25% crack.

2. Every time a machine is started up or shut down, data (in the form of 1X and 2X Bode and polar plots) should be taken and compared to earlier data. Look for significant changes in 1X and 2X behavior through resonances, a decrease in one or more resonance speeds, or other abnormal behavior. Significant changes in startup or shutdown machine response should be a cause for concern and investigated. This kind of monitoring has provided warning as early as a 20% crack.

3. 1X slow roll vectors should be logged and compared to earlier data. As a crack propagates, the bow of the rotor is likely to change, and the amplitude and phase of the 1X slow roll vectors will also change.

While there are no guarantees, careful and thoughtful machine monitoring gives you a very good chance of detecting a crack before a catastrophic failure occurs.

Summary

A shaft crack is a slowly growing fatigue fracture of the rotor. When the reduced cross section of the rotor is unable to withstand the static or dynamic loads that are applied to it, the rotor fails in a fast brittle fracture mode, a catastrophic failure.

Cyclic stresses cause shaft cracks to start in high local stress regions of the shaft, such as near step changes in shaft diameter, shrink fits, keyways, drilled holes, or other discontinuities. Cracks start at the microstructure level, where surface machining imperfections, chemical surface damage, or material discontinuities (produced by voids, slag inclusions, or chemical impurities) can produce high, local stress concentrations.

Once initiated, the crack tip will slowly propagate in a direction perpendicular to the orientation of the tensile stress field that exists at the crack tip. If a rotor is subjected only to simple bending stresses, then the stress field will be oriented along the long axis of the rotor, and the crack will propagate directly into the rotor, a transverse crack. Torsional stress will produce a spiral crack that is oriented at 45° relative to the shaft axis.

Shaft cracks reduce the bending stiffness of the shaft, due to the reduced available cross-section area, and the stiffness often becomes anisotropic. These characteristics lead to the two rules of crack detection:

1. *If a shaft is cracked, then it is most likely bowed.* This produces 1X vibration behavior that changes as the crack evolves. 1X vibration changes are the most reliable indicator of a shaft crack.

2. *If a cracked shaft is subjected to a static radial load and is operated at one-half of a resonance, then 2X vibration can appear.* This effect is due to the crack-induced, rotating anisotropic stiffness of the shaft.

Both 1X and 2X vibration can be caused by a large number of other malfunctions that must be excluded before making a diagnosis.

Shaft cracks usually result from a combination of design shortcomings, improper machine installation, or poor operating practice. There are several things that can contribute to the initiation and propagation of a shaft crack: stress concentrations, such as keyways, notches, drilled holes, and step changes in shaft diameter; shrink fits; retaining-pin holes and grooves; misalignment; high radial load; thermal shock; high vibration; and operation of machines on or near resonances, or at half of any lateral or torsional resonance.

For crack detection, 1X and 2X vibration vectors should be trended at slow roll, during startup and shutdown, and at steady state operation, with Bode, polar, and APHT plots.

Case Histories

Chapter 25

High Vibration in a Syngas Compressor Train

This case history presents an example of an "unbalance" problem that wasn't unbalance. As is often the case, as the problem was investigated, the real root cause turned out to be something completely unexpected. Transient data provided the additional information needed to correctly diagnose the problem.

A new methanol plant was being commissioned on an island in the Caribbean. The plant produced liquid methanol from local natural gas, and the process depended upon a synthesis gas (syngas) compressor train, which moved partially reformed product to the plant's final process reactor. The machine train consisted of a single-case, HP/LP steam turbine and tandem LP and HP barrel compressors (Figure 25-1). Table 24-1 lists the nameplate and operating data for this machine train.

The turbine and LP compressor were connected with a shim-pack, spool-type coupling that was not the coupling that had shipped with the unit. During final assembly, mechanics had discovered that, because of a foundation error, the original coupling was too short. On short notice, the coupling manufacturer sent another coupling that had been high-speed balanced at the factory.

Plant construction engineers tested the compressor train at low speed, then continued low-speed operation while the entire plant was started up. It took several days for the reactor beds upstream of the compressor to reach operating temperatures and pressures.

Production began, and operators started to bring the compressor up to its 10 480 rpm operating speed. The operators noticed that, as speed increased, so did vibration at bearing 3 on the LP compressor. On the vibration monitor, direct vibration increased dramatically as the compressor neared its operating speed,

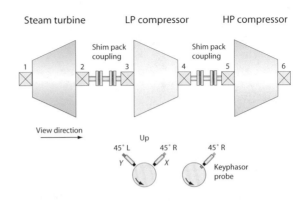

Figure 25-1. The synthesis gas (syngas) compressor train. An HP/LP steam turbine drives LP and HP barrel compressors in tandem.

Table 25-1. Operating parameters for the syngas compressor train.

Steam Turbine

Power	22 MW (30 000 hp)
Inlet press.	52 bar (750 psia)
Inlet temp.	400 °C (750 °F)
Exhaust press.	1 bar (15 psia)
Exhaust temp.	130 °C (270 °F)
Trip speed	11 200 rpm
First critical	3650 rpm
Max cont. speed	10 800 rpm
Bearing type	5 pad tilting pad
Diametral clearance	300 μm (12 mil)

LP Compressor

Gas	Reformed natural gas
Capacity	300 m^3/min (10 500 ft^3/min)
Speed	10 800 rpm
Inlet conditions	1.7 bar @ 38 °C (25 psia @ 100 °F)
Discharge conditions	17 bar @ 107 °C (250 psia @ 225 °F)
First resonance	5200 rpm
Bearing type	5 pad tilting pad
Diametral clearance	225 μm (9 mil)

HP Compressor

Gas	Reformed natural gas
Capacity	130 m^3/min (4500 ft^3/min)
Speed	10 800 rpm
Inlet conditions	12 bar @ 120 °C (175 psia @ 250 °F)
Discharge conditions	31 bar @ 220 °C (450 psia @ 425 °F)
First resonance	4300 rpm
Bearing type	5 pad tilting pad
Diametral clearance	225 μm (9 mil)

reaching 50 μm pp (2.0 mil pp) at 10,200 rpm. At that point, operators slowed the machine train down to avoid damage. At 9500 rpm, vibration was acceptable, but plant output was limited to 85% of capacity.

The problem had to be resolved quickly. The plant could not operate at full capacity until the compressor was repaired. Any shutdown for repairs would be expensive; each day the machine train was shut down, they would have to vent product to a flare stack and stop downstream production. Deadlines were approaching for both the owner's acceptance of the plant and for delivery contracts. The machine had to be repaired quickly, in a single shutdown. The contractor asked Bently Nevada machinery specialists to document the machine behavior and help determine the cause of the compressor vibration.

Steady State Analysis

Bently Nevada specialists set up their equipment while the machine was running. There were only eight channels available in the data acquisition equipment, enough for only two machines. Because coupling unbalance was suspected, they decided to concentrate on the steam turbine and the LP compressor. When they were ready, the compressor was brought back up to 10,385 rpm and they collected steady state machinery data and began to analyze the problem.

Orbit plots of data from the inboard turbine bearing (bearing 2) and the inboard LP compressor bearing (bearing 3) showed similar behavior (Figure 25-2). At both locations, the shaft moved in large, nearly circular orbits, with a predominant, 1X frequency component. However, the 1X vibration amplitude at bearing 3 was more than twice the vibration amplitude at bearing 2.

The compressor manufacturer (OEM) and the plant construction engineers suspected that the replacement coupling was unbalanced because

1. Compressor vibration amplitudes had been significantly lower in factory tests than on-site. The turbine and LP and HP compressors were shop tested prior to shipment and ran very well; vibration amplitudes were on the order of 4 - 6 μm pp (about 0.2 mil pp).

2. The vibration measured on-site had properties that were typical of an unbalanced shaft: a circular orbit, predominantly 1X vibration, and vibration amplitude that appeared to increase in proportion to the square of rotor speed.

The OEM and construction engineers attributed the difference in vibration amplitudes to the great difference in the masses of the turbine and compressor rotors. The mass of the turbine rotor was approximately eight times greater than that of the compressor rotor.

Based on this analysis, a decision was made to balance the coupling, and they developed a plan to minimize downtime. Before shutdown, they prepared the tooling and calculated the balance weights they would need. At the same time, the Bently Nevada specialists prepared to capture shutdown (transient) data.

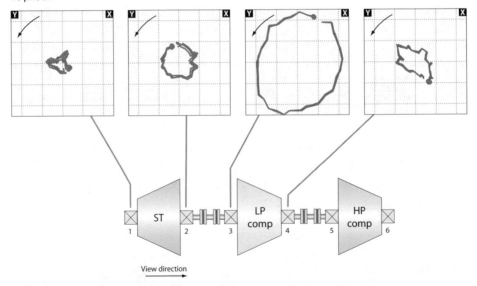

Figure 25-2. Steady state orbits at full speed before shutdown. The uncompensated, direct data shows that the orbits at bearings 2 and 3 are predominantly 1X and circular. The bearing 3 orbit is around 50 μm pp (2.0 mil pp), suggesting an unbalance problem.

Transient Data Analysis

Transient data was collected during the machine shutdown. While maintenance crews prepared to balance the coupling, the Bently Nevada specialists and engineers reviewed the new data.

With slow roll data available, the high-speed orbits could be waveform compensated. The orbits then revealed a different behavior (Figure 25-3). The *compensated* vibration from the inboard turbine bearing (bearing 2) was actually very small. Most of the uncompensated vibration at bearing 2 was actually due to runout. The compensated orbits showed that most of the vibration was centered at the LP compressor bearing 3. Also, the bearing 4 compensated orbit showed a flattening in the lower left quadrant that suggested a high radial load.

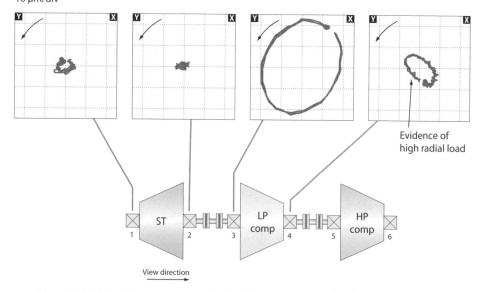

Figure 25-3. Waveform compensated orbits. Transient data allowed capture of slow roll waveforms, which were used to compensate the full speed orbits. A very different dynamic picture emerged. The compensated orbit at bearing 2 is quite small, which does not suggest an unbalance problem. The orbit at bearing 3 is little changed, while the bearing 4 orbit is partially flattened, suggesting the presence of a high radial load.

A more important piece of information was discovered. According to factory test data, the LP rotor first balance resonance should have been between 4900 and 5400 rpm. Polar and Bode plots of the shutdown data (Figure 25-4) showed some evidence of a resonance in this speed range. However, above the resonance region, the amplitude increased approximately as the square of rotor speed, while the phase lag continued to change at a constant rate. The behavior of the vibration amplitude implied that the resonance had shifted to somewhere near or above the 10,480 rpm operating speed.

A machine's balance resonance speed is a function of the rotor mass and spring stiffness:

$$\Omega_{res} = \sqrt{\frac{K}{M}} \qquad (25\text{-}1)$$

where K is the rotor system spring stiffness, and M is the rotor mass (see Chapter 11).

Increasing the balance resonance speed would require increasing K or reducing M. It was unlikely that the rotor mass of the compressor had changed; it was much more likely that something had changed in the machine in a way that increased the spring stiffness.

The behavior of the bearing 3 vector plots is similar to what might be expected of a rub (Chapter 21). When a shaft contacts a stationary part, the average system spring stiffness is increased. If the contact occurs as the machine approaches a resonance, the increasing stiffness moves the resonance farther ahead of the machine speed. As speed and the unbalance force increase, the dwell time of the contact can increase, further increasing K and the resonance speed. Unless the system changes in some way that breaks the contact, the rotor system can chase the resonance to ever higher speeds. During this period, the phase change associated with passage through the resonance is delayed while the amplitude continues to increase.

The specialists and engineers began to search for a clue to what might have caused the stiffness increase. They examined mechanical drawings of the compressor and learned that it was equipped with floating ring seals. These types of seals float on the shaft in lubricated, close contact and move with the shaft. These seals have been known to lock up, preventing them from floating properly. The locked seal then acts much like a very close clearance bearing, constraining shaft motion and increasing the rotor system spring stiffness.

The specialists theorized that the floating seal near bearing 3 had locked up, resulting in behavior like a rub. The increased spring stiffness could have shift-

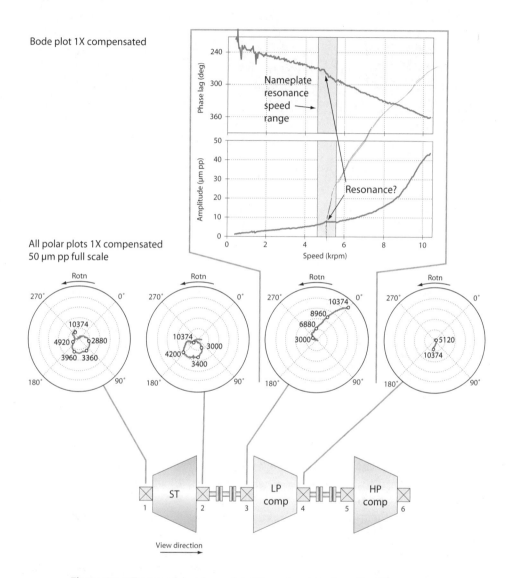

Figure 25-4. Transient shutdown data. The polar plots show the 1X, compensated, shutdown data from the *X* probes at bearings 1 through 4, and the Bode plot shows bearing 3 data. The data shows some evidence of a resonance in the nameplate speed range (nominally 5200 rpm). Above the resonance region, though, the amplitude increases dramatically, and the phase lag continues to change at a constant rate. This behavior implies that the resonance has shifted to somewhere near or above the 10 480 rpm operating speed.

ed the compressor's balance resonance to near its operating speed. The nearby resonance would amplify the normal unbalance response of the machine, producing the observed high 1X vibration.

Shaft centerline data (Figure 25-5) also supported the conclusion. The vertical movement of the shaft centerline plot is normal for a tilting pad bearing machine; however, the plot showed that the rotor was operating near the exact center of the bearing clearance, which is unusual. Some of the rise could be explained by the machine's tilting pad bearings, which can cause a shaft to operate at an eccentricity ratio of 0.2 or so, much less than for a shaft supported by plain sleeve bearings. However, the shaft in bearing 3 was operating very close to the center of the bearing, an abnormal position.

The bearing 4 shaft centerline plot showed the rotor operating at an unusually *high* eccentricity ratio; this, together with the flattened orbit shape at this location, suggested a possible misalignment between the LP and HP compressors.

Inspection and Modification of the Machine

Bearing 3 and its nearby seal were removed from the LP compressor and inspected. The rotor showed evidence of a wipe in the contact area of the seal, and the bearing showed signs of a rub. Also, inspection of the seal revealed that it was not floating correctly; thus, it had probably acted as a poor bearing, constrained the rotor, and caused the stiffness increase and the rubbing.

The engineers concluded that the floating seal was too wide, and when it thermally expanded during operation, it locked within the stationary sleeve. The seal rubbed because the clearance between the seal and the shaft is much tighter than bearing clearances. As speed increased, the rotor/seal contact evolved into a forward, full annular rub.

To ensure that the seal would float freely, the OEM reduced the intermediate ring width by 0.1 mm (4 mils) and elongated the locating pin slots. After the modifications were completed, the machine was reassembled.

The data acquisition system was reconfigured to examine the LP and HP compressors during the startup. The unit was restarted and went through its normal startup cycle while Bently Nevada specialists captured the data. It showed that the LP compressor balance resonance was now between 4900 and 5400 cpm (Figure 25-6), consistent with factory test data. The phase change through resonance was now normal at the inboard LP compressor bearing. At full speed, vibration at bearing 3 had decreased, from 44 μm pp (1.7 mil pp) to 3 μm pp (0.1 mil pp). Note that, above the resonance, the Bode plot shows a small jump in both amplitude and phase near 5700 rpm that suggests the presence of slight rub in the machine, perhaps at another location.

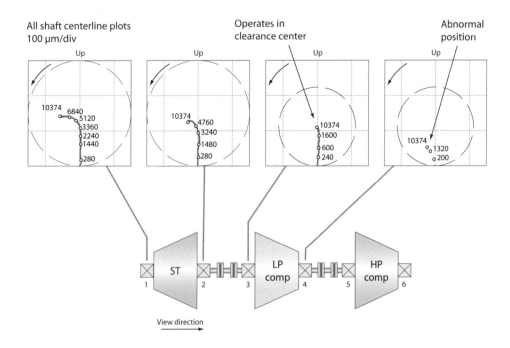

Figure 25-5. Shutdown shaft centerline plots. The vertical movement of the shaft centerline is normal for a tilting pad bearing machine. At bearing 3, the rotor operates near the exact center of the bearing clearance, which is unusual. At bearing 4, the rotor operates at an unusually *high* eccentricity ratio; this and the flattened orbit shape at this location suggests a possible misalignment between the LP and HP compressors.

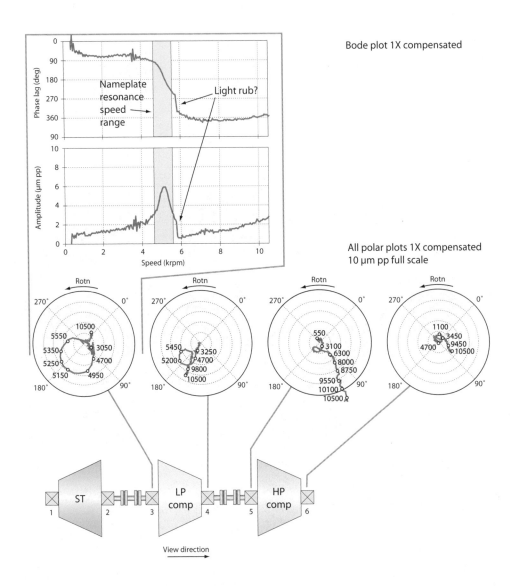

Figure 25-6. Startup data after repair of the seal near bearing 3. The data is for bearings 3 through 6, and the scale is now 10 μm pp full scale. The LP rotor exhibits a normal looking, in-phase resonance, and high-speed vibration levels are normal. Immediately above the resonance, the Bode plot shows a jump in both amplitude and phase that suggests that a slight rub still exists in the machine.

Although vibration amplitudes at bearing 3 were low at operating speed, the shaft centerline plots (Figure 25-7) still indicated abnormal shaft positions at running speed. The HP compressor rotor appeared to be operating too high in the bearings, and LP bearing 3 also showed a high rotor position. It is possible that the actual bearing clearance was greater than reported by the OEM, in which case the data plots would not accurately represent the rotor position relative to the center of the bearing.

More likely is that the position anomalies may have been due to the cold startup. Cold machines take some time to thermally grow and reach operating position. The hotter the machine's operating temperature, the more the position is likely to change. (Note that, in Figure 25-7, the HP compressor, which runs hottest, shows the most abnormal looking centerline plots when cold.)

While a machine heats up, shaft centerline position is likely to change; for this reason, a shaft centerline position which is abnormal looking when the machine is cold should not be taken too seriously unless it can be confirmed later when the machines are hot.

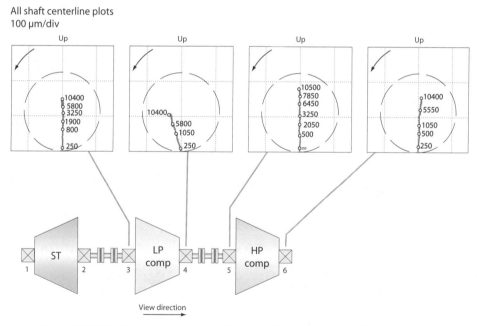

Figure 25-7. Cold startup shaft centerline plots after the seal repair. The rotor positions in bearings 3 and 4 have changed and are higher (compare to Figure 24-5). The rotor also appears to be too high in bearings 5 and 6. All of this data is somewhat suspect because the machines have not had time to reach operating temperature.

Summary

Transient data is almost always needed for machinery diagnostics, although it is usually more difficult to obtain than steady state data. However, steady state data contains significantly less information, and it can be misleading because of the relatively small amount of information available. You should always be careful when attempting to diagnose a machine problem using only steady state data.

In this case, the steady state data and some historical information seemed to indicate that the problem was a coupling unbalance. Because slow roll data was not available, the uncompensated orbit from the inboard turbine bearing was interpreted as being due to unbalance. The transient data revealed much more information: the compensated orbits showed different behavior, and the Bode and polar plot data pointed toward a rub of some sort. Rub is always a secondary malfunction that is caused by some other root cause; in this case, the underlying problem was the locked floating seal.

Chapter 26

Chronic High Vibration in a Draft Fan

A BENTLY NEVADA MACHINERY SPECIALIST WAS ASKED to balance an induced draft (ID) fan at a grain distillery. The fan was located on the sixth floor of a sixty-year-old power house, a very flexible support structure.

The plant had three ID fans, all operating at the same speed. The other two were located next to each other on the fifth floor directly below ID Fan 1. All three fans had been replaced with larger fans when the plant's boiler was upgraded two years earlier. Since installation, ID Fan 1 had experienced a chronic unbalance problem; it had been balanced 24 times, an average of once per month.

The fan was a horizontal, squirrel cage design approximately 15 ft (4.6 m) in diameter, weighing 5000 to 6000 lb (2300 to 2700 kg), with an internal, hollow, conical section for guiding air flow. The fan was located midway between its fluid-film sleeve bearings. It was driven through a flexible coupling by a 3-phase, 8-pole, 400 hp (300 kW) induction motor, turning at around 890 rpm. The motor was also equipped with fluid-film bearings (Figure 26-1).

When the specialist arrived, there were no permanently mounted vibration transducers installed on the machine train. Hand-held velocity transducers had been used on the fan during previous balancing attempts. This is undesirable for several reasons. First, hand-held transducers can suffer from measurement repeatability problems due to changes in measurement location and poor contact between the transducer and machine casing. Second, fluid-film bearings generally do not transmit shaft relative vibration to the casing very well. For this kind of machine, casing vibration amplitudes are typically less than one third of shaft relative vibration amplitudes, and the fluid-film bearing can produce a phase delay in the casing vibration; thus, casing mounted velocity probes usually provide a poor picture of what is happening with the shaft and make accurate balancing more difficult. Third, because of the structural flexibility of the building, the two fans on the floor below (which operated at the same speed) could transmit vibration through the building structure to the casing of the fan being balanced, where it could be detected by casing-mounted velocity probes.

Before balancing, the fan was sandblasted clean to remove any accumulated fouling. *XY* shaft relative proximity transducers were installed on the fan at bearings 3 and 4 at 15° L and 75° R, and a Keyphasor transducer was installed to provide a phase reference.

Moving-coil, *XY* velocity transducers (Seismoprobes) were also installed, using magnetic bases, on the motor at 0° and 90° R near bearings 1 and 2, and on the fan at 15° L and 75° R near bearings 3 and 4. These transducers were installed because of the possibility of significant casing motion, which might affect shaft relative measurements. However, the frequency of the fan, about 890 cpm, was close to the minimum rated frequency response (600 cpm) of the velocity transducers. At 600 cpm, the amplitude would be down by 30%, and the phase would lead vibration by 90°. At running speed, a significant, phase-lead error of more than 50° could be expected. Thus, vibration data from these transducers would have to be used cautiously.

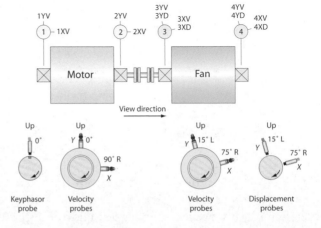

Figure 26-1. Machine train diagram. Only velocity transducers were installed on the motor at 0° and 90° R. Both shaft relative and velocity transducers were installed on the fan at 15° L and 75° R.

After the transducers were installed, the transducer suite was connected to a Bently Nevada, computer-based, data acquisition system. The velocity transducers on the fan measured nearly 5 integrated mil pp (130 μm pp), mostly vertical vibration, *with the fan stopped!* This was vibration being transmitted from the other two fans through the building structure. The shaft relative transducers showed no vibration.

The specialist prepared to get baseline data after the fan was brought up to full speed. With an induction motor, the startup is usually so rapid that you can't get good data (a tape recorder can help here); during coastdown, the speed usually changes more slowly, which results in better data. For that reason, power to the motor was cut, and data was taken during the coastdown.

1X, compensated polar plots of the shutdown are shown in Figure 26-2. The bottom row shows shaft relative vibration for all four fan transducers. The top row shows casing vibration, integrated to displacement, for the associated velocity transducers. The approximately 180° phase change in the velocity data is due to the *transducer* resonance at its rated frequency and does not accurately reflect casing vibration. Given the probable transducer phase error at running speed, better estimates of amplitude and phase values are indicated by the blue dots.

The two sets of polar plots show that, for each transducer location, the shaft relative and casing vibration are about the same amplitude; the (adjusted) relative phase shows that they are within 90° of each other. Thus, the two vibrations will add in a way that produces a very high shaft absolute vibration. The high level of 1X vibration suggests a large amount of unbalance.

The First Balancing Attempt

Ideally, given the large amount of casing vibration present, it might have been best to use shaft absolute vibration for balancing. However, there was significant phase error associated with the velocity data; also, the casing vibration was approximately in phase with the shaft relative vibration. For these reasons, the specialist decided to use the shaft relative data for balancing purposes.

Since the shaft relative vibration amplitudes from the X transducers were higher than from the Y transducers, the specialist decided to use the 1X, compensated X data for balancing the fan. The original vibration vectors, $\boldsymbol{O}$, measured at running speed, were:

$$\boldsymbol{O}_{3X} = 13.0 \text{ mil pp } \angle 259° \ (330 \text{ μm pp } \angle 259°)$$
$$\boldsymbol{O}_{4X} = 14.8 \text{ mil pp } \angle 282° \ (376 \text{ μm pp } \angle 282°)$$

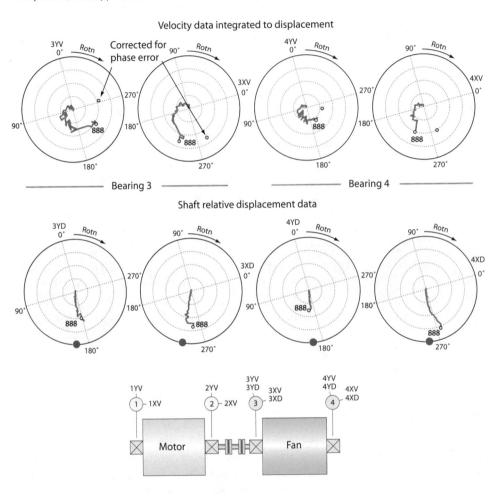

Figure 26-2. Original shutdown data for the fan. The bottom row shows shaft relative vibration for all four fan transducers. The top row shows velocity data, integrated to displacement, from the associated velocity transducers. The blue dots show better estimates for the running speed vibration vectors, compensating for the probable velocity transducer phase error. The two sets of polar plots show that, for each transducer location, the shaft relative and casing vibration at running speed are approximately in phase and about the same amplitude. The heavy spots indicated by the displacement data are shown as red dots.

The behavior of the shaft relative data suggests that the fan was operating below the first balance resonance. This made location of the heavy spot a relatively simple task, and the estimated heavy spot locations are shown as red dots on the shaft relative polar plots. The indicated heavy spot direction suggested adding weight approximately opposite the vibration readings, at 60° to 90° relative to the X transducers. Based on previous experience with this kind of machine and the large amount of unbalance present, the specialist decided to add a calibration weight, $m_{cal} = 12$ oz $\angle75°$ (340 g $\angle75°$). At this location, the weight would be opposite the indicated heavy spot and would likely reduce the unbalance. At the same time, it would serve as a calibration weight for calculating influence vectors. The weight was installed at a location close to the midspan and near the outer perimeter of the fan. Thus, the radius of attachment was nearly the fan radius, about 7.5 ft (2.3 m). A weight at this radius would produce a force of 1500 lb (6.7 kN) at running speed and affect both measurement planes nearly equally. The fan was restarted, and a new set of coastdown data was obtained.

The results were very surprising (Figure 26-3, top row). The vibration should have decreased; instead, the vibration actually *increased*, and the indicated heavy spot location moved only about 40° in the direction of rotation. The situation is summarized in the middle row of Figure 26-3. The new vibration vectors, T, represent the total response of the fan to the original unbalance and the calibration weight:

$$T_{3X} = 27.0 \text{ mil pp } \angle213° \text{ (686 µm pp } \angle213°)$$
$$T_{4X} = 27.8 \text{ mil pp } \angle229° \text{ (706 µm pp } \angle229°)$$

The calibration weight produced a change in the vibration, $C = T - O$, of

$$C_{3X} = 20.3 \text{ mil pp } \angle186° \text{ (516 µm pp } \angle186°)$$
$$C_{4X} = 22.3 \text{ mil pp } \angle197° \text{ (566 µm pp } \angle197°)$$

Since the fan was operating below the first balance resonance, the change in vibration should have been toward m_{cal}, not away from it.

The influence vector, H, can be calculated using this equation (from Chapter 16):

$$H = \frac{C}{m_{cal}} \qquad (26\text{-}1)$$

This yields

$$H_{3X} = 1.69 \text{ mil pp/oz } \angle 111° \ (1.52 \text{ μm pp/g } \angle 111°)$$
$$H_{4X} = 1.86 \text{ mil pp/oz } \angle 122° \ (1.66 \text{ μm pp/g } \angle 122°)$$

The phase of an influence vector is directly related to the heavy spot/high spot relationship in the rotor system. If a machine was operating well below the resonance, as the shutdown data had been suggesting, then the influence vector phase should have been closer to 0°. The influence vectors for both measurement planes are very similar, *but the phase angle suggests operation slightly above the resonance*. This was the first sign that something was not happening as expected. The specialist rechecked his calculations and obtained the same result. He decided to continue and calculate a balance solution for the next run:

$$m = \frac{-O}{H} \qquad (26\text{-}2)$$

Figure 26-3. Results of the first calibration run. At top are the polar plots from the fan's two *X* shaft relative probes. The original run is shown in green. A 12 oz calibration weight was added to the fan at 75° relative to the *X* probes. The next shutdown is shown in blue. The middle pair of plots show the graphical construction for 890 rpm, using the vector values from the polar plots above. The *C* vector shows the change in vibration from the first run to the second. The bottom row shows the graphical balance solution. The calibration weight is modified and rotated to produce −*O*.

1X compensated, 20 mil pp full scale

Figure 26-3

Figure 26-3

Bearing 3

Bearing 4

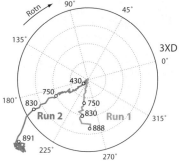

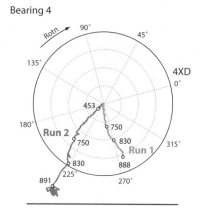

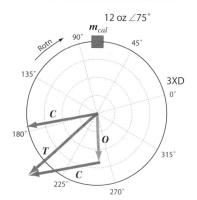

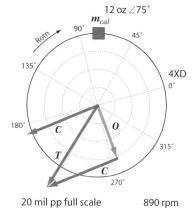

20 mil pp full scale   890 rpm

20 mil pp full scale   890 rpm

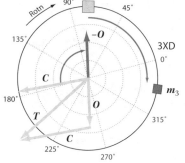

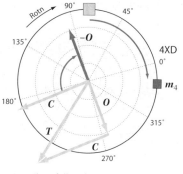

20 mil pp full scale   890 rpm

20 mil pp full scale   890 rpm

When he did this for each measurement plane, he obtained

$$m_3 = 7.7 \text{ oz } \angle 328° \text{ (220 g } \angle 328°)$$
$$m_4 = 8.0 \text{ oz } \angle 340° \text{ (230 g } \angle 340°)$$

The two calculated solutions show good agreement with each other. The graphical balance solution is shown in the bottom row of Figure 26-3. The calibration weight was rotated and reduced in size until the new response was equal to $-O$. There is a small discrepancy between the calculated values in the text and the indicated graphical solution. The calculation uses values that were obtained from the instrumentation when the fan was running at steady state. The graphical solution was derived from the polar plot vectors that were obtained during the shutdown; the vibration data was slightly different.

The calibration weight was removed, and $m = 8.4 \text{ oz } \angle 332°$ was installed in the fan. This weight and location were the closest available to the calculated solution. This weight installation should have resulted in a dramatic reduction of the unbalance response. The fan was restarted and a new set of vibration vectors was measured as

$$T_{3X} = 12.8 \text{ mil pp } \angle 247° \text{ (325 µm pp } \angle 247°)$$
$$T_{4X} = 13.9 \text{ mil pp } \angle 268° \text{ (353 µm pp } \angle 268°)$$

While lower, these responses were not even close to the values that should have been seen based on the balance solution. This was not a simple unbalance problem; as the influence vectors had suggested, something else was wrong with this machine.

The Real Problem

Knowing the past balancing difficulty with this fan and having had a similar experience with an induced draft fan at a coal mine, the specialist wondered if dust or dirt was trapped in the interior of the fan hub. The dirt would form a heavy spot that could shift every time the fan was shut down.

He planned a simple test to determine if this was the cause of the problem. The fan would be started from a resting position 180° from the last starting point. This point was known because of the installation of the balancing weight. If the vibration was the same after starting from a different position, then dirt was probably not the problem. If, however, there was a significant change, this would indicate that dirt might be shifting and affecting the balance state of the fan.

Power was cut to the fan motor, and the fan coasted down. When the fan reached 10 rpm, maintenance personnel removed the access cover. As the fan continued to slow, a cloud of dust appeared every time the fan passed a certain point. The specialist knew he was on the right track.

Further investigation revealed that an open area surrounding the anchor bolts let dust into the hub of the fan. Every time the fan was shut down, the dirt would shift to a different position in the hub and change the unbalance. To solve the problem, two holes were cut at the outer diameter of the hub, and the contaminating dirt was blown out with compressed air. After cleaning, all of the holes were sealed, and the balancing procedure was repeated.

After two balancing runs, the 1X vibration was reduced to less than 1.5 mil pp (38 μm pp). Table 26-1 shows the measurements, weights, and influence vectors for the fan. Note that the phases of the influence vectors were now consistent with what would be expected for a machine operating below the resonance.

Table 26-1. ID Fan 1 balancing data after cleaning and sealing. The final balancing weight was 38 oz ∠6° (1.1 kg ∠6°).

Probe location	*O*	*H*	**Final vibration**
3XD	22.0 mil pp ∠229° 559 μm pp ∠229°	0.56 mil pp/oz ∠46° 0.50 μm pp/g ∠46°	1.4 mil pp ∠169° 36 μm pp ∠169°
4XD	22.4 mil pp ∠248° 569 μm pp ∠248°	0.60 mil pp/oz ∠63° 0.54 μm pp/g ∠63°	0.8 mil pp ∠114° 20 μm pp ∠114°

The process was successfully repeated with the other two fans, which suffered the same problem. All of the fans were running more than two years later with no unbalance problem or interruption in service.

The root cause of the problem was dirt that was trapped in the hub of the fan. When the fan stopped rotating, the dirt would settle to the bottom of the approximately 5 ft (1.5 m) radius hub. When the fan was started, the dirt would be held in position by centrifugal force. This caused the fan to have an ever changing source of unbalance. Repeated balancing of this machine had not and would never have solved the problem. Whenever a machine fails to respond as expected to repeated balancing attempts, there are two possibilities: the method being used is incorrect, or there is another problem in the machine that must be discovered.

Chapter 27

A Generator Vibration Puzzle

Bently nevada machinery specialists traveled to a power plant to document the startup of a steam turbine generator set following a rotor overhaul. They were asked to document the vibration response characteristics during startup, load tests, and shutdown. They were also asked to review the dynamic data and evaluate the current mechanical condition of the unit based on the vibration measurements.

The machinery specialists arrived at the site and set up their computer-based data acquisition equipment. The machine was a 150 MW, 3600 rpm, steam turbine generator in a tandem-compound, double flow configuration (Figure 27-1). The opposed flow HP/IP turbine was connected to a single, dual flow LP unit and a generator. The generator was connected to an 897 rpm exciter through a flexible coupling and gearbox. The turbine and generator bearings (1 through 6) were instrumented with *XY* proximity probes. The gearbox and exciter bearings were not instrumented. Table 27-1 shows the machine train parameters.

The existing Keyphasor probe observed a split hub on the machine. This arrangement made it difficult to obtain a reliable, once-per-turn signal because the transducer picked up the split line on both sides of the hub as well as the Keyphasor slot. This arrangement caused problems with the Keyphasor signal, which resulted in a partial loss of startup data.

During the startup, the unit was brought up to a speed of 2300 rpm and maintained near that speed for a five hour heat soak. After the heat soak, the unit was brought up to full speed and run at no load for the next twelve hours. During the startup, machine behavior was normal, with direct vibration reaching a maximum of around 3.6 mil pp (90 µm pp) at bearing 4.

Figure 27-1. Machine train diagram. The rigidly coupled HP/IP and dual flow LP steam turbines drive a 150 MW, 60 Hz generator. Rotation is *Y* to *X* (CW).

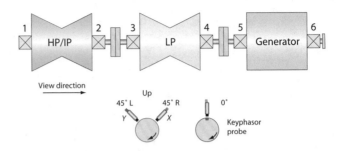

Table 27-1. Machine train operating parameters.

Steam Turbines

Power	150 MW
Speed	3600 rpm
Inlet press.	100 bar (1450 psig)
Inlet temp.	540 °C (1000 °F)
Reheat temp.	540 °C (1000 °F)
Exhaust press.	64 mm Hg abs (2.5 in Hg abs)

Generator

Apparent power	183 824 kVA
Power	156 250 kW
Voltage	18 000 V
Current	5896 A
Power factor	0.85
Frequency	60 Hz
Hydrogen press.	3 bar (45 psig)

Exciter

Power	980 kW
Voltage	375 V
Current	2615 A
Speed	897 rpm

Unusual Vibration Behavior

The next morning, the machinery specialists prepared to take load test data. After starting data acquisition, they noticed that the vibration in bearing 5, the generator inboard bearing, was acting strangely. Immediately after startup, the 1X vibration measured by the X transducer at bearing 5 had been 1.4 mil pp $\angle 238°$ (36 µm pp $\angle 238°$). Now the vibration amplitude was slowly changing, alternating between 3.5 and 0.8 mil pp (90 and 20 µm pp). The vibration amplitude changed from high to low and back to high, completing a cycle in about 2 hours (Figure 27-2). Direct orbits from bearing 5 showed that, when the amplitude was highest, the vibration was predominantly 1X.

Figure 27-2. Modulation of vibration amplitude. The vibration at bearing 5 slowly changes in amplitude, alternating between 3.5 and 0.8 mil pp (90 and 20 µm pp), completing a cycle in about 2 hours. Direct, uncompensated orbits from bearing 5 show that, when the amplitude is highest, the vibration is predominantly 1X.

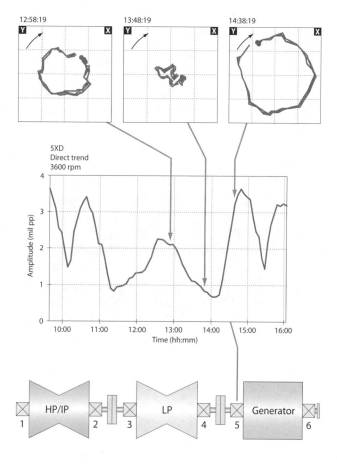

This vibration was studied for the next 6 hours by plant operators, OEM representatives, and the Bently Nevada specialists. During this period, the OEM representatives decided to change the oil temperature and pressure in the generator hydrogen seal to see if that would eliminate or reduce the vibration. Nothing worked, and the vibration continued its slow cycling.

The vibration behavior was puzzling, but, since the amplitudes were not high enough to constitute an immediate problem, plant operators decided to proceed with the load tests. The machinery specialists prepared to take more data during the load test and shutdown. Perhaps the changing load would shed some light on the problem.

Over a 4 hour period, operators increased the load to 151 MW. During this time, the periodically changing vibration continued in much the same way, with no significant relationship to load. Then operators shed the load on the generator and shut the machine down while the machinery specialists captured transient data.

Data Analysis

1X polar plots of data taken during the load tests showed that the vibration vectors at the LP turbine and generator bearings were very slowly rotating in a *forward* direction (Figure 27-3), with a period of over an hour. The largest changes occurred at generator bearing 5. (Changes in vibration in the HP/IP bearings were due to load changes and were not periodic.) The 1X orbits from the generator and LP turbine confirmed the polar plot data.

The Bently Nevada machinery specialists were puzzled. The 1X vibration vectors changed by moving in a forward direction. This was unusual; a loose rotating part will rotate more slowly than the rotor and produce a 1X vibration change in the lag direction (Chapter 21).

It was proposed that the observed behavior on the data plots was actually *reverse*, but appeared to be forward because of sample aliasing. Aliasing occurs when twice the sampling period is more than the period of the phenomenon being measured. Before the load test, the sample period was 5 minutes and, during the load test, 9 minutes. If the vibration completed a full change in less than 10 minutes (2 x 5 minutes), it is possible that a reverse moving vector would appear as a forward moving vector in both data sets, much the same as a movie of a rotating wagon wheel can make the spokes appear to move backwards.

However, other data confirmed the forward nature of the vibration change. The last two samples in the database were taken 30 seconds apart and showed a phase change of 1 degree *forward*. While limited by poor resolution, this phase change provided an estimate of 3 hours per cycle of vibration change, confirming the observed long cycle time. Separate instrumentation also confirmed the

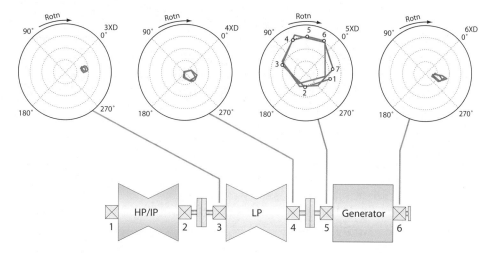

Figure 27-3. Steady state operation with changing 1X vibration. Polar APHT plots show approximately 2 hours of vibration data at 3600 rpm, sampled 9 minutes apart. The first 7 samples for bearing 5 are numbered and show that the 1X vibration vector rotates in a forward direction, completing 1 revolution in about 1 hour. The largest change in vibration amplitude occurs at bearing 5, but all four bearings show changes in vibration.

observation of forward movement. An oscilloscope and a tape recorder used during the data acquisition process provided continuous data that supported the periodically sampled data.

A 1X rub at the location of the rotor high spot can produce a phase change. The rub causes local heating and a thermal bow, which produces a new, effective heavy spot, shifting the high spot response. The simple rotor model of Chapter 10 predicts that the high spot will lag the heavy spot by between 0° and 180°, depending on where the rotor speed is relative to the resonance. For this model, a thermal bow in the direction of the high spot (which lags the heavy spot) will produce a phase change in the *lagging* direction (see Chapter 19). However, to explain the observed *leading* phase change, the high spot would have to lag the heavy spot by more than 180° (or lead the heavy spot by less than 180°), behavior that the simple model cannot support. A different explanation was needed.

While the cause of the forward moving vector was puzzling, the most likely cause of the periodic vibration seemed to be a rub. More data would be needed to support this theory.

The machinery specialists decided to look at the startup and shutdown generator data for clues. Unfortunately, during the startup, a problem with the Keyphasor signal caused a loss of part of the startup data. Also, during shutdown, the maximum number of samples was reached at 880 rpm, cutting off data below that speed. This prevented acquisition of hot slow roll vectors that could have been used for compensation of the shutdown data.

The machinery specialists decided to use the cold slow roll vectors from the startup data to compensate the hot shutdown data. This was done cautiously, because they did not know if thermal growth had caused the slow roll vectors to change. The two sets of compensated data are plotted with the same amplitude and speed scales in Figure 27-4. The results were surprising. The startup data (blue) was very different from the shutdown data (red). In the figure, the data from the X probe at bearing 5 is shown, but data from the other generator probes showed similar differences in behavior.

The shutdown data showed a clear resonance near 1400 rpm. The startup showed a very different picture; there was no clearly defined resonance below 2400 rpm, the speed where the data was cut off, and the amplitude and phase lag increased steadily. The data suggested that a balance resonance existed somewhere near 2400 rpm.

The startup and shutdown phase changes have a similar overall pattern, but the pattern during startup appears to be shifted to a higher frequency. Also, the shutdown phase lag is shifted by about 120° (compare left and right scales), indicating that a significant change in the location of the heavy spot has taken place.

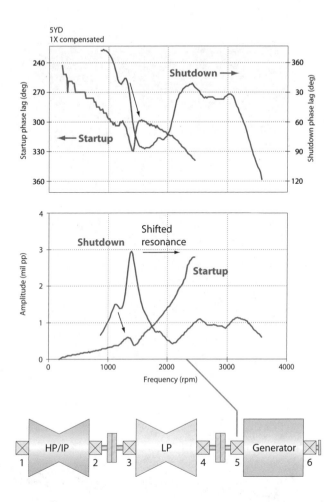

Figure 27-4. Startup and shutdown data for bearing 5. The shutdown data (red) shows a clear resonance at the inboard end of the generator at 1400 rpm. The startup shows a very different picture, with no clearly defined resonance below 2400 rpm. The startup (blue) data suggests that a balance resonance exists somewhere near 2400 rpm, indicating the presence of a rub during the startup. The phase data shows very different behavior, with the phase shifted nearly 120° between startup (left scale) and shutdown (right scale).

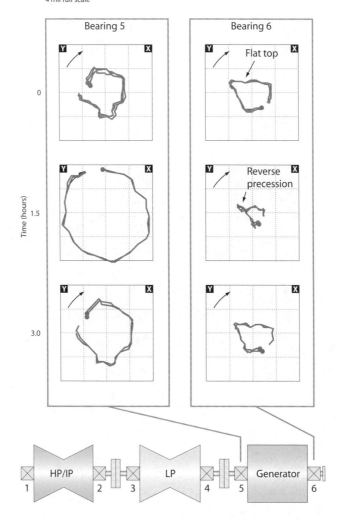

All orbits direct, uncompensated
3600 rpm
4 mil full scale

Figure 27-5. Orbit changes during steady state operation. Direct, uncompensated orbits for bearings 5 and 6 show modulation of vibration amplitude and phase. The bearing 6 orbit (top right) has a flat top that suggests a constraint. After a period of 1 1/2 hours (middle row), the bearing 5 orbit is large and circular, while the bearing 6 orbit shows evidence of partial reverse precession. After 3 hours have passed, the behavior is similar to that at the beginning.

The data from both generator bearings was very similar and strongly suggested the presence of a rub during the startup. A rub, by constraining the motion of the rotor, will increase the spring stiffness of the rotor system and move the resonance to a higher speed. The data clearly supports the rub diagnosis. Evidently, the rub was reduced or eliminated just before the final shutdown, allowing the resonance to return to 1400 rpm. The change in phase also suggests a thermally induced bow that modified the effective heavy spot.

Even more interesting was the pattern of the direct orbits at bearings 5 and 6 during the vibration cycling (Figure 27-5). When the orbit at bearing 5 was relatively small, the orbit at bearing 6 was larger and more open; when the orbit at bearing 5 was largest, the orbit at bearing 6 was small and had a sharp corner at the upper left with a small amount of reverse precession. The reverse precession at bearing 6 was highly suggestive of a rub; the friction at the rub contact acts to briefly accelerate the rotor in a direction opposite to rotation (see Chapter 21).

Overall, the data seemed to clearly support the diagnosis of a rub. But how could the specialists explain the forward movement of the vibration vector? They knew that rotor systems with multiple modes exhibit much more complicated behavior than can described by the simple model. The mixture of multiple mode responses and bow can cause the high spot response vector to have any phase, depending on the dynamic conditions.

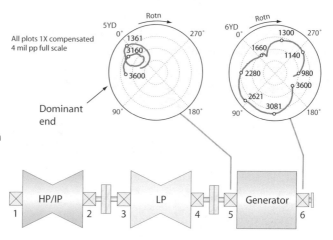

Figure 27-6. Shutdown data for both generator bearings. The generator operates above the second mode, and bearing 5 is the dominant end of the machine, as shown by the nested polar loops. At running speed, the high spot location leads the indicated first mode heavy spot. See also the bearing 5 shutdown data in Figure 27-4.

They proposed this explanation: most large generators operate above the second mode. A generator with a *dominant end*, where the first and second mode heavy spots are in the same quadrant, could produce a high spot response that lags the indicated heavy spots by more than 180°. If this were to happen, a rub-induced thermal bow could produce a new heavy spot that would shift *both* modal heavy spots in the forward direction. The magnitude of the new vibration vector would depend on the relative magnitudes of the original heavy spots and the bow. In this scenario, a forward rotating response vector would be possible.

Polar plots of the shutdown (Figure 27-6) revealed that the generator was operating above the second mode, that bearing 5 was the dominant end of the machine, and that, at running speed, the high spot location was leading the indicated first mode heavy spot. This information supported the theory.

Conclusions

All the data clearly suggested to the machinery specialists that a rub occurred in the generator, near bearing 5. The most likely location for such a rub would be the carbon ring of the hydrogen seal, which could have been installed incorrectly, resulting in an internal misalignment between the ring and the shaft. Even though the seal was lubricated, direct contact between the shaft and the carbon ring could produce high friction in the area of the rub. The shutdown data suggested that the rub had opened up the clearance, which eliminated the rub, sometime before the shutdown.

The forward-moving, 1X vibration vector was most likely caused by rub-induced local heating of the surface of the generator rotor, which was operating above the second resonance.

After the machine was restarted, the unusual vibration behavior reappeared, but later disappeared without any further action. Most likely, the rub worked itself out as it increased the seal clearance.

Chapter 28

High Vibration in an Electric Motor

Operators of a synchronous-motor-driven, syngas compressor had been experiencing episodes of high vibration on the motor. Occasionally, the vibration would suddenly become high enough that the unit would trip. The lost production, and concerns about the health of the machine train, prompted the plant operators to ask Bently Nevada to obtain vibration data and help diagnose the problem with the machine.

When the Bently Nevada machinery specialist arrived at the plant, the machine was operating. The machine train (Figure 28-1) consisted of a 10 000 hp (7450 kW), 1800 rpm, synchronous motor driving a syngas barrel compressor at 4459 rpm through a speed-increasing gearbox, using flexible couplings. Fortunately, the machine train was well instrumented: *XY* proximity probes were installed at all eight fluid-film bearings, and Keyphasor probes observed both the low- and high-speed rotors. Table 28-1 lists the nameplate data for this machine train.

The operators told the machinery specialist that the unit had been experiencing sporadic periods of high vibration in the motor bearings, with the highest on bearing 2. During the episodes of high vibration, vibration in the gearbox and compressor remained normal. Occasionally, the motor vibration would become so high that the unit would trip. After trips, while at slow roll speed, the monitors would show high vibration readings from bearing 2. The specialist asked whether the vibration was correlated with any changes in process conditions, but the operators had not noticed if this was the case.

The machinery specialist set up his equipment and prepared to take data. At the start of data acquisition, the specialist noted that the direct vibration was about 2 mil pp (50 µm pp) on bearing 1 and a little over 3 mil pp (75 µm pp) on

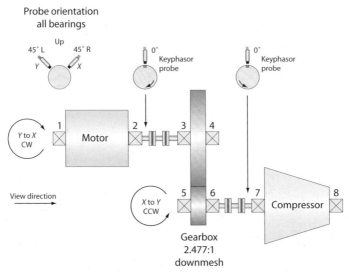

Figure 28-1. Machine train diagram. A 10 000 hp (7450 kW), 1800 rpm, synchronous motor drives a 4459 rpm syngas barrel compressor through a speed-increasing gearbox and flexible couplings. Shaft relative proximity probes are installed at all eight fluid-film bearings, and Keyphasor probes observe both the low- and high-speed rotors.

Table 28-1. Machinery nameplate data.

Synchronous motor		Compressor	
Poles	4	Gas	Synthetic gas
Speed	1800 rpm	Mole weight	15.94
Voltage	13 200 V		
Current	370 A	**Rated conditions**	
Apparent power	8460 kVA	Inlet pressure	21.3 bar (309 psi)
Power factor	0.90	Inlet temperature	536 °F (280 °C)
Power	10 200 hp (7614 kW)	Volume	23 900 acfm
Service factor	1.0		(678 m³/min)
		Discharge pressure	367 psi (25.3 bar)
Gearbox		Max. cont. speed	4680 rpm
Input speed	1800 rpm	1st critical	2400 rpm
Output speed	4459 rpm		
Ratio	2.4771		
Service power	8500 hp		
Service factor	1.4		

bearing 2. After a period of time, the vibration in both motor bearings started to rise; at bearing 2 it suddenly increased to 9 mil pp (230 µm pp), and the machine tripped. The specialist continued to capture data during the coastdown.

Data Analysis

The trend plot of direct vibration at the motor bearings, starting about 10 minutes before trip, is shown in Figure 28-2, along with selected orbits. The motor vibration was steady for most of the data collection period, but started increasing dramatically about 4 minutes before the trip. The gearbox and compressor data did not show any increase in vibration.

Both motor bearings appeared to be heavily loaded; the first set of direct orbits were flattened on top, showing clear evidence of constrained rotor motion. Both orbits showed reverse precession.

Bearing 1 orbits (blue) maintained approximately the same shape from the start of the data until 01:12:45, just before the trip, at which time the orbit became significantly distorted, approaching a figure eight shape. After the trip, the orbit became banana shaped and switched to forward precession below 1400 rpm.

Orbits from bearing 2 also showed evidence of a large radial load. A small external loop developed by 1:09:17. By 1:12:45, just seconds before the trip, an external loop had developed in the bottom of the orbit, which had significantly higher amplitude. Precession switched to forward at this time. Direct vibration at bearing 2 approached 9 mil pp (230 µm pp) just before the trip, probably close to the available bearing clearance.

The direct orbits at the moment of trip are shown for the entire machine train in Figure 28-3. It was clear that the vibration problem was in the motor; the gearbox and compressor bearings showed very little vibration.

The 1X APHT plots (Figure 28-4) showed significant changes in 1X vectors at the motor bearings before the trip; the 1X vector movement was much larger on bearing 2. APHT plots for other bearings in the machine train showed no change in the 1X vectors during this period.

The shaft centerline plots for the motor also showed evidence of a rub. As vibration amplitude increased, the shaft centerlines at both bearings shifted up and to the right by nearly a mil (25 µm), with more vertical change occurring in bearing 2.

The shaft centerline position in the motor showed more unusual behavior during the shutdown (Figure 28-5). The centerline positions in both bearings initially moved down to the left; this is not the behavior one would expect from fluid-film bearings with Y to X shaft rotation. Below about 700 rpm, the shaft centerline behavior appeared normal until the speed reached about 70 rpm, the

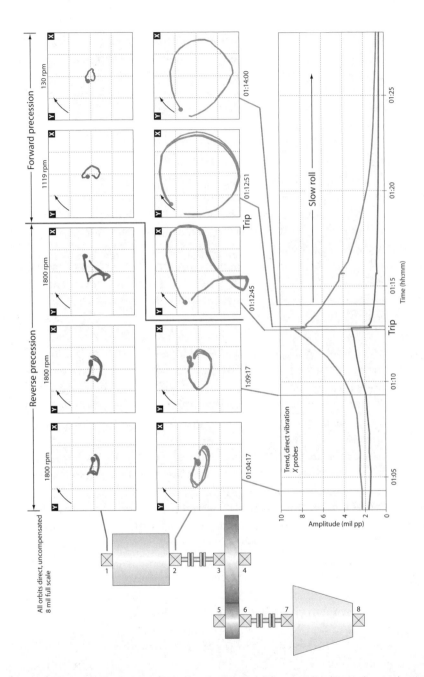

Figure 28-2. Direct vibration trend plots and orbits for the motor. Bearing 1 data is shown in blue; bearing 2 in green. See the text for a full description.

All orbits direct, uncompensated
8 mil full scale

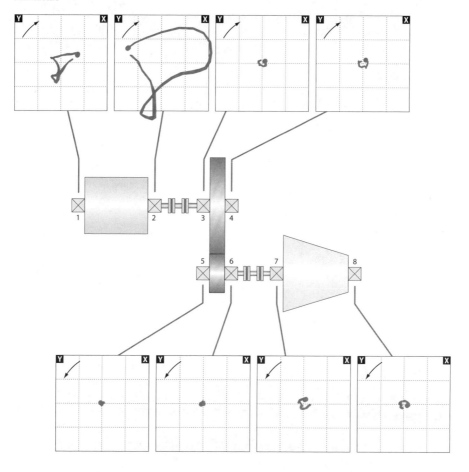

Figure 28-3. Direct, uncompensated orbits along the machine train just before the trip. It is clear that the vibration problem is in the motor; the gearbox and compressor bearings show very little vibration.

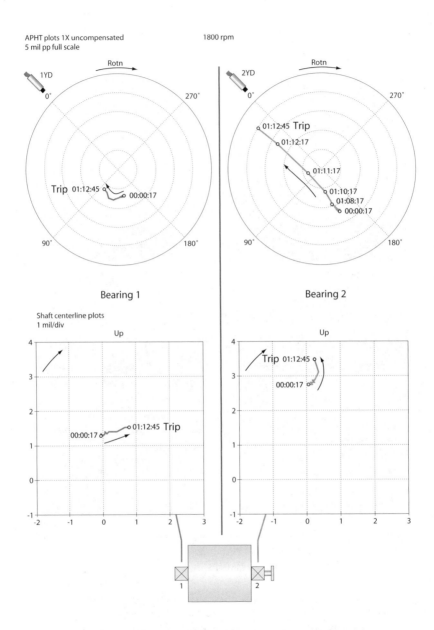

Figure 28-4. Motor bearing APHT and shaft centerline plots at 1800 rpm. The arrows indicate the direction of change during this period. There are significant changes in 1X vectors, especially at bearing 2. As vibration amplitude increases, the shaft centerline at bearing 2 shifts up and to the right by nearly a mil (25 μm) and slightly more at bearing 1.

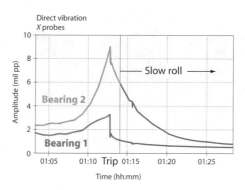

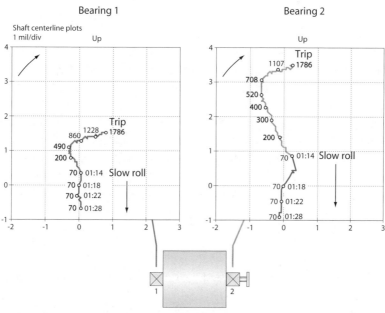

Figure 28-5. Motor bearing shaft centerline position during shutdown. The centerline positions both initially move down to the left. Below around 700 rpm, shaft centerline behavior appears normal until about 70 rpm, the slow roll speed. Once on slow roll, the shaft continues to move down about one mil (25 μm) in bearing 1 and almost two mils (50 μm) in bearing 2 over the next 15 minutes. During this period, the direct vibration trend plot (top) shows that the shaft slow roll vibration at bearing 2, which is mostly 1X, decreases from 5.6 mil pp (140 μm pp) to 0.8 mil pp (20 μm pp).

slow roll speed. Once on slow roll, over the next 15 minutes *the shaft continued to move down* another mil (25 μm) in bearing 1 and almost two mils (50 μm) in bearing 2. During this period, as shown in the accompanying trend plot, the shaft vibration in bearing 2, which was mostly 1X, decreased from 5.6 mil pp (140 μm pp) to 0.8 mil pp (20 μm pp).

Diagnosis

At this point, it was clear to the specialist that there was a problem in the motor, most likely near bearing 2. The direct orbits clearly suggested that a rub was taking place. The large change in the 1X vector during steady state operation could be explained by the development of a thermal bow. This would be consistent with a 1X rub; the heating at the rub contact point would cause local thermal expansion of the shaft and rotor bow. As the rotor heated during the rub, the large unbalance that was created changed the 1X vibration.

The bow produced a large, mostly 1X runout at slow roll speed. As the rotor cooled while on slow roll, the thermal bow slowly disappeared over a 15 minute period, leaving a residual runout of less than 0.8 mil pp (20 μm pp). This explained the operators' observation regarding high vibration immediately after shutdown.

Why and where did the rub occur? Virtually no unusual vibration appeared in either the gearbox or the compressor. Whatever happened had to be associated with the motor. One possibility was an internal misalignment of the dust or oil seals in the motor. Another possibility was an alignment problem that reduced the air gap, but this should have produced vibration at twice line frequency. No such vibration was evident.

The specialist recommended that a thorough inspection be performed on the motor. The inspection should include the motor bearings, and internal and external alignment checks, including all seals and the motor air gap. He also recommended that the motor shaft be checked at several axial locations for any signs of a permanent rotor bow.

The seal clearances were measured and found to be very uneven, with zero clearance on one side of the motor dust seal at bearing 1 (Table 28-2). Measurements indicated that this seal was positioned too low and too far to the right, resulting in a large clearance at the bottom and zero clearance at left. When technicians removed the seals, they found evidence of rub at both ends of the machine.

Based on this data, the machinery specialist developed a theory as to what happened. The zero clearance at the bearing 1 dust seal pointed toward that seal as the primary source of the problem. A heavy rub on the dust seal thermally bowed the rotor, causing the vibration at bearing 2 to increase, which eventually caused a rub on the bearing 2 oil seal. When this second rub occurred, vibration increased rapidly and tripped the machine. The thermal bow caused the high vibration at slow roll until the rotor cooled down.

After the seals were reassembled and clearances adjusted, the unit ran smoothly with no problems.

Table 28-2. Measured dust and oil seal clearances on the motor. Dimensions are in mils, and directions are as viewed from the motor looking toward the gearbox. Evidence of rub was found where noted. The clearances were set to the indicated values.

Dust seals

	Top	Right	Left	Bottom
Outboard	12	35	0 (rub)	96
Set to	20	20	20	20
Inboard	18	18	16	250
Set to	25	25	25	70

Bearing 1 oil seals

	Top	Right	Left	Bottom
Outboard	8	11	8	14
No changes	-	-	-	-
Motor side	15	13	15	13
No changes	-	-	-	-

Bearing 2 oil seals

	Top	Right	Left	Bottom
Motor side	5 (rub)	11	20	20
Set to	12	11	11	14
Coupling side	16	9	11	12
Set to (min)	11	11	11	11

Chapter 29

Problems with a Pipeline Compressor

A GAS PIPELINE OPERATOR IN SOUTH AMERICA had purchased a number of compressor packages for installation during expansion of the pipeline. Each package consisted of a gas turbine-driven compressor.

At several of the compressor stations, high vibration trips and/or high vibration alarms occurred during the startup test runs. Initial data acquired by field personnel at one station indicated the trips were due to the onset of high amplitude, subsynchronous vibration at both compressor bearings. If the machines did not trip, then the subsynchronous vibration would subside as the discharge pressure increased.

The pipeline operator asked Bently Nevada to acquire additional startup, shutdown, and steady state vibration data under various process conditions and to assist field personnel with identification of the root cause of the problem. A Bently Nevada machinery specialist traveled to the site to examine the compressor package.

The Machine Train

The machine train consisted of a 3200 kW (4300 hp), industrial gas turbine that was used as a gas generator. An overhung, aerodynamically coupled power turbine, rotating at around 15 000 rpm, drove the compressor through a flexible coupling (Figure 29-1).

The compressor was a modification to an older, 7-stage, single flow design; for the pipeline application, a compressor with comparable flow and half the head was needed. The modification replaced the center stage with a labyrinth seal and the final three wheels with the same wheels used in the first three stages. This produced two, 3-stage compressors on one shaft, supported by two

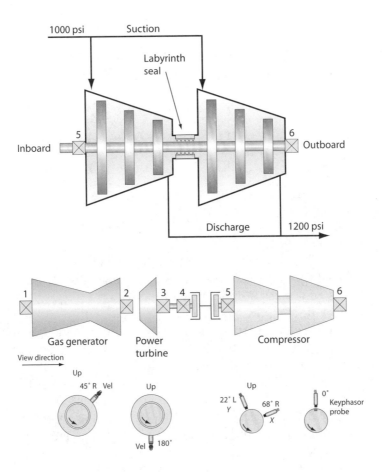

Figure 29-1. Gas turbine compressor train diagram. A 3200 kW (4300 hp), industrial gas turbine is used as a gas generator. An overhung, aerodynamically coupled power turbine drives the compressor at around 15 000 rpm through a flexible coupling. A seven-stage compressor was modified to produce two, three-stage compressors on one shaft, supported by two tilting pad bearings. The two compressors are operated in parallel with identical suction and discharge pressures. A midspan labyrinth seal separates the suction and discharge sides.

tilting pad bearings. The two compressors were operated in parallel, with identical suction and discharge pressures. The midspan labyrinth seal separated the discharge end of the first compressor from the suction end of the second compressor.

With this modification, the discharge pressure at rated load was 83 bar (1,200 psi) when the suction pressure was 70 bar (1,000 psi), for a pressure ratio of 1.2 and a differential pressure of 14 bar (200 psi).

The compressor was equipped with *XY* proximity probes on bearings 5 and 6 and with a Keyphasor probe, while the power turbine and gas generator each had a single velocity transducer mounted on the outer casing. The machinery specialist connected his data acquisition equipment to the buffered monitor outputs and prepared to take data.

The specialist was told that the compressor had floating ring seals at each end. The seals were designed for axially balanced thrust loading of the seal faces. The balanced design was intended to maintain a free floating seal so that it would not lock up and constrain the rotor. These seals also had an antirotation pin to prevent spinning. The pipeline operator suspected that the seals might be the source of the problem; perhaps the antirotation pins were causing the seals to lock up, or the seals were triggering a fluid-induced instability that was the source of the subsynchronous vibration.

The operators also suspected that the machine had insufficient damping, which was contributing to the instability problem. This last theory seemed improbable to the Bently Nevada specialist; fluid-induced instability problems usually have low sensitivity to damping and are primarily caused by circulating fluid trapped between the rotor and stator somewhere in the machine (see Chapter 22).

To discover the root cause of the vibration, the operators scheduled a series of tests based on different mechanical configurations of the compressor. The first series would be with the machine in its current configuration: pinned, balanced floating seals and the standard tilting pad bearings. Then, if the vibration problem still occurred, a second series of tests would use seals with a design that excluded the antirotation pin. The final series would use fluid-film bearings surrounded by a squeeze film damper to increase the damping in the machine. Because the vibration had been observed to disappear when the discharge pressure built up, each series of tests would include changing the suction or discharge pressures.

Tests With Pinned Seals

When the cold machine with pinned seals was started, intermittent low level subsynchronous vibration appeared in both compressor bearings starting at 10,300 rpm. As the machine reached 14,300 rpm, it reappeared and grew to high amplitude as the rotor speed increased to 14,700 rpm. The machine was shut down, and the data was analyzed.

Figure 29-2 shows a cascade plot for bearing 5 (bearing 6 data was similar) and unfiltered (direct) shaft orbits at 14,700 rpm for both bearings. The multiple Keyphasor dots indicate that the vibration was at a subsynchronous frequency well below running speed. Also, the orbit shapes were fairly circular.

The cascade plot shows several important features. First, relatively high amplitude, 1X forward vibration occurred between approximately 4,000 and 7,000 rpm. This suggested a balance resonance, which could be confirmed with Bode or polar plots. Second, the subsynchronous vibration began to appear at a little over 10,000 rpm and eventually grew in amplitude with increasing rotor speed. The frequency of this vibration was about 5,500 cpm, or 3,7% of the 14,700 rpm running speed, at approximately the same frequency as the earlier high 1X vibration. This strongly suggested that the subsynchronous vibration was associated with the compressor natural frequency. The subsynchronous vibration was almost purely forward; the reverse component at that frequency was very small.

The cascade plot also shows a low level, approximately ½X vibration that tracked running speed during the startup. While barely visible during the 1X resonance, it reappeared suddenly at just over 10,000 rpm, where it coincided with the rotor natural frequency and was amplified. At that speed, the machine acceleration suddenly increased when the gas generator fired up (the very rapid acceleration smeared and laterally displaced the 1X spectral data at this time). The frequency of this low level component could not be determined exactly due to the limited resolution of the spectrum, but it was clearly forward and tracking, suggesting a fluid-induced instability.

The 1X Bode plot (Figure 29-3) confirmed the resonance and revealed some additional, important information. The amplitude behavior was abnormal during the balance resonance between 5,000 and 6,600 rpm. The growth in amplitude was truncated and was followed by a sharp drop at 6,600 rpm. The phase change through the resonance was also abnormal: the phase slope became more gradual at 5,000 rpm and showed a sharp drop at 6,600 rpm. Finally, the phase plots from each bearing were almost identical, indicating that this resonance was an in-phase mode, most likely the first bending mode of the compressor rotor.

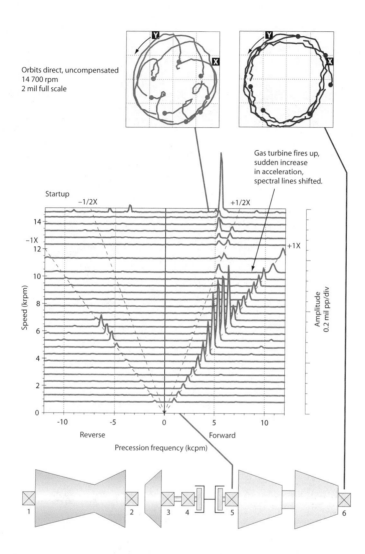

Figure 29-2. Cold startup data from bearing 5. The multiple Keyphasor dots on the 14,700 rpm orbits from bearings 5 and 6 indicate that the vibration is at a subsynchronous frequency well below running speed. The orbit shapes are fairly circular. On the full spectrum cascade plot, relatively high amplitude, 1X forward vibration occurs between approximately 4,000 and 7,000 rpm. A low level, approximately 1/2X, forward vibration tracks running speed during the startup. While barely visible during the 1X resonance, it reappears at just over 10,000 rpm when the gas turbine fires up, where it coincides with the rotor natural frequency and is amplified. Subsynchronous, forward vibration, locked to this frequency, continues intermittently until 14,300 rpm, then suddenly grows to high amplitude at 14,700 rpm.

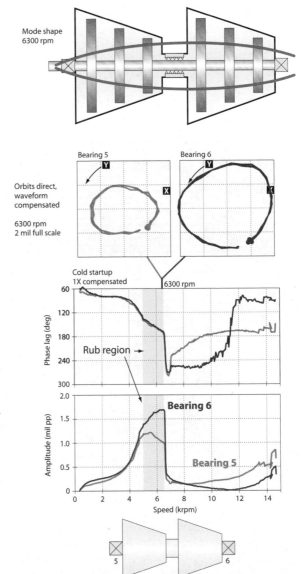

Figure 29-3. Compressor resonance behavior during the cold start with the original configuration. The 1X Bode plot shows an extended balance resonance region around 6000 rpm. The amplitude and phase behavior through the resonance are abnormal, indicating a probable rub. The 6300 rpm direct orbits are predominantly 1X and in phase, indicating that this is the first bending mode of the compressor rotor. Given the mode shape of the resonance, the highest 1X vibration amplitude during the resonance would occur at midspan (top); thus, it is most likely that the rub is occurring at the midspan labyrinth seal. The orbits show only mild distortion, indicating that the rub was probably not close to either bearing.

At this point, there was enough evidence to support a preliminary diagnosis. All of the data was consistent with fluid-induced instability as the source of the subsynchronous vibration at high speed: the vibration was forward, the frequency was not a simple integer ratio of running speed, and the vibration appeared suddenly at a frequency that appeared to be related to the resonance frequency. The instability did not track running speed; it appeared to lock onto the natural frequency of the rotor first bending mode, a characteristic of whip.

Also, the Bode plot amplitude and phase behavior during the resonance were classic symptoms of a 1X rub (see Chapter 21). Given the mode shape of the resonance, the highest 1X vibration amplitude during the resonance would occur at midspan; thus, it was most likely that the rub was occurring at either the midspan labyrinth seal or a nearby interstage seal. Direct orbits at both bearings (Figure 29-3) showed only mild distortion, indicating that the rub was probably not close to either bearing.

The problem now was to determine the location of the instability. The operators still suspected the floating seals. However, the machinery specialist had noted that the subsynchronous vibration due to the instability had appeared simultaneously at both compressor bearings. Also, the vibration amplitude, as shown by the direct orbits (Figure 29-2), had similar magnitudes at both bearings. Finally, the waveforms of the subsynchronous vibration (Figure 29-4) indicated an in-phase relationship for the subsynchronous vibration. This supported the cascade plot data and suggested that the vibration was associated with excitation of the first bending mode of the rotor. The data strongly suggested an

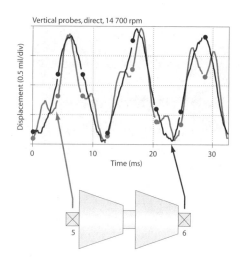

Figure 29-4. Waveforms of the subsynchronous vibration. Subsynchronous vibration, which is essentially in phase, dominates the direct (unfiltered) waveforms, supporting the idea that it is associated with the first bending mode of the rotor.

instability source near the rotor midspan, and the midspan labyrinth seal appeared to be the most likely location.

The operators continued with the series of tests. After restarting the machine, they changed the temperature of oil supplied to the radial bearings and the oil seals; this produced no improvement in stability.

During a hot coastdown following one of these test runs, it became evident that the compressor behavior had changed (Figure 29-5). The data on the Bode plot now appeared normal; there was no evidence of rub in either the amplitude, which now peaked at 4900 rpm, or the phase data. The vibration increase above 12 000 rpm suggested the presence of a second balance resonance somewhere above operating speed. The specialist calculated the Synchronous Amplification Factor (SAF) using the Half-power Bandwidth method as 5.2.

The frequency of the resonance peak at 4900 rpm was below the instability frequency of 5500 cpm, yet the specialist knew that fluid-induced instability is always associated with a natural frequency of the rotor system. The natural frequency, ω_n, is approximately

$$\omega_n = \sqrt{\frac{K}{M}} \tag{29-1}$$

where K is the rotor system spring stiffness and M is the rotor mass. It is unlikely that the rotor mass changed; the observed shift in natural frequency implied a change in K, where

$$\frac{\omega_{n2}}{\omega_{n1}} = \sqrt{\frac{K_2}{K_1}} \tag{29-2}$$

Thus, for the natural frequency to increase from 4900 cpm to 5500 cpm, K had to increase by a factor of

$$\frac{K_2}{K_1} = \left(\frac{\omega_{n2}}{\omega_{n1}}\right)^2 = \left(\frac{5500}{4900}\right)^2 = 1.26$$

What could produce a 26% increase in spring stiffness? One possibility was a higher dynamic eccentricity ratio in the bearings when the whip instability was present. However, the orbits during the instability were less than 2 mil pp. In this case it is more likely that, given the mode shape of the instability, the rotor was using most of the available clearance at midspan, perhaps even directly contacting the midspan labyrinth seal; an increase in stiffness at midspan would have the greatest potential to modify the natural frequency of the rotor first mode. Thus, the significant change in spring stiffness supported the possibility that the source of the instability was at the midspan seal.

The operators isolated the entire station from the pipeline and used the station surge control bypass piping to run the compressor in a closed loop. This provided the opportunity to control suction and discharge pressures independently by pinching the flow at various points in the loop. During these test runs, the unit tripped on high vibration at significantly different rotor speeds. The compressor appeared to have an instability threshold that varied with differential pressure and speed.

During one closed loop test with around 14 bar (200 psi) suction and 15 bar (220 psi) discharge pressures, the machine was able to reach 100% speed without experiencing any subsynchronous vibration. The machine seemed to run

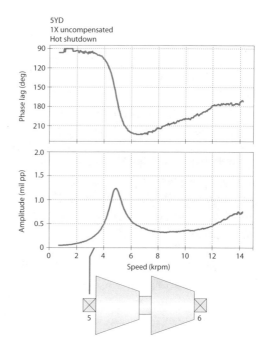

Figure 29-5. Bode plot of hot shutdown data from the bearing 5 vertical probe, original configuration. The 1X behavior now appears normal; the amplitude and phase show no evidence of a rub, and the resonance peak is at 4900 rpm. The vibration increase above 12 000 rpm suggests the presence of a second balance resonance somewhere above operating speed. The SAF, using the Half-power Bandwidth method, is 5.2.

fine at this low suction pressure. What would happen if suction pressure was increased while the machine kept running at full speed?

The operators increased suction pressure from 14 bar (200 psi) while the compressor ran at over 15,000 rpm in a closed loop. As suction pressure increased, discharge pressure approximately increased by the pressure ratio of 1.2, and differential pressure increased slowly. When the suction pressure reached 28 bar (410 psi), high subsynchronous vibration suddenly appeared, and the machine tripped (Figure 29-6).

During this test, the low level, ½X, forward vibration component again appeared. This component still showed evidence of tracking running speed as the machine tripped and began coasting down. A check of other transducer data showed that this component did not appear on any bearing 6 data, but it *did* appear in the power turbine casing vibration data. This suggested that the origin of this low level vibration was in the power turbine, not the compressor.

Tests With Unpinned Seals

The operators suspected that the floating ring seals were the source of the instability, so they replaced the seals with a different design. To eliminate the possibility that the antirotation pins were preventing free seal motion, the pins were not included in the new design. The replacement seals did not have as good a design for balanced axial loading of the seal faces, so there was still some risk that the seals might lock up.

The replacement seals did not correct the problem, but a hot coastdown showed that they may have stiffened the rotor system, shifting the location of the first balance resonance from 4,900 rpm to 5,000 rpm. Also, there no longer was evidence of a second balance resonance near running speed.

Several tests were performed with the unpinned seals at various suction and discharge pressures. Two startups were done with suction pressures of about 33 bar (475 psi). When the differential pressure was between 13 and 14 bar (190 and 200 psi), the Threshold of Instability was 14,800 rpm. When differential pressure was reduced to 13 bar (180 psi), the Threshold of Instability dropped to 14,100 rpm. This evidence suggested that stability was enhanced with higher differential pressure.

Tests With Damper Bearing

The operators still suspected that the instability was due to insufficient damping in the rotor system. To test this theory, they replaced bearing 5 with a special, squeeze-film-damped, fluid-film bearing, a bearing with two concentric oil films that was designed to provide additional damping.

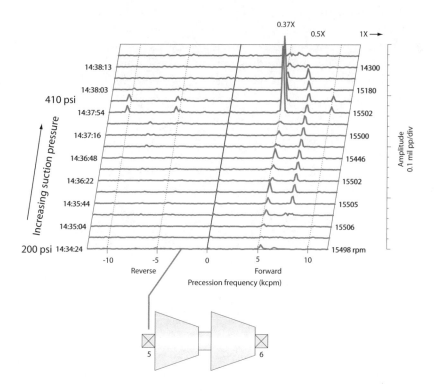

Figure 29-6. Full spectrum waterfall plot of closed loop tests with changing suction pressure, original configuration. While the compressor ran in a closed loop at over 15 000 rpm, the operators increased suction pressure from 14 bar (200 psi). As suction pressure increased, discharge pressure increased by a factor of approximately 1.2, slowly increasing the differential pressure. When the suction pressure reached 28 bar (410 psi), high amplitude, subsynchronous vibration suddenly appeared and tripped the machine. During this test, the low level, 1/2X forward vibration component again appeared.

During subsequent tests, the machine reached 98% of full speed at normal operating pressures without evidence of instability. Several runs were made, but the instability did not reappear. Hot shutdown data showed that the damper bearing had significantly altered the rotor system characteristics (Figure 29-7).

Two changes were immediately apparent in the data. First, the phase slope was more gradual than that shown in Figure 29-5. This indicated that the effective damping (actually, the Quadrature Dynamic Stiffness) of the rotor system had increased significantly; in fact, the SAF had been reduced from 5.2 to 2.5.

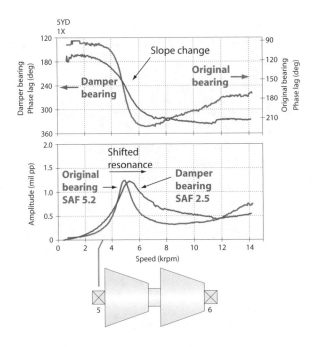

Figure 29-7. Comparison of hot shutdown data from original and damper bearing. Data from the original bearing (blue) is the same as in Figure 29-5. The damper bearing (red) has altered the rotor system characteristics: the phase slope is more gradual and the first balance resonance has moved from 4900 to 5300 rpm. These changes indicate that the Quadrature Dynamic Stiffness of the rotor system has increased significantly and that the damper bearing is stiffer than the original bearing.

Second, the first balance resonance had moved from 4900 to 5300 rpm. This indicated that damper bearing was stiffer than the original bearing.

Additional Analysis

The Bently Nevada machinery specialist reviewed what he had learned so far:

1. During the cold start test, low level, subsynchronous vibration appeared intermittently starting about 10 300 rpm, reappeared at 14 300 rpm, and grew to a very high level at 14 700 rpm.

2. Experience with the machine over a longer operating period showed that, at full speed, the subsynchronous vibration disappeared after discharge pressure built up.

3. During the cold startup, evidence of a rub appeared when the compressor passed through the first balance resonance, an in-phase bending mode. Given the mode shape, the rub most likely occurred on the midspan labyrinth seal.

4. The subsynchronous vibration was forward, it appeared suddenly and remained locked to the modified natural frequency, and the frequency was not a simple integer ratio of running speed.

5. The subsynchronous vibration was approximately the same amplitude at both bearings, and it was in phase, confirming excitation of the first bending mode.

6. Changes in bearing and seal oil temperature had little effect on the subsynchronous vibration at operating speed.

7. The instability frequency was higher than the hot shutdown resonance frequency, indicating a 26% stiffening of the rotor system when the instability was active.

8. During closed loop testing at low suction and discharge pressures, the machine was able to reach 100% speed without experiencing any subsynchronous vibration.

9. During the same test, at a constant speed over 15 000 rpm, the vibration appeared when the suction pressure was increased to 28 bar (410 psi).

10. New floating ring seals without antirotation pins had no significant effect on the instability.

11. When the suction pressure was increased to a moderate value of about 33 bar (475 psi), the higher differential pressure increased the Threshold of Instability (increased stability).

12. The damper bearing installed at bearing 5 increased system damping, reducing the SAF to 2.5. It also increased rotor system spring stiffness, moving the first balance resonance from 4900 to 5300 rpm. With this bearing, the compressor was stable at 98% of full speed and load.

What was the pattern in all this information? The damper bearing seemed to have solved the problem, at least temporarily, but the Bently Nevada specialist still suspected that the midspan seal was the real root cause of the problem. He realized that two things had been changed when the damper bearing was installed: damping and stiffness.

The specialist considered the equation for the Threshold of Instability, Ω_{th}, that was derived from the simple rotor model in Chapter 14:

$$\Omega_{th} = \frac{1}{\lambda}\sqrt{\frac{K}{M}} \tag{29-3}$$

where λ is the Fluid Circumferential Average Velocity Ratio and K and M are the rotor system spring stiffness and mass. This expression defines the speed at which the rotor system will begin the subsynchronous vibration associated with fluid-induced instability. At speeds below this value, the machine will be stable.

To stabilize the rotor system, Ω_{th} must be increased to some value above the maximum running speed of the machine. This could be done by increasing the rotor system natural frequency, usually by increasing K, or by reducing the fluid circulation in the midspan seal, λ, which he suspected was responsible for the instability.

There was a way to check if the increase in K due to the damper bearing was large enough to stabilize the machine. The specialist could estimate λ from the hot shutdown resonance speed of 4900 rpm and the observed cold startup Threshold of Instability of 14 300 rpm. Solving Equation 29-3 for λ,

$$\lambda = \frac{1}{\Omega_{th}}\sqrt{\frac{K}{M}} = \frac{1}{14\ 300\ \text{rpm}}\,4900\ \text{rpm} = 0.34$$

Now the specialist assumed that, after installation of the damper bearing, λ in the seal remained the same. This was reasonable; no changes were made to the seal during the damper bearing installation. Using Equation 29-3, the system should now have a Threshold of Instability of

$$\Omega_{th} = \frac{1}{\lambda}\sqrt{\frac{K}{M}} = \frac{1}{0.34}(5300\ \text{rpm}) = 15\ 600\ \text{rpm}$$

This speed was above the speeds that were reached during testing. It was quite possible that the beneficial effect of the damper bearing was due to the higher spring stiffness, K, of the bearing.

Could increasing the bearing damping have also improved stability? There is no damping term in Equation 29-3. This is a result of the rotor model that was used to derive the expression. However, Muszynska [1] originally developed a slightly more complex model than the one that was presented in Chapter 10. This expanded model includes the effects of damping, D, and a new damping term, the *system damping*, D_S. In the full model, the primary damping term, D, is associated with λ and Ω in the region where the destabilizing tangential force ($jD\lambda\Omega r$ in the model) originates. The system damping term, D_S, accounts for all other sources of damping forces in the system. (In this model, the *total* damping force becomes $-(D_S + D)\dot{r}$.)

In Muszynska's model, the Threshold of Instability is

$$\Omega_{th} = \left(1 + \frac{D_S}{D}\right)\frac{1}{\lambda}\sqrt{\frac{K}{M}} \tag{29-4}$$

In our rotor model of Chapters 10 and 14, we assumed that $D_S = 0$; applying that here, Equation 29-4 reduces to Equation 29-3.

To see the possible effect of the damper bearing, the specialist assumed that the source of the instability was in the midspan seal, where the parameters D and λ were presumed to exist. The damping in the rest of the compressor, including the bearings, was lumped into D_S. (The bearings were tilting pad designs, with inherently low λ by design. Although the oil control rings and the floating seal rings *were* potentially capable of producing a significant destabilizing tangential force, they were ignored for this qualitative analysis.) When the damper bearing was installed, D_S increased (he knew this from the change in SAF), and, according to Equation 28-4, Ω_{th} would also increase.

The question was how much? The sensitivity of Ω_{th} to changes in D_S depends on the relative sizes of the two damping terms. Without knowing the values of D and D_S, it was difficult to say how sensitive Ω_{th} was in this situation. The large change in SAF with the damper bearing argued for a large enough ratio of D_S/D to produce good sensitivity. It seemed safe to conclude that, because of the system damping increase, Ω_{th} was likely to be somewhere above 15 600 rpm. Thus, it is likely that the increased stiffness and damping of the new bearing both acted to stabilize the machine.

The damper bearing testing pointed toward a possible solution to the stability problems in these compressors, but the fix was a rather complex and expensive retrofit. The specialist still believed that the primary source of the instability was the seal, and the best solution should address the root cause of the problem.

There were still unsolved puzzles about the behavior of this machine. Why didn't the instability appear during the 14 bar (200 psi) closed loop tests? Why did it appear at moderate suction pressures, but improve with increasing differential pressure?

The answer to the first question might have to do with the density of the gas in the seal. At low pressures, the density would be relatively low, perhaps too low to develop destabilizing tangential forces. That would explain the stability of the machine at low pressures.

When suction pressure was increased, discharge pressure also increased, approximately by the pressure ratio of 1.2. Thus, the average pressure and density in the seal also increased. The higher density would increase the strength of the tangential force in the seal (most likely by increasing D) until it destabilized the machine. This would explain why the compressor was stable until it reached moderate suction pressure.

Another factor was the fluid circulation term, λ. The value of λ would depend partially on the internal geometry of the seal and partially on the axial flow rate of gas through the seal. As gas traversed the seal from the high-pressure side to the low-pressure side, the rotor would spin it up to some average circumferential velocity, $\lambda\Omega$. The value of λ would partially depend on the amount of time the gas remained in the seal.

Increasing differential pressure would reduce that time. With low differential pressure, the time would be relatively long, and λ would be relatively high. With high differential pressure, the gas would move through relatively fast, and λ would be lower. Lower λ would increase the Threshold of Instability, stabilizing the machine. This could be the reason why the compressors would stabilize when discharge pressure built up to maximum. The axial flow in the seal would reduce λ and increase the Threshold of Instability to above operating speed.

In addition to these pressure effects, the rub had probably opened up the seal clearance, increasing the axial flow. It was quite possible that, as the seal clearance opened up because of rubs, axial flow velocity through the seal region would increase, λ would drop, and compressor stability would be enhanced. There was no historical data showing whether the Threshold of Instability had increased over time, but it was quite possible that the numerous cold startups during the testing may have caused repeated seal rubs that altered the machine behavior during the course of the testing. The observed increase in the Threshold of Instability associated with the damper bearing may have been partially due to increased seal clearances.

Conclusions and Recommendations

The Bently Nevada machinery specialist concluded that the most likely source of the instability was the midspan labyrinth seal of the compressor. This conclusion was supported by the fact that the whip vibration was similar in amplitude and in phase at both ends. If the whip were occurring at either the bearing or floating seal, it would produce larger whip amplitudes at the nearest bearing.

This conclusion was also supported by the effect that changes in average pressure and pressure differential had on stability. Gas present in the seal was capable of affecting the rotor system spring stiffness, K, and seal damping, D. At low average pressures, the density of the gas in the seal area was too low to produce instability. Equation 29-4 shows that, if D were very small, then Ω_{th} would be high, resulting in a stable machine. Under this circumstance, Ω_{th} would be very sensitive to changes in D. As average pressure and gas density increased, the increase in D would drop Ω_{th} to below operating speed, resulting in the appearance of the instability. This decrease in stability was partially offset by the effect differential pressure had on λ; as differential pressure increased, axial flow increased, reducing λ and increasing Ω_{th}. Thus, the appearance of the instability depended on two, independent factors with opposite effects, both of which were likely associated with the midspan seal.

The specialist also concluded that, during the cold startup, the compressor entered a rub condition at 5000 rpm and left the rub condition at about 6600 rpm. The Bode plot of the startup had shown classic resonance broadening due to a radial rub. In addition, the direct orbits from both compressor bearings during the rub showed only minimal distortion. For these reasons, the rub was not suspected to be near either bearing, supporting a location at the midspan seal.

The specialist recommended modification of the midspan seal rather than use of the damper bearing. Evidence strongly pointed to the seal as the source of the instability; any design fix should concentrate on the root cause of the problem. The seal could be shortened to improve axial flow, possibly sacrificing some efficiency, or a new design could be used that incorporated antiswirl injection. This would involve injecting gas at discharge pressure into the seal with a tangential velocity component *against* the direction of rotation, which would reduce λ and stabilize the machine.

The operators conducted additional field tests and found that the damper bearings provided acceptable stability. They decided to install the damper bearings on some of the compressor packages for more testing. On some of these machines, the new bearings caused the second balance resonance to move close to running speed, causing a high sensitivity to unbalance. Thus, it became evident to the operators that the damper bearings were not a good, long term solution.

Following the specialist's original recommendation, the operators modified the midspan labyrinth seal of the compressor. They shortened the seal length and applied the antiswirl concept by injecting gas at discharge pressure into the seal. The modified seals provided a good, long-term solution to eliminating the stability problem, and the fix was incorporated in all of the compressor packages.

References

1.   Muszynska, A, "One Lateral Mode Isotropic Rotor Response to Nonsynchronous Excitation," *Proceedings of the Course on Rotor Dynamics and Vibration in Turbomachinery*, von Karman Institute for Fluid Dynamics, Belgium (September 1992): pp. 21-25.

Appendix

Appendix 1

Phase Measurement Conventions

THE ROTOR MODEL PRESENTED IN CHAPTER 10 uses phase and amplitude measurement conventions that are convenient for the mathematical description of the rotor system. They are different from those commonly used by machinery instrumentation systems.

When you compare the measured behavior of a machine to the prediction of a mathematical model, you must convert between the two measurement systems. This chapter will explain the differences between the systems, starting with the instrumentation convention, and show how to convert between them.

The Instrumentation Convention

In Chapter 2 we defined phase as the time delay between two events. When event "B" occurs some time after event "A," we say that event "B" *lags* event "A." If we start a timer when event "A" occurs, the time increases until event "B" occurs. The time delay, or *lag*, between the two events is expressed in degrees of a vibration cycle, a positive number called *positive phase lag*, or typically, *phase lag*.

Most machine-oriented instrumentation systems use a positive phase lag convention. In this *instrumentation convention*, increasing time delay produces a larger positive number. When the time delay represents *absolute* phase lag, the "A" event is the Keyphasor event and the "B" event is the next positive peak of the vibration waveform; the difference is expressed as an angle. A phase lag between 180° and 360° is sometimes called a *phase lead*, and could be expressed as a negative lag number between −180° and 0°. When some machines pass through resonances, phase changes greater than 360° can be measured. However, angles in the instrumentation convention are typically converted to a positive number between 0° and 360° for display on instrumentation or data plots.

This is equivalent to reducing the phase angle *modulo 360* (abbreviated *mod 360*): for phase numbers greater than 360°, repeatedly subtract 360° until the result falls between 0° and 360°; for negative numbers, repeatedly add 360°. For example, using this convention, a calculated phase angle of –60° would be displayed as 300°, and a phase angle of 740° would be displayed as 20°. Note that *phase should not be reduced mod 360 before performing difference calculations.*

In the instrumentation convention, the amplitude of shaft relative displacement vibration is normally displayed in peak-to-peak units (for example, 20 µm pp) and velocity and acceleration are displayed in zero-to-peak (peak, or pk) units.

As we showed in Chapter 3, the amplitude and absolute phase lag of the filtered signal describe a vibration vector that rotates at the filter frequency, in the direction of rotation. The transducer sensitive axis defines the zero degree reference position, and the Keyphasor event behaves like a strobe that illuminates the position of the rotating vector.

In the instrumentation convention, the phase lag represents the time delay between the Keyphasor event and when the vibration vector arrives at the transducer position. This phase lag angle defines the angular position of the vibration vector when the Keyphasor event occurs. If, after the Keyphasor event occurs, the vector rotates 220° in the direction of rotation to point at the transducer, then you must rotate it 220° *against* rotation, from the transducer, to see where it pointed when the Keyphasor event occurred.

Figure A1-1 (top) shows two examples of vector plotting using the instrumentation convention. The same vector (150 µm pp ∠220°) is plotted in the transducer response plane for different rotation directions. At left, the machine rotation direction is X to Y (counterclockwise); at right, it is Y to X (clockwise).

The Mathematical Convention

In the mathematical convention, the phase is the angle of the vibration vector when the Keyphasor event occurs, measured from the X axis, in the positive (counterclockwise) direction. The transducer sensitive axis defines the X axis of a complex plane.

While it is possible to define different mathematical coordinate systems that are dependent on the direction of shaft rotation, it is simplest to use a coordinate system that is independent of this variable. In this system, the vibration vector is always assumed to rotate in the positive mathematical sense (counterclockwise), regardless of the direction of shaft rotation.

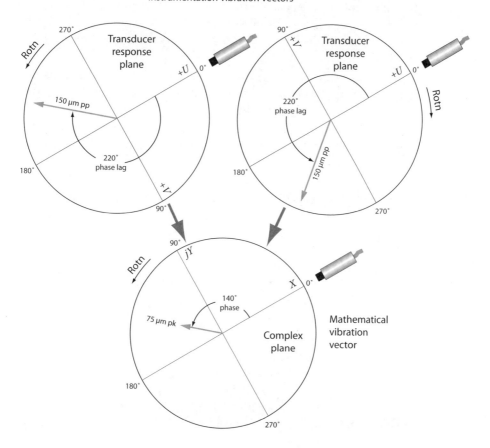

Figure A1-1. Phase measurement conventions. At top are two examples of vector plotting using the instrumentation convention. The same vector (150 μm pp ∠220°) is plotted in the transducer response plane for different rotation directions, X to Y (counterclockwise) at left, Y to X (clockwise) at right. In the mathematical convention (bottom), the phase is the angle of the vibration vector when the Keyphasor event occurs, measured from the X axis, in the positive (counterclockwise) direction. The transducer sensitive axis defines the X axis of a complex plane.

Mathematical phase can be measured as a positive or negative number and can exceed 360°. When subtracting phase numbers, the form that retains negative values is best. After calculations have been completed, it is recommended that the results be displayed modulo 360.

Note that the isotropic mathematical model of Chapter 10 implicitly assumes, for convenience, that the transducer is located at horizontal right; the actual measurement transducer (and its associated coordinate system) may be at any orientation.

In the mathematical model of the rotor system, displacement is measured from the origin of the coordinate system. Thus, mathematical vibration amplitudes are zero-to-peak, not peak-to-peak.

Figure A1-1, bottom shows the mathematical convention equivalent of the instrumentation convention vectors at top. Both instrumentation vectors can be expressed as the same mathematical vector shown.

Converting Between The Two Conventions

Phase conversion is simple:

$$\Phi_{math} = -\Phi_{inst} \qquad \text{(A1-1)}$$

where Φ_{math} is the phase in the mathematical convention and Φ_{inst} is the phase in the instrumentation convention. This can be verified by examining Figure A1-1. In the figure, the instrumentation phase, $\Phi_{inst} = 220°$ phase lag. Applying Equation A1-1,

$$\Phi_{math} = -220°$$

This result is mathematically correct. However, because we prefer to display the result modulo 360,

$$\Phi_{math} = -220° + 360° = 140°$$

The result agrees with that shown in Figure A1-1.

Displacement amplitude conversion is also simple. The mathematical convention amplitude (pk) is one half of the instrumentation amplitude (pp). If you discover a discrepancy of a factor of two in the displacement amplitude, it is likely this little detail was overlooked. Remember that velocity and acceleration amplitudes are already typically displayed as peak values in instrumentation.

Phase On Bode and APHT Plots

The difference in phase measurement conventions is most obvious on a Bode (Figure A1-2) or APHT plot. The left side of the phase plot is labeled as *phase lag* in the Bently Nevada convention, where the phase lag becomes *more positive* in a downward direction. The right side of the plot is labeled as *phase* using the mathematical convention, where the phase becomes *more negative* in a downward direction. As speed increases through the resonance, the phase data moves toward the bottom of the plot; the *phase lag* is increasing, but the *phase* is decreasing.

Figure A1-2. Bode plot showing instrumentation and mathematical phase labeling. The left side of the phase plot is labeled using the Bently Nevada convention, where phase lag becomes more positive downward. The right side of the plot is labeled using mathematical phase (mod 360), where phase becomes more negative in a downward direction. Both are correct, but the Bently Nevada convention is preferred.

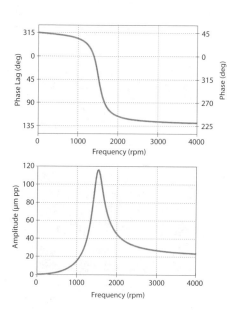

Plots in technical literature sometimes show phase lag increasing upward; often this is a result of plotting phase lag data using the autoscaling features of the plotting software. This can lead to confusion and misinterpretation of the data.

We know that, normally, phase lag increases as machine speed increases through a resonance, but there are several possible ways to present this data. Figure A1-3 shows different ways of plotting the same phase data. At top, the Bently Nevada instrumentation convention is used, and this is the recommended method for general machinery work. Next are two ways of labeling the same data using the mathematical convention; one uses the continuum of real negative numbers, the other reduces the phase modulo 360. Note that the data plots the same way, with phase data moving lower with increasing speed. The bottom plot inverts instrumentation phase, so that phase lag increases in the upward direction. This is confusing because it inverts the critical visual characteristic of leading and lagging phase and is not recommended.

When examining unfamiliar data, be sure to check which phase plotting convention is being used. The easiest way to verify the data is to look for the phase change through a resonance.

Finally, on Bode and APHT plots, the phase is displayed modulo 360. If the changing phase passes through 360°, simple plotting routines can produce jump discontinuities in the phase plot. These discontinuities can be eliminated by a process called *unwrapping*, which removes the phase jump discontinuities and unites the end points to create a continuous curve. Some software packages have a function for this purpose (in MATLAB, the *unwrap* function).

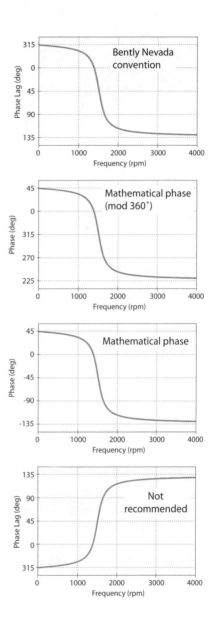

Figure A1-3. Different phase plotting methods. The top plot uses the Bently Nevada convention, where phase lag increases downward. The next two plots, where the phase decreases downward, use the mathematical convention. Two methods are shown: phase modulo 360° and continuous phase. All three plots present the phase data the same way; the Bently Nevada convention is preferred. In the bottom plot, where phase lag increases upward, the curve is inverted, producing a phase plot that can cause confusion. This method is not recommended.

Appendix 2

Filtered Orbit and Timebase Synthesis

In chapter 4, we showed how the unfiltered timebase plot is a representation of the unfiltered, ac signal voltage from a single transducer. The signal is converted to the appropriate engineering units and displayed versus time. In Chapter 5, we showed how an unfiltered orbit is reconstructed from the unfiltered waveforms from two, orthogonal transducers. In that situation, the signals are converted to engineering units of displacement, which describe the instantaneous position coordinates of the shaft centerline.

A *filtered* timebase and *filtered* orbit are constructed using a different process. When electronic vector filters are used, they will produce a rapidly changing (dynamic), analog output signal. An oscilloscope can display the signals as separate filtered timebase waveforms or combine them to produce a filtered orbit, where the instantaneous signal values define the coordinates of the shaft centerline on the filtered orbit.

Computers synthesize the filtered waveforms and orbits from vibration vectors, which are complex numbers representing amplitude and phase. The vectors can be generated in hardware, firmware, or software, but in any case, vector data is essentially *static* in that it does not change rapidly with time. An individual vector can be stored in rectangular form (sometimes called *in-phase* and *quadrature* components) or in polar form as amplitude and phase lag.

This chapter will present a computational algorithm that can be used to create filtered timebase and orbit plots from vector data. In the following discussion, we will assume the vector data has been converted to engineering units and stored in polar form, using positive phase lag (the instrumentation convention, see Appendix 1).

Timebase Synthesis

The amplitude and phase of the nX displacement vibration vector is $\boldsymbol{x}_{inst}$,

$$\boldsymbol{x}_{inst} = A_{inst} \angle \alpha_{inst} \tag{A2-1}$$

where A_{inst} is the filtered vibration amplitude provided by the instrumentation, and α_{inst} is the phase lag in the instrumentation convention.

In order to synthesize the timebase waveform, the vector must be converted from the instrumentation convention to the mathematical convention,

$$\boldsymbol{x} = A \angle \alpha \tag{A2-2}$$

In the instrumentation convention, the amplitudes of displacement vibration vectors are in peak-to-peak (pp) units, while velocity and acceleration vector amplitudes are in zero-to-peak (pk) units. Thus, for displacement vectors with peak-to-peak amplitude,

$$A = \frac{A_{inst}}{2} \tag{A2-3}$$

and for velocity and acceleration vectors,

$$A = A_{inst} \tag{A2-4}$$

Phase in the mathematical convention is the negative of the instrumentation phase (Appendix 1):

$$\alpha = -\alpha_{inst} \tag{A2-5}$$

At a rotor speed, Ω, in rpm, the nX vector frequency, ω, in rad/s, is

$$\omega(\text{rad/s}) = n\frac{\pi}{30}\Omega(\text{rpm})$$ (A2-6)

Using the compact and convenient exponential notation, the *rotating* vibration vector can be described as

$$\boldsymbol{x} = Ae^{j(\omega t + \alpha)}$$ (A2-7)

To synthesize the filtered waveform, the nX filtered vibration vector is rotated in the complex plane at the filter frequency (Figure A2-1). In the figure, the same instrumentation convention vector is plotted two ways, corresponding to different directions of shaft rotation. Regardless of the direction of shaft rotation, *the mathematical convention* nX *vector is always assumed to rotate in a positive mathematical direction* (X to Y, or counterclockwise). This is shown in the middle of the figure.

At time $t = 0$ (the Keyphasor event), the orientation of the vector corresponds to the phase, α, of the filtered vibration. The instantaneous projection of the rotating vector on the transducer sensitive axis corresponds to the filtered position of the shaft as seen by the transducer. This projection is the real part of Equation A2-7,

$$x = A\cos(\omega t + \alpha)$$ (A2-8)

When x is plotted against time on the horizontal axis, this is a timebase plot. The period of one cycle of vibration is given by

$$T = \frac{2\pi}{\omega}$$ (A2-9)

The Bently Nevada plot standard places the Keyphasor dot at the time of each Keyphasor event. Thus, for Equation A2-8, the Keyphasor dot would be plotted at the beginning of the plot ($t = 0$), and *once per revolution of the shaft* thereafter. The time (in seconds) to plot the kth Keyphasor dot is

$$t_k = \frac{60(k-1)}{\Omega(\text{rpm})} \tag{A2-10}$$

The blank is created by omitting several points before the Keyphasor dot.

Figure A2-1. Timebase synthesis from a vibration vector. A 1X displacement vibration vector (150 μm pp ∠220°) is plotted in the transducer response plane (top). The same instrumentation convention vector is plotted two ways, corresponding to different rotation directions. The location of the vectors shown corresponds to the Keyphasor event. Both instrumentation vectors convert to the same mathematical vibration vector, which is plotted in the complex plane (middle). The real part of the rotating vector, the projection of the vector on the transducer sensitive axis, produces the synthesized timebase waveform. Keyphasor dots are added at the beginning and at intervals of one shaft rotation, which, because this is a 1X vector, equals one cycle of vibration.

Figure A2-1.

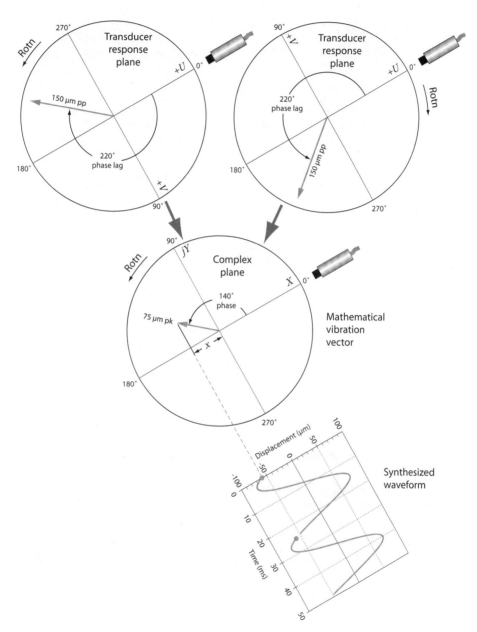

Instrumentation vibration vectors

Orbit Synthesis

Synthesis of a filtered orbit proceeds along similar lines. Now, however, there are two, orthogonal transducers (at least they should be). Thus, we have two rotating vibration vectors, each associated with its own transducer,

$$\boldsymbol{x} = Ae^{j(\omega t + \alpha)}$$
$$\boldsymbol{y} = Be^{j(\omega t + \beta)}$$

(A2-11)

where the mathematical amplitudes and phases are found following the procedure above. Note that *each phase is referenced to its own transducer sensitive axis*. For circular orbits, the amplitudes will be the same, and the phase will differ by 90°, the difference in transducer mounting orientation. However, in general, filtered orbits will not be circular; the amplitudes will be different and the phases of the two vectors will not differ by 90°.

Each transducer and its vector exist in a separate complex plane; the real axis of each plane is oriented with the transducer's sensitive axis. In Figure A2-2, the real axis of the X transducer plane and its vector (green) and the real axis of the Y transducer plane and its vector (blue) are overlaid to produce a response plane with two real axes.

This leads to an important point. Since the real axes are aligned with their respective transducers, at any moment in time the filtered physical coordinates, (x, y), of the shaft centerline are the real parts of the rotating vectors,

$$x = A\cos(\omega t + \alpha)$$
$$y = B\cos(\omega t + \beta)$$

(A2-12)

The orbit is synthesized by rotating the vectors in the positive direction (X to Y), regardless of the direction of shaft rotation, and calculating a set of coordinates for each value of t. Note that Y to X precession will be correctly handled because the phase lag of the parent vectors will reflect this precession.

The period of one vibration cycle (one complete orbit) is given by Equation A2-9. The first Keyphasor dot is plotted at $t = 0$, and subsequent Keyphasor dots are plotted at times corresponding to Equation A2-10. In the figure, the Keyphasor dot is located at $t = 0$ on the synthesized orbit at the point (x, y) defined by the projection of each vector on its sensitive axis.

More complex orbits can be synthesized by adding orbital components that are filtered to different frequencies, such as 1X + 2X, or 1X + 2X + 3X. This can allow construction of complex orbits when only vector data is available.

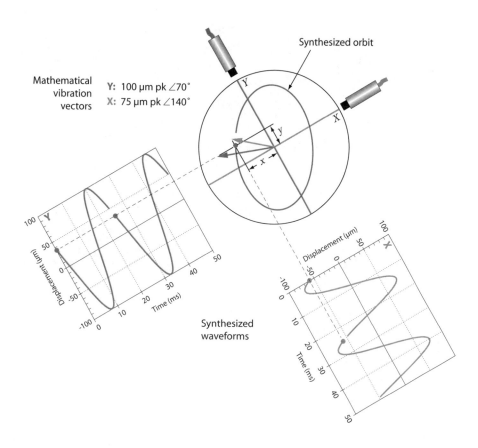

Mathematical vibration vectors

Y: 100 µm pk ∠70°
X: 75 µm pk ∠140°

Synthesized orbit

Synthesized waveforms

Figure A2-2. Filtered orbit synthesis from vibration vectors. Each transducer/vector combination exists in a separate complex response plane, which has its real axis oriented with its transducer's sensitive axis. The two response planes have been overlaid in the figure, producing real *X* and *Y* axes, and each vector is located at its phase with respect to its real axis. The orbit is synthesized by rotating the vectors at the filter frequency in the positive (*X* to *Y*) direction and calculating a set of coordinates for each value of *t*. The coordinates are defined by the instantaneous projection of each vector on its sensitive axis. The projections of the vectors in the figure define the coordinates of the Keyphasor dot on the orbit.

Appendix 3

The Origin of the
Tangential Stiffness Term

IN CHAPTER 10, WE DEVELOPED A SIMPLE ROTOR MODEL that is quite useful for explaining rotor system behavior. A key part of this behavior depends on the tangential force that is produced by the fluid-film in bearings and seals. This force produces a component of rotor response at 90° to the rotor displacement, and it is ultimately responsible for the onset of fluid-induced instability.

As part of the derivation of that model, we stated an expression for the tangential force,

$$\boldsymbol{F}_T = jD\lambda\Omega\boldsymbol{r} \qquad \text{(A3-1)}$$

where D is the damping, λ is the Fluid Circumferential Average Velocity Ratio, Ω is the rotor speed in rad/s, and $\boldsymbol{r}$ is the position vector of the rotor measured relative to the origin of the coordinate system, which was taken to be the center of the bearing. Finally, $j=\sqrt{-1}$, which, in our model, indicates that the force is directed at 90° from the displacement in the direction of rotation.

In this chapter, we will show how this expression can be derived from the concept of a rotating system of fluid forces.

Modeling the Pressure Wedge

As we stated in Chapter 10, the physical source of the tangential force is the pressure distribution that forms when a rotating rotor is displaced from the center of a fluid-film bearing. The fluid, which has been dragged into motion by the rotor, now encounters a reduction in available clearance and slows down. The deceleration of this fluid produces an increase in the local pressure in the fluid near the area of minimum clearance between the rotor and the bearing surface

(Figure A3-1). The fluid produces a circumferential *pressure wedge* that pushes on the rotor and moves it to the side.

When the applied load is static, the rotor moves until the force produced by the pressure wedge exactly opposes the force applied to the rotor. This pressure wedge produces a spring-like force that is the primary means of rotor support in hydrodynamic journal bearings. When the rotor centerline moves in response to dynamic forces, the pressure wedge shifts position, orienting itself relative to the instantaneous position of the shaft. At the same time, the fluid produces damping forces that oppose rotor centerline motion.

Any mathematical model of the fluid force system must take these static and dynamic behaviors into account, and the resulting model behavior must be a good fit to observed rotor system behavior.

It is possible to model this complex fluid behavior with a relatively simple system of rotating springs and dashpots. The springs provide the spring stiffness, and the dashpots provide damping. These elements surround the rotor, which has angular velocity Ω, and they rotate more slowly, at the average fluid angular velocity, $\lambda\Omega$. The elements maintain a radial orientation as they move around the clearance. The clearance at any location is a measure of the length of the springs and dashpots.

When the rotor is centered in the clearance (Figure A3-2, top), there is no change in the length of the springs and dashpots as they move around the rotor; thus, the forces due to the surrounding fluid are balanced around the rotor.

When the rotor is moved to a static position below the center (Figure A3-2, bottom), the springs change length as they move around the clearance. The

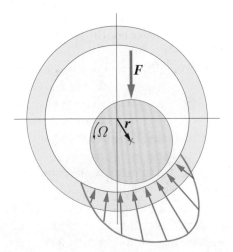

Figure A3-1. The fluid pressure wedge. When an applied force, F, moves a rotating rotor to an eccentric position in the bearing, the gap between the journal and bearing surfaces is partially closed. When the moving fluid encounters this restriction, the fluid pressure increases (red arrows). The pressure distribution creates a force that is equal and opposite to the applied force.

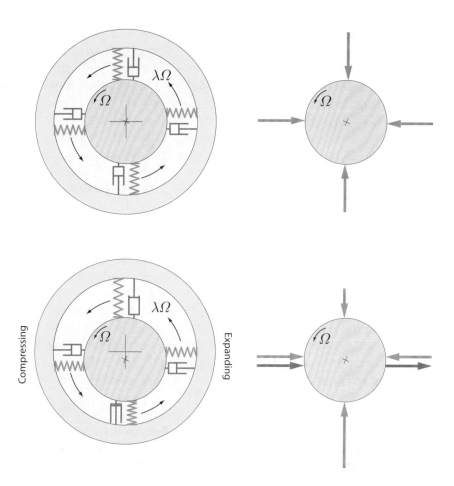

Compressing

Expanding

Figure A3-2. Spring and dashpot model of the fluid force system. The springs and the dashpots, which represent spring stiffness and damping, rotate at the average fluid angular velocity, $\lambda\Omega$, a fraction of rotor speed. The elements maintain a radial orientation to the shaft as they move around the clearance, which is greatly exaggerated for clarity. The length of the spring is equal to the available clearance at its location. When the rotor is centered in the clearance (top), the springs and dashpots do not change length as they move around the rotor; thus, the forces due to the surrounding fluid are balanced around the rotor. When the rotor is moved to a static position below the center (bottom), the elements change length as they move around the clearance, producing an unbalanced system of forces. See the text for more details.

force produced by a spring is proportional to its compression. As the springs reach the top, they are longer, producing a smaller compression force; when they reach the bottom, they are shorter, producing a larger force. Thus, the net spring force is directed upward toward the center, equilibrium position.

The dashpot behavior is similar, but there is an important subtlety. The force produced by a dashpot is proportional to the *change* in length per unit time (the speed of compression or extension). As the dashpots move across the top of the rotor in the figure, there is no extension or compression, and no force is produced. As the dashpots move down through the left of center, they compress to fit the reduced clearance between the rotor and the bearing or seal surface. This compression produces a force that tries to push the rotor to the right. As the dashpots move across the bottom, there is no compression, and they produce zero force. As they move around to the right, they extend to fit the increased clearance; this produces a force that tries to pull the rotor to the right. Thus, the effect of the dashpots is to produce a net force to the right, similar to the tangential force we are trying to model.

Now assume that the rotor moves from the center downward. During the time that the rotor centerline is moving with downward velocity, the dashpots at the top no longer have zero extension speed; they produce a force that tries to pull the rotor up. At the same time, the dashpots at bottom are compressed, and they try to push the rotor up. Thus, when dynamic motion is taking place, the rotating dashpot system produces a force that opposes the direction of rotor motion and is proportional to the velocity of the rotor centerline; this mimics the behavior of the fluid damping force. This force adds to the forces produced by displacement of the rotor.

This system of mechanical elements can be modeled by using conventional spring and damping forces in a coordinate system that rotates at $\lambda\Omega$. We will use a displacement vector, $\boldsymbol{r}_{rot}$, that represents the displacement of the rotor as seen in the *rotating* coordinate system. The fluid forces on the rotor can be described [1] in this rotating coordinate system as

$$\boldsymbol{F}_{rot} = -K\boldsymbol{r}_{rot} - D\dot{\boldsymbol{r}}_{rot} \tag{A3-2}$$

where K is the overall fluid spring constant, and D is the overall fluid damping coefficient. As the elements move around the available clearance at $\lambda\Omega$, this expression duplicates the behavior we have been discussing. This expression cannot be used directly in our rotor model because the model is derived in a stationary coordinate system; thus, we must transform the expression from the rotating coordinate system to the stationary system.

Transformation to Stationary Coordinates

The rotating coordinate system, to which the spring and dashpot are attached, is rotating at angular velocity $\lambda\Omega$. The angle that it makes with the stationary coordinate system is $\lambda\Omega t$ (Figure A3-3).

A position vector, r, when observed in the rotating system, appears to fall behind (rotate in the opposite direction). Even though we wish to transform Equation A3-3 to stationary coordinates, the easiest way to do this is to find an expression that transforms the position vector from the stationary system to the rotating system. To transform r to the rotating system, we must rotate it in the opposite direction. The transform becomes

$$\boldsymbol{r}_{rot} = \boldsymbol{r}e^{-j\lambda\Omega t} \tag{A3-3}$$

For the damping force term, we will also need to transform the velocity, which is obtained by differentiating Equation A3-3 with respect to time. Assuming that r is also a function of time,

$$\dot{\boldsymbol{r}}_{rot} = \dot{\boldsymbol{r}}e^{-j\lambda\Omega t} - j\lambda\Omega\boldsymbol{r}e^{-j\lambda\Omega t} \tag{A3-4}$$

which reduces to

$$\dot{\boldsymbol{r}}_{rot} = (\dot{\boldsymbol{r}} - j\lambda\Omega\boldsymbol{r})e^{-j\lambda\Omega t} \tag{A3-5}$$

The terms in parentheses represent the stationary coordinate description of the velocity vector in the rotating system.

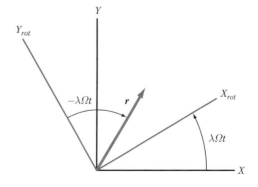

Figure A3-3. Fixed and rotating coordinate systems. The spring and dashpot are attached to the rotating coordinate system (red), which is rotating at angular velocity $\lambda\Omega$ relative to the stationary coordinate system (black). The angle that it makes with the stationary coordinate system is $\lambda\Omega t$. To an observer in the rotating system, the position vector, r, will appear to rotate backwards.

We now substitute the stationary coordinate descriptions of the vectors into Equation A3-2 and obtain the expression for the force in stationary coordinates,

$$F = -Kr + jD\lambda\Omega r - D\dot{r} \qquad \text{(A3-6)}$$

The middle term is the tangential force expression used in our rotor model.

Reference

1.   Muszynska, A., and Bently, D. E., "Frequency-Swept Rotating Input Perturbation Techniques and Identification of the Fluid Force Models in Rotor/Bearing/Seal Systems and Fluid Handling Machines," *Journal of Sound and Vibration* 143, no. 1, (1990): pp. 103-124.

Appendix 4

SAF Calculation

The synchronous amplification factor (SAF) is a measure of how much 1X vibration is amplified when the system passes through a resonance. Systems with low Quadrature Dynamic Stiffness have narrow resonances with high amplification of the unbalance response; those with high quadrature stiffness have relatively broad resonances with low amplification (Figure A4-1).

Figure A4-1. The Synchronous Amplification Factor (SAF). Systems with low Quadrature Dynamic Stiffness have a narrow resonance, high amplification of the unbalance response, and a rapid phase change (blue); those with high quadrature stiffness have a relatively broad resonance, low amplification, and relatively slow phase change (green).

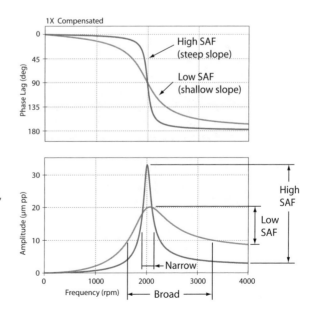

There are four methods used to measure the SAF, three (Peak Ratio, Half-power Bandwidth, and Phase Slope) based on the Bode plot, and one (a variation of the Half-power Bandwidth method) based on the polar plot. The methods are summarized in Figure A4-2. Since the Half-power Bandwidth method was discussed in Chapter 7, in this chapter we will show how to calculate the SAF using the other three methods.

The SAF is based on the dynamic response of rotor systems to a rotating unbalance force. Because of this, *all methods for measuring the SAF use 1X, compensated, polar and Bode plots.* Slow roll compensation removes the part of the rotor response that is not due to unbalance. The following discussions assume that the 1X data has been compensated.

A word of caution is appropriate here. All methods for measuring the SAF are based on ideal, isotropic rotor behavior. Real rotor systems can (and usually do) have some degree of anisotropy in the support stiffness. This causes the measurement of SAF using *any* method to be sensitive to the mounting angle of the measurement probes. Be sure to see Chapter 13 before applying any of the SAF measurement methods to data from your machine.

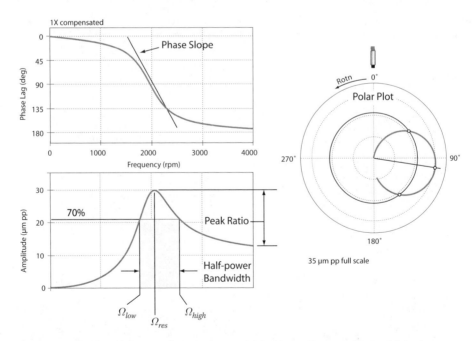

Figure A4-2. SAF graphical calculation methods. The Half-power Bandwidth and Peak Ratio methods utilize the Bode amplitude plot. The Phase Slope method uses the Bode phase plot, and the Polar Plot method uses the polar plot.

Because of the presence of anisotropic stiffness, all of these methods are approximate, and the precision of any SAF calculation is usually meaningful to only one or two significant figures.

Peak Ratio Method

The *Peak Ratio* method is probably the most intuitive (Figure A4-3).

1. On the Bode plot, find the amplitude at the resonance peak and the amplitude at some speed well above resonance.

2. The SAF is the ratio of these two values:

$$SAF = \frac{A_{res}}{A_{fast}} \qquad (A4\text{-}1)$$

For example, in the figure, $A_{res} = 30$ μm pp, and $A_{fast} = 13$ μm pp. Applying Equation A4-1,

$$SAF = \frac{30}{13} = 2.3$$

The rotor behavior shown in the figure is from the ideal, isotropic rotor model developed in Chapter 10. In practice, after the rotor passes through a resonance and experiences a decline in vibration amplitude, a higher mode will usually cause the vibration to increase again. For closely spaced modes, if the next mode amplitude rises before the previous mode amplitude falls to a limiting value, the SAF calculated using this method will not be accurate.

Figure A4-3. The Peak Ratio method. Identify the amplitude at the resonance peak, A_{res}, and the amplitude at a speed well above the resonance, A_{fast}. To calculate the SAF, divide A_{res} by A_{fast}, Equation A4-1.

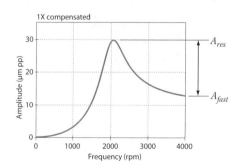

A variation of the SAF is sometimes used for estimating shaft relative alarm limits. Ideally, we want to shut down a machine so that it can safely pass through one or more resonances without rubbing. To estimate the vibration limit at running speed,

1.   Determine the maximum permissible vibration amplitude at all resonances, using knowledge of the mode shapes of the machine and its internal clearances.

2.   Calculate the ratio of the vibration amplitude at the most critical resonance peak to the amplitude *at running speed*.

3.   Divide the maximum permissible resonance vibration by the ratio. This defines the maximum allowable vibration amplitude at running speed.

In most machines, unfiltered vibration is predominantly 1X, but may contain significant amounts of other frequency components. If alarms are based on unfiltered vibration amplitude, calculate the ratio from a plot of unfiltered vibration amplitude.

This method only provides one small view of the problem of setting alarms for machinery vibration, and it should be used cautiously. Vibration alarm levels should be set based on manufacturers' recommendations and personal experience with the particular type of machine and its application. This method provides additional perspective, but it is not the complete solution to the problem.

Phase Slope Method

When a rotor system passes through a resonance, the phase lag increases. The slope of the phase change is usually steepest near the peak of the resonance. The *rate* of this change is related to the Quadrature Dynamic Stiffness, $jD(1-\lambda)\Omega$, of the system. Systems with low damping or high lambda will have low effective damping, $D(1-\lambda)$, a high rate of change of phase during resonance, and a high SAF. Systems with high effective damping will have a relatively low rate of change of phase.

Calculate the SAF using the maximum slope of the phase on a Bode plot using this procedure (Figure A4-4):

1.   Generate a Bode plot using the Bently Nevada Convention (*degrees phase lag*), where all phase angles are between 0° and 360°.

2. Draw a line parallel to the steepest part of the phase plot in a convenient location.

3. Select two arbitrary points on the line, far enough apart to provide good resolution of the data.

4. For each point, identify the speed and phase, $\Omega_1\, \alpha_1$ and $\Omega_2\, \alpha_2$, where $\Omega_2 > \Omega_1$.

5. If $\alpha_2 < \alpha_1$, add 360° to α_2. For example, if $\alpha_1 = 350°$ and $\alpha_2 = 10°$, then $\alpha_2 = 10° + 360° = 370°$.

6. Identify the speed at which the slope of the phase is steepest. For the simple rotor model, this is the speed where the high spot lags the heavy spot by 90°, Ω_{90}.

7. Calculate the SAF:

$$SAF = \frac{\pi}{360°}\,\Omega_{90}\left[\frac{\alpha_2 - \alpha_1}{\Omega_2 - \Omega_1}\right] \qquad (A4\text{-}2)$$

In the figure, $\Omega_1 = 1550$ rpm, $\alpha_1 = 0°$, $\Omega_2 = 2600$ rpm, $\alpha_2 = 180°$, $\Omega_{90} = 1900$ rpm, and

$$SAF = \frac{\pi}{360°}(1900\text{ rpm})\left|\frac{180° - 0°}{2600\text{ rpm} - 1550\text{ rpm}}\right| = 2.8$$

Figure A4-4. The Phase Slope method. Draw a line parallel to the steepest slope of the phase. Choose two arbitrary points and determine their phase and speed values. The steepest slope of the plot identifies the rotor speed where the high spot lags the heavy spot by 90° for that mode. Calculate the SAF using Equation A4-2.

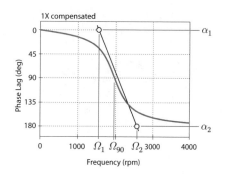

Polar Plot Method

The polar plot contains the same information as a Bode plot, so it is not surprising that it can be used to calculate the SAF. This method is actually a polar plot transformation of the Half-power Bandwidth method. For the ideal rotor model, on a polar plot, the half-power points are located 45° before and after the resonance peak. When rotor behavior deviates from ideal, the half-power points will not be at 45°. It is best to locate these points by finding the 70% amplitude levels. This will provide good agreement with the results obtained using a Bode plot.

The SAF is calculated using the following procedure (Figure A4-5):

1. Identify the resonance peak by locating the maximum amplitude on the plot. Draw a line from the origin through this peak. This identifies the resonance speed, Ω_{res}.

2. Draw a circle on the plot centered on the origin with a radius equal to 70% of the peak amplitude. The half-power bandwidth speeds, Ω_{low} and Ω_{high}, are found where the circle intersects the plot. These speeds may have to be interpolated between existing data points.

3. Calculate the SAF:

$$SAF = \frac{\Omega_{res}}{(\Omega_{high} - \Omega_{low})} \qquad \text{(A4-3)}$$

In the figure, $\Omega_{res} = 2050$ rpm, $\Omega_{high} = 2550$ rpm, and $\Omega_{low} = 1700$ rpm, and

$$SAF = \frac{2050 \text{ rpm}}{(2550 \text{ rpm} - 1700 \text{ rpm})} = 2.4$$

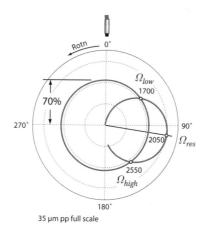

35 μm pp full scale

Figure A4-5. The Polar Plot method. The maximum amplitude identifies the resonance speed. Draw a circle (red) at 70% of the maximum amplitude to identify the speeds used to calculate the half-power bandwidth. Calculate the SAF using Equation A4-3.

Appendix 5

Vector Transforms

I<small>N CHAPTER</small> 13, <small>WE SHOWED THAT, FOR SYSTEMS</small> with anisotropic stiffness, measurement of rotor vibration can be highly viewpoint dependent. Anisotropic stiffness can adversely affect measurement of the Synchronous Amplification Factor (SAF) and make identification of the heavy spot ambiguous.

Two methods of vector transformation have been developed to improve our understanding of anisotropic rotor behavior: vector data can be transformed to what would be measured by a set of *virtual probes* mounted at any desired orientation, or vector data can be transformed to *forward* and *reverse* responses.

This chapter will present the mathematical algorithms used for these transforms. Both transforms operate on vibration vectors from a pair of orthogonal transducers. The transforms can be applied to a pair of vectors measured at one operating speed, or they can be applied to a full set of startup or shutdown vectors. The transforms are usually applied to displacement data, but they can be applied to velocity or acceleration data from orthogonal transducers.

Virtual Probe Rotation

Virtual probes are imaginary orthogonal probes that we can mount at any angle we choose. Suppose a pair of probes are mounted on the machine at 0° and 90° R, and that, after taking vector data, we wish to know what vibration vectors would have been measured if the probes had been installed at some other orientation, perhaps 30° L and 60° R. We can mathematically transform the measured vector data to produce the vectors that would have been measured by these virtual probes.

As we discussed in Chapter 3, vibration vectors are complex numbers that can be expressed in polar or rectangular form. Most coordinate transforms involve operations on scalar quantities, usually position coordinates. The special quality of this transform is that it operates directly on the complex vibration vectors.

We start with a pair of orthogonal (XY) transducers, which we will call the *physical* transducers. The transducers measure a pair of vibration vectors, x_{inst} and y_{inst}, where

$$x_{inst} = A_{inst} \angle \alpha_{inst}$$
$$y_{inst} = B_{inst} \angle \beta_{inst}$$

(A5-1)

The subscript *inst* refers to the instrumentation measurement convention (Appendix 1), A_{inst} and B_{inst} are the amplitudes, and α_{inst} and β_{inst} are the measured phase lags. The phases are measured relative to the transducer axes: α_{inst} is measured relative to the X transducer sensitive axis, and β_{inst} is measured relative to the Y transducer sensitive axis.

What vibration vectors would be measured by a pair of orthogonal transducers mounted at a different orientation (virtual probes)? To answer this question, we assume that the new, virtual probes are created by rotating the physical probes through an arbitrary angle, θ, as shown in Figure A5-1.

In the figure, the vibration vectors, x and y, are shown in a real XY plane which is formed by the combination of the two complex transducer response planes. Each vector is complex, with its real part aligned with its transducer's sensitive axis.

First, the measured vectors are converted to the mathematical phase measurement convention (Appendix 1) and then to rectangular form,

$$x = x_d + jx_q$$
$$y = y_d + jy_q$$

(A5-2)

where x_d and x_q are the *in-phase* (real part) and *quadrature* (imaginary part) components of x, and y_d and y_q are the corresponding components of y.

Then we apply a standard coordinate transform,

$$\begin{pmatrix} x_R \\ y_R \end{pmatrix} = \begin{bmatrix} \cos\theta & \sin\theta \\ -\sin\theta & \cos\theta \end{bmatrix} \begin{pmatrix} x \\ y \end{pmatrix}$$

(A5-3)

where $\boldsymbol{x}_R$ and $\boldsymbol{y}_R$ are the vibration vectors that would be measured by the virtual probes. Substituting Equations A5-2 and expanding,

$$\boldsymbol{x}_R = (x_d \cos\theta + y_d \sin\theta) + j(x_q \cos\theta + y_q \sin\theta)$$
$$\boldsymbol{y}_R = (y_d \cos\theta - x_d \sin\theta) + j(y_q \cos\theta - x_q \sin\theta)$$

(A5-4)

The transformed vectors can be converted back to polar form and to the instrumentation convention for comparison to the original vectors.

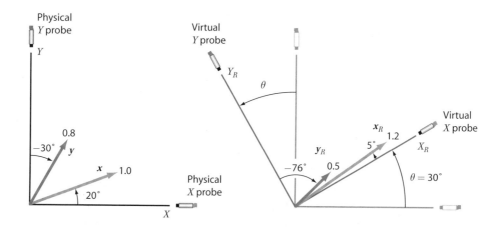

Figure A5-1. Physical and virtual probe coordinate axes. A set of physical *XY* probes are shown at left with their respective vibration vectors, *x* and *y*. The vectors are plotted using the mathematical convention, and their amplitudes and phases are shown. A set of virtual probes, X_R and Y_R are created by mathematically rotating the physical probes through an angle, θ. The new vibration vectors (right), $\boldsymbol{x}_R$ and $\boldsymbol{y}_R$, are what would have been measured by the virtual probes and will generally have different amplitudes and phases.

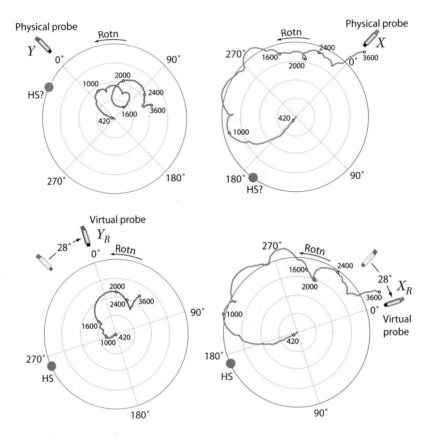

Figure A5-2. Virtual probe data from a gas turbine generator set. This is a fluid-film bearing machine with probes mounted at ±45° from the vertical. On the physical probe polar plots (top), the indicated locations of the heavy spots disagree. On the virtual probe polar plots (bottom), where the probes have been rotated 28° clockwise, the heavy spot locations show good agreement.

The transformed vectors are plotted the same way as the vibration vectors from the physical probes: the phase lag starts at zero degrees *relative to the virtual probe* and increases in a direction opposite to rotation (Figure A5-2). In the figure, virtual probes have been constructed at 28° clockwise relative to the physical probes, and the data is plotted on a separate set of polar plots.

Polar plots generated for virtual probes are interpreted in the same way as for physical probes. For example, the indicated heavy spot in the figure is located about 260° relative to the *virtual*, Y_R, probe location. You must add 28° to the phase lag to arrive at its location relative to the physical probe.

The Forward and Reverse Transform and Full Spectrum

In Appendix 2, we showed how a filtered orbit can be reconstructed from a pair of vibration vectors. The same orbit can be constructed from a pair of forward and reverse vectors that rotate in opposite directions at the filter frequency, ω (Figure A5-3). The forward vector rotates in the same direction as rotor rotation. Research [1] has shown that, at speeds well below the resonance, the forward response always points toward the heavy spot, making it a valuable tool for balancing.

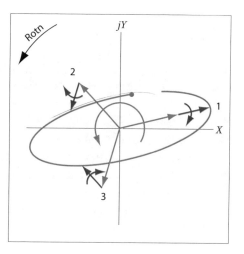

Figure A5-3. Forward and reverse vectors and the filtered orbit. Forward (red) and reverse (violet) rotating vectors are shown at three moments in the complex plane. At any instant in time, the vector sum locates the coordinates of the rotor centerline in the filtered orbit.

The forward/reverse transform starts with a pair of vibration vectors, x_{inst} and y_{inst}, from orthogonal (XY) probes. The vibration vectors are first converted to the mathematical convention (positive phase lead and zero-to-peak amplitude) as discussed in Appendix 1. These vectors can be expressed in rotating form as

$$x = Ae^{j(\omega t+\alpha)}$$
$$y = Be^{j(\omega t+\beta)}$$

(A5-5)

where A, B, α, and β are the amplitudes and phases of the vibration vectors in mathematical convention. α is measured relative to the X transducer axis, and β is measured relative to the Y transducer axis. Thus, the physical coordinates of the rotor centerline on the filtered orbit are (x, y), where

$$x = A\cos(\omega t+\alpha)$$
$$y = B\cos(\omega t+\beta)$$

(A5-6)

The transform to forward and reverse uses the identity,

$$\cos\theta = \frac{e^{j\theta}+e^{-j\theta}}{2}$$

(A5-7)

This identity is substituted into Equation A5-6 to obtain

$$x = \frac{1}{2}A\left[e^{j(\omega t+\alpha)}+e^{-j(\omega t+\alpha)}\right]$$
$$y = \frac{1}{2}B\left[e^{j(\omega t+\beta)}+e^{-j(\omega t+\beta)}\right]$$

(A5-8)

Note that the exponential expressions contain terms that represent vectors that are rotating in the mathematically positive direction, $e^{j\omega t}$, which is equivalent to *forward* precession, and the negative direction, $e^{-j\omega t}$, which is equivalent to *reverse* precession.

We now multiply the second equation in A5-8 by j, add the two equations together, and combine forward and reverse parts to obtain

$$x + jy = \frac{1}{2}\left[Ae^{j(\omega t+\alpha)} + jBe^{j(\omega t+\beta)}\right] + \frac{1}{2}\left[Ae^{-j(\omega t+\alpha)} + jBe^{-j(\omega t+\beta)}\right] \quad \text{(A5-9)}$$

The sum of these four complex, rotating vectors represents the instantaneous position of the rotor centerline in the filtered orbit. This orbit exists in what is now a complex plane $(X + jY)$ with the real axis aligned with the X transducer. The two vectors in the left bracket rotate in the forward direction $(+\omega)$; the two in the right bracket are reverse $(-\omega)$. Setting $t = 0$ gives us the filtered position at the Keyphasor event in terms of the measured vibration vectors,

$$(x + jy)_{t=0} = \frac{1}{2}(Ae^{j\alpha} + jBe^{j\beta}) + \frac{1}{2}(Ae^{-j\alpha} + jBe^{-j\beta}) \quad \text{(A5-10)}$$

Equations A5-9 and A5-10 can be used in a computer program (such as MAT-LAB) that supports complex numbers in this form.

However, we wish to find expressions for the amplitude and phase of the forward and reverse vectors. Equation A5-9 can be described by the sum of two forward and reverse rotating vectors,

$$x + jy = A_F e^{j(\omega t+\phi_F)} + A_R e^{j(-\omega t-\phi_R)} \quad \text{(A5-11)}$$

where A_F and A_R are the amplitudes of the forward and reverse vectors, and ϕ_F and ϕ_R are the phases, both measured relative to the X axis. Comparing the right sides of Equations A5-9 and A5-11 at $t = 0$,

$$\begin{aligned} A_F e^{j\phi_F} &= \frac{1}{2}(Ae^{j\alpha} + jBe^{j\beta}) \\ A_R e^{-j\phi_R} &= \frac{1}{2}(Ae^{-j\alpha} + jBe^{-j\beta}) \end{aligned} \quad \text{(A5-12)}$$

The exponential functions can be expanded into trigonometric functions using Euler's identity,

$$e^{j\theta} = \cos\theta + j\sin\theta \quad \text{(A5-13)}$$

Applying Euler's identity to the right sides of Equations A5-12, and, after some algebra and a trigonometric identity or two, we obtain

$$A_F = \frac{1}{2}\left[A^2 + B^2 + 2AB\sin(\alpha - \beta)\right]^{0.5}$$

$$A_R = \frac{1}{2}\left[A^2 + B^2 - 2AB\sin(\alpha - \beta)\right]^{0.5} \tag{A5-14}$$

and

$$\phi_F = \arctan\left(\frac{A\sin\alpha + B\cos\beta}{A\cos\alpha - B\sin\beta}\right)$$

$$\phi_R = \arctan\left(\frac{A\sin\alpha - B\cos\beta}{A\cos\alpha + B\sin\beta}\right) \tag{A5-15}$$

The phase angles should be calculated using the *arctangent2* function to yield angles between ±180° (which can be reduced mod 360 if desired), and the data should be unwrapped to prevent jump discontinuities.

It is important to remember that these expressions are based on a mathematical convention where *both* of the phase angles are measured relative to the X (real) axis, which is aligned with the X transducer sensitive axis, and ϕ_F is measured in the positive (counterclockwise) direction. However, as a result of the phase angle definition in equation A5-8 for the reverse vector, positive ϕ_R is measured in the *clockwise* direction, the reverse of the usual convention.

Before plotting, the forward and reverse vectors should be converted to the instrumentation convention (the negative of the mathematical phase) to be consistent with other data plots.

When plotted on a polar plot (Figure A5-4), as the phase lag of the forward response increases (the mathematical phase decreases), it will move in a direction opposite to rotation (the same as standard vibration vectors); on a Bode plot, it will move downward.

As the phase lag of the *reverse* response increases, it will move in the *same* direction as rotation on the polar plot, and, if plotted on a Bode plot together with the forward response, it will move upward.

A full spectrum (Chapter 8) can be calculated using the same algorithm. Full spectrum uses the time delay between events on X and Y transducers to deduce the X to Y or Y to X precession direction information. For this reason, full spectrum computation requires that the unfiltered waveform data from an orthogonal (XY) pair of transducers be sampled simultaneously and with the same sam-

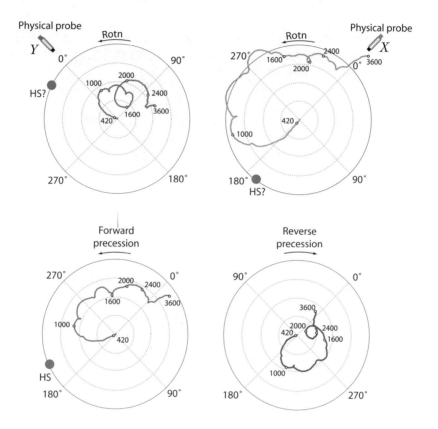

Figure A5-4. Forward and reverse polar plots. The polar plots (bottom) show the forward (left) and reverse (right) vectors transformed from the vibration vectors in the standard *XY* polar plots above. The phase is plotted in degrees lag relative to the direction of precession. The low speed phase of the forward plot points toward the heavy spot and agrees with the location found using virtual probe rotation in Figure A5-2. For any speed, the sum of the forward and reverse vectors will reconstruct the original filtered orbit, including its orientation. The low speed phase of the reverse polar plot does not, typically, point in the direction of the heavy spot.

pling frequency. The direction of shaft rotation is needed to determine whether the calculated precession direction is forward or reverse.

In a half spectrum, the X and Y waveforms are each subjected to a fast Fourier transform (FFT). For each frequency bin in the resulting spectra, the FFT produces a complex number that contains both amplitude and phase information. When a half spectrum is plotted, only the amplitude of each frequency is used, and the phase information is thrown away.

Full spectrum uses all of the complex information in the FFT. For each frequency bin, the two X and Y FFT complex numbers are computationally equivalent to the complex x and y vibration vectors discussed above. Thus, for each bin, the forward and reverse frequency amplitudes can be calculated using Equation A-14. When this process is repeated for all of the frequency bins in the FFT data, the result is a full spectrum.

References
1. Franklin, W., and Bently, D. E., "Balancing Nonsymmetrically Supported Rotors Using Complex Variable Filtering." Paper presented at the Vibration Institute 21st Annual Meeting, New Orleans, Louisiana, June 1997.

Appendix 6

Eigenvalues of the Rotor Model

Iᴛ ɪs ᴘᴏssɪʙʟᴇ ᴛᴏ ᴅᴇʀɪᴠᴇ ᴀɴ ᴇxᴘʟɪᴄɪᴛ ᴇxᴘʀᴇssɪᴏɴ for the eigenvalues (also called *roots*, or in control theory, *poles*) of the simple rotor model presented in Chapters 10 and 14. The derivation we will use will follow Muszynska's [1].

The free vibration rotor model of Equation 14-7 is restated here:

$$M\ddot{r} + D\dot{r} + (K - jD\lambda\Omega)r = 0 \tag{A6-1}$$

We assume a solution of the form

$$r = Re^{st} \tag{A6-2}$$

Solution leads to the *characteristic equation,*

$$Ms^2 + Ds + K - jD\lambda\Omega = 0 \tag{A6-3}$$

The eigenvalues, s, are the roots of this equation; because the equation is quadratic, there will be two. We find them using the standard solution to a quadratic equation,

$$s_{1,2} = \frac{-b \pm \sqrt{b^2 - 4ac}}{2a} \tag{A6-4}$$

The important feature here is that the c term is a complex number. Applying Equation A6-4, we obtain

$$s_{1,2} = \frac{-D \pm \sqrt{D^2 - 4M(K - jD\lambda\Omega)}}{2M} \qquad (A6\text{-}5)$$

which leads to

$$s_{1,2} = -\frac{D}{2M} \pm \sqrt{\left(\frac{D}{2M}\right)^2 - \frac{K}{M} + j\frac{D\lambda\Omega}{M}} \qquad (A6\text{-}6)$$

Note that, if either Ω or λ is zero, then the imaginary term under the radical disappears, and the eigenvalues are the same as those of a simple harmonic oscillator,

$$s_{1,2} = -\frac{D}{2M} \pm \sqrt{\left(\frac{D}{2M}\right)^2 - \frac{K}{M}} \qquad (A6\text{-}7)$$

This situation would apply to a rotor that has negligible fluid interaction, such as an electric motor with rolling element bearings. It would also apply to a stopped rotor supported by externally pressurized (hydrostatic) bearings. For now, we will examine Equation A6-7 in detail; we will return to Equation A6-6 later.

There are three possible cases for the term under the radical: it is either zero, greater than zero, or less than zero.

If the term is equal to zero, then

$$\left(\frac{D}{2M}\right)^2 - \frac{K}{M} = 0 \qquad (A6\text{-}8)$$

Solving for the damping, D, leads to the definition of *critical damping*, D_{cr}:

$$D = D_{cr} = 2\sqrt{MK} \qquad (A6\text{-}9)$$

If we substitute this expression into Equation A6-7, Equation A6-2 becomes

$$r = R_1 e^{s_1 t} + R_2 e^{s_2 t} \qquad (A6\text{-}10)$$

where R_1 and R_2 depend on the initial conditions, and

$$s_1 = s_2 = \gamma_1 = \gamma_2 = -\sqrt{\frac{K}{M}} \qquad \text{(A6-11)}$$

The eigenvalues are real, consisting only of two equal values of the growth/decay rate, γ; thus, for critical damping there is no natural frequency term, ω_d, and no precession. For zero initial centerline velocity, the disturbed rotor system will move back to the equilibrium position *in a straight line* without overshooting or oscillation. On the root locus plot, the two eigenvalues will plot at the same point on the horizontal axis in the left half plane at the location given by Equation A6-11.

The expression for critical damping leads to the definition of the *damping factor*, ζ, which is the ratio of the damping to the critical damping:

$$\zeta = \frac{D}{D_{cr}} = \frac{D}{2\sqrt{KM}} \qquad \text{(A6-12)}$$

Thus, when $\zeta = 1$, the system is critically damped.

Returning to Equation A6-7, if the term under the radical is greater than zero, then both eigenvalues are real and *unequal*. Substituting the eigenvalues into Equation A6-2, we obtain the free response of the system,

$$\boldsymbol{r} = \boldsymbol{R}_1 e^{s_1 t} + \boldsymbol{R}_2 e^{s_2 t} \qquad \text{(A6-13)}$$

where the values of $\boldsymbol{R}_1$ and $\boldsymbol{R}_2$ depend on the initial conditions, and

$$s_1 = \gamma_1 = -\frac{D}{2M} + \sqrt{\left(\frac{D}{2M}\right)^2 - \frac{K}{M}}$$

$$s_2 = \gamma_2 = -\frac{D}{2M} - \sqrt{\left(\frac{D}{2M}\right)^2 - \frac{K}{M}} \qquad \text{(A6-14)}$$

Again, the eigenvalues are real; when disturbed and released with zero initial velocity, the system will also return slowly back to the equilibrium position in a straight line, without overshoot. For this case, $D > D_{cr}$, $\zeta > 1$, and the system is *supercritically damped*, or *overdamped*; the system will return to the equilibrium position more slowly than for the critically damped case. The two eigenvalues will be located at two points on the horizontal axis of the root locus plot; both points will be in the stable, left half plane.

In the third case, the term under the radical in Equation A6-7 is negative. For this case, $D < D_{cr}$, $\zeta < 1$, and the system is *subcritically damped*, or *underdamped*. Factoring out the –1, we obtain

$$s_{1,2} = -\frac{D}{2M} \pm j\sqrt{\frac{K}{M} - \left(\frac{D}{2M}\right)^2} \qquad \text{(A6-15)}$$

The eigenvalues are now complex, of the form $\gamma \pm j\omega_d$, and the system will oscillate. The rotor response is given by

$$r = R_1 e^{\gamma_1 t} e^{j\omega_d t} + R_2 e^{\gamma t} e^{-j\omega t} \qquad \text{(A6-16)}$$

where

$$\gamma_1 = \gamma_2 = -\frac{D}{2M}$$

$$\omega_d = \sqrt{\frac{K}{M} - \left(\frac{D}{2M}\right)^2} \qquad \text{(A6-17)}$$

The eigenvalues are complex conjugates and are located above and below each other on the root locus plot, with equal positive (forward precession) and negative (reverse precession) frequencies. The growth/decay rates are equal, and the two, counterrotating vectors produce a line orbit that decreases in amplitude with time. The decay in amplitude determined by the value of γ.

The natural frequency, ω_d, is the classical definition of the *damped natural frequency*, which is lower than the *undamped natural frequency*, ω_n,

$$\omega_n = \sqrt{\frac{K}{M}} \qquad \text{(A6-18)}$$

We have been exploring the situation where either Ω or λ is zero. When Ω and λ are *both nonzero*, the rotor system will have eigenvalues given by Equation A6-6. The term under the radical is complex, and we must convert this equation to a form where j is outside the radical. The conversion can be found in a good mathematics handbook [2]:

$$\sqrt{a + jb} = \sqrt{\frac{\sqrt{a^2 + b^2} + a}{2}} \pm j\sqrt{\frac{\sqrt{a^2 + b^2} - a}{2}} \qquad \text{(A6-19)}$$

When this expression is applied to Equation A6-6, after some algebra, we obtain expressions for the two eigenvalues of the form

$$s_{1,2} = \gamma_{1,2} + j\omega_{r1,2} \qquad \text{(A6-20)}$$

where

$$\gamma_1 = \left[-\frac{D}{2M} + \frac{1}{\sqrt{2}}\sqrt{-\omega_d^2 + \sqrt{\omega_d^4 + \left(\frac{D\lambda\Omega}{M}\right)^2}} \right]$$

$$\gamma_2 = \left[-\frac{D}{2M} - \frac{1}{\sqrt{2}}\sqrt{-\omega_d^2 + \sqrt{\omega_d^4 + \left(\frac{D\lambda\Omega}{M}\right)^2}} \right]$$

$$\omega_{r1} = j\left[\frac{1}{\sqrt{2}}\sqrt{\omega_d^2 + \sqrt{\omega_d^4 + \left(\frac{D\lambda\Omega}{M}\right)^2}} \right]$$

$$\omega_{r2} = -j\left[\frac{1}{\sqrt{2}}\sqrt{\omega_d^2 + \sqrt{\omega_d^4 + \left(\frac{D\lambda\Omega}{M}\right)^2}} \right] \qquad \text{(A6-21)}$$

and ω_d is the damped natural frequency of Equation A6-17.

Here, we are using ω_r to indicate that this is the damped natural frequency of precession of the *rotating* rotor system with significant fluid interaction. (This subscript will only be used here to emphasize the distinction between the rotating and nonrotating natural frequencies. Elsewhere in the book, ω_d will be used to indicate a damped natural frequency for either a rotating or nonrotating system.)

All of the terms contain the tangential stiffness, $D\lambda\Omega$; thus, all are functions of both lambda and rotor speed. There are two unequal values of γ; thus, the eigenvalues are not conjugate pairs. The damped natural frequency of precession, ω_r, is a much more complicated expression than that of Equation A6-17, and the tangential stiffness term makes the natural frequency of the rotor system increase with increasing rotor speed or λ.

The only way the term under the radical in Equation A6-6 can be zero is if the real and imaginary parts of the term are both zero simultaneously. The straight line behavior of critically and supercritically damped systems derived from the fact that the term under the radical was either zero, or real and positive. For nonzero values of λ and Ω, this is no longer possible, which means that *a rotor system with fluid interaction and nonzero rotor speed cannot move in a straight line in free vibration*. Once the rotor starts turning, the tangential stiffness term will guarantee that, if disturbed from equilibrium, the rotor will move in some sort of spiral orbit, at a natural frequency, ω_r.

For a rotor system with nonzero λ and damping equal to or greater than D_{cr}, the eigenvalues will plot on the horizontal axis only when $\Omega = 0$. As soon as the rotor starts turning, the two eigenvalues will move off the horizontal axis, and the frequency of precession given by ω_r will be nonzero. Figure A6-1 summarizes the eigenvalue positions for each of the cases we have discussed.

The Threshold of Instability

The Threshold of Instability speed, Ω_{th}, is the speed at which the growth/decay rate, γ, is zero, and it can be found by setting the real parts of $\gamma_{1,2}$ equal to zero:

$$-\frac{D}{2M} \pm \frac{1}{\sqrt{2}}\sqrt{-\omega_d^2 + \sqrt{\omega_d^4 + \left(\frac{D\lambda\Omega_{th}}{M}\right)^2}} = 0 \qquad (A6\text{-}22)$$

which leads to

$$\Omega_{th} = \frac{1}{\lambda}\sqrt{\frac{K}{M}} \qquad (A6\text{-}23)$$

This is identical to Equation 14-5, which was derived from the Dynamic Stiffness.

References

1. Muszynska, A, "One Lateral Mode Isotropic Rotor Response to Nonsynchronous Excitation," *Proceedings of the Course on Rotor Dynamics and Vibration in Turbomachinery*, von Karman Institute for Fluid Dynamics, Belgium, September 1992, pp. 21-25.
2. Tuma, Jan J., and Walsh, Ronald A. (contributor), *Engineering Mathematics Handbook*, 4th Ed. (New York: McGraw-Hill Book Company, 1997).

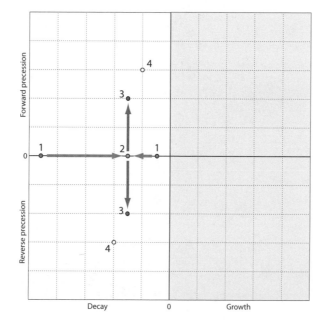

Figure A6-1. Eigenvalue locations on the root locus plot for different damping factors for a one-degree-of-freedom system. Points 1, 2, and 3, are for systems where either λ or $\Omega = 0$. Eigenvalues of a supercritically damped system ($\zeta > 1$) will plot as two separate points on the horizontal axis (points labeled 1). Eigenvalues of a critically damped system ($\zeta = 1$) will plot as one point (2). Both of these systems have real eigenvalues. Subcritically damped systems ($\zeta < 1$) have complex eigenvalues that are conjugates and plot off the horizontal axis (3). Systems where both λ and Ω are nonzero have complex eigenvalues that are not conjugate (4).

Appendix 7

Units of Measurement

Metric/US Customary Unit Conversions

All conversion factors are presented in four significant figures except when the conversion is exact.

All conversions are of the form
 A   =   B

Displacement

1 in	25.4 mm
1 in	25.4×10^{-3} m
1 m	39.37 in
1 mil	1×10^{-3} in
1 mil	25.4×10^{-3} mm
1 mil	25.4 µm
1 mm	39.37×10^{-3} in
1 mm	39.37 mil
1 mm	1×10^{3} µm
1 µm	39.37×10^{-6} in
1 µm	39.37×10^{-3} mil
1 µm	1×10^{-3} mm

Velocity

1 in/s	25.4 mm/s
1 in/s	25.4×10^{-3} m/s
1 m/s	39.37 in/s
1 m/s	1×10^{3} mm/s
1 mm/s	39.37×10^{-3} in/s
1 mm/s	1×10^{-3} m/s

Acceleration; "g" is the standard acceleration of gravity at sea level, 45° latitude.

1 g	386.1 in/s^2
1 g	32.17 ft/s^2
1 g	9.807 m/s^2
1 in/s^2	2.590×10^{-3} g
1 ft/s^2	31.08×10^{-3} g
1 m/s^2	102.0×10^{-3} g

Displacement, velocity, and acceleration: d is the amplitude of displacement vibration, v is velocity, and a is acceleration; ω is the frequency of vibration in rad/s, and f is the frequency of vibration in hertz. These equations are applicable to sinusoidal motion (single frequency) only.

d	v/ω
d	$v/2\pi f$
d	a/ω^2
d	$a/(2\pi f)^2$
v	ωd
v	$2\pi f d$
v	a/ω
v	$a/2\pi f$
a	$\omega^2 d$
a	$(2\pi f)^2 d$
a	ωv
a	$2\pi f v$

Amplitude, A, peak-to-peak (pp), peak (pk), and rms. The formulas for rms are for a sine wave (single frequency) only.

A_{pk}	$1/2\,A_{pp}$
A_{pp}	$2\,A_{pk}$
A_{rms}	$0.7071\,A_{pk}$
A_{pk}	$1.414\,A_{rms}$
A_{pp}	$2.828\,A_{rms}$

Phase, Φ, of displacement, velocity, acceleration.

Φ_{disp}	$\Phi_{vel} - 90°$
Φ_{disp}	$\Phi_{accel} \pm 180°$
Φ_{vel}	$\Phi_{disp} + 90°$
Φ_{vel}	$\Phi_{accel} - 90°$
Φ_{accel}	$\Phi_{disp} \pm 180°$
Φ_{accel}	$\Phi_{vel} + 90°$

Phase, Φ, instrumentation and math conventions. See Appendix 1.

Φ_{math}	$-\Phi_{inst}$

Force, weight, and mass. See the last section for a discussion of force, weight, and mass in the US customary system. In the following, "g" is the symbol for gram.

1 g	1×10^{-3} kg
1 g	2.205×10^{-3} lb
1 g	5.711×10^{-6} lb · s²/in
1 g	68.53×10^{-6} lb · s²/ft
1 g	35.27×10^{-3} oz
1 kg	1×10^3 g
1 kg	2.205 lb
1 kg	5.711×10^{-3} lb · s²/in
1 kg	68.53×10^{-3} lb · s²/ft
1 kg	35.27 oz
1 lb	453.6 g
1 lb	453.6×10^{-3} kg
1 lb	2.590×10^{-3} lb · s²/in
1 lb	31.08×10^{-3} lb · s²/ft
1 lb	4.448 N
1 lb	16 oz
1 lb · s²/in	175.1×10^3 g
1 lb · s²/in	175.1 kg
1 lb · s²/in	386.1 lb
1 lb · s²/in	6.178×10^3 oz
1 lb · s²/ft	14.59×10^3 g
1 lb · s²/ft	14.59 kg
1 lb · s²/ft	32.17 lb
1 lb · s²/ft	514.7 oz
1 N	224.8×10^{-3} lb
1 N	3.597 oz
1 oz	28.35 g
1 oz	28.35×10^{-3} kg
1 oz	62.50×10^{-3} lb
1 oz	161.9×10^{-6} lb · s²/in
1 oz	1.943×10^{-3} lb · s²/ft
1 oz	278.0×10^{-3} N

Stiffness

1 lb/in	175.1 N/m
1 N/m	5.710×10^{-3} lb/in

Damping

1 lb · s/in	175.1 N · s/m
1 N · s/m	1 kg/s
1 N · s/m	5.710×10^{-3} lb · s/in

Unbalance

1 g · mm	1.389×10^{-3} in · oz
1 in · oz	720.1 g · mm

Speed and frequency

1 cpm	16.67×10^{-3} Hz
1 Hz	60 cpm
50 Hz	3000 cpm
60 Hz	3600 cpm
1 rad/s	104.7×10^{-3} rpm ($\pi/30$ rpm)
1 rpm	9.549 rad/s ($30/\pi$ rad/s)

Pressure

1 atm	1.013 bar
1 atm	29.92 in Hg
1 atm	101.3 kPa
1 atm	14.70 lb/in^2
1 atm	760 mm Hg
1 bar	986.9×10^{-3} atm
1 bar	29.53 in Hg
1 bar	100 kPa
1 bar	14.50 lb/in^2
1 bar	750.1 mm Hg
1 in Hg	33.42×10^{-3} atm
1 in Hg	33.86×10^{-3} bar
1 in Hg	3.386 kPa
1 in Hg	491.2×10^{-3} lb/in^2
1 in Hg	25.4 mm Hg
1 kPa	9.869×10^{-3} atm
1 kPa	10×10^{-3} bar
1 kPa	295.2×10^{-3} in Hg
1 kPa	145.0×10^{-3} lb/in^2
1 kPa	7.501 mm Hg
1 lb/in^2	68.03×10^{-3} atm
1 lb/in^2	68.95×10^{-3} bar
1 lb/in^2	2.036 in Hg
1 lb/in^2	6.895 kPa
1 lb/in^2	51.71 mm Hg
1 mm Hg	1.316×10^{-3} atm
1 mm Hg	1.333×10^{-3} bar
1 mm Hg	$39.37 \; 10^{-3}$ in Hg
1 mm Hg	133.3×10^{-3} kPa
1 mm Hg	19.34×10^{-3} lb/in^2

Temperature

Use the following for temperature *differences* only.

1 °C	5/9 °F
1 °C	5/9 °R
1 °C	1 K
1 °F	9/5 °C
1 °F	1 °R
1 °F	9/5 K
1 °R	9/5 °C
1 °R	1 °F
1 K	1 °C
1 K	5/9 °F

Use the following for general temperature conversion.

X °C	5/9 (Y °F − 32°)
Y °F	(9/5 X °C) + 32°
X K	Y °C + 273.15
X °R	Y °F + 459.67
1 °R	9/5 K
1 K	5/9 °R

Torque

1 lb · in	113.0×10^{-3} N · m
1 lb · ft	12 lb · in
1 lb · ft	1.356 N · m
1 N · m	737.6×10^{-3} lb · ft
1 N · m	8.851 lb · in

Mass moment of inertia

1 in · lb · s^2	113.0×10^{-3} kg · m^2
1 kg · m^2	8.852 in · lb · s^2

Torsional stiffness

1 lb · ft/deg	1.356 N · m/deg
1 N · m/deg	737.6×10^{-3} lb · ft/deg

Torsional damping

1 lb · ft · s/deg	1.356 N · m · s/deg
1 N · m · s/deg	737.6×10^{-3} lb · ft · s/deg

Power

1 hp	745.7×10^{-3} kW
1 hp	550 ft · lb/s
1 kW	1.341 hp
1 kW	1 kJ/s
1 kW	737.6 ft · lb/s

Unit Prefixes

Multiple	Prefix	Symbol
10^{-18}	atto	a
10^{-15}	femto	f
10^{-12}	pico	p
10^{-9}	nano	n
10^{-6}	micro	μ
10^{-3}	milli	m
10^{-2}	centi	c
10^{-1}	deci	d
10^{1}	deka	da
10^{2}	hecto	h
10^{3}	kilo	k
10^{6}	mega	M
10^{9}	giga	G
10^{12}	tera	T
10^{15}	peta	P
10^{18}	exa	E

Unit Abbreviations

Abbreviation	Meaning	Comments
bhp	brake horsepower	
cpm	cycle per minute	frequency, but not shaft speed
deg	degree	
ft · lb	foot pound	work or energy, but not torque
g	acceleration of gravity	
g	gram	
hp	horsepower	
Hz	hertz (cycles per second)	
in · lb	inch pound	work or energy, but not torque
in/s	inch per second	
kcpm	thousands of cycles per minute	
kHz	kilohertz	
krpm	thousands of revolutions per minute	
kW	kilowatt	
lb	pound	
lb · in	pound inch	torque or moment, but not work
lb · ft	pound foot	torque or moment, but not work
mil	0.001 inch	
mm/s	millimeter per second	
mV/(in/s)	millivolt per in/s	velocity sensor scale factor
mV/(m/s^2)	millivolt per m/s^2	accelerometer scale factor
mV/(mm/s)	millivolt per mm/s	velocity sensor scale factor
mV/µm	millivolt per micrometer	displacement sensor scale factor
mV/g	millivolt per g	accelerometer scale factor
mV/mil	millivolt per mil	displacement sensor scale factor
MW	megawatt	
µm	micrometer	
N · m	newton meter	torque, moment, or work
N · m/s	newton meter per second	power; equal to a watt
oz	ounce	
pk	peak (zero-to-peak)	
pp	peak-to-peak	
rad	radian	
rad/s	radian per second	
rms	root-mean-square	
rpm	revolution per minute	shaft rotative speed
shp	shaft horsepower	
V	volt	
Vac	volt alternating current	
Vdc	volt direct current	
W	watt	

Force, Weight, and Mass in the US Customary System

Often, units of force and mass are written as *lbf* and *lbm*, for the pound, or *ozf* and *oz* for the ounce. Pounds and ounces are, fundamentally, units of *force*; thus, throughout this book, the units *lb* and *oz* are used with the understanding that force is implied. We find it more convenient to express US customary units of *mass* as $lb \cdot s^2/in$ or $lb \cdot s^2/ft$. (1 $lb \cdot s^2/ft$ is also called a *slug*, a derived unit of mass weighing 32.17 lb, but this is not a convenient unit for calculations which involve dimensional bookkeeping.)

According to Newton's Law, when a mass is subjected to an acceleration, in this case due to the earth's gravity, it produces a force, W:

$$W = mg \qquad\qquad (A7\text{-}1)$$

We perceive (and measure) this force as a *weight*. Using this equation, a balance weight that has a mass of $162 \times 10^{-6}\ lb \cdot s^2/in$, will weigh

$$W = \left(162 \times 10^{-6}\ \frac{lb \cdot s^2}{in}\right)\left(386.1\ \frac{in}{s^2}\right)$$

$$W = 0.0626\ lb\left(16\ \frac{oz}{lb}\right) = 1\ oz$$

This balance weight exerts a force, W, on your hand of 1 oz when held stationary in our 1 g gravitational field. However, when installed in a 3600 rpm rotor at a radius of 24 in, the force produced by this weight will be very different. This force can be found by substituting the centripetal acceleration, a, of the rotor for the acceleration due to gravity:

$$F = \left(\frac{W}{g}\right)a \qquad\qquad (A7\text{-}2)$$

Here $a = r_u \Omega^2$, where r_u is the radius of attachment, and Ω is the rotor speed in rad/s. Thus, Equation A7-2 becomes

$$F = \left(\frac{W}{g}\right)r_u \Omega^2 = mr_u\Omega^2 \qquad\qquad (A7\text{-}3)$$

where m is the mass of the weight, W/g.

We can calculate the force, F, using the middle part of Equation A7-3,

$$F = \left[\frac{1\text{ oz}}{386.1\text{ in/s}^2}\right]\left\{(24\text{ in})\left[(3600\text{ rpm})\left(\frac{\pi\text{ rad/s}}{30\text{ rpm}}\right)\right]^2\right\}$$

$$F = 8800\text{ oz}\left(\frac{1\text{ lb}}{16\text{ oz}}\right) = 550\text{ lb}$$

Or, using the right side of Equation A7-3, we can apply the conversion factor from a previous section,

$$F = \left[(1\text{ oz})\left(162 \times 10^{-6}\ \frac{\text{lb}\cdot\text{s}^2/\text{in}}{\text{oz}}\right)\right](24\text{ in})\left[(3600\text{ rpm})\left(\frac{\pi\text{ rad/s}}{30\text{ rpm}}\right)\right]^2$$

$$F = 550\text{ lb}$$

Appendix 8

Nomenclature

THROUGHOUT THIS BOOK, SCALARS (magnitude only) are displayed as *italic*; vectors (magnitude and direction) are displayed as ***bold italic***.

Upper case Roman

A	amplitude
A_F	amplitude of the forward rotating vector
A_{inst}	amplitude of a vibration vector in the instrumentation reference frame
A_R	amplitude of the reverse rotating vector
B_{inst}	amplitude of a vibration vector in the instrumentation reference frame
D	damping constant
D_{cr}	critical damping
D_E	effective damping
D_S	system damping
D_T	torsional damping
E	modulus of elasticity (Young's modulus)
F	force vector
F$_B$	radial force component
F$_D$	damping force
F$_P$	perturbation force
F$_S$	spring force
F$_T$	tangential force component
G	shear modulus
HS	heavy spot
I	(mass or section) moment of inertia
J	polar moment of inertia

K	spring stiffness constant
K_{strong}	strong spring stiffness in anisotropic systems
K_{weak}	weak spring stiffness in anisotropic systems
K_B	bearing spring stiffness
K_D	Direct Dynamic Stiffness
$\boldsymbol{K}_N$	nonsynchronous Dynamic Stiffness
K_Q	Quadrature Dynamic Stiffness
$\boldsymbol{K}_S$	synchronous Dynamic Stiffness
K_T	torsional spring stiffness
K_x	spring stiffness in X direction
K_y	spring stiffness in Y direction
L	length of shaft section
L	transducer orientation angle *left* of reference direction
M	rotor mass
P	power
Q	Synchronous Amplification Factor
$\boldsymbol{R}$	Arbitrary constant displacement vector
R	transducer orientation angle *right* of reference direction
T	period of a vibration signal
T	torque
U	transducer response plane axis that is aligned with the transducer
U	unbalance
V	transducer response plane axis that is perpendicular to the U axis
W	partial weight of the rotor supported by a particular bearing
X	multiple (order) of rotor speed (1X, 2X, ...)
X	axis of rectangular coordinate system
XY	coplanar, orthogonal transducers
X_R	rotated virtual X probe
Y	axis of rectangular coordinate system
Y_R	rotated virtual Y probe
Z	axial coordinate axis of rectangular coordinate system
Z	peak amplitude of response in axial direction

Lower case Roman

a	acceleration
c	radial clearance
d	displacement
d	differential, as in dt
e	base for natural logarithm, 2.718281828...
e	eccentricity

f	frequency
$f(\ )$	function
i	element counter, as in the ith position, x_i
j	$\sqrt{-1}$
j	element counter, as in the jth position, x_j
k	integer
l	unsupported rotor length
m	unbalance mass
n	multiplier of rotor speed (nX)
r	radius of outer surface of shaft
$\boldsymbol{r}$	shaft position or vibration vector
$\boldsymbol{r}_s$	shaft absolute vibration vector
$\boldsymbol{r}_c$	casing absolute vibration vector
$\boldsymbol{r}_{sr}$	shaft relative vibration vector
$\dot{\boldsymbol{r}}$	shaft velocity vector
$\ddot{\boldsymbol{r}}$	shaft acceleration vector
r_e	distance between mass center and geometric center of shaft
r_u	distance of unbalance mass from geometric center of shaft; typically, the radius of the balance ring
$s_{1,2}$	eigenvalues (roots) of the characteristic equation
t	time
$\boldsymbol{u}$	dummy vector variable
u	position in the direction of the U coordinate axis in the transducer response plane
v	linear velocity
v_{avg}	average angular velocity of swirling fluid
v	position in the direction of the V coordinate axis in the transducer response plane
x	position in the direction of the X coordinate axis
$\boldsymbol{x}$	vibration vector measured by X probe
x_d	in-phase (real) component of the complex vibration vector, $\boldsymbol{x}$
$\boldsymbol{x}_{inst}$	vibration vector measured by the X transducer, using instrumentation phase
x_q	quadrature (imaginary) component of the complex vibration vector, $\boldsymbol{x}$
$\boldsymbol{x}_R$	vibration vector measured by virtual X probe
y	position in the direction of the Y coordinate axis
$\boldsymbol{y}$	vibration vector measured by Y probe
y_d	in-phase (real) component of the complex vibration vector, $\boldsymbol{y}$
$\boldsymbol{y}_{inst}$	vibration vector measured by the Y transducer, using instrumentation phase

y_q quadrature (imaginary) component of the complex vibration vector, $\boldsymbol{y}$

$\boldsymbol{y}_R$ vibration vector measured by virtual Y probe

z position in the directions of the Z coordinate axis

Upper case Greek

Ø	Phi	used in KØ to symbolize the Keyphasor probe or event
$\varPhi$	Phi	general phase angle
$\varPhi$		amplitude of torsional vibration
$\varPsi$	Psi	attitude angle
$\varOmega$	Omega	shaft rotative speed
$\varOmega_{res}$		resonance speed
$\varOmega_{th}$		Threshold of Instability

Lower case Greek

α	alpha	phase of $\boldsymbol{r}$ with respect to measurement transducer at $t = 0$ (KØ event), expressed in the mathematical measurement convention
α_{inst}		phase lag angle in the instrumentation measurement convention
β_{inst}	beta	phase lag angle in the instrumentation measurement convention
δ	delta	angular location of the force vector at $t = 0$ (KØ event)
δ		logarithmic decrement
γ	gamma	growth/decay rate
ε	epsilon	eccentricity ratio
ζ	zeta	damping factor
θ	theta	angle of $\boldsymbol{r}$ with respect to the measurement axis in the complex plane
θ		angular deflection of a shaft
θ_K		angle of the Keyphasor transducer with respect to a reference direction
θ_T		angle of the vibration transducer with respect to a reference direction
λ	lambda	Fluid Circumferential Average Velocity Ratio, a measure of fluid circulation
π	pi	the ratio of the circumference of a circle to its diameter, 3.141592654...
τ	tau	torsional shear stress
ϕ	phi	relative angular displacement (angle of twist) of a shaft, measured between two axial locations

$\dot{\phi}$		relative angular velocity of a shaft, measured between two axial locations
$\ddot{\phi}$		relative angular acceleration of a shaft, measured between two axial locations
ϕ_F		phase of the forward vector in the mathematical measurement convention
ϕ_R		phase of the reverse vector in the mathematical measurement convention
ω	omega	any nonsynchronous frequency
ω_d		damped natural frequency of vibration
ω_n		undamped natural frequency of vibration

Glossary

⅓X, ⅖X, ½X, 4/9X, etc.

In a complex vibration signal, signal components having frequencies equal to fractions of rotative speed. Also called subsynchronous and, when the numerator is 1, subharmonic.

1X

In a complex vibration signal, the signal component that occurs at the same frequency as rotative speed (1 times rotor speed). Also called synchronous.

2X, 3X, etc.

In a complex vibration signal, signal components having frequencies equal to integer multiples of shaft rotative speed. Also called harmonic, superharmonic, and supersynchronous.

Absolute phase

The timing difference between a once-per-turn reference event (Keyphasor event) and the first positive peak of a filtered vibration signal (filtered to a harmonic of running speed), expressed as degrees phase lag.

Absolute vibration

Vibration of an object measured relative to an inertial (fixed) reference frame. Accelerometers and velocity transducers measure absolute vibration, typically of machine housings or structures; they are often referred to as seismic or inertial transducers.

Acceleration

The rate of change of velocity with time. Acceleration is the first derivative of velocity and the second derivative of displacement. Acceleration is a zero-to-peak (pk) measurement.

Accelerometer

An inertial transducer that converts acceleration into an electrical signal.

Acceptance region

On a 1X or 2X polar APHT plot, a region of acceptable steady state response defined by amplitude and phase boundaries. Based on normal historical data for the machine, the user defines one or more acceptance regions for each radial vibration measurement and operating condition. Acceptance regions can also be defined in terms of the normal average shaft centerline position.

Accuracy

The degree of conformity of a calculation or measurement to a standard or true value. It is often expressed as a ratio, in percent, of the error to the full-scale meter reading, or of the error to the actual input value. Accuracy is not the same as precision (repeatability).

Aeroderivative

Aircraft jet (gas turbine) engines that have been modified for industrial use.

Aerodynamic instability

An abnormal aerodynamic flow in a compressor. Stall and surge are caused by flow separation in blades or impellers; choke is caused by supersonic flow. Aerodynamic instabilities can couple to the rotor dynamics of the machine.

Alarm

See: Alert

Alert (point)

The parameter value that activates a warning of a condition requiring corrective action or investigation. Synonymous with *alarm*.

Aliasing

In measurements, false indication of frequency components caused by sampling a dynamic signal at too low a sampling frequency. According to the Nyquist criterion, the sampling frequency must be at least twice the highest frequency component in the signal. Aliasing can be eliminated by adjusting the sampling frequency or by using a low-pass filter on the signal prior to sampling (antialias filter). The primary disadvantage of antialias filtering is that it causes phase and amplitude errors (as is the case with virtually any type of filtering).

Alignment

A machine is in perfect internal alignment when the average shaft centerline position is in the center of each interstage diaphragm or seal and the average shaft centerline of the rotor operates at the design position in the bearing. Two machines are in perfect external alignment when the shaft centerlines are collinear at the coupling and operate in their design axial positions within each machine. Also, the process of positioning machine components such as bearings, diaphragms, rotors, casing, foundation, piping, etc., with respect to each other so that they are aligned within an acceptable tolerance under normal operating conditions.

Amplification Factor, Nonsynchronous

See: Nonsynchronous Amplification Factor

Amplification Factor, Synchronous

See: Synchronous Amplification Factor

Amplitude

The magnitude of periodic dynamic motion (vibration) or position. Amplitude is typically expressed in terms of peak-to-peak, zero-to-peak, root-mean-square, or average.

Amplitude modulation

The process whereby variation in the amplitude of a vibration signal results in a variation of the amplitude of a carrier signal. AM is used when high frequency signal recordings are needed (for example, for gear mesh frequencies). AM (also called direct) tape recorders have a finite lower frequency response above zero hertz (dc). They capture dynamic data above the lower response frequency, but not the average shaft position data (dc voltage), which is also available from a proximity probe signal.

Anisotropy

A system or material property such as stiffness, damping, elasticity, density, composition, conductivity, etc., that varies with respect to the direction it is measured.

Antialias filter

A low-pass filter which is used to prevent false frequency components from appearing in the spectrum of a digitally sampled signal.

Antinode

A location on a mode shape where the vibration amplitude is maximum.

Antiswirl

A technique used in the bearings and seals of pumps and compressors to improve rotor stability. To decrease or prevent fluid circumferential flow around the rotor, fluid is injected into the clearance in the direction opposing the fluid dragged into rotation.

Antiswirl injection

The injection of fluid tangentially into a bearing or seal, against rotation, to control a fluid-induced instability problem. Antiswirl injection increases the Threshold of Instability by decreasing λ.

APHT plot (Amplitude-PHase-Time)

A trend plot of filtered vibration amplitude and phase lag angle data in a rectangular or polar format. Commonly used for 1X, 2X and nX vibration data.

API

The American Petroleum Institute is a national trade organization representing the petroleum industry. API was formed in 1919 to standardize specifications for oil drilling and production equipment.

Apparent power

The product of the applied rms voltage times the rms current.

Asymmetry

A geometric property of an object such that when it is divided by a plane, the pieces are not similar, or when it is subjected to a certain operation (rotation, inversion, etc.), it does not appear the same unless the operation returns it to its original condition.

Asymmetric rotor

A rotor whose cross section, when rotated at any angle about its geometric center, does not appear the same unless returned to its original orientation; for example, an elliptical cross section, a rotor with a keyway, or a rotor section with a crack.

Asynchronous

Not synchronized with a timing signal. Two waveforms sampled at slightly different times are said to be asynchronous waveforms.

Attenuation

A reduction in amplitude of a signal. Also, the decrease in amplitude that results from the transmission of vibration energy from one machine part to another (for example shaft to fluid-film bearing housing).

Attitude angle

In a bearing, the angle between the resultant of the radial loads acting on a rotor and a line connecting the bearing and shaft centers, measured in the direction of rotation. Sometimes confused with rotor position angle.

Auxiliary machines

Machines that assist process machines. Auxiliary machines include lube oil systems, sealing systems, fuel delivery systems, cooling systems, and, in power plants, condensate feedwater systems. Lube oil systems supply fluid-film bearings with clean lubricant at the correct pressure, flow rate, and temperature. Sealing systems, which can be quite complex, provide buffer oil or gas where needed. Cooling systems range from elaborate cooling tower systems in power plants, to interstage cooling systems, to lube oil cooling systems.

Average amplitude

An amplitude measurement rarely used for vibration signals; the half cycle average amplitude of a sine wave is 0.637 x zero-to-peak (pk) amplitude. This formula applies to sinusoidal (single frequency) signals only.

Average shaft centerline plot

A transient data or trend plot of the average shaft centerline position, presented in an *XY* (rectangular) format.

Average shaft position

The average position of the shaft relative to the displacement probe and its mounting. The most common application is rotor axial (thrust) position relative to the thrust bearing. Another important application is average shaft radial position. These measurements are made using the dc (position) component of the proximity probe signal. Two proximity probes mounted in an *XY* configuration are required for a two-dimensional, radial position measurement.

Axial

In the same direction as the shaft centerline (the axis of shaft rotation).

Axial Dynamic Stiffness

The ratio of the dynamic axial force to the dynamic axial response of a rotor system.

Axial position

The average position or change in position of a rotor in the axial direction with respect to some fixed reference. Typically, the reference is the thrust bearing support structure or other casing member to which the displacement probe is mounted. The probe may observe the thrust collar or some other integral, axial shaft surface. Also called thrust position.

Axial vibration

Vibration of the rotor shaft or machine casing in the axial direction.

Balance-of-plant machinery

All machinery in a plant that is considered neither critical nor essential. Many of these machines have tandem or spared installations (redundant installations).

Balance plane

A specific axial location in a machine at which balance weights may be installed.

Balance resonance speed

The shaft rotative speed which approximately coincides with a rotor system natural frequency. The vibration characteristics are a peak in the 1X amplitude together with a significant increase in the 1X vibration phase lag angle.

Balancing

The act of adjusting the radial mass distribution of a rotor at one or more balance planes so that the center of mass (principal axis of inertia) is within an acceptable distance from the rotor geometric center. This reduces the 1X lateral vibration of the rotor.

Band-pass filter

A filter that has a single transmission band extending from a lower corner frequency to an upper corner frequency. The amplitude at the corner frequencies is 70% (-3 dB) of the amplitude at the center frequency.

Bandwidth

The span between the corner frequencies of a band-pass filter. Normally expressed in terms of frequency for constant bandwidth filters and as a percent of the center frequency for constant Q (constant percentage) filters.

Baseline data

A set of reference data acquired when a machine is in acceptable condition, usually after installation, overhaul, or turnaround.

Baseplate

A cast or fabricated steel support for a machine. The baseplate would normally include the pedestals for all the machines in the machine train. The baseplate can be directly grouted and bolted to a foundation. Also called a soleplate.

Bearing

Any low friction structure which supports the rotor and provides dynamic constraint in the radial (lateral) and/or axial (thrust) directions. The main categories are fluid-film bearings, rolling element bearings, magnetic bearings, and foil bearings.

BEP (Best efficiency point)

The flow at which a pump operates with maximum efficiency (the minimum amount of losses). The BEP is important for two reasons: operating costs are minimized and radial (side) loads are minimized.

Blade passing frequency

The number of blades (on a disk or stage) times shaft rotative speed. The blade passing frequency is a potential vibration frequency on any machine with blades (a turbine, axial compressor, fan, propeller, etc.).

Bode plot

A pair of graphs in rectangular (Cartesian) format displaying the amplitude and phase of the 1X vibration vector as a function of shaft rotative speed. The Y axis of the top graph represents 1X phase, measured as positive phase lag, increasing downward; the Y axis of the bottom graph represents 1X amplitude. Both X axes represent shaft rotative speed or perturbation frequency. Sometimes called an unbalance response plot. Also used for 2X, 3X, etc. vibration vectors.

Bow

A condition of plastic deformation of a shaft which results in a bent geometric shaft centerline. Often the centerline is bent in a single plane, due to gravity sag, thermal warping, etc.; however, the bow may be three dimensional (corkscrew). Shaft bow can be detected by measuring the shaft relative displacement (the eccentricity) with a proximity probe at rotor slow roll speed.

Cage frequency

See: Fundamental train frequency

Calibration weight

A weight of known magnitude which is placed on the rotor at a known axial and angular location, in order to measure the resulting change in machine 1X vibration response at known operating conditions. Sometimes called a trial weight.

Campbell diagram

A plot of rotor system natural frequencies (vertical axis) versus excitation frequencies (horizontal axis). The plot allows a designer to detect when frequencies produced by the machine, including the harmonics of running speed, are close to a natural frequency of the system. Diagonal lines represent the frequencies that could be produced by the rotor system. Horizontal lines represent natural frequencies as they exist in the machine at operating speed.

Cartesian format

See: XY plot

Cascade plot

See: Spectrum cascade plot

Casing expansion

A measurement of the axial position of the machine casing relative to a fixed reference, usually the foundation. The measurement is typically made with a linear variable differential transformer (LVDT) installed on the foundation at the opposite end of the machine from the point where the casing is attached to the foundation. Changes in casing axial position are the result of thermal expansion and contraction of the casing during start-up and shutdown.

Casing transducer

A velocity or acceleration transducer that measures the absolute vibration of the machine housing or structure. These transducers measure absolute vibration relative to an internal inertial reference and are referred to as seismic or inertial transducers.

CCW

Counterclockwise. See: *X to Y*

Center frequency

For band-pass filters, the arithmetic center of a constant bandwidth filter or the geometric center (midpoint on a logarithmic scale) of a constant percentage filter.

Centerline position

See: Average shaft position

Channel

A single transducer and the instrumentation hardware path to display or record its output signal.

Characteristic equation

A polynomial in s that describes the free vibration behavior of a system. For a second order system, the characteristic equation is a quadratic polynomial in s. The values of s that satisfy this equation are the roots of the equation and are also called the eigenvalues, characteristic values, or poles.

Characteristic values

The roots, or eigenvalues, of the characteristic equation.

Clearance circle

The circle or ellipse traced out by the shaft centerline as the shaft walks around in contact with the bearing or seal. The clearance circle should be documented on the average shaft centerline plot.

Clearance, diametral

The diameter of the available clearance in which the shaft can move. The diameter of the clearance circle.

Clearance, radial

The distance from the bearing or seal center to the shaft centerline when the shaft contacts the bearing or seal. The radius of the clearance circle.

Coastdown

A machine speed change from higher to lower rpm during shutdown; typically, when a machine goes from operating speed to zero, or near zero, speed.

Complex conjugate

A complex number formed by changing the sign of the imaginary (quadrature) term of a complex number. The result of multiplying a number by its complex conjugate is a real number equal to the sum of the squares of the two terms.

Cold water stands

An arrangement of piping and brackets installed along a machine foundation for hot alignment measurements. Proximity probes observe exposed shaft areas or targets on the machine casing from brackets through which water circulates. This provides a thermally stable reference for the alignment measurement.

Compensation

See: Runout compensation

Complex number

A number of the form $x + jy$, where $j = \sqrt{-1}$. A complex number is equivalent to a point that is plotted in the complex plane. In mathematics, a complex number has a real part and an imaginary part. In machinery applications, complex numbers are used for rotor modeling and to represent vibration vectors. Dynamic Stiffness is a complex number; the two parts are referred to as direct and quadrature, respectively. Complex numbers can be added, subtracted, multiplied, and divided.

Conditional baseline data

Reference data sets used for a short term comparison of correlation, typically under different operating conditions.

Constant bandwidth filter

A band-pass filter having a fixed frequency bandwidth regardless of the value of the center frequency.

Constant percentage filter

A band-pass filter whose bandwidth is a fixed percentage of the center frequency. Also called a constant Q filter.

Constant Q filter

See: Constant percentage filter

Critical

Defined by the API [7] as any balance resonance frequency with a Synchronous Amplification Factor > 2.5.

Critically damped

See: Damping factor

Critical machinery

Machinery that represents such large business risks, including economic, safety, government compliance, or production interruption, that failures cannot be tolerated.

Critical speed

In general, any shaft rotative speed which is associated with high vibration amplitudes. When it corresponds to the resonance frequency of a rotor radial vibration mode that is excited by rotor unbalance, it is more correctly called the *balance resonance speed*.

Critical speed map

An *XY* (Cartesian) diagram used in rotating machinery design as a tool to approximate the effect of changes in bearings, supports, and pedestal designs on system natural frequencies. The X axis represents bearing stiffness and the Y axis represents rotor system natural frequency.

Cross-axis sensitivity

The ratio of change in the signal output to an incremental change in the input along any axis perpendicular to the sensitive axis of an inertial (seismic) transducer.

Crosstalk

Interference or noise in a transducer signal or channel which originates in another transducer or channel. Crosstalk can occur when the tips of two proximity probes are too close together. The interaction of the probes' electromagnetic fields causes a noise component in each of the transducers' output signals. The frequency of the noise component is the difference (beat frequency) of the two Proximitor oscillator frequencies.

CW

Clockwise. See: Y to X

Cycle

One complete sequence of values of a periodic quantity. A cycle of vibration represents one complete set of signal values.

Cylinder expansion

See: Casing expansion

Damped natural frequency

The natural frequency of a mechanical system that includes the effects of damping. Damping shifts the natural frequency of a system to slightly below the undamped natural frequency.

Damping factor

The damping factor, ζ, is the ratio of the damping to the critical damping, a nondimensional number that defines the behavior of a freely vibrating mechanical system. If $\zeta < 1$, the system is *subcritically damped* (underdamped) and, when disturbed, will oscillate with decreasing amplitude. The larger (closer to 1) the damping factor, the more quickly the vibration will die away. When $\zeta = 1$, the system is *critically damped* and will not vibrate, but will return to the equilibrium position in the shortest possible time without overshooting (oscillating). When $\zeta > 1$, the system is *supercritically damped* (overdamped) and will return relatively slowly to the equilibrium position without any overshoot or oscillation.

Damping force

A force that is proportional to the speed of a body and acts in a direction opposite to the velocity: $F = -D\dot{r}$, where D is the damping constant, and $\dot{r}$ is the velocity of the body. The damping force is produced by the viscosity of the fluid through which the body is moving.

Damping stiffness

In the simple rotor model, the dynamic stiffness term produced by the damping force. The damping stiffness is $jD\omega$, where D is the damping, ω is the frequency of vibration, and $j = \sqrt{-1}$. The j indicates that the damping stiffness acts at 90° to the direction of the applied dynamic force. Like the mass stiffness, the damping stiffness is a dynamic stiffness, and it only appears when the rotor centerline has nonzero velocity.

Danger (point)

A parameter value at which immediate action is required, up to and including automatic or manual shutdown of a system.

Decibel (dB)

The logarithm of the ratio of the power (P) or voltage (V) levels of electrical signals. $dB = 10 \log P_1 / P_2 = 20 \log V_1 / V_2$.

Degree(s) of freedom

In rotor system modeling, the number of independent displacement variables. For example, a rotor system modeled with one rotor mass using the complex variable $r = x + jy$, has one complex degree of freedom (1-CDOF), but the same rotor system modeled treating the two real variables, x and y, independently has two real degrees of freedom (2-DOF or 2-RDOF).

Detector

See: Transducer

Diagnostics

The process of finding an answer or solution to a problematic situation. Diagnostics is inherently reactive in nature. It requires a problem to exist before an answer is sought.

Differential expansion

The measurement of the axial position of the rotor with respect to the machine casing at some distance from the thrust bearing. Changes in axial position relative to the casing affect axial clearances and are usually the result of different rotor and casing thermal expansion rates during startup and shutdown. The measurement is typically made with a proximity probe transducer mounted to the machine casing and observing an axial surface (for example, collar) of the rotor. The measurement is usually incorporated as part of a Turbine Supervisory Instrumentation system.

Differential phase

A technique which measures the phase difference between vibration signals filtered to the same frequency at different axial locations on a rotor system. It is primarily used for determining the location of the source of an instability. The vibration signal whose phase leads all others usually indicates the transducer location which is closest to the source of the instability.

Digital runout compensation

The process of digitally sampling the unfiltered signal from the proximity transducer at slow roll speed and subtracting it from the signal at any other speed. It requires a phase reference such as a Keyphasor signal.

Digital vector filter

See: Vector filter

Direct

In Dynamic Stiffness, acting in the same or opposite direction to the applied dynamic force. See: Dynamic Stiffness, Direct.

Direct data

Data or a signal that represents the original transducer signal. Sometimes called unfiltered, raw, all pass, or overall data.

Disk

A wheel, usually solid and axially slim, on which the mechanical work of a rotating machine is performed or from which work is extracted. Disks may be integral to or mounted on the shaft. Examples of disks are a turbine disk, compressor wheel, and pump impeller.

Displacement

The change in position of an object relative to a reference. Machinery displacement vibration is typically a peak-to-peak measurement of the observed oscillating motion and is usually expressed in units of mil pp or μm pp. Proximity probes measure displacement directly.

Dominant end

The end of a machine where most of the unbalance is concentrated. For a two-mode machine, the indicated heavy spots for the two modes will be approximately in the same direction on the polar plot from the dominant end.

Driven

Most driven machines take input in the form of rotating kinetic energy and convert it to useful work. Driven machines include blowers, fans, generators, exciters, pumps, and compressors. These machines increase the energy state of the working fluid or product.

Driver

Drivers are machines that act as prime movers; most convert some form of energy to the kinetic energy of rotation. Internal combustion engines and gas turbines utilize the chemical energy of fuel, steam turbines use the potential and kinetic energy of high pressure and high temperature steam, and electric motors use the energy of electricity. Two types of drivers convert the kinetic energy of one substance to the kinetic energy of rotation: wind turbines use moving air, and hydro turbines use moving water, which was previously stored as gravitational potential energy.

Dual probe

A pair of transducers, consisting of a proximity probe and velocity transducer, installed at the same point (usually in a common junction box on the machine bearing housing) with the same radial orientation. Four separate measurements are provided by this transducer system: shaft relative radial position within the bearing clearance, shaft dynamic motion relative to the bearing, machine casing absolute vibration measured by the velocity transducer, and shaft absolute motion represented by the summation of the velocity signal integrated to displacement and the shaft relative signal.

Dwell time

During a rub, the period of time during which the rotor maintains contact with the stationary part.

Dynamic data

Data, such as a waveform, which is rapidly changing. Dynamic data usually mimics the raw data in a way that allows further signal processing, such as for direct orbit and timebase displays, and spectrum. From dynamic data, it is possible to derive static data signal parameters, such as direct amplitude, filtered amplitude, and phase lag angle. See: Static data

Dynamic equilibrium

While moving in an orbit, a rotor is in dynamic equilibrium if, when it is subjected to some temporary, disturbing force, it eventually returns to the original orbit; the growth/decay rate, γ, is less than zero.

Dynamic motion

See: Vibration

Dynamic Stiffness

The ratio of the applied dynamic force to the dynamic response of a mechanical system. Dynamic Stiffness consists of the spring stiffness of the mechanical system complemented by the dynamic effects of mass and damping. Dynamic Stiffness is a characteristic of a system, and it opposes an applied dynamic force to limit vibration response.

Dynamic Stiffness, Direct

The component of complex Dynamic Stiffness, consisting of spring stiffness and mass stiffness, which acts at 0° or 180° to (collinear with) the applied dynamic force. In mathematical terms, it is called the real component.

Dynamic Stiffness, Quadrature

The component of complex Dynamic Stiffness, which acts at 90° to the applied dynamic force. In mathematical terms, it is the imaginary part of Dynamic Stiffness, which is indicated by j in the equation.

Dynamic transducer

A transducer that is capable of capturing high-frequency transient events. For example, a pressure transducer with a frequency response in the kHz range would be considered to be a dynamic transducer. This is in contrast to a transducer with a very slow time response that essentially produces static (averaged) data, such as a thermocouple imbedded in bearing backing.

Eccentricity

The radial displacement of the rotor journal centerline from the geometric center of a fluid-film bearing.

Eccentricity, peak-to-peak

The difference between the positive and negative extremes of the slow roll rotor bow at the measurement location, usually near the free end of a shaft. The shaft bow may be due to permanent mechanical bow or temporary thermal bow.

Eccentricity position (obsolete)

See: Average shaft position

Eccentricity ratio

A dimensionless quantity representing the average position of the shaft within the bearing compared to the available clearance. It is calculated by dividing the distance between the bearing center and the shaft centerline position by the available radial clearance. The eccentricity ratio is zero when the shaft is at the center of the bearing, and one when the shaft is in contact with the bearing wall. The *average* eccentricity ratio is obtained by using the distance between the average position of the shaft centerline and the bearing (seal) centerline. The *dynamic* eccentricity ratio is obtained by using the *instantaneous* position of the shaft within the bearing.

Eccentricity, slow roll

See: Eccentricity peak-to-peak

Eddy current

A localized electric current induced in a conductive material which experiences a changing magnetic field. The operating principle of the eddy current proximity probe.

Effective damping

In synchronous rotor behavior, the damping after modification by the effects of fluid circulation. The effective damping, D_E, of the synchronous rotor system is $D_E = D(1-\lambda)$, where D is the damping, and λ is the Fluid

Circumferential Average Velocity Ratio. Because λ is usually a positive number less than 0.5, the effective damping for a system is usually less than the actual damping constant, D. The effective damping is the slope of the synchronous Quadrature Dynamic Stiffness.

Eigenvalue

A complex number that contains information about the free vibration behavior of a system. It is also called a root of the characteristic equation, a characteristic value, or a pole of the system. The real part of the eigenvalue is the growth/decay rate; the imaginary part is the damped natural frequency of the system.

Elastic bow

Rotor bow due to static radial loads that do not exceed the yield strength of the rotor. They can be caused, for example, by process fluid loads in pumps, internal misalignment, and partial arc steam admission in steam turbines, but most commonly, in a horizontal machine, by the weight of the rotor.

Electrical runout

A noise component in the output signal of an eddy current transducer system due to nonuniform properties of electrical conductivity or magnetic permeability, or local (spot) magnetic fields on the circumference of the observed shaft surface. Runout produces a change in the output signal which does not result from a probe gap change. The error repeats exactly with each shaft revolution as long as the shaft does not change axial position.

Element Passage Frequency (EPx)

In rolling element bearings, the frequency at which rolling elements pass a fixed point on either the inner or outer race. Harmonics of the element passage frequency are then indicated as 2EPx, 3EPx, ..., nEPx.

Ellipticity

The difference between the major and minor axes of an ellipse, divided by the major axis: 0 denotes a circle and 1 denotes a straight line.

Engineering units

Units of measurement; typically, for vibration, μm, mil, mm/s, in/s, g, or similar.

Error

The difference between the indicated value and the true value of the measured variable. It is often expressed as relative error, that is, as a percent of the output reading of the transducer.

Essential machinery
Machinery that can cause partial production interruption or some other form of business loss (such as an emissions violation) if it fails or runs at reduced capacity.

Externally pressurized bearing
A fully lubricated, fluid-film bearing that derives its primary support force from hydrostatic pressure supplied by a source external to the bearing. Also called a hydrostatic bearing.

Filter
Electronic circuitry designed to pass or reject a specific frequency band of a signal.

Flexible rotor
Rotors that experience significant bending modes. The first mode of a flexible rotor with its mass supported between bearings is usually a simple, predominantly in-phase bending mode. The second mode of a flexible rotor is usually an out-of-phase, S-shaped bending mode. Machines with fluid-film bearings can have rigid body behavior in the very lowest modes and transition to flexible rotor behavior at higher modes.

Fluid Circumferential Average Velocity Ratio, (lambda, λ)
The dimensionless ratio of the average angular velocity of a fluid in a bearing, seal, or other rotor-to-stator clearance, divided by shaft angular velocity, Ω. $\lambda\Omega$ is the average angular velocity of the circulating fluid.

Fluid-film bearing
A bearing which supports the shaft on a thin film of oil. The fluid-film layer may be generated primarily by journal rotation (an internally pressurized, or hydrodynamic bearing) or by external pressure (an externally pressurized, or hydrostatic bearing). Film thickness is normally in the range of several micrometers to tens of micrometers.

Fluid-induced instability
Self-excited rotor lateral vibration caused by interaction between the rotor and a surrounding fluid.

Foil bearing
A gas bearing comprised of a cylindrical shell lined with corrugated bump foils topped with a thin flat foil. The foil complies to the hydrodynamic pressure distribution of the gas inside the bearing, resulting in a larger gap than would be present for an identically loaded, rigid gas bearing.

Forced mode shape
The deflection shape of the rotor at a particular operating speed. It is the sum of several free vibration (natural) mode shapes, each of which is excited to varying degrees by the unbalance distribution of the system.

Forced vibration

The response vibration of a mechanical system due to a forcing function (exciting force). Typically, forced vibration has the same frequency as that of the exciting force.

Forward component

See: Forward and reverse vectors

Forward and reverse vectors

A pair of counterrotating vectors that, when added, reconstruct a filtered orbit. Both vectors rotate at the same frequency; the ratio of the amplitudes determines both the ellipticity and direction of precession of the orbit.

Forward precession

Precession of a shaft in the same direction as its rotation.

Fracture toughness

A measure of a material's resistance to fast fracture. It is a function of the alloy, heat treatment, temperature, and rate of loading.

Free vibration

Vibration response of a mechanical system following an initial disturbance. If the system is underdamped (subcritically damped), the mechanical system vibrates at one or more of its natural frequencies with decaying amplitude. If it is critically damped or overdamped (supercritically damped), the system will not vibrate, but will return slowly to the equilibrium position with no oscillation (overshoot).

Frequency

The repetition rate of a periodic vibration per unit of time. Frequency is typically expressed in units of cycles per second (Hz), cycles per minute (cpm), or radians per second (rad/s).

Frequency component

The amplitude, frequency, and phase characteristics of a dynamic signal after it has been filtered to a single frequency.

Frequency modulation

Variation of the frequency of a carrier signal caused by variation in the amplitude of a vibration signal. FM tape recordings have a frequency response down to zero hertz (dc). This allows recording of proximity probe dc gap voltages, which represent average shaft position.

Friction instability

An instability in rotors caused by friction between disks and the rotor or by internal material friction. It manifests itself as large amplitude, subsynchronous vibration. Elastic bow in built up rotors has been known to cause friction instability.

Full annular rub

    Rub that maintains continuous contact over all of the vibration cycle. It may occur with either forward or reverse precession.

Full spectrum

    A spectrum of an orbit, calculated from the simultaneously sampled waveforms from a pair of *XY* transducers. It displays the amplitudes versus frequency of precession of the forward and reverse components of the orbit, with forward precession to the right and reverse precession to the left.

Full spectrum cascade plot

    See: Spectrum cascade plot

Full spectrum waterfall plot

    See: Spectrum waterfall plot

Fundamental

    The lowest frequency of a series in frequency analysis. Integer (1, 2, 3, …) multiples of this frequency are called harmonics. Usually, in rotor systems, the fundamental frequency is rotative speed, 1X. Higher harmonics are 2X, 3X, etc.

Fundamental train frequency

    In rolling element bearings, the frequency at which the cage and element assembly completes one revolution of the bearing. For bearings with fixed outer races, the fundamental train frequency is near ½X.

g

    The standard acceleration due to earth's gravity at 45° latitude and sea level. By international agreement, $g = 9.807 \text{ m/s}^2 = 386.1 \text{ in/s}^2 = 32.17 \text{ ft/s}^2$

Gain

    See: Signal gain

Gap voltage

    The voltage output of a proximity transducer system indicating the distance (gap) between the transducer and the object observed.

Gear mesh forces

    The contact forces that result from tooth contact in gears. The lateral gear mesh force can be resolved into a tangential force and a radial separation force as a function of the pressure angle. The tangential force is directly related to the torque delivery of the gears, the product of the tangential force and the pitch radius of the gear. The radial separation force attempts to separate the gears; for a typical 20° pressure angle, it is about 37% of the tangential force. Single helical gearing can also produce an axial force.

Gear mesh frequency

    The number of gear teeth times shaft rotative speed.

General purpose machinery

See: Balance of plant machinery

Glitch

The combination of mechanical and electrical runout in the proximity probe viewing area. Glitch produces a signal variation that does not represent vibration.

Grout

An epoxy-based material used to fill all voids between a soleplate, or baseplate, and the foundation to improve the load transfer between the machine and the ground.

Growth/decay rate, γ

The real part of the complex eigenvalue that describes how free vibration amplitude changes over time. The magnitude and sign of γ control how fast the vibration amplitude increases or decreases.

Half-power Bandwidth method

A method, adopted by API, to measure the Synchronous Amplification Factor. It is the dimensionless ratio of the rpm of the resonance peak to the half-power bandwidth (at 70% of resonance amplitude).

Half spectrum

A display of the amplitude as a function of frequency of a signal's components calculated from the waveform from a single transducer. See: Full spectrum

Half spectrum cascade plot

See: Spectrum cascade plot

Half spectrum waterfall plot

See: Spectrum waterfall plot

Harmonic

A vibration frequency that is an integer multiple of the fundamental, or lowest frequency in a series.

Harmonic series

A series of vibration signal components whose frequencies are integer multiples of the fundamental, or lowest frequency, vibration component; for example, 1X, 2X, 3X, etc., or ½X, 1X, ³⁄₂X, etc.

Harmonic vibration

Sinusoidal vibration with a single frequency component.

Heavy spot (HS)

The angular location of the unbalance at a specific axial location on a rotor.

Hertz

Unit of frequency measurement in cycles per second (Hz).

High-eccentricity natural frequency

The natural frequency of a rotor system operating at a high eccentricity ratio in a fluid-film bearing. The high-eccentricity natural frequency is usually close to the nameplate resonance.

High frequency

A frequency range, typically above 5 kHz, used to measure the very high vibration frequencies generated in structures by rolling element bearing components with microscopic faults.

High-pass filter

A filter having a transmission band extending from a lower corner frequency (where amplitude is attenuated by 3 dB) to the upper frequency response limit of the transducer or instrument.

High spot

In 1X vibration, the location on the shaft directly under the vibration probe when the shaft makes its closest approach to that probe. It corresponds to the positive peak of the vibration waveform.

Homogeneous equation

A differential equation in which the forcing function is zero.

HS

Abbreviation for heavy spot.

Hydraulic load

A fluid radial load which appears in pumps because of asymmetries in the design of the volute or operation of the pump off its best efficiency point (BEP). Also called a preload or sideload.

Hydrodynamic bearing

See: Internally pressurized bearing

Hydrostatic bearing

See: Externally pressurized bearing

Hysteretic damping

A form of internal material loss that will remove energy from vibrating systems. The hysteretic damping force is directly proportional to the velocity and inversely proportional to the frequency of the vibration.

Impulse response

The response to a well-defined, short duration, impulsive force such as produced by a hammer. The force is considered to be of such short duration that no significant system changes occur during that time.

Inboard

When identifying the location of an object on a single machine, it is the side toward the inside of the machine case; for example, the seal is *inboard* of the bearing. When identifying the location of two similar components of a machine case, it is the one toward the driver coupling; for example, the *inboard* bearing of the HP compressor. When there is a chance of ambiguity, the components should be defined and a written record kept.

In phase

A response in the same direction as the applied force vector. The magnitude of the response vector times the cosine of the angle between the force and response vectors.

Inertially referenced

Referenced to a mass element whose inertia is presumed to keep it stationary; a transducer with an internal inertial reference mass.

Influence coefficient

See: Influence vector

Influence vector

A complex number that describes how the 1X amplitude and phase of vibration change when a balance weight is added to the machine. Each influence vector is specific to a particular combination of weight and measurement planes and to a particular set of operating conditions, including speed, load, temperature, and alignment state.

Influence vector, direct

An influence vector where the measured vibration vector and the unbalance force vector are in the same or closely associated planes along the rotor axis.

Influence vector, inverse

An influence vector whose magnitude is the reciprocal of the magnitude of a standard influence vector.

Influence vector, longitudinal

An influence vector where the measured vibration vector and the unbalance force vector are in distinctly different planes along the rotor axis.

Inner race ball pass frequency

In rolling element bearings, the frequency at which rolling elements pass a fixed point on the inner race.

Instability

See: Fluid-induced instability; Stability

Integrator

An electronic circuit that converts a velocity signal to a displacement signal or converts an acceleration signal to a velocity signal.

Interference diagram

See: Campbell diagram

Internally pressurized bearing

A fluid-film bearing that, in normal conditions, is partially lubricated and derives its primary support force from dynamic pressure of the lubricating fluid produced by rotation of the journal. Also called a hydrodynamic bearing.

ISO

International Organization for Standardization.

Isotropic supports

Rotor support systems that provide uniform Dynamic Stiffness in all radial directions.

Isotropy

A system or material property such as stiffness, damping, elasticity, density, composition, etc., which is constant in all directions.

j

The square root of negative 1 ($j = \sqrt{-1}$).

Jeffcott rotor

An early, simple rotor model developed by H. H. Jeffcott. It was introduced in his paper, "The Lateral Vibration of Loaded Shafts in the Neighbourhood of a Whirling Speed.—The Effect of Want of Balance," Philosophical Magazine 6, vol. 37 (1919): pp. 304-314.

Journal

The portion of a shaft inside the fluid-film bearing. It transmits the rotor load through the fluid to the bearing supports.

Keyphasor event

The sudden voltage change caused by a once-per-turn shaft marker passing a Keyphasor transducer. This signal provides a reference for measuring vibration phase lag angle and also serves to measure shaft rotative speed. The period between successive Keyphasor events represents one revolution of the shaft.

Keyphasor pulse

See: Keyphasor event

Keyphasor transducer

A transducer that produces a once-per-turn voltage pulse, called the Keyphasor event. The Keyphasor transducer is typically a proximity probe, but can be an optical pickup or a magnetic pickup.

Lambda (λ)

See: Fluid Circumferential Average Velocity Ratio

Lateral vibration

See: Radial vibration

Lift test

A method to quickly check the bearing clearance on smaller, horizontal machines when the machine is stopped. A dial indicator is used to record position changes when the shaft is moved from one side of the bearing to another. A correction factor must be applied for tilting pad bearings, because pad movement can give the false impression of greater diametral clearance.

Linear system

A mechanical system with constant parameters (such as mass, stiffness, and damping) that can be modeled by linear differential equations. Linear systems have output that is proportional to input and output frequency equal to input frequency.

Lissajous curve

The plot of two, simple-harmonic-motion (sine wave) signals versus each other on a rectangular format. The shape of the curve identifies the relative frequency and phase characteristics of an unknown signal versus a known signal. An orbit is a form of Lissajous curve.

Load

The resultant of all forces (static and dynamic) applied to the rotor system. These forces can be either axial or radial and can be due to either internal or external mechanisms. Because the load can affect the shaft centerline position in a fluid-film bearing or seal, it can act to stabilize or destabilize the dynamic condition of the machine. Static load is sometimes referred to as preload.

Also, the output power being delivered by a rotating machine; for example, the electrical load of a generator.

Load zone

A region in a rolling element bearing where, when a radial or axial force is applied to the shaft, there is solid contact between the shaft, inner race, elements, and outer race of the bearing. The angular size of the load zone depends on the tolerance class of the bearing, with close tolerance bearings having wide load zones.

Low-eccentricity natural frequency

The natural frequency of a rotor system operating at a low eccentricity ratio in a fluid-film bearing. The system stiffness, the series combination of the bearing stiffness and the shaft stiffness, approaches its lower limit when the average and dynamic eccentricity ratio of the rotor approach zero.

Low-pass filter

A filter having a transmission band extending from zero frequency (or the lower frequency response limit of the transducer or instrument) to some upper corner frequency (where the amplitude is attenuated by 3 dB).

LVDT

Linear variable differential transformer. A contacting displacement transducer consisting of a movable core and a stationary transformer. Typically, the core is attached to the moving part and the transformer is attached to a fixed reference. A change in core position causes a change in output voltage.

Machinery management

The use of products to provide data or information that is interpreted and applied by humans to assess the condition of their machinery and correctly operate, maintain, and improve its operation.

Machinery protection

The use of products to provide automatic shutdown of a machine or return it to a safe or nondestructive mode of operation without human intervention

Magnetic bearing

A rotor support system that uses strong magnetic fields to suspend the rotor.

Margin of Stability

The frequency range between the zero values of the Direct Dynamic Stiffness and the nonsynchronous Quadrature Dynamic Stiffness.

Mass center

The principal axis of inertia of a rotor. At any axial location, the mass center is the point where all the mass of the body appears to be located. On a rotor, the mass centerline connects the mass centers of adjacent cross sections of the rotor.

Mass stiffness

In the simple rotor model, the negative dynamic stiffness term produced by the inertia of the rotor: $-M\omega^2$, where M is the mass, and ω is the frequency of vibration. The mass stiffness only appears when the rotor centerline vibrates.

Mechanical runout

A noise component in the output signal of a transducer system due to geometric imperfections. In proximity probes, this produces a probe gap change that is not caused by a shaft centerline position change. Common sources include an out-of-round shaft, scratch, chain mark, dent, rust, conductive buildup on the shaft, stencil mark, flat spot, and engraving. An out of round shaft can also transmit a noise signal to velocity and acceleration transducers.

Microinch

A unit of length or displacement equal to 10^{-6} inches or 10^{-3} mils.

Micrometer

A unit of length or displacement equal to 10^{-6} meters. Also called micron (obsolete).

Mil

A unit of length or displacement equal to 0.001 inch. One mil equals 25.4 micrometers.

Misalignment

See: Alignment

Modal damping

The actual damping force available to the system when mode shape effects are included. The actual damping force depends on the damping constants of the individual bearings and seals and the local shaft lateral velocities in those bearings and seals. For example, rigid body modes produce large amplitudes of vibration in fluid-film bearings, larger damping forces, and higher modal damping, while bending modes tend to produce smaller amplitudes of vibration in the bearings, smaller damping forces, and lower modal damping.

Modal mass

The effective dynamic mass of the system. Modal mass stores the kinetic energy associated with vibration. The modal mass will be different for each mode, and, except when an entire rotor moves rigidly, the modal mass of the rotor will usually be less than the static weight of the rotor. Successively higher modes have more nodal points that prevent shaft motion and reduce modal mass.

Modal stiffness

The effective stiffness of a system in dynamic motion. The rotor shaft behaves like a beam with bending stiffness related to the unsupported length. Successively higher modes have more nodal points that act as pinned supports from a stiffness perspective, decreasing the effective unsupported length and increasing the modal stiffness. Modal stiffness includes the series/parallel combination of all stiffness elements in the rotor and support system.

Mode identification probes

Probes that are installed to help with the identification of the shaft mode shape. Mode shapes must normally be interpolated between a small set of measurement points, which do not always provide enough information to measure complicated, higher-order mode shapes. Additional mode identification probes can be installed to provide more information.

Model

A mathematical representation of a system that is designed to mimic certain important features to help us understand system behavior. The rotor model is an attempt to describe the function of the black box that transforms dynamic forces into vibration. Applying a model beyond the limits expressed in the assumptions will usually lead to error.

Mode shape

The three-dimensional vibration pattern of a rotor system in free vibration (*free* mode shape) or due to a dynamic force distribution (*forced* mode shape). For large, distributed systems, the vibration amplitude and phase will change continuously along the rotor, and the machine casing will participate in the vibration in some complicated way. The forced mode shape changes with rotor speed.

Moment of inertia, mass

The sum of the products of each differential mass element times the square of its distance from the rotational axis

NARF

Acronym for Natural Axial Resonant Frequency; usually refers to axially compliant couplings.

Nameplate

A placard on a machine that contains basic information about the machine, such as the manufacturer, model number, rated power, power factor, operating speed, resonance speeds, pressures, temperatures, etc.

Nameplate resonance

Normal resonance speed(s) for a particular machine as indicated by the manufacturer on the nameplate. Typically the high-eccentricity natural frequency.

Natural frequency

The frequency of free vibration of a mechanical system. Each natural frequency is associated with a particular vibration pattern, called a mode shape, and each mode shape is independent of all the other mode shapes of the system.

See: Damped natural frequency; Undamped natural frequency

Natural mode

See: Natural frequency

Nodal point (node)

A point of minimum (or zero) shaft deflection in a specific mode shape. Nodal points can change axial location due to changes in speed or Dynamic Stiffness. Vibration on opposite sides of a node is usually 180° out of phase.

Noise

Any component of a transducer signal which does not represent the variable intended to be measured.

Nonlinear function

A function which cannot be expressed as $a_1x_1 + a_2x_2 + \ldots a_nx_n = y$. Examples of nonlinear functions are of a parabola, $y = x^2$, and a trigonometric function, $y = \sin x$.

Nonlinear system

A system with dynamic behavior characteristics that cannot be modeled by linear differential equations. The mathematical model must include nonlinear functions of displacements and/or velocities, which result in a set of nonlinear differential equations. Nonlinear systems can have output that is not proportional to input and output frequencies that include harmonics of the input frequency.

See: Linear system

Nonsymmetric rotor

See: Asymmetric rotor

Nonsynchronous

A vibration frequency component which is different than shaft rotative speed.

Nonsynchronous Amplification Factor

A measure of the susceptibility of rotor vibration response to a *nonsynchronous* harmonic force at a rotor system natural frequency. Typically, this is the ratio of the response amplitude at resonance to the response amplitude well away from any resonance.

Nonsynchronous Dynamic Stiffness

The generalized form of Dynamic Stiffness, in which the perturbation frequency is different than the rotative speed. See: Dynamic Stiffness.

Normal-loose

A behavior where a rotor, because of high vibration, moves to a position where the average stiffness decreases significantly. A worn bearing or loose support structure can allow normal-loose behavior.

Normal-tight

A behavior where a rotor contacts a bearing wall, seal, or some other part for a portion of the vibration cycle (a partial rub), increasing the average stiffness significantly.

Not-1X

Vibration data from which the 1X response has been removed, by either notch filtering or waveform subtraction.

Notch filter

A filter which has a rejection band extending from a lower cutoff frequency to an upper cutoff frequency. Frequencies within the rejection band are eliminated or attenuated while frequencies outside the rejection band are retained. The opposite of a band-pass filter.

Nyquist criterion

See: Aliasing

Nyquist limit

The highest frequency that can be reproduced in a digitally sampled waveform without aliasing. The Nyquist limit is one-half of the sampling frequency; thus, to ensure the proper frequency content in a sampled waveform, the sampling rate is typically set to some number greater than twice (for example, 2.2 times) the highest desired frequency.

Observed damping

See: Effective damping

Octave

A 2 to 1 ratio between two frequencies. An octave higher than a particular frequency is twice the frequency; an octave lower is one-half the frequency.

Offset balancing

Balancing used to compensate a repeatable thermal- or strain-induced unbalance. Even generators in new condition can have small asymmetries caused by slots, windings, and cooling gas flow that produce uneven heating and thermal bow. Manufacturers will often offset balance a generator so that it will run smoothly at full load. However, changes in load or excitation can produce temperature changes that lead to a different thermal bow, causing an increase in 1X vibration.

Oil whip

See: Whip

Oil whirl

See: Whirl

Optical pickup

A noncontacting transducer with an internal LED, typically infrared, and a phototransistor that detects the level of reflected light. It is most commonly used as a temporary Keyphasor transducer, observing a once-per-turn change in shaft reflectivity (a dark or light paint spot or a small strip of highly reflective tape on the shaft).

Orbit

The two dimensional path of the shaft centerline. The orbit can be observed when *XY* vibration transducers are connected to an oscilloscope in *X* versus *Y* mode. A Keyphasor dot is usually added to provide phase and precession information. An orbit is a specific form of a Lissajous curve.

Order lines

Diagonal lines starting at the origin on a spectrum cascade plot or vertical lines on a waterfall plot that indicate frequencies that maintain a fixed ratio to running speed; for example, 1X, 2X, 0.47X, etc.

Orientation

See: Probe orientation

Orthogonal probes

Probes whose sensitive axes intersect at right angles and which are in a plane at right angles to the rotor axis.

Oscillator-demodulator

See: Proximitor sensor

Outboard

When identifying the location of an object on a single machine, it is the side toward the outside of the machine case; for example, the probe is *outboard* of the bearing. When identifying the location of two similar components of a machine case, it is the one away from the driver coupling; for example, the *outboard* bearing of the HP compressor. When there is a chance of ambiguity, the components should be defined and a written record kept.

Outer race

In rolling element bearings, the track for the rolling elements in the outer ring of the bearing.

Outer race ball pass frequency

In rolling element bearings, the frequency at which rolling elements pass a fixed point on the outer race.

Out of phase

Having a 180°, or essentially 180°, phase relationship. Occasionally used to mean not exactly in phase.

Overdamped

See: Damping factor

Parameter

A rotor system parameter is a property of the system that affects system response. Mass, stiffness, damping, and λ are examples of rotor system parameters.

Partial rub

Rub in which contact between the rotor and stator is maintained for only part of the vibration cycle.

Peak

An amplitude measurement. For a sine wave signal, the amplitude is measured from the average signal level (the middle) to the peak value. For complex signals containing many frequencies, the peak value is found by taking one-half of the peak-to-peak amplitude. Peak is abbreviated pk.

Peak-to-peak

An amplitude measurement based on the difference between positive and negative peaks of an electronic signal or dynamic motion. Abbreviated pp.

Period

The time required for one complete oscillation or for a single cycle of events. The reciprocal of frequency.

Periodic vibration

Oscillatory motion that repeats itself identically at regular intervals.

Permanent bow

A bending deformation of the rotor that is not self-reversing without special intervention. For this to be true, the stresses in some part of the rotor must have exceeded the yield strength of the material.

Perturbation

Use of an external or internal (such as unbalance) device to apply a known forcing function to a system to study the system characteristics.

Perturbator

A mechanism that produces a variable frequency, synchronous or nonsynchronous perturbation of a shaft or casing. The perturbator may apply the force unidirectionally or circularly. A Keyphasor mark on the perturbator provides a phase and speed reference.

Phase lag angle

The timing relationship between two vibration signals, such as a Keyphasor pulse and a vibration signal; also, the phase difference between two signals, such as an input force signal and an output response signal. Phase lag is expressed in degrees of the vibration cycle, where the number of degrees is a positive number between 0° and 360°.

Pickup

See: Transducer

Pipe strain

Deformation of a machine casing caused by excessive force applied to the casing by the attached piping. This force may be due to poor piping fit or a malfunctioning support system.

Pitch radius

In a gear, the radius of the pitch circle, the imaginary circle that rolls without slipping on the pitch circle of the mating gear.

Pivotal mode shape

A mode shape where the principal node is more or less in the middle and each end is out of phase. For a rigid body mode, the rotor traces out the shape of two coaxial cones attached at their points, the nodal point. Also used to describe the S-shaped bending mode of a rotor.

pk

See: Peak

pp

See: Peak-to-peak

Polar plot

A graphical format consisting of a center reference point surrounded by concentric circles for plotting the amplitude and absolute phase of a set of vibration vectors. Amplitude is represented by the distance from the center of the plot and phase by the angular position relative to the transducer orientation. A polar plot can be constructed from steady state or transient data.

Poles

In control theory, the eigenvalues of the system. They are also known as the characteristic values or roots of the characteristic equation. In an electric motor or generator, locations on opposite sides of a rotor equivalent to the north and south ends of a bar magnet.

Position angle

The angle between an arbitrary reference line drawn through the center of a bearing (typically vertical down in a horizontal machine) and the line connecting the bearing and shaft centers, measured in the direction of rotor rotation.

Power factor

The sine of the phase angle between the instantaneous voltage and the resulting current. The apparent power multiplied by the power factor equals the actual power.

Precession

The lateral, two-dimensional motion or vibration of the rotor geometric center in the XY plane, which is perpendicular to the axis of the rotor. Precession is also known as orbiting or vibration. Precession is completely independent of rotation.

Precision

A measure of the random error of a repeated measurement. Assuming no change in the parameter being measured, a measuring instrument is said to have high precision (repeatability) if repeated measurements of the parameter are clustered closely together.

Pressure angle

In gears, the angle between the normal to the tooth profile at the pitch circle and the tangent to the pitch circle at that point.

Pressure wedge

A region of local high pressure that forms in a fluid-film bearing or seal, produced when a shaft rotates at an eccentric position. The shaft draws the circulating fluid into an area of reduced clearance; some of the fluid escapes axially, but the fluid near the axial center of the bearing produces a circumferential pressure distribution that supports the rotor and moves it to the side. This pressure distribution is the primary means of rotor support in internally pressurized (hydrodynamic) journal bearings.

Preswirl

The injection of a fluid into a bearing or seal, intentionally or unintentionally, with a tangential angular velocity component in the direction of rotor rotation. In this case, the value of λ can be considerably greater than 0.5.

Prime Spike

In the operation of rolling element bearings, a frequency range that encompasses, as a minimum, the ball pass frequencies and their harmonics.

Probe

Typically, an eddy current proximity transducer, although often used to describe any transducer.

Probe gap

The physical distance (gap) between the face of a proximity probe tip and the observed surface. The distance can be expressed in terms of displacement (mils, micrometers) or voltage (millivolts).

Probe orientation

The angular location of a probe, in a plane perpendicular to the rotor centerline, with respect to a unique reference direction. Typically, 0° is at top dead center (vertical or up) for a horizontal machine train and at a compass point or some significant feature for a vertical machine. The angle is measured from 0° to 180° to the left or the right.

Protection

See: Machinery protection

Proximitor sensor

A Bently Nevada signal conditioning device which sends a radio frequency signal to an eddy current proximity probe, demodulates the response, and provides an output signal proportional to probe gap distance. Also called an oscillator-demodulator.

Proximity probe

A noncontacting probe, most commonly an eddy current probe, which measures the displacement of an observed surface relative to the probe mounting location.

Q

See: Synchronous Amplification Factor

Quadrature

In Dynamic Stiffness, the component of a response that lies in a direction perpendicular to the applied force vector. See: Dynamic Stiffness, Quadrature.

Radial

A direction on a machine which is perpendicular to the shaft centerline.

Radial position

See: Average shaft position

Radial vibration

Shaft dynamic motion or casing vibration, sometimes called lateral vibration, measured in a direction perpendicular to the shaft axis.

REBAM

The acronym for Rolling Element Bearing Activity Monitor, which is a Bently Nevada system for monitoring and analyzing the performance of rolling element bearings using eddy current transducers and MicroPROX sensors.

Reference data

Recorded machine measurements, at defined conditions, for comparison and correlation with measurements taken at a later time or at different operating conditions.

Relative phase

The timing difference between equivalent events (such as positive peaks or zero crossings) on two signals filtered to the same frequency. Relative phase is expressed in degrees of the vibration cycle, "Signal A leads (or lags) signal B (the reference signal, in this case) by (the number of) degrees."

Relative vibration

Vibration measured relative to a chosen reference, which may also be vibrating. Proximity probes measure shaft dynamic motion and position relative to the probe mounting, usually the bearing or bearing housing.

Repeatability

The quality of a transducer or readout instrument to produce measurements of the same variable, under the same conditions, with small dispersion (random error). Such a device is said to have high repeatability (precision).

Resolution

The smallest change in a signal that will produce a detectable change in an instrument output. In a spectrum, the line width, equal to the span divided by the number of lines in the spectrum.

Resonance

The increase in amplitude and change in phase that occurs when the frequency of an applied periodic force coincides with a natural frequency of the system. During startup or shutdown, a resonance typically is identified by an amplitude peak, accompanied by a significant change of phase.

Restoring force

A force that acts in the direction of the original position, attempting to restore the system to equilibrium.

Reverse component

See: Forward and reverse vectors

Reverse (backward) precession

Precession of a shaft in the opposite direction of its rotation.

Rigid rotor

A rotor where the bending of the rotor is relatively small compared to the motion of the rotor in the bearings, produced by a high ratio of rotor stiffness to support stiffness. In many cases, the very lowest modes are an in-phase (cylindrical) or an out-of-phase (pivotal) rigid body mode.

rms

See: Root-mean-square

Rolling element bearing

A bearing in which the low friction property derives from mechanical rolling (usually with fluid lubrication), using ball or roller elements between two constraining rings.

Rolling elements

In a rolling element bearing, the rollers or balls that support the rotating load of a shaft.

Root locus

A graphical presentation of the eigenvalues (roots) of a system as a system parameter is changed. It gives us a qualitative description of the system's transient performance and stability and provides a quantitative measure of the damped natural frequency, Threshold of Instability, Synchronous Amplification Factor, and Margin of Stability.

Root-mean-square (rms)

A measure of amplitude that is the square root of the arithmetic mean of a

set of squared instantaneous values. For sine waves only,
rms $= 1/\sqrt{2}$ x (pk amplitude) $= 0.707$ x (pk amplitude) $= 0.354$ x (pp amplitude).

Roots

The characteristic values, eigenvalues or, in control theory, poles of a mechanical system.

Rotating stall

Partial flow separation in a compressor that creates one or more regions of impaired flow. These regions rotate around the rotor disk or diffuser at a subsynchronous frequency.

Rotation

Rotation is the angular motion of the rotor about its axial geometric center, or shaft centerline.

Rotative Speed

See: Shaft rotative speed

Rotor

The rotating part of a machine. A rotor usually consists of an assembly of components attached to a shaft or it can consist of a massive shaft.

Rotor mode

The state of rotor vibration identified by several characteristics: natural frequency, hierarchy (first, second, third, etc.), deflection shape (rigid or flexible), or end-to-end relative phase (in phase or out of phase).

Rotor position angle

See: Position angle

Rotor system

The rotor system includes all parts of the machine that are involved with vibration. This includes the shaft with any attached disks, the bearings that support the shaft, the structures that support the bearings, the machine casing, the foundation system, coupled machines, and attached piping systems or unsecured cabling. The rotor system can also include all of the plant equipment that is involved in the process in which the machine is imbedded.

Rotor vibration region

A frequency range which includes the principal frequency components of rotor vibration: typically, from ¼X to approximately 3X.

RTD

The abbreviation for Resistance Temperature Detector; a sensor which measures temperature through a change in resistance.

Rub

Contact between the rotating and stationary parts of the machine. Rub is always a secondary effect caused by a malfunction that reduces the available clearance between the rotor and the stator.

Runout

See: Electrical runout, Mechanical runout

Runout compensation

Correction of a transducer output signal for the error resulting from mechanical or electrical runout.

SAF

See: Synchronous Amplification Factor

Scalar

A parameter or variable possessing only magnitude. Unlike a vector, a scalar has no direction information. For example, voltage, temperature, distance, and speed are scalars.

Scale factor

The change in output per change in input of a transducer. Also, the factor by which a signal is amplified or attenuated to meet the input requirements of an instrument. Also called sensitivity.

Seismic transducer

A vibration transducer that measures the absolute vibration of an object relative to an internal inertial reference. Examples are accelerometers and velocity transducers.

Self-excited vibration

The periodic vibration of a system at a natural frequency that occurs when an internal feedback mechanism of the system converts a supply of external energy, which may not be oscillatory in nature, to an oscillatory force.

Sensitivity

The ratio of the change in the output to a change in the input. A typical sensitivity for a proximity probe transducer is 200 millivolts per mil (7.84 volts per millimeter). Also called scale factor.

Service factor

An additional load capability that a machine (typically electric motors and gearboxes) can tolerate for brief periods without damage. The rated power is multiplied by the service factor to arrive at an allowable, brief overload capacity.

Shaft

A rod or a beam, usually with circular cross section, on which a disk may be carried, either integrally or by shrink fitting. Shafts rotate about their long axis.

Shaft absolute vibration

The radial vibration of a rotor shaft measured relative to an inertial, or fixed, reference frame. If a machine casing were absolutely rigid and motionless, the shaft vibration measured by an eddy current transducer mounted to the case would be shaft absolute. When significant casing vibration exists, the eddy current measurement must be added to the integrated casing vibration to obtain shaft absolute.

Shaft average centerline plot

See: Average shaft centerline plot

Shaft centerline

The axial geometric centerline of the rotor.

Shaft relative transducer

Typically, a proximity probe, mounted on a bearing or bearing housing, that observes shaft motion. The output signal includes the effects of the shaft motion and the transducer motion.

Shaft relative vibration

Shaft radial vibration that is measured by a transducer mounted on a structure that can vibrate. The vibration signal will include the effects of transducer vibration.

Shaft rotative speed

The frequency at which a shaft is rotating, usually expressed in units of revolutions per minute (rpm). It may also be expressed in radians per second (rad/s).

Shear

The parallelogram distortion produced by the relative parallel displacement of two parallel planes in a material.

Shim

A metal spacer, preferably stainless steel, placed between the machine foot and the foundation to correct the height of the machine at that location

Signal conditioner

A device placed between a signal source and a readout instrument to change the signal. Examples include attenuators, preamplifiers, filters, and signal converters (for changing voltage to current or analog to digital, etc.).

Signal gain

The relative attenuation or amplification of a signal, usually presented in dB. Also, the amplification of small electronic signals to match the scale range on instruments, such as FM tape recorders, to improve the resolution of the measurement.

Signal-to-noise ratio

The number formed by dividing the magnitude of the signal by the magnitude of the noise present in the signal. A low noise signal has a high signal-to-noise ratio, while a high noise signal has a low signal-to-noise ratio.

Signature

All the information necessary to uniquely identify a state. The term is sometimes applied to a vibration frequency spectrum that is specific to a particular machine, component, system, or subsystem at a specific point in time, under specific machine operating conditions. It is used for historical comparison of mechanical condition over the operating life of the machine.

Sine wave

The waveform that results from filtering a vibration signal to a single frequency. It is described by the function $y = A\sin(\omega t)$, where y is the instantaneous value of the signal, A is the peak or peak-to-peak amplitude, ω is the circular frequency in rad/s, and t is time.

Single amplitude

(Obsolete) See: Peak

Skid

A term usually used to identify a massive, fabricated support made of structural members. On small machines, it can be used without a foundation; on large machines, it may be bolted and grouted to the foundation.

Slip frequency

In an induction motor, a measure of how fast the loaded rotor is turning compared to the no load ideal. $\text{Slip} = 2(f/p) - \Omega$, where f is the line frequency, p is the number of poles, and Ω is the rotor speed.

Slow roll compensation

Slow roll compensation is the subtraction of slow roll data from vibration data taken from the same measurement point in order to remove the effects of mechanical and electrical runout. The resultant vibration data will only reflect the dynamic response of the rotor. Compensation can be performed using vectors or waveforms.

Slow roll runout

A combination of electrical and mechanical runout measured at a slow speed where the dynamic effects associated with rotation are negligible. Normally it can only be measured with a proximity probe because of the low frequency of the signal.

Slow roll speed

A rotor speed low enough that the dynamic effects of unbalance are negligible. Typically, slow roll speed is less than 10% of the first balance resonance speed.

Slow roll vector

A constant or very slowly varying component of the vibration vector that represents nondynamic action observed by a transducer. It consists of thermal, electrical, and mechanical effects, such as a bowed rotor, mechanical or electrical runout, or a coupling problem. The slow roll vector will be different for each measurement transducer.

Soft foot

Machine feet that are not coplanar with the soleplate (baseplate) or foundation. When feet are not properly supported, tightening them down will warp the machine casing, changing the alignment of machine components.

Soleplate

A steel plate grouted and bolted to a foundation. If a soleplate is used, the machine is bolted to the soleplate. Also called a baseplate.

Spall

In rolling element bearings, a flake or chip of metal from a bearing race or rolling element.

Span

The range of displayed frequencies in a spectrum.

Spectrum

See: Half spectrum

Spectrum cascade plot

A series of half or full spectrum plots taken over a range of speeds of a machine, such as during a startup or shutdown, usually at set speed intervals.

Spectrum waterfall plot

A series of half or full spectrum plots taken over a range of time, usually during constant speed operation.

s-plane

The XY plane of the root locus plot; the coordinates of the plot represent the components, γ and ω_d, of the complex eigenvalues, or roots, s, of the characteristic equation.

Split resonance

Two balance resonances that have a similar mode shape, but are separated in frequency.

Spring stiffness

The series and parallel combination of all the springlike elements of the rotor system, including shaft bending stiffness, bearing fluid-film direct stiffnesses, and any support and foundation stiffnesses; usually represented by the symbol K. When a system is displaced from the equilibrium position, spring stiffness produces a force that is proportional to displacement and directed toward the equilibrium position.

Stability (Liapunoff definition, stability "in the small")

The dynamic regime of a physical system is stable if an external, small perturbation of its steady-state regime causes a transient response that decays to the same steady state regime. A system is unstable if an external, small perturbation results in an increasing response.

Stability (practical definition)

A system is stable if a transient perturbation does not result in a system response with amplitudes exceeding an acceptable level.

Stability threshold

See: Threshold of Instability

State space matrix

The matrix resulting from the reduction of a second order system to a system of first order differential equations. The state space matrix produces a set of velocities from a corresponding set of input displacements. The eigenvalues of the system can be calculated from the state space matrix.

Static data

Data which represents a processed value of some measured parameter. Examples of static data include vibration amplitude, phase lag angle, frequency, average shaft position, shaft rotative speed, time, date, and monitor alarm and OK status. See: Dynamic data

Stator

The stationary part of the machine in which the rotor rotates.

Steady state

Operation at a constant shaft rotative speed.

Steam whip

See: Whip

Stiffness axes

The resolution of an anisotropic, radial stiffness distribution into orthogonal major and minor stiffnesses. The orientation of the major and minor stiffnesses identify the directions of the stiffness axes. The major axis of the low-speed, 1X orbit tends to align with the minor stiffness axis.

Strain gauge

A transducer attached to a deformable solid which reacts to changes in strain, typically through changes in resistance.

Stress

The force acting on a body per unit area, usually measured in terms of lb/in^2 or N/m^2.

Structural resonance

Excitation of a natural frequency of an attached structural component, often by rotor vibration. A structural resonance can appear as a small loop on a polar plot.

Subcritical damping

See: Damping factor

Subharmonic

A component of a vibration signal that is a submultiple (integer fraction) of a fundamental frequency, for example ½, ⅓ etc.

Subsynchronous

A component of a vibration signal which has a frequency less than shaft rotative speed.

Supercritical damping

See: Damping factor

Superharmonic

A component of a vibration signal that is an integer multiple, $n > 1$, of a fundamental frequency.

Supersynchronous

A component of a vibration signal which has a frequency greater than shaft rotative speed.

Support structure

The entire support system for a machine, usually including a foundation, grout, soleplate, pedestals, shims, and bolts. This structure transmits machinery and related loads to the ground and may transmit external loads from the ground to the machine.

Surface-to-core thermal gradient

A temperature gradient across a rotor cross section that appears because of heating or cooling of the outer surface of the rotor.

Sweep frequency filter

A type of band-pass filter which is automatically swept (tuned) through a frequency range of interest. An instrument which incorporates this type of filter can be used to generate a vibration frequency spectrum.

Swirl ratio

See: Fluid Circumferential Average Velocity Ratio

Symmetric rotor

A rotor whose cross section, when rotated about its geometric center, appears the same at all angular orientations; for example, a circular cross section.

Symmetry

A geometric property of an object such that, when it is subjected to certain operations (rotation, inversion, etc.), the object appears the same as before the operation.

Synchronous

The component of a vibration signal that has a frequency equal to the shaft rotative speed (1X).

Synchronous Amplification Factor (SAF)

A measure of the sensitivity of a rotor system to unbalance when shaft rotative speed is equal to a rotor system natural frequency. A high Synchronous Amplification Factor produces relatively high vibration at a resonance and indicates low system Quadrature Dynamic Stiffness; a low amplification factor produces relatively low vibration at a resonance and indicates high system Quadrature Dynamic Stiffness. Also called Q.

Synchronous Dynamic Stiffness

The ratio of the applied, synchronous dynamic force to the dynamic response of a mechanical system. In rotor systems, the synchronous force is usually rotating unbalance. See: Dynamic Stiffness

Synchronous precession

Rotor precession with frequency equal to rotor speed (1X).

Synthetic gas (Syngas)

An intermediate product consisting primarily of methane.

System

The interacting combination of rotors, bearings, casing, and surrounding fluid. The system responds as an entity to dynamic excitation.

System mode shape

The complicated vibration pattern produced by all the elements of a vibrating system.

Tangential stiffness

A springlike stiffness produced by the converging fluid pressure wedge when the rotor is at an eccentric position in a bearing or seal. It can be modeled as $+jD\lambda\Omega$, where D is the damping, λ is the Fluid Circumferential Average Velocity Ratio, Ω is rotor speed, and $j = \sqrt{-1}$. The tangential stiffness acts at 90° to the displacement vector, in the direction of rotation.

Temperature stratification

A temperature gradient that forms in the casing of a steam turbine after shutdown, with higher temperatures at the top of the casing.

Temporary bow

A rotor bow that does not involve plastic deformation of the rotor material; the rotor returns to its original shape when the cause of the bow disappears.

Thermal bow

A rotor bow that forms in response to a temperature gradient in the rotor. When the temperature returns to equilibrium, the bow disappears.

Thermal fatigue

Fatigue cracks that form as a result of thermal shock during startup or shutdown.

Thermal shock

A sudden temperature change on the outer surface of an object that produces surface temperatures significantly different from those in the interior. The thermal expansion or contraction of the surface layers are constrained by the underlying material; thus, thermal shock can generate very large stresses capable of producing cracks. Sudden surface heating will produce tensile stresses in the interior; sudden surface cooling will produce tensile stresses on the surface.

Thermocouple

A temperature transducer comprised of two dissimilar metal wires which, when heated or cooled, produce a proportional change in electrical potential at the point where they join.

Threshold

The level at which a trigger or other function is initiated.

Threshold of Instability

The speed, Ω_{th}, at or above which a machine will experience a fluid-induced instability.

Thrust position

See: Axial position

Timebase Plot

A presentation of the instantaneous values of a signal as a function of time: a waveform. The vibration waveform can be observed on an oscilloscope in the time domain.

Torque

A measure of the tendency of a force to cause rotation; a force couple, equal to the force multiplied by the perpendicular distance between the line of action of the force and the center of rotation.

Torque, average

The average value of the torque applied to a rotor in order to sustain rotational speed, angular acceleration, or load requirements.

Torque, dynamic

The instantaneous value of the time-varying component of the torque applied to a rotor, typically resulting from a variation in driving load or torque.

Torque, static

The force times the perpendicular distance between the line of action of the force and the center of rotation (moment) as applied to a structure (nonrotating).

Torsional vibration

Oscillation of the angle of twist of a shaft, typically measured in tenths of degrees peak-to-peak.

Track

To maintain a specific frequency ratio with another vibration component, usually 1X, which is changing frequency. For example, ½X rub can *track* running speed over a limited speed range during startup or shutdown.

Tracking filter

See: Vector filter

Transducer

A device for converting the magnitude of one quantity into another quantity for the purpose of measurement. The second quantity often has units of measure different from the first. For example, displacement vibration transducers convert mechanical position into a voltage signal proportional to displacement.

Transient

Changing; commonly, when machine speed is changing, usually during startup or shutdown. Mathematically, the dynamic response (*transient response*) associated with free vibration that usually decays with time. See: Growth/decay rate

Transient vibration

The temporary vibration of a mechanical system, such as a machine, associated with instantaneous changes in machine condition, such as speed, load, etc.

Translational mode shape

See: Mode shape

Transmission device

A machine or machine part that connects a driver to a driven machine. Transmission devices include gearboxes, couplings, and clutches.

Transverse sensitivity

See: Cross-axis sensitivity

Trend data

Periodically sampled data that is used for the purpose of observing changes in machine behavior as a function of time.

Trend interval

The time period between consecutive data points on a trend plot.

Trend period

The time frame (beginning to end of data) of a trend plot.

Trend plot

A presentation in rectangular (Cartesian) or polar format of a measured variable versus time.

Trigger

Any event which is used as an initial timing reference. A trigger signal for a digital vector filter is a Keyphasor pulse, which provides a reference for measuring the amplitude and phase lag angle.

Trip

The shut down, often automatic, of a machine, based on predetermined levels of measured parameters or observed conditions.

Trip multiplier

In a monitor system, the function that temporarily increases the alarm (Alert and Danger) setpoint values by a specific multiple (usually two or three). This function is normally applied by manual (operator) action during startup to allow a machine to pass through high vibration speed ranges without monitor alarm indications. Also called setpoint multiplier.

TSI

Abbreviation for Turbine Supervisory Instrumentation. A TSI system is a continuous monitoring system generally used on turbogenerator sets. The TSI system consists of measurement transducers, monitors, interconnecting wiring, and a microprocessor-based monitoring, data acquisition, and processing system.

Unbalance

Unequal radial mass distribution in a rotor; a shaft condition where the mass centerline (principal axis of inertia) does not coincide with the geometric centerline.

Unbalance response

The amplitude and phase of rotor synchronous precession at a given speed, caused by the dynamic forcing action of rotating unbalance.

Undamped natural frequency

The natural frequency of a mechanical system without the effects of damping.

Underdamped

See: Damping factor

Unfiltered Data

See: Direct data

Unstable

See: Stability

Valve position

A measurement of the position of the process inlet valves on a machine, usually expressed as a percentage of the valve opening; zero percent is fully closed, 100 percent is fully open. The measurement is usually made with an LVDT or rotary transducer as part of a Turbine Supervisory Instrumentation system.

Vane passing frequency

A potential vibration frequency on vaned-impeller compressors, pumps, and other machines with vaned rotating elements. It is the number of vanes (on an impeller or stage) multiplied by shaft rotative speed.

Vector

A quantity which has both magnitude and angular orientation.

See: Vibration vector

Vector filter

An electronic instrument that measures the amplitude and phase lag angle of, primarily, 1X and 2X components of a vibration signal.

Velocity

The rate of change of displacement with time. Typical units for velocity are in/s or mm/s peak. Velocity measurements are used to evaluate machine housing and other structural response characteristics. Integration of a velocity signal yields dynamic displacement, but not average position.

Velocity transducer

An electromechanical transducer, typically with an internal inertial reference, with an output in units of velocity.

Velocity profile

A collection of velocity vectors that describe the velocity distribution of fluid flow in a defined region; for example, the velocity distribution in the lubricating fluid between a rotating journal and the bearing wall.

Vibration

The oscillatory (back and forth) motion of a physical object.

Vibration form

The appearance of the vibration signal when displayed in various formats. While form can also be seen in timebase and spectrum formats, for rotor shafts, it is best seen in the orbit, which combines the vibration characteristics of amplitude, phase, and frequency in a two dimensional display; the form is determined by the shape and direction of the dynamic path of the shaft centerline.

Vibration vector

For displacement, velocity, or acceleration, a vector that represents the amplitude and absolute phase of a filtered vibration signal. A vibration vector is actually a complex number and can be expressed in rectangular or polar form.

Virtual probe rotation

A mathematical transform of vector data from an existing XY pair of vibration transducers to produce vectors that would be measured by XY probes mounted at some other, arbitrary orientation.

Waterfall plot

See: Spectrum waterfall plot

Waveform

The instantaneous value of a signal displayed as a function of time. A vibration waveform can be observed on a timebase plot or on an oscilloscope in the timebase mode.

Waveform compensation

Point by point subtraction of a slow roll waveform from an unfiltered waveform measured by the same transducer at some other speed.

Waveform plot

See: Timebase plot

Whip

Subsynchronous, fluid-induced instability vibration that is locked to a bending mode natural frequency of the rotor system. When the source of the instability is in a fluid-film bearing, it is sometimes called *oil whip*; *steam whip* is a fluid-induced instability caused by steam interaction with the rotor. All of these are different manifestations of fluid-induced instability.

Whirl

Also called *oil whirl*; a subsynchronous, fluid-induced instability vibration that tracks rotor speed. Typically, whirl occurs at frequencies below ½X. Also, an obsolete term used to describe an orbit.

Window function

A digital signal processing technique applied to the sample record to reduce noise in the calculated spectrum. Typically, it gradually and smoothly forces the signal values to zero at the beginning and end of the record. In the frequency domain, a window appears as a band-pass filter.

X to *Y*

> The direction of rotation using the rectangular coordinate system as a reference. *X* to *Y* is equivalent to counterclockwise (CCW).

XY

> Orthogonal (mutually perpendicular) axes in a rectangular (Cartesian) coordinate system. Usually used to indicate orthogonal radial vibration transducers. Mathematically, *Y* is the vertical axis, and *X* is the horizontal axis, but the axes can be aligned with the *X* and *Y* measurement transducers for convenience.

XY plot

> A rectangular graphical format consisting of a vertical (*Y*) axis and a horizontal (*X*) axis. This format is used to graph the results of one variable as a function of another; for example, vibration amplitude versus time (trend), or amplitude versus frequency.

XY probes

> Two radial probes, in the same plane, oriented 90 degrees from each other.

Y to *X*

> The direction of rotation using the rectangular coordinate system as a reference. *Y* to *X* is equivalent to clockwise (CW).

Zero-to-peak

> See: Peak

References

1. Electrical Transducer Nomenclature and Terminology: ISA-S37.1-1975 (Philadelphia: The Instrumentation, Systems, and Automation Society of America, 1982).
2. Christiansen, Donald, ed. *Electronics Engineers' Handbook*, 4th ed. (New York: McGraw-Hill, Inc., 1996).
3. Avallone, Eugene A., Baumeister, Theodore, eds. *Marks' Standard Handbook for Mechanical Engineers*, 10th ed. (New York: McGraw-Hill, Inc., 1996).
4. American Petroleum Institute, Mechanical Equipment Standards for Refinery Service (Washington, D.C.: American Petroleum Institute,)
5. Taylor, Barry N., *Guide for the Use of the International System of Units (SI)*, National Institute of Standards and Technology, Special Publication 811, 1995 ed. (Washington: U.S. Government Printing Office, 1995)
6. American Petroleum Institute, *Tutorial on the API Standard Paragraphs Covering Rotor Dynamics and Balancing: An Introduction to Lateral Critical and Train Torsional Analysis and Rotor Balancing*, API Publication 684, 4th ed. (Washington, D.C.: American Petroleum Institute, 1996)

Index

About the Authors

DONALD E. BENTLY is the former Chairman of the Board and Chief Executive Officer of Bently Nevada Corporation, which was sold to GE Power Systems in 2002. He is now Chairman and Chief Executive Officer of Bently Pressurized Beariing Company. Mr. Bently pioneered the successful commercial use of the eddy current proximity transducer to measure vibration and other critical parameters in rotating machinery. His visionary work in this area gave rise to an entire industry surrounding the use of vibration instrumentation to protect and diagnose machinery. His active research of rotor dynamics has allowed him to make significant theoretical and practical contributions in this field. He is a globally recognized authority on these subjects and has authored or co-authored more than 140 papers. He has received numerous awards for his work. Mr. Bently earned his Bachelor's degree in Electrical Engineering (with Distinction) in 1949, followed by his Master's degree in 1950 from the University of Iowa. In 1987 he was awarded an honorary Doctorate in Engineering from the University of Nevada, Reno, and an honorary A.A. degree from Western Nevada Community College in 1998.

CHARLES T. HATCH joined Bently Nevada Corporation in 1989. He worked in Custom Products Engineering for several years before joining Bently Rotor Dynamics Research Corporation, where he performed research in Dynamic Stiffness, Root Locus, and Virtual Probe Rotation. He also served in the Technical Training Department as an instructor in the Machinery Diagnostics and Advanced Machinery Dynamics seminars. He holds B.S. and M.S. degrees in Mechanical Engineering from the University of California at Berkeley.

BOB GRISSOM joined Bently Nevada Corporation in 1978. He was manager of the Customer Training Department for several years before joining Bently Rotor Dynamics Research Corporation (BRDRC) as Technical Editor. Bob was also the Technical Editor for the ORBIT magazine for three years. Bob earned a B.A. in Physics from the University of California, Irvine, and is a member of Sigma Pi Sigma and IEEE.

About Bently Nevada and Bently Pressurized Bearing Company

Bently Nevada Corporation began in 1955 as Bently Scientific Company in Berkeley, California. Don Bently formed his own company to design, build, and sell his eddy current "distance detectors" via mail order. His conversion of the basic transducer system design from vacuum tubes to transistors made it robust and cost-effective for industrial applications.

In 1961, Bently Scientific moved to its present-day location in Minden, Nevada, a small community 45 miles south of Reno, and changed its name to reflect its new home. The proximity probe soon found its niche as a sensor for directly observing the position and vibration of rotating shafts inside industrial machinery, and Bently Nevada's business grew exponentially during this period.

In the mid-1960s, Bently Nevada began offering monitoring systems as well as transducers. The monitors accepted inputs from Bently transducers, provided continuous monitoring of vibration and position, and compared monitored parameters against user-established alarm limits. In the years since, the number of monitored parameters has grown to encompass rotative speed, phase, temperature, thermal expansion, valve position, pressure, and numerous other machine-related conditions.

In the 1970s, Bently Nevada developed a services organization to diagnose machinery problems as well as install, calibrate, and repair instrumentation. Bently also began offering training to customers on the fundamentals of vibration, the use and calibration of instruments, and machinery diagnostics.

The 1980s saw the establishment of Bently Rotor Dynamics Research Corporation, founded to conduct fundamental research, led by Dr. Agnes Muszynska for many years. Bently Nevada also introduced computerized, online, condition monitoring software as part of a growing emphasis on machinery protection and proactive management of machinery through the use of real-time data.

The 1990s brought further refinements in Bently Nevada's capabilities and scope, adding thermodynamic condition monitoring capabilities. At the same time, a significant growth in its services organization took place to address the shrinking staff of machinery engineers in many customers' plants and to provide system integration and turnkey project management expertise.

In 2002, Bently Nevada Corporation was purchased in a friendly acquisition by GE Power Systems. The purchase of Bently Nevada enabled Donald E. Bently to focus on another area of rotor dynamics that he believes is fertile ground for development. That area is bearings. Mr. Bently formed Bently Pressurized Bearing Company in 2002 in order to develop new bearing technology that gives machinery engineers greater ability to control machine condition and behavior.

The new millennium sees Mr. Bently continuing his leadership position in pioneering innovations to improve rotating machinery performance.